Species Management:

Challenges and Solutions for the 21st Century

The Natural Heritage of Scotland

Periodically, since it was founded in 1992, Scottish Natural Heritage has organized or jointly organized a conference which has focused on a particular aspect of Scotland's natural heritage. The papers read at the conferences, after a process of refereeing and editing, have been brought together as a book. The fifteen titles already published in this series are listed below (No. 6 was not based on a conference).

This is the sixteenth book in the series.

Species Management:

Challenges and Solutions for the 21st Century

Edited by: John M. Baxter and Colin A. Galbraith

Scottish Natural Heritage
All of nature for all of Scotland

Edinburgh: TSO Scotland

First published in 2010 by The Stationery Office Limited
26 Rutland Square, Edinburgh, EH1 2BW

Applications for reproduction should be made to Scottish Natural Heritage,
Great Glen House, Leachkin Road, Inverness, IV3 8NW

British Library Cataloguing in Publication Data
A catalogue record for this book is available from the British Library

ISBN 978 0 11 497348 3

80%

Printed on paper containing 80% recycled fibre content.

The views expressed in the chapters of this book do not necessarily represent views of the editors or the organizations that supported the conference and this publication.

Cover: Studio 9 (Scotland) Ltd.

All cover images are © Lorne Gill/SNH with the exception of the beaver on the front cover which is © Scottish Beaver Trial and the stag beetle on the back cover which is © Laurie Campbell/SNH.

Acknowledgements

The production of this book has involved a great many people working in a variety of capacities. We are especially grateful to the authors of the chapters who have provided a wonderful source of information and insight. Each chapter has been independently reviewed and we are grateful to all those who helped with this process. Thanks are due also to the various photographers who have allowed us to use their wonderful images to illustrate the book, and especially Betty Common for her invaluable help in researching and sourcing many of the images.

The original conference, organized by Scottish Natural Heritage involved the work of many people, and we are grateful to them all for their contributions. In particular, however, the conference could not have happened without the behind the scenes organizational work by Marion Whitelaw, Amy Campbell, Helen King and Paul Robertson. The conference was held at the Edinburgh Conference Centre, Heriot-Watt University. We thank Janet Hunter and all her staff for their helpful and friendly support that helped to make the event such a success.

Finally we thank The Stationery Office for their support in the production of this book. Special thanks are due to Shona Struthers and Jon Dalrymple for their patience and expert advice and assistance.

Contents

Contributors

Arjun Amar, RSPB Scotland, Dunedin House, 25 Ravelston Terrace, Edinburgh, EH4 3TP, UK.

John M. Baxter, Scottish Natural Heritage, Silvan House, 231 Corstorphine Road, Edinburgh, EH12 7AT, UK.

Colin W. Bean, Scottish Natural Heritage, Caspian House, Mariner Court, Clydebank Business Park, Clydebank, G81 2NR, UK.

Philip J. Boon, Scottish Natural Heritage, Silvan House, 231 Corstorphine Road, Edinburgh, EH12 7AT, UK.

Ian L. Boyd, Sea Mammal Research Unit, Gatty Marine Lab, University of St Andrews, St Andrews, Fife, KY16 8LB, UK.

Peter Bridgewater, Joint Nature Conservation Committee, Monkstone House, City Road, Peterborough, PE1 1JY, UK.

Peter Brotherton, Natural England, Northminster House, Northminster Road, Peterborough, PE1 1UA, UK.

Mike T. Burrows, Scottish Association for Marine Science, Dunstaffnage Marine Laboratory, Oban, Argyll, PA37 1QA, UK.

Mary Christie, Scottish Natural Heritage, Battleby, Redgorton, Perth, PH1 3EW, UK.

Mairi Cole, Scottish Natural Heritage, Silvan House, 231 Corstorphine Road, Edinburgh, EH12 7AT, UK.

Roy Dennis, Highland Foundation for Wildlife, Middle Lodge, Dunphail, Forres, Moray, IV36 2QQ, UK.

David W. Donnan, Scottish Natural Heritage, Battleby, Redgorton, Perth, PH1 3EW, UK.

Alison Dyke, Reforesting Scotland, 58 Shandwick Place, Edinburgh, EH2 4RT, UK.

Robert W. Furness, Faculty of Biomedical and Life Sciences, Graham Kerr Building, University of Glasgow, Glasgow, G12 8QQ, UK.

Colin A. Galbraith, Scottish Natural Heritage, Silvan House, 231 Corstorphine Road, Edinburgh, EH12 7AT, UK.

Martin Gaywood, Scottish Natural Heritage, Great Glen House, Leachkin Road, Inverness, IV3 8NW, UK.

Lisbeth Gederaas, The Norwegian Biodiversity Information Centre, Erling Skakkesgt. 47, 7491, Trondheim, Norway.

David Genney , Scottish Natural Heritage, Great Glen House, Leachkin Road, Inverness, IV3 8NW, UK.

Dave Goulson, School of Biological & Environmental Sciences, University of Stirling, Stirling, FK9 4LA, UK.

Rhys E. Green, RSPB and Conservation Science Group, Department of Zoology, University of Cambridge, Downing Street, Cambridge, CB2 3EJ, UK.

Nick R. Halfhide, Deer Commission for Scotland, Great Glen House, Leachkin Road, Inverness, IV3 8NW, UK.

Mike O. Hammill, Maurice Lamontage Institute, Fisheries and Oceans Canada, P.O. Box 1000, 850 route de la Mer, Mont. Joli, QC. Canada, G5H 3Z4.

Bradley P. Harris, Department of Fisheries Oceanography, School for Marine Science and Technology, Marine Fisheries Institute, University of Massachusetts Dartmouth, 200 Mill Road, Suite 300, Fairhaven, Massachusetts, USA 02719.

John Harwood, Centre for Research into Ecological and Environmental Modelling, University of St Andrews, St Andrews, Fife, KY16 8LB, UK.

Steve J. Hawkins, School of Ocean Sciences, Bangor University, Menai Bridge, Anglesey, LL59 5AB, UK.

Liana N. Joseph, The Ecology Centre, School of Integrative Biology, University of Queensland, St Lucia, Australia, 4072.

Robbie P. Kernahan, Deer Commission for Scotland, Great Glen House, Leachkin Road, Inverness, IV3 8NW, UK.

Paul Kirkland, Butterfly Conservation, Balallan House, Allan Park, Stirling, FK8 2QG, UK.

David W. Macdonald, Wildlife Conservation Research Unit, Recanati-Kaplan Centre, University of Oxford, Department of Zoology, Tubney House, Tubney, Oxfordshire, OX13 5QL, UK.

Iain Macleod, Hebridean Mink Project, Scottish Natural Heritage, 32 Francis Street, Stornoway, HS1 2ND, UK.

Richard F. Maloney, Research and Development Group, DOC, P.O. Box 13049, Christchurch 8141, New Zealand.

Fiona J. Manson, Scottish Natural Heritage, Battleby, Redgorton, Perth, PH1 3EW, UK.

Michael C. Marino II, Department of Fisheries Oceanography, School for Marine Science and Technology, Marine Fisheries Institute, University of Massachusetts Dartmouth, 200 Mill Road, Suite 300, Fairhaven, Massachusetts, USA 02719.

Nova Mieszkowska, The Marine Biological Association of the UK, The Laboratory, Citadel Hill, Plymouth, PL1 2PB, UK.

John A. Milne, Deer Commission for Scotland, Great Glen House, Leachkin Road, Inverness, IV3 8NW, UK.

Simon Milne MBE, Scottish Wildlife Trust, Cramond House, 3 Kirk Cramond, Edinburgh, EH4 6HZ, UK.

Tony J. Mitchell-Jones, Biodiversity Team, Natural England, Northminster House, Peterborough, Northminster Road, PE1 1UA, UK.

Tom P. Moorhouse, Wildlife Conservation Research Unit, Recanati-Kaplan Centre, University of Oxford, Department of Zoology, Tubney House, Tubney, Oxfordshire, OX13 5QL, UK.

Donald G. Newman, Research and Development Group, DOC, P.O. Box 10-420, Wellington 6143, New Zealand.

Shaun M. O'Connor, Research and Development Group, DOC, P.O. Box 10-420, Wellington 6143, New Zealand.

Catherine E. O'Keefe, Department of Fisheries Oceanography, School for Marine Science and Technology, Marine Fisheries Institute, University of Massachusetts Dartmouth, 200 Mill Road, Suite 300, Fairhaven, Massachusetts, USA 02719.

James Pearce-Higgins, RSPB Scotland, Dunedin House, 25 Ravelston Terrace, Edinburgh, EH4 3TP, UK.

Hugh P. Possingham, The Ecology Centre, School of Integrative Biology, University of Queensland, St Lucia, Australia, 4072.

Tom Prescott, Butterfly Conservation, Balallan House, Allan Park, Stirling, FK8 2QG, UK.

Chris D. Preston, Biological Records Centre, CEH Maclean Building, Benson Lane, Crowmarsh Gifford, Wallingford, Oxfordshire, OX10 8BB, UK.

Chris Quine, Centre for Human and Ecological Sciences, Forest Research, Northern Research Station, Roslin, EH25 9SY, UK.

Duncan Ray, Centre for Human and Ecological Sciences, Forest Research, Northern Research Station, Roslin, EH25 9SY, UK.

Robert Raynor, Scottish Natural Heritage, Great Glen House, Leachkin Road, Inverness, IV3 8NW, UK.

Steve Redpath, Aberdeen Centre for Environmental Sustainability, Aberdeen University and The Macaulay Institute, Aberdeen, AB24 2TZ, UK.

Tim M. Reed, EcoText Ltd., Hughfield House, Fenstanton Road, Hilton, Cambridgeshire, PE28 9JA, UK.

Ingrid Salvesen, The Norwegian Biodiversity Information Centre, Erling Skakkesgt. 47, 7491, Trondheim, Norway.

Rosalind F. Shaw, Wildlife Conservation Research Unit, Recanati-Kaplan Centre, University of Oxford, Department of Zoology, Tubney House, Tubney, Oxfordshire, OX13 5QL, UK.

Arnór Sigfússon, VST Consulting Engineers, Armula 4, 108 Reykjavik, Iceland.

Adam Smith, Game and Wildlife Conservation Trust, Couston, Newtyle, Angus, PH12 8UT, UK.

Chris J. Spray MBE, Professor of Water Science and Policy, UNECSO Centre for Water Law, Policy and Science, Dundee University, Dundee, DD1 4HN, UK.

Judy Stroud, Natural England, Northminster House, Northminster Road, Peterborough, PE1 1UA, UK.

Garry B. Stenson, Northwest Atlantic Fisheries Centre, Fisheries and Oceans Canada, P.O. Box 5667, St John's, NL, Canada, A1C 5X1.

Kevin D.E. Stokesbury, Department of Fisheries Oceanography, School for Marine Science and Technology, Marine Fisheries Institute, University of Massachusetts Dartmouth, 200 Mill Road, Suite 300, Fairhaven, Massachusetts, USA 02719.

Øystein Størkersen, Directorate for Nature Management, Tungasletta 2, 7485 Trondheim, Norway.

David A. Stroud, Joint Nature Conservation Committee, Monkstone House, City Road, Peterborough, PE1 1JY, UK.

Heather E. Sugden, School of Ocean Sciences, Bangor University, Menai Bridge, Anglesey, LL59 5AB, UK.

Simon Thirgood*, Aberdeen Centre for Environmental Sustainability, Aberdeen University and The Macaulay Institute, Aberdeen, AB24 2TZ, UK.

Des B.A. Thompson, Scottish Natural Heritage, Silvan House, 231 Corstorphine Road, Edinburgh, EH12 7AT, UK.

Åslaug Viken, The Norwegian Biodiversity Information Centre, Erling Skakkesgt. 47, 7491, Trondheim, Norway.

Martin S. Warren, Butterfly Conservation, Manor Yard, East Lulworth, Dorset, BH20 5QP, UK.

Jon Webb, Natural England, Northminster House, Northminster Road, Peterborough, PE1 1UA, UK.

David Windmill, The Royal Zoological Society of Scotland, Edinburgh Zoo, 134 Corstorphine Road, Edinburgh, EH12 6TS, UK.

* Tragically, Professor Simon Thirgood was killed in an accident shortly after completing his contribution to this book.

Introduction

This book contains the papers presented at a conference held to review the management of species in the new Millennium. It was held at a pivotal time for nature conservation, at both the global and local levels. The 2010, Year of Biodiversity was already on the horizon and the discussion relating to the 2010 target to stop the loss of biodiversity at the global level, and how this assessment might influence the conservation of biodiversity had begun. The concept of the "Ecosystem Approach" and discussion about the value of ecosystem services was developing in scientific circles, and importantly, was already finding its way into policy thinking in Governments around the world. In Scotland, these ideas were being actively discussed in relation to new legislation on climate change and in relation to the management of the seas around the country. Both these legislative areas present new and complex challenges to the scientist and policy maker alike.

So how then should species management be taken forward within this context, and against a background of rapid change in the ecology of habitats in Scotland? Changes due to climate change, the spread of alien species and the cumulative, long-term effects of grazing regimes, especially in the uplands, all bring pressures to bear on the species found across Scotland. Yet it is not all bad news and difficulty. Recent schemes to bring back some of the most iconic species to Scotland, such as the white-tailed sea eagle (*Haliaeetus albicilla)*, red kite (*Milvus milvus*) and European beaver (*Castor fiber)* have all demonstrated that with vision, determination and enthusiasm a lot can be achieved, to not just maintain what we have, but to enhance the overall biodiversity of the country.

Clearly, the conservation of species has to be seen in the context of the wider ecosystem and of the value that they bring to its functioning. Conservation has, however, always gone beyond looking at functionality, and has in many ways been an expression of what people want to see in "their" countryside. In Scotland, as in many other countries, our wildlife is part of our cultural heritage, responsible in part for shaping our art and literature over the years. Stories of eagles and wildcats abound in our literature, both in English and in our native Gaelic, and pictures of red deer stags have become iconic symbols of Scotland.

There is enormous public interest in the well being of many of these iconic species, and growing awareness of just what a superb resource we have in Scotland. This public interest is likely to grow and mean that issues will still need to be addressed at the individual species level in years to come. Public interest rightly focuses also on the welfare of individual animals in the wild. Aligning the discussion between animal welfare standards and the need for the active control of some species in the wild is a key area yet to be fully resolved. Some of the studies in this book do, however, highlight that the two areas, welfare and control, can be compatible.

With the vast array of species in Scotland and a multitude of issues to be resolved, how can management be effectively focused so that resources are best used and the key problems are dealt with? In response to this challenge Scottish Natural Heritage (SNH) developed a "Species Action Framework" in 2007. This approach, designed primarily to help prioritize the work of SNH, has had much wider value in providing a structure in which priorities can be set. It identified four categories for action:

- Species in need of conservation action. Given the wide range of species in need of action in Scotland it will always be difficult to prioritize, but in practice with finite resources, hard decisions have to be taken, ideally based on a sound information base.
- Dealing with invasive alien species. This has been identified as an area where the problem is becoming greater, with new species arriving in the country and others spreading into new areas, possibly as a result of climate change enabling species to expand their range where they were previously constrained by one or more climatic factors.
- Conflicts of interest between native species. In some ways this is perhaps one of the most complex areas for the managers of species to grapple with. How do you decide what species is a priority and how can an effective balance in their respective ecology be achieved? Some of the most intransigent problems in conservation within Scotland relate to just this question. For example, resolving the management issues between hen harriers (*Circus cyaneus)* and red grouse (*Lagopus lagopus scotica)* will demand innovation and a detailed understanding of their respective ecology, and of the dynamics of the habitats that support them. This book contains the details of studies seeking the solution to this, and other similar situations.
- Finally, the sustainable use of species is seen as a key aim. In situations where there is a direct harvest and therefore a direct economic return, then the need for sustainable use is obvious, yet in many cases difficult to achieve. The history of species management is littered with examples of over-exploitation leading to the destruction of the population being harvested. The overfishing of the native oyster (*Ostrea edulis*) in the Forth estuary is one well known example but there are many others from around the world. Learning from these mistakes is crucial to future management and to sustaining the direct economic return from populations of wild animals.

Whichever way we manage species, there are some general principles that have come from a variety of "best practice" studies over the years, and that relate to using the ecosystem approach in planning and in problem resolution. Firstly, managing species is a shared responsibility; something to be undertaken, with all interest groups and individuals involved where possible. Starting from a point of inclusiveness in the management of species is a significant departure from previous management where it was done by particular managers or by government in some cases. Secondly, it is important to take account of the ecological and economic issues involved. Gaining an understanding of the ecology of species is fundamental to good management but so too is developing an awareness of the economic issues involved. Thirdly, whilst taking a strategic approach; laying out options and taking a wider view is clearly wise, it is necessary to be adaptive; learning from mistakes and successes, trying new approaches and being flexible to achieve results. It could be said that some management of species in Scotland today is too traditional and that a more adaptive approach is required for the new challenges the country faces. Can the effects of climate change really be tackled if we continue to manage our species and habitats in the same way that we have done for the past 100 years?

Finally, it is important to note that the management of species in Scotland cannot be viewed in isolation from the rest of the world. We have a responsibility to manage species in a sustainable way, especially for those migratory species that we share with other countries. Looking after migratory salmon, geese and seabirds, for example, is important to us as they are part of our natural heritage, and part of the natural heritage of many other countries. Several of the chapters in this book relate to studies in other countries; allowing us to learn from their work and to see how different approaches may be deployed.

The book is intended to generate discussion and debate. We welcome your thoughts!

Colin A. Galbraith and John M. Baxter February 2010.

Part 1

How do we manage species?

This first section of the book provides an overview of the key issues involved in the conservation of species, and gives a valuable insight into conservation management in Norway and in New Zealand.

Peter Bridgewater reveals the difficulties involved in decision making in setting priorities for action. He stresses that prioritizing is difficult but necessary if action is to be taken. He stresses also the need to take a holistic approach, considering the full range of issues involved in management problems. He advocates the use of the Ecosystem Approach to planning, and encourages greater attention on the full range of species involved in ecosystems, not just the iconic ones. Finally, he stresses the need for a new approach and innovation for the new Millennium.

Shaun O'Conner and his co-authors provide us with an overview of conservation work in New Zealand, a country with a staggering 2,700 threatened taxa, many being endemic to the country. We see from the experience of those responsible for the conservation of these species that the development of a systematic approach, through the Natural Heritage Monitoring System (NHMS) is increasingly being viewed as essential. The system provides a decision support tool, providing information on priority planning and monitoring plans. The information held in the system will progressively allow managers to assess how effective their actions may be and to make clear choices about where best to deploy their resources.

The chapter by Øystein Størkersen, Des Thompson and John Baxter gives us an insight into how wildlife is managed in Norway. The country is rich in biodiversity, with a strong link to national culture and way of life. The Directorate for Nature Management has a key responsibility for the management of wildlife, especially the conservation of biodiversity, regulation of hunting and the control of alien species. The importance of developing an effective network of protected areas and a network of protected water courses is stressed, each as a building block towards the effective management of the resource overall. They note especially the importance and profile of the marine environment, highlighting the need for a sound information base on marine species. This becomes ever more important given the recent rise in interest in the marine environment in terms of energy generation in particular.

Taken together, these three chapters set the scene and provide examples of management practices that will be explored further in the other sections of this book.

Opposite – Royal hakea (*Hakea victoria*). © Peter Bridgewater

Chapter 1

What management? Which species?

Peter Bridgewater[1]

Summary

1. While it is true that species readily attract public attention, they are not the only aspect of biodiversity important for conservation.
2. Using the full complement of the biodiversity hierarchy can deliver better conservation and management results for species.
3. Species management in the 21st century may have to be on a different basis than before – working with the impacts of climate and other changes to habitats and landscapes to deliver the optimal results.
4. Optimal results are best judged by continued delivery of ecosystem services, not just which species survive.
5. Inevitably we will have to make choices, mostly unpleasant, about which species it is sensible to invest effort in saving or managing. Application of the Ecosystem Approach of the Convention on Biological Diversity, which brings a socio-cultural focus to conservation and sustainable use, can be of help here.

[1] Chair, Joint Nature Conservation Committee, Monkstone House, City Road, Peterborough, PE1 1JY, UK

1.1 Introduction

Red kangaroo (*Macropus rufus*). © Peter Bridgewater

In Barcelona on Monday 6 October 2008 the fourth World Conservation Congress opened with pomp and ceremony. The key headline was "at least 1,141 of the 5,487 mammals on Earth are known to be threatened with extinction..." The reaction of the Director General of IUCN, was to suggest **"We must** *now set clear targets for the future to reverse this trend to ensure that our enduring legacy is not to wipe out many of our closest relatives"* – and that this extinction rate for species was *"a frightening sign of what is happening to the ecosystems where they live".*

But this misses a crucial point. Simply setting targets for species will not achieve anything, except to produce more lists, goals and targets – of the also growing list of species which have left or are leaving us!! For species management in this century, the key challenge is accelerating global change, mostly driven by climate change. But there are other challenges. The need to understand the bio-cultural context of species is critical – why do we spend so much time and effort on so-called charismatic species when those on which the earth's future depends are neglected in comparison? In part it is because these are unseen and for the most part unknown. And species loss and change is important, but is it fully reflected in changes to the delivery of ecosystem services?

Before the IUCN held World Conservation Congresses they called General Assemblies; the last in 1994 in Buenos Aires. A key item on the Agenda of that meeting, and the World Conservation Congresses held in 1996, 2000 and 2004 was the Red List and its conclusions – simply put, an increasing list of species facing extinction, or moving to the departure lounge. There was some good news, however, IUCN (2008b) suggesting some species are improving their status.

Also on the agenda of the 1994 meeting was sustainable use of wild resources (or sustainable development); an area where there was much polarity between the government and non-government sectors and between developed and developing countries. Fast forward to Barcelona in 2008, and the same scenario obtains. No-one seems prepared to grab the nettle of sustainable use, and many are quite happy to describe it as (oxy)moronic. Yet if we are really to give effect to the actions under the Convention on Biological Diversity (CBD) we must understand more clearly how far we can go to match conservation and management of wildlife with social desires and aspirations – not to mention the need to recognize conservation as a key to the reduction of poverty.

Despite the theme of the 1994 assembly (caring for the earth and its people) it was also obvious that, for many, *people* are not seen as being part of biodiversity. Of course we are, and if we do not realize biodiversity conservation is about our own conservation, whether we live in the intellectual safety of York, Edinburgh or Bangor; the gritty reality of the Tanami, Serengeti, or Gobi deserts or the verdancy of the Amazon or Congo; we are certainly deservedly doomed to extinction. We must conquer our natural tendency to view all other organisms as somehow part of a different world. Once we accept that reality, it all becomes just a little bit easier.

Therefore I would say at the outset *"It's not just the species, stupid!"* I argue we have spent too long focused on species as the only way to achieve conservation – and in so doing we have actually lost sight of the role of ecosystems as a key focus for achieving nature conservation. Of course we do understand, comprehend and relate to species as units. Public appreciation of wild nature is almost always expressed through a species lens – with rare and endangered species attracting most attention. But it is fitting that other chapters deal with the ecosystem approach –this chapter starts there as well. Because, to understand the species which need attention, and what management to apply to them, we need clarity on the role of species in the biodiversity hierarchy. Following the definition of biodiversity in the text of the CBD, it is clear it is a hierarchical concept, from genes, through species to ecosystems. Of course even those boundaries blend downwards towards the molecular, and upwards to landscapes and ultimately the biosphere.

So far I have used the terms species, wildlife and biodiversity. Our conservation lexicon is becoming rather crowded, and for clarity I subsequently use the term biodiversity, qualified as necessary. To revisit the definition of biodiversity; the CBD defines it as:

> *"the variability among living organisms from all sources including,* inter alia, *terrestrial, marine and other aquatic ecosystems and the ecological complexes of which they are part; this includes diversity within species, between species and of ecosystems."*

Too often, however, biodiversity is simply used as an equivalent word for species. Witness the Biodiversity Hotspots of Conservation International (Myers *et al.,* 2000). These are certainly areas of great endemic species richness, but are not necessarily – indeed usually not at all – centres for high biodiversity in the sense of the Convention's definition. There have been several attempts to clarify this hotspot concept, (e.g. Possingham and Wilson, 2000) among the more interesting, a recent blog on the website of The Nature Conservancy (TNC, 2008).

1.2 Sustainability

Government policies in all countries of the UK, more widely in Europe and through much of the developed world, respond to and generally reflect the majority views of society. Interest in biodiversity conservation is generally species orientated and is often stimulated by the campaigns and lobbying activities of dedicated non-government conservation organizations (NGOs). All too often, however, animal welfare issues (and we must never minimize them) are presented veiled as conservation problems.

Much debate has taken place in recent times on the need to conserve biodiversity and formulate policies that ensure that the future development of the UK at large and its devolved administrations is sustainable. These two policy objectives are not mutually exclusive. Achieving practical formulae that provide for an improved quality of life for Britons without further impoverishing our natural resources for future generations is the core issue. Economists have become more ecological in their focus, looking at ways to value species, communities and ecosystems - most usefully through the ecological services they provide (e.g. Balmford *et al.*, 2002; EC, 2008).

But there are other issues. Promoting the cause for biodiversity conservation is sometimes disappointing because of its seeming reduction to nothing but demands for more and larger totally protected areas. Protected areas certainly have a major role to play in biodiversity conservation – yet such conservation without understanding that protected areas need the support of well managed surrounds will be destined to failure. Chief among the causes of biodiversity decline are habitat loss and fragmentation, and resulting disruptions in ecological processes (Bridgewater, 1997; Bennett, 2003; Nassauer, 2006). Fragmentation impairs the ability of a species to adapt to the rapidly shifting habitat patterns and ecological processes that result from climate change, further weakening their resilience.

Successful long-term conservation of biodiversity will depend ultimately on formulating strategies which integrate principles of resource conservation and sustainable development *and* which are acceptable to society at large. Policies must be practical and readily achievable if they are to be embraced by land managers and those who live with biodiversity. In this regard there is clearly a need to collaborate with community-based groups and develop complementary strategies which can be implemented by organizations and individuals other than governments.

IUCN Recommendation 18.24 (IUCN, 2008a) provided the basis for the IUCN to establish a sustainable use of wildlife programme. This programme had some successes in the neotropics and Francophone Africa, and to some extent the Asia-Pacific region. All this may sound heresy to dedicated conservationists committed to the conventional approach to conserving wildlife through the acquisition and management of national parks and nature reserves. However, if one steps back from that approach and examines the issues objectively, it warrants serious consideration. Use of wildlife is not a new phenomenon. Since they became recognizable as a sentient species with highly invasive tendencies, humans have interacted with wildlife for food, shelter, warmth and companionship. It is now axiomatic that the demands on living resources by increasing numbers of humans has resulted in many such uses becoming unsustainable.

The concept of using the commercial or other values of wildlife as a means of creating the incentives necessary to develop sustainable use and conserve those species and their habitats represents a departure from traditional western conservation ideology. But it does not represent anything radical to indigenous communities who have depended on and coexisted with wildlife for millennia. Such peoples, because of their reliance on certain wildlife to exist; have often, though not exclusively, exercised safeguards in using wildlife to ensure that resources are not depleted in a manner which threatens options for future use.

Unfortunately there are all too many examples of wild plants and animals which have been harvested for commercial purposes at levels or periods which are unable to be sustained by the wild resource. Although this is obviously cause for concern, the threat of wholesale extinctions from habitat shrinkage and disappearance is even greater. Destruction of essential habitats in the face of competing land uses and the resulting disappearance of their associated biotas seem irreversible. While all of the above would seem a compelling reason for a programme under IUCN to flourish it has instead languished in favour of more traditional approaches. Part of the reason for this is lack of support from some IUCN members who prefer to see conservation in black and white rather than the rainbow hue it actually is.

1.3 Kangaroos

Some 69 species of kangaroo (and wallaby) are recognized by systematists, with most having quite restricted populations. Australia has 53 of these species, with six having gone extinct since 1770, and many others currently endangered. Endangerment is not, however, an issue for populations of the large Maropod species. Kangaroo management in Australia has been important and has a key role in the future management of arid and semi-arid regions of Australia.

In any country, competition between certain species and agriculture *sensu lato* generally results in the persecution of the native species concerned and destruction of its habitat to reduce the conflict. There still exists some antipathy by Australian pastoralists to conservation. This is particularly true in areas adjacent to national parks and other protected areas of natural vegetation – as well as key species. Protected areas are regarded both as fire hazards and as reservoirs for native species which regularly venture onto neighbouring farmlands causing damage to crops. And none more so than some of the kangaroo species – making these species useful models of the considerations we now must give to species management; a holistic integrated approach that takes account of the role of species in the biodiversity hierarchy.

Conflicts over kangaroos merely serve to polarize pastoralists and rural communities against urban conservationists. Conservation agencies thus become the middleman in these arguments, unable to cull, and yet legally responsible for ensuring ecosystem health. It is axiomatic that in developing plans of management for such areas the views of local communities must be taken into account. The long-term viability of the conservation estate will be enhanced if local communities perceive a degree of "ownership" in the way in which such lands are managed – and the same is true for species.

Human settlement of Australia has been accompanied by extensive changes to the landscape – first from Aboriginal people and their manipulation of landscape through fire, and latterly by settlers from Europe who have continued use of fire, though with different regimes, as well as extensive technologically-aided changes to agriculture, resulting in significant changes to hydrology.

Agriculture (including pastoralism) in Australia has resulted in conversion of native vegetation into more 'productive' land-uses, especially for people. While this habitat conversion has been detrimental to some species of native plants and animals it has undoubtedly been beneficial to others. Red and grey kangaroos and some native parrots and cockatoos in particular found themselves with an abundance of food resources - and competed directly with agricultural interests.

These species rapidly became perceived as pests by rural communities, who, in addition to having to contend with climatic conditions such as flooding and frequent, often prolonged, droughts, regularly faced extensive damage to crops and competition for fodder by native wildlife. This led the various State and Federal governments in Australia to agree a process for management of certain species of kangaroos, essentially predicated on their nature as an agricultural pest.

This management is carried out under the Environment Protection and Biodiversity Conservation (EPBC) Act 1999 (DEWHA, 2008), where Australian (Federal) Government approval is required for the State kangaroo management plans. Before approval, kangaroo management plans must demonstrate that they have no net detriment to either the harvested species or their ecosystems. These plans thus promote the long term conservation of these species, within a framework of sustainable harvesting – although it is a moot point whether control or harvesting is the main motive.

Kangaroo harvesting results in meat (suitable for human consumption) and skins for leather. It is estimated that 70% of meat and 30% of skins are used domestically, with the remainder being exported to over 25 countries (DEWHA, 2008). Four species are currently subject to harvesting:

- Red kangaroo (*Macropus rufus*), (Range: Qld, NSW, SA, WA)[1]
- Eastern grey kangaroo (*M. giganteus*), (Range: Qld, NSW)
- Western grey kangaroo (*M. fuliginosus*), (Range: NSW, SA, WA)
- Common wallaroo or euro (*M. robustus*), (Range: Qld, NSW, SA)

It is clear from an analysis over the last 20 years that there has been no detriment to the populations (Figure 1.1a) with the total estimated population of all harvested species showing a peak in 1990, and again in 2000. Each of these years had particularly good rainfall in the preceding years across inland Australia. When the rangelands are well vegetated, after prolonged rains, the kangaroo population is able to expand rapidly, due to its special reproductive abilities (Walton and Richardson, 1989). Figure 1.1b shows the cull quota of the target species, and the total quota. Actual cull is always lower than the quota. But as the population rose in high productivity years the quota rose before falling away again. In the last five years Australia has been in the grip of a severe drought and the overall population figures reflect this. Yet the harvesting operation has not caused kangaroo populations to crash – and limited cull is still practised, and necessary.

The effects of climate change, and the need to adapt to carbon based economies is showing new ways of reacting to species management. For kangaroos, Wilson and Edwards (2008) advance a very interesting argument, based on the low levels of methane produced by kangaroo grazing, compared to cattle and sheep. The latter two species, through ruminant activity, account for 11% of Australia's Greenhouse Gas (GHG) emissions. The authors postulate that removing 7 million cattle and 36 million sheep from Australia's rangelands, and allowing the kangaroo population to expand to 175 million would save 3% of Australia's GHG emissions. Further, the grazing patterns for sheep and cattle, together with their hoofed feet has caused incalculable damage to the soil surface structures of Australia's arid areas. Lunney (2001) has estimated around 20 of the mammal extinctions in Australia in the last 50 years are due to grazing damage to native ecosystems from sheep and cattle.

[1] Qld –Queensland; NSW – New South Wales; SA – South Australia; WA – Western Australia

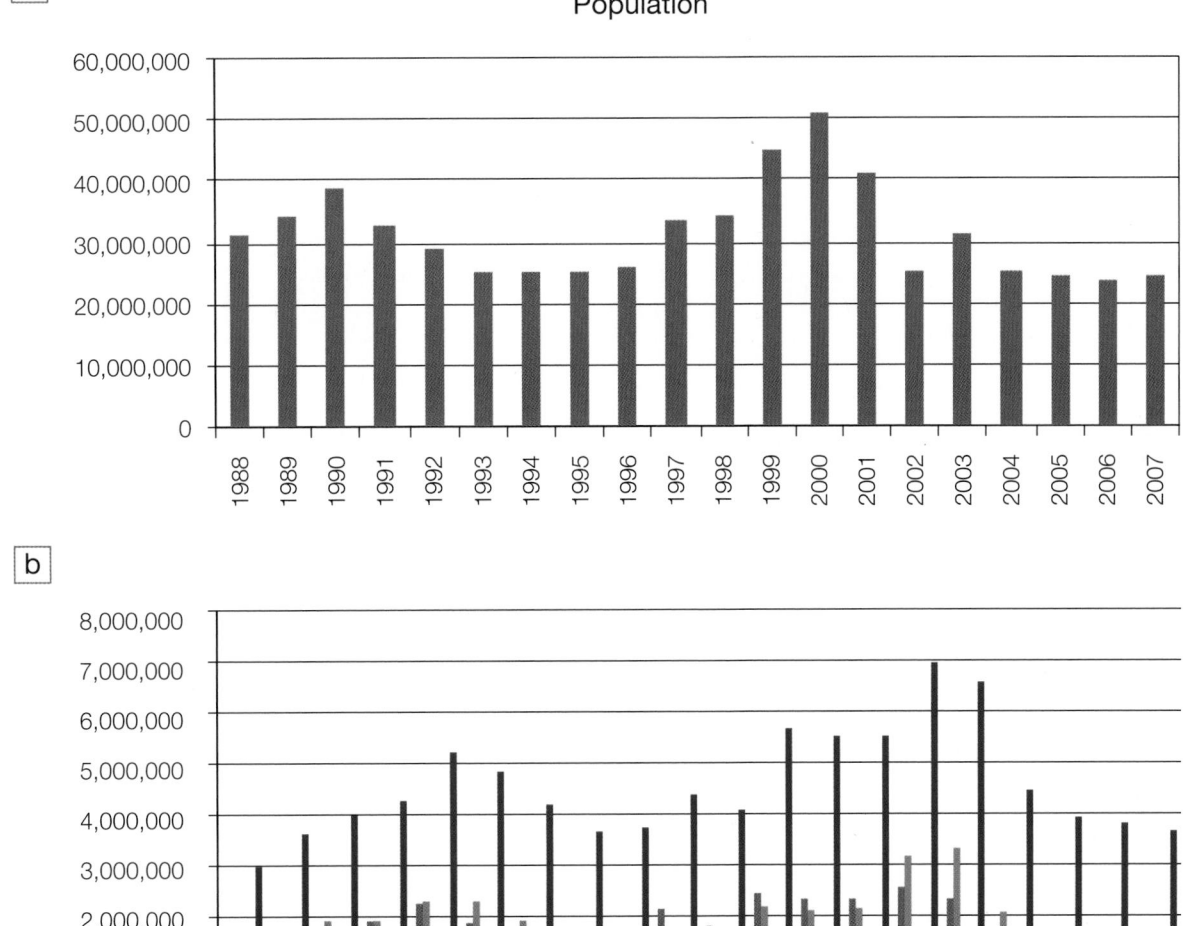

Note: *M. parryi* was always at very low quotas, and ceased to be allocated quota from 2003.

Figure 1.1 Cull quota and population data for harvested species of *Macropus* in Australia, 1988 – 2008. a) Total estimated population data for the harvested kangaroo species, based on data held by the Department of the Environment, Canberra. b) Cull quota for the five kangaroo species harvested across Australian Rangelands, 1988 – 2008.

Plate 1.1 Western grey kangaroo (*Macropus fuliginosus*) in forested landscape, Western Australia. © Peter Bridgewater

Wilson and Edwards (2008) note such a change would require great cultural and social change – among rural landholders and especially conservationists/animal welfare organizations who see kangaroo culling by shooting as cruel and inhumane. They also note that bison in America, red deer in Scotland and springbok in South Africa are now thriving on private lands integrated with agriculture. So there are ways to manage species, within a changing ecosystem context.

1.4 Animal welfare and conservation

The relationship between wildlife conservation and sustainable utilization was reinforced at the 1992 meeting of the Conference of the Parties to the Convention on International Trade in Endangered Species of Wild Fauna and Flora (CITES) when a resolution was adopted which recognized the potential benefits deriving from the sustainable use of certain species to both the conservation of the species and the economic well-being of rural communities. But ever since then we have had continuing controversy in CITES over many species, the flames of controversy often fanned by NGOs and governments not with a real cause for wildlife protection, but as a means to advance animal welfare objectives. Clearly welfare issues are important, yet they cannot – indeed must not – be the driving force to set conservation objectives.

It is bizarre that in this century it is apparently less difficult to show and explain away human casualties on battlefields than whales, elephants, kangaroos, or other charismatic animals also killed in their own battlefields. It is true that when you set targets to cull (which while it sounds like kill has quite a different etymological origin) the "kill" will never be perfect, just as the best run slaughter houses are never 100% on target.

Welfare considerations emerged in the discussion of kangaroo management in Australia decades ago. But not really as issues of welfare – instead falsely portrayed as issues of conservation, species endangerment and the like. Yet it is in the oceans that welfare and conservation have become maximally blurred – seals certainly fall into this, but primarily whales are the set of charismatic species which have become entwined between welfare and conservation.

Australian, U.K. and many other government positions on whaling have been criticized by some as inconsistent with other policies which allow sustainable use, while being praised by others. Australia's position was transformed from a pro-whaling stance in the 1970s to an ultra-protectionist position by many events, most notably by the report by Sir Sydney Frost in 1978 (Australia, 1978). The Whaling Industry was in fact an example, par excellence, of a non-sustainable use of wildlife. The industry was badly focused and driven largely by a combination of greed, expediency and the need to find materials to continue the industrial revolution. Use of whales for food and sustenance, has, of course, always occurred but has been largely limited to far northern communities in the northern hemisphere, with occasional takes in other parts of the world on the migratory pathways of particular species. The International Whaling Commission has developed possibly the most sophisticated wildlife management model for any sort of species. While this model has been tested through simulation it has yet to be applied in the real world.

Aside from the science, there are, of course sociological and marketplace aspects. Getting agreement on inspection and other controls, and ensuring they are effective, will be essential to avoid a repeat of the post-war pelagic whaling juggernaut. It is also obvious that we are still uncertain of the stock numbers to make the model work. And despite numerous sessions at the IWC on welfare issues it is quite clear that harpooning a large speeding mammal from a pitching and tossing vessel is unlikely to have high success rates in "instant painless death".

Despite the clear issues of welfare, and the validity on welfare grounds alone, from questioning any remaining whaling activities, many of those opposed to whaling, including official government positions, dress the arguments as conservation. "Whale species are heading for extinction..." is a familiar refrain. Yet we learn from the latest IUCN Red list analysis that the humpback whale (*Megaptera novaeangliae*) at least is now being regarded as no longer endangered, along with several other species. (IUCN, 2008b) Rightly, the total protection afforded whale species by the 1982 IWC moratorium (IWC, 2008) has resulted in population recovery, and will continue to do so.

The question is, however, whether this success will produce its own dilemma: as whale populations regain strength they are likely to do so in a different balance than pre-whaling numbers. This will mean, at the ecosystem level, increasing perturbations between whales, their prey, and others who indirectly or directly prey on their prey!! It will be ironic if one of the results of the whaling moratorium is, in 50 years time, a new need for whaling, sealing or other species culls, to manage populations of various species, especially in the southern ocean.

The whaling industry is a clear lesson of how to get it wrong. But it is not a signal that we cannot get it right – if we approach the issues dispassionately, and with full humanity and indeed humility. Mclaren *et al.* (2006) examine the general question of welfare and conservation. They say, *inter alia*, "*Accepting that intervention, with potential animal welfare implications, is necessary for much of conservation biology, a combined welfare and conservation ethic could be that the rights to exist and be left alone should only be waived if there is sufficient justification.*" And later "*Ultimately, however, welfare science must be able to provide biologists with the tools and predictive power to be able to plan successful conservation interventions. We judge that conservationists have a duty to evaluate whether the animal welfare implications of their work are outweighed by conservation benefits.*"

This puts additional demands and pressures on those practising conservation science, which, as Mclaren *et al.* (2006) rightly emphasize, is in reality intervention and management. The implications are clear, conservation is not just about genes, species, or ecosystems – it is about how *Homo sapiens* as a species has and can continue to interact with, and retain, the maximum biodiversity on this planet. And in part, whether the specific epithet is deserved! Macdonald *et al.* (2006) note:

> "*Once, the emphasis was protection. Now, it is integration. The most obvious reason for this change is that the world's human population has more than trebled since 1900, from less than two billion to 6.5 billion.*"

So, how should we look at the other species with which we share the planet, and what management, and at what level, should we be considering?

1.5 Triage

In 1991, the Ecological Society of America proposed the Sustainable Biosphere Initiative, a research agenda directed towards the establishment of research priorities which will provide the information necessary for future informed decisions on environmental matters (Lubchenco *et al.*, 1991). That same year, IUBS-SCOPE-UNESCO produced a research agenda for biodiversity (Solbrig, 1991). These two agendas have received much support. While there are the inevitable differences of opinion, the world's research ecologists appear remarkably united, in a way not seen since Arthur Tansley coined the term *ecosystem* (Tansley, 1935), in their support for the ideas of these agendas and the importance of scientific information in the decision-making process. The Millennium Ecosystem Assessment (MEA, 2005)

Plate 1.2 Abbott's booby (*Papasula abbotti*) formerly widespread in the Indian Ocean and now confined to Christmas Island, Indian Ocean. Its future depends on effective management of the rainforest on the island, including through re-afforestation. © Peter Bridgewater

continued this process of natural and social sciences working together to provide the best possible policy options.

Although we must in no way diminish the contribution of these research agendas, the processes of establishing priorities, making and implementing decisions (all using the very best scientific information) are functions of management (q.v. McLaren *et al.*, 2006). The crucial linkages, often overlooked, are between the managers and the researchers. Research methodology is basically reductionist, while management is integrative and holistic. The challenge for the manager is where to apply the available information and to clearly establish what new information is needed. The challenge for the research scientist is to provide useable information for conservation managers.

For example, is the keystone-species concept (cf. Mills *et al.,* 1993) helpful? To single out for research or other community attention any taxon or ecological grouping is certain to generate both support and discord. While individual biologists have a favourite taxon or ecological grouping, in reality *all* species and *all* ecological groups are important. And biodiversity redundancy - does it exist? How much do we need? – is a vital question to be answered for managers.

Much recent effort on the protection of threatened or endangered species has been through the use of protected areas and through the development of special survival programmes for those species which were considered to be endangered. Macdonald *et al.* (2006) note that *"…it is not uncommon to meet conservationists who seem to believe that all conflict in Nature's garden would vanish if only their misinformed opponents 'understood'. This hopeful vision imagines that the lions that eat cattle (and a number of cattle-herders that is not inconsequential to those involved) would become welcome denizens of everybody's backyard if only people understood them better (often in the cornucopian embrace of eco-tourism)."*

So we need to think about both endangered species - and endangered spaces. McCloskey (in Bridgewater, 1997), clearly articulated that *"We need to go beyond 'saving what's left'—it's as if mainline environmental movements are running a hospital with only an emergency ward."* This echoes some of the views of McIntyre *et al.* (1992) on species triage, and Bridgewater and Walton (1995), who put it as: *"we must not concentrate solely on saving the man over-board while the ship sinks"*. The implication being that we must make choices on what to save, based on what we can sensibly manage. Of course, many more genes can be saved by *ex-situ* conservation of propagules and individuals in seed and germplasm banks, zoos and botanic gardens. We must also address the crises in our landscapes and seascapes, not concentrate solely on endangered species. Endangered species are a symptom of crisis, and as such also a tool to help solve the crisis, by helping develop and map out a new strategic approach to biodiversity management.

1.6 The other side of the coin

Invasive alien species and the threats they pose to global conservation efforts are well documented, not least through the CBD (CBD, 2008a). Yet there are other ways to look at this – for while there are some seriously damaging species operating now in many habitats, there are many more which are being integrated into native ecosystems, and forming new combinations (novel ecosystems, *sensu* Hobbs *et al.*, 2006.)

There is evidence that these species are actually contributing to the ultimate conservation of endangered native species. Lundberg *et al.* (2008) describe the contribution of *Opuntia* species planted in the southern part of Madagascar. The area is a landscape heavily fragmented by human interventions and clearing. The remaining forest patches are actually mostly sacred groves, an anthropic landscape feature which none-the-less conserves biodiversity. *Opuntia* (mostly *O. ficus-indica*) is planted as hedges, largely to provide for an emergency crop in case of other crop failure, and also as the principal food source for cattle. The result is that the high biodiversity parts of this considerably fragmented landscape are effectively connected, affording protection for many rare and endemic species.

There are ironies, however, in that in an adjacent area *O. stricta* has become established as a very invasive species, and has worked to reduce biodiversity. This simply demonstrates that conservation needs to retain many pathways to ensure ecosystem resilience.

A further example is the Norfolk Island green parrot (*Cyanoramphus cookii*) (Hill, 2002). It is one of the rarest and most endangered bird species in Australia, found only on Norfolk Island in the South Pacific where it is largely restricted to natural or semi-natural forests within the Norfolk Island National Park. It probably originally occurred on the adjoining and smaller Phillip Island. The total population size is currently estimated to be 160 with 14 known breeding pairs.

The total population size will be limited by the availability of predator-free breeding habitat and nesting sites and ultimately by habitat loss and the small area of remaining suitable habitat. The current recovery plan proposes establishing and maintaining sufficient predator-free nest sites for 25 breeding pairs on Norfolk Island, replanting 4 ha of potential breeding habitat each year, establishing a second breeding population on Phillip Island and investigating the possibility of establishing a true second population either captive on the Australian mainland or introduced to nearby Lord Howe Island.

Green parrots forage in all habitats within the park (except for a small area of eucalypt plantation) and in some areas outside of the park. The principal diet of adult green parrots appears to be a variety of native seeds, fruits, flowers, and leaves, with seeds, fruit and bark of some invasive alien species also consumed (Forshaw, 1981: Hicks and Preece, 1991).

Seeds from the highly invasive African olive and red guava may now form a significant part of the diet of newly-fledged juveniles (Davidson, 1997). Not only does the fact that the recovering populations are feeding on alien, highly invasive species raise an eyebrow, the establishment of suitable sites for establishment on Phillip Island would almost certainly need to be *via* seeding with these aliens, as the island was totally devegetated by goats and rabbits during the last half of the 20th century. Seeding with native species is as yet uncertain, but is a long term aim. This is ecosystem and species manipulation on a large scale. And yet it can be done, and should be done – it is a good case study of the Ecosystem Approach in action.

1.7 The Ecosystem Approach

The Ecosystem Approach of the CBD (CBD, 2008b) is:

> *"...the primary framework for action under the Convention of Biological Diversity. The ecosystem approach provides a framework within which the relationship of protected areas to the wider landscape and seascape can be understood, and the goods and services flowing from protected areas can be valued."*

But it is also about species conservation as well. It has 12 principles, of which Principle 8 states:

> *"Recognizing the varying temporal scales and lag-effects that characterize ecosystem processes, objectives for ecosystem management should be set for the long term".*

Macdonald *et al.* (2006) proposed 11 themes for conservation, with the 9th being

"The goals of conservation are often arbitrary, and we should recognize the different arguments for conserving process and for preserving the products of that process."

This theme fits well with the ecosystem approach, which is almost a coded way of "living well with nature". It is primarily about linking people with nature at various spatial and temporal scales (UNESCO-MAB, 2000). It is a framework against which the whole of the CBD can be realized.

As we move into the 21st century the demands placed on wild living resources will require innovative strategies to help us deliver effective management. In developing countries, sustainable use of wildlife has the potential to be applied as a strategy to create incentives to conserve species outside protected areas.

Plate 1.3 Pig-nosed turtle (*Carettochelys insculpta*) depicted in Aboriginal rock art, Kakadu National Park, Australia. The species is found in New Guinea and Northern Australia, the northern Australian populations being regarded as a separate sub-species. Not only in Australia, indigenous (bio-cultural) knowledge of species and their management is passed on through art, legend and song. © Peter Bridgewater

In developed countries we need to find a new paradigm which balances relentless development with a better place for all of biodiversity, including people, to live.

Whether in developing or developed countries, governments cannot afford the luxury of continuing to acquire land for conservation purposes, especially in the face of climate and other global changes. Conservation of biological diversity will not be achieved merely through protective legislation and the acquisition of a fixed arbitrary percentage of lands and territorial waters for inclusion in the "conservation estate". So, we do need a completely new pragmatic approach to conservation, where species *can* and *should be* the focus, with an eye to ensuring genetic diversity is maintained or enhanced, and ecosystems are not only conserved but are managed for their services.

To conclude, I can do little better than quote Holdgate (1993);

"This whole issue needs to be seen in context - the context of environmentally sound and sustainable development and the equitable apportionment of its benefits... Each community needs to judge for itself how it can best conserve its environment and use it optimally... Dialogue between all sectors of the community (will be needed), and especially (between) environmentalists who understand the value of the services nature provides, and the limits of nature's tolerances, economists, who face the challenge of incorporating these values into their models and equations, governments as custodians of the economy and regulators of policy and action, and local people who are the custodians of the land and its living resources. IUCN will endeavour to promote that dialogue, and guide it to solutions, that cater for the interests of both people and wildlife."

It's not clear that 15 years on from this remark, and 60 years after its foundation, IUCN has delivered on that promise. And dialogue, if it exists, is too often a dialogue of the deaf. Leopold (1949), wrote, when today's environmental problems were still a whisper;

"... the evolution of a land ethic is an intellectual as well as an emotional process. Conservation is paved with good intentions which prove to be futile, or even dangerous, because they are devoid of critical understanding either of the land, or of economic land-use.

... by and large our present problem is one of attitudes and implements".

Taking his words as a prescient setting for our current focus on species conservation, it is clear we need to develop new attitudes, refine the tools we have available – in short, shift to a new paradigm. Such a paradigm shift should link adaptive management, create partnerships between all sectors of society and develop a land/seascape focus using the ecosystem approach.

1.8   Acknowledgements

I acknowledge with pleasure papers supplied by David Macdonald and George Wilson, and assistance with kangaroo data from Cindy Steensby. Conversations with too many to mention over the years have contributed to the ideas synthesized here, so thanks to many anonymous discussants!

References

Australia. (1978). *Inquiry into Whales and Whaling*. A.G.P.S. Canberra.

Balmford, A., Bruner, A., Cooper, P., Costanza, R., Farber, S., Green, R.E., Jenkins, M., Jefferiss, P., Jessamy, V., Madden, J., Munro, K., Myers, N., Naeem, S., Paavola, J., Rayment, M., Rosendo, S., Roughgarden, J., Trumper, K. & Turner, K.T. (2002). Economic reasons for conserving wild nature. *Science* **297**: 950–953.

Bennett, F. A. (2003). *Linkages in the landscape.* IUCN Forest Conservation Programme, Conserving Forest Ecosystems Series No. 1. IUCN, Gland.

Bridgewater, P. B. (1997). The Global Garden: Eden revisited. In Hale, P and Lamb, D. *Conservation outside of Reserves*, Surrey Beatty, Chipping Norton, New South Wales. pp 35 - 38.

Bridgewater, P. & Walton, D.W. (1995). The species triage: are we trying to retrieve the man overboard while the ship sinks? In *Reintroduction Biology of Australian and New Zealand Fauna.* Ed. M. Serena, Surrey Beatty & Sons, Chipping Norton, New South Wales. pp. ix-xii.

Convention on Biological Diversity. (2008a). http://www.cbd.int/invasive/

Convention on Biological Diversity. (2008b). http://www.cbd.int/ecosystem/

Davidson, P.M. (1997). *Movements and Behaviour of Juvenile Green Parrots Determined by Radio-tracking.* Environment Australia, Canberra. Unpublished Report.

Department of the Environment, Water, Heritage and the Arts. (2008). http://www.environment.gov.au/biodiversity/trade-use/wild-harvest/kangaroo/biology.html#kanfam

Department of the Environment, Water, Heritage and the Arts. (2008). Environment Protection and Biodiversity Conservation Act, 1999. Canberra Australia. http://www.environment.gov.au/epbc/about/history.html

European Communities. (2008). The economics of ecosystems and biodiversity. Interim report. Welzel + Hardt, Wesseling, Germany.

Forshaw, J. (1981). *Australian Parrots.* Lansdowne Editions, Melbourne.

Hicks, J. & Preece, M. (1991). *Green Parrot. 1991 Recovery Plan.* Australian Parks and Wildlife Service, Canberra. Unpublished Report.

Hill, R. (2002). *National recovery plan for the Norfolk Island Green Parrot* Cyanoramphus novaezelandiae cookii. Environment Australia, Unpublished Report.

Hobbs, R.J., Arico, S., Aronson, J., Baron, J.S., Bridgewater, P., Cramer, V.A., Epstein, P.R., Ewel, J. J., Klink, C.A., Lugo, A.E., Norton, D., Ojima, D., Richardson, D.M., Sanderson, E.W., Valladares, F., Vilà, M., Zamora, R. & Zobel. M. (2006). Novel ecosystems: theoretical and management aspects of the new ecological world order. *Global Ecology and Biogeography* **15**: 1–7.

Holdgate, M. W. (1993). *Can wildlife pay for itself?* IUCN focus series, Gland.

International Union for Conservation of Nature. (2008a).
	http://cmsdata.iucn.org/downloads/resolutions_recommendation_en.pdf
International Union for Conservation of Nature. (2008b). http://cmsdata.iucn.org/downloads/cetacean_table_for_website.pdf
International Whaling Commission. (2008). http://www.iwcoffice.org/_documents/commission/schedule.pdf
Leopold, A. (1949). *A Sand County Almanac*. Oxford University Press. New York.
Lubchenco, J., Olson, A.M., Brubaker, L.B., Carpenter, S.R., Holland, M.M., Hubbell, S.P., Levin, S.A., MacMahon, J.A., Matson, P.A., Melillo, J.M., Mooney, H.A., Peterson,C.H., Pulliam, H.R., Real, L.A., Regal, P.J. & Risser, P.G. (1991). The sustainable biosphere initiative: an ecological research agenda. *Ecology* **72:** 371-412.
Lundberg, J., Pyykönen, M. & Elmqvist, T. (2008). Introducing an Alien keystone in the midst of a global endemic hotspot for conservation. in *Rethinking Urban Nature*. , Lundberg, J. Doctoral Thesis, Stockholm University. pp VI 1 - 24.
Lunney, D. (2001). Causes of the extinction of native animals of the Western Division of New South Wales: an ecological interpretation of the nineteenth century historical record. *Rangeland Journal* **23**: 44 – 70.
Millennium Ecosystem Assessment. (2005). *Millennium Ecosystem Assessment. Ecosystems and Human Well-being: Synthesis.* Washington, Island Press,.
Macdonald, D.W., Collins, N.M. & Wrangham, R. (2006). Principles, practice and priorities: the quest for 'alignment'. In *Key Topics in Conservation Biology* Eds. D.W. Macdonald and K. Service, Blackwell publishing. Oxford. pp. 273 – 292.
McIntyre, S., Barrett, G.W., Kitching, R.L. & Recher, H.F. (1992). Species Triage - Seeing Beyond Wounded Rhinos. *Conservation Biology* **6:** 604-606.
McLaren, G., Bonacic, C. & Rowan, A. (2006). Animal welfare and conservation: measuring stress in the wild. In *Key Topics in Conservation Biology* Eds. D.W. Macdonald and K. Service, Blackwell publishing. Oxford. pp 120- 133.
Mills, L.S., Soulé, M.E. & Doak, D.F. (1993). The keystone-species concept in ecology and conservation. *BioScience* **43**: 219-224.
Myers, N., Mittermeier, R.A., Mittermeier, C.G., da Fonseca, G.A.B. & Kent, J. (2000). Biodiversity hotspots for conservation priorities. *Nature* **403**: 853–858.
Nassauer, J.I. (2006). Landscape Planning and Conservation Biology: Systems Thinking Revisited. *Conservation Biology* **20:** 677-678.
Possingham, H. P. & Wilson, K. A. (2000). Biodiversity: Turning up the heat on hotspots. *Nature* **404**: 990-992.
Solbrig, O.T. (Ed.). (1991). *From Genes to Ecosystems: A Research Agenda for Biodiversity* . IUBS . Cambridge, Mass.
Tansley, A.G. (1935). The use and abuse of vegetational concepts and terms. *Ecology* **16:** 284-307.
http://ec.europa.eu/environment/nature/biodiversity/economics/pdf/teeb_report.pdf
The Nature Conservancy. (2008). http://www.nature.org/tncscience/science/art20328.html
UNESCO-MAB. (2000). *Solving the Puzzle: The Ecosystem Approach and Biosphere Reserves*. UNESCO, Paris.
Walton, D.W. & Richardson, B.J. (Eds). (1989). *Fauna of Australia Vol. IB. Mammalia*. AGPS, Canberra.
Wilson, G.E. & Edwards, M.J. (2008). Native wildlife on rangelands to minimize methane and produce lower-emission meat: kangaroos versus livestock. *Conservation Letters* **XX**: 1-10.

Bridgewater, P. (2010). What management? Which species? In: *Species Management: Challenges and Solutions for the 21st Century*, ed. by J.M. Baxter and C.A. Galbraith. TSO Scotland, Edinburgh. pp. 3-19

Chapter 2

Development of a new approach to threatened species management in New Zealand

*Shaun M. O'Connor[1], Richard F. Maloney[2], Donald G. Newman[1],
Liana N. Joseph[3] and Hugh P. Possingham[3]*

Summary

1. New Zealand biota evolved in the absence of predatory and browsing mammals making it particularly vulnerable to the arrival of humans and the species they introduced.
2. New Zealand has in excess of 2,700 threatened taxa (species and subspecies), more than can be managed individually with resources currently available.
3. The Department of Conservation (DOC) is the central government organization charged with conserving the natural heritage of New Zealand.
4. DOC is developing a Natural Heritage Management System (NHMS) to create a nationally consistent, scientifically sound system of natural heritage management, enabling better prioritization, planning, monitoring and reporting of achievement.
5. Prioritisation will use decision tools, underpinned by an optimization model, to support senior managers in making cost-effective decisions for resources. We will demonstrate the utility of the optimization model in supporting decisions to achieve the most cost-effective projects which secure the greatest number of threatened species that are unique to New Zealand, and most at risk of extinction. The tool is currently at a late stage of development and is being considered for implementation.
6. The national application of a species optimization model would probably be a world first and its implementation will involve significant cultural change in DOC, in other agencies, and in the community as it informs and guides future conservation management.

[1] Research and Development Group, DOC, P.O. Box 10-420, Wellington 6143, New Zealand
[2] Research and Development Group, DOC, P.O. Box 13049, Christchurch 8141, New Zealand
[3] The Ecology Centre, School of Integrative Biology, University of Queensland, St Lucia, Australia, 4072

2.1 Introduction

Tuatara (*Sphenodon punctatus*). D. Veitch. Crown copyright: DOC N.Z. 1980

Isolated by oceans for tens of millions of years, the New Zealand archipelago developed or retained unique and varied plants and animals, many of which are found nowhere else in the world (Cooper *et al.*, 2001; McGlone *et al.*, 2001; Ericson *et al.,* 2002). Amongst these are the tuatara (*Sphenodon punctatus*), the kakapo (*Strigops habroptila*) kiwi (*Apteryx* spp.), native frogs (*Leiopelma* spp.), and an exceptionally diverse range of land snails. Unfortunately, New Zealand also has a record of species extinctions. The biota evolved in the absence of predatory and browsing mammals; making it particularly vulnerable to the arrival of humans and the species they introduced (Holdaway, 1989). At last reckoning, New Zealand had 2788 threatened taxa (species and subspecies), although this number is an under estimate because insufficient information was available to judge the threat status of a further 3031 taxa (Hitchmough *et al.*, 2007).

The Department of Conservation (DOC) is the central government organization charged with conserving the natural and historic heritage of New Zealand. The overarching purpose of the Department is to increase the value that New Zealanders attribute to conservation. (DOC, 2008 a,b) To do this, amongst other things, DOC seeks to be recognized as an effective manager of the lands, waters, species, historic places and roles entrusted to it (DOC, 2008 a,b). A vital component of effective management is restoring and maintaining a representative range of biodiversity in a healthy and functioning state. DOC intends that its actions will ensure the survival of those populations of threatened species that have been targeted for management. Decision-making on threatened species work is supported by the New Zealand Threat Classification System and a new decision tool which is presently at a late stage of development. This tool identifies the most cost-effective means of achieving security for the greatest number of threatened species, prioritized by uniqueness to New Zealand and extinction risk (Joseph *et al.*, 2009).

The new decision tool is one of a suite of similar prioritization tools that DOC has in development. These encompass security from extinction and long-term recovery of threatened species, and the health and functioning of examples of the full range of New Zealand ecosystems. All of these tools will be components of a Natural Heritage Management System (NHMS) which will facilitate nationally consistent and scientifically sound natural heritage management, including prioritization, planning, monitoring and reporting of achievements. Here, we briefly outline the New Zealand Threat Classification System and NHMS, and describe how the first of the new decision tools, that for optimizing threatened species management to achieve security objectives, will work.

2.2 The New Zealand Threat Classification System

The New Zealand Threat Classification System is a national system led by DOC. It uses objective criteria and information drawn from a wide range of experts to rigorously assess the risk of extinction faced by New Zealand plants, animals and fungi. Each taxon (species and subspecies) is placed in a category that

Plate 2.1 Great spotted kiwi (*Apteryx haastii*). R. Morris. Crown Copyright: DOC, N.Z. 1975

reflects the level of risk it faces. The system is specifically designed to be relevant to New Zealand's unusual ecological and geographic conditions (de Lange and Norton, 1998). This system is intended to complement, not compete with, the International Union for the Conservation of Nature (IUCN) Red Lists of threatened species.

The key difference between the two systems relates to the treatment of species which have limited distributions (de Lange and Norton, 1998). The IUCN Red Lists were designed to detect rarity and decline of species at global and continental scales. Since many New Zealand species are naturally very restricted in distribution (e.g. to one small island group or mountain range), the seriousness of their status is exaggerated using the IUCN criteria (de Lange and Norton, 1998). Therefore, this system was considered too coarse a tool for assessing the status of many New Zealand taxa.

Plate 2.2 Kakapo (*Strigops habroptila*). V. Smith. Crown Copyright DOC N.Z. 2007

The first version of the New Zealand Threat Classification System was published in 2002. In 2002 and 2007, DOC published lists of threatened taxa using the 2002 criteria (Hitchmough *et al.*, 2007). Following a review of the system, a revised manual was recently published (Townsend *et al.*, 2008). Taxa (species, sub-species, forms, varieties) are now classified into nine categories: not threatened, extinct, threatened (three categories), or at risk (four categories), as shown in Figure 2.1.

While DOC is accountable for developing and reviewing the system, the listings draw upon the knowledge of the entire community of relevant scientific and conservation experts in New Zealand. There is an expert panel for each taxonomic group (e.g. bats, birds, etc.) that makes assessments about the threat status of individual taxa within that group. Starting in July 2007, DOC has initiated a three-yearly cycle of review, where one taxonomic group will be reviewed at a time (for example, vascular plants, birds and fungi were reviewed during the past year), with all groups covered over a three-year cycle.

The threat status of a taxon is one criteria used by DOC and the New Zealand conservation community to help prioritize management effort based on risk of loss. The system itself is one of the critical databases supporting DOC's Natural Heritage Management System.

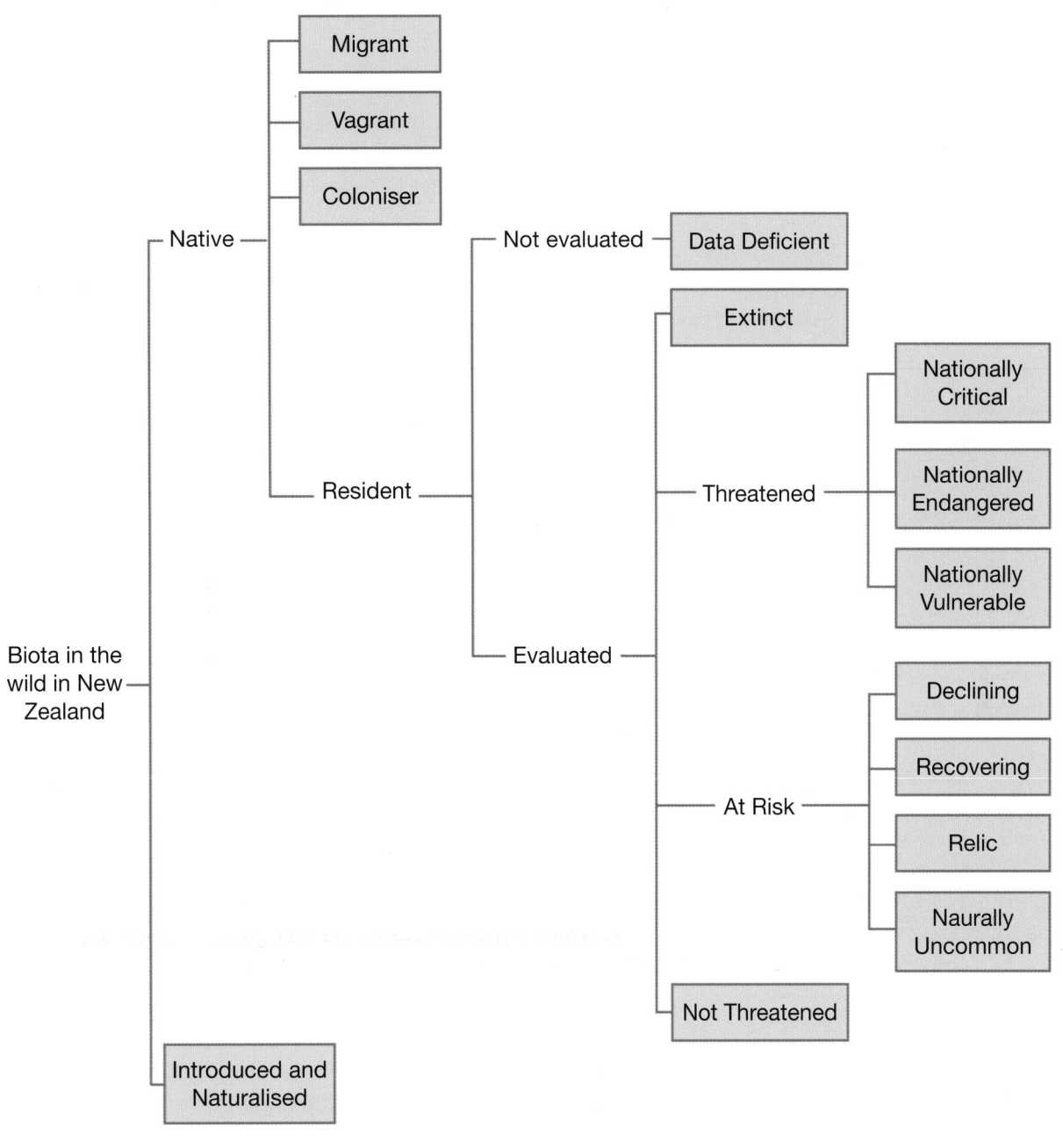

Figure 2.1 Structure of the New Zealand Threat Classification System.

2.3 The Natural Heritage Management System (NHMS)

2.3.1 Why build NHMS?

Since its establishment in 1987, DOC's approach to managing natural heritage has been evolving. For many years, a single species approach was favoured, with programmes aimed at recovering specific threatened species and controlling individual pest species. Since 2000, however, the focus has moved from single species work towards integrated management at particular sites (Saunders and Norton, 2001), and from threatened species protection to protection of threatened ecosystems. There has been increasing recognition of the need to manage for "ecosystem services", such as soil and water protection, and to measure the broader economic benefits of management of conservation areas (Farber *et al.*, 2002). Increasing awareness of the scale and extent of decline in the biodiversity under threat in New Zealand, and a heightened realization that resources are limited, has made it clear that specific goals must be set and work prioritized to achieve the best net conservation return (Mace *et al.*, 2006; Joseph *et al.*, 2008). Integrated management at key sites can optimize resources and maximize outcomes.

The Department of Conservation has also recognized that the context of conservation in New Zealand is changing. Regional and local councils are focusing increasingly on biodiversity. Private trusts and landowners are doing significant conservation work. Maori landowners are becoming more and more involved in managing the biodiversity on their own land. In effect, there has been a progressive move away from DOC as a control agency, protecting "its" estate, towards greater community engagement and cooperation in managing biodiversity on both public conservation lands and on private land.

This changing environment and approach has led DOC to adopt a new strategic direction, which can be expressed as follows:

"The overarching purpose of the Department of Conservation is to increase the value that New Zealanders attribute to conservation. This leads to enhanced care of New Zealand's unique heritage for people to benefit from and enjoy.", (DOC, 2008 a,b).

This direction reflects the reality that if people do not value conservation, it will not get funded, and therefore work that is needed to halt the decline in biodiversity in New Zealand will not be done. Pragmatically, the new strategic objective also recognizes that halting the decline in New Zealand's biodiversity is far too big a job for DOC to do on its own, and it needs to work with others if the best conservation outcome for New Zealand is to be achieved.

Legislation and government priorities are the primary drivers of DOC's work. They guide its strategic direction which, in turn, helps to set the direction of the annual statement of intent. A key overarching strategy for natural heritage work in New Zealand is the New Zealand Biodiversity Strategy (DOC & MfE, 2000) which sets, as one of its visions, that *"The full range of New Zealand's indigenous ecosystems and species thrive from the mountains to the ocean depths"*. It has an associated goal to *"Halt the decline in New Zealand's indigenous biodiversity*" (DOC & MfE, 2000). These statements provide a vision that can guide an overall approach, but offer limited direction on which values should be managed first with a limited resource. Embedded in DOC's Statement of Intent (DOC, 2008a) is an Outcome Statement and a subset of seven Intermediate Outcome Statements. Three of these directly relate to natural heritage (see Figure 2.2). Senior managers in DOC determine what resource will be allocated to each of these seven Intermediate Outcomes.

Figure 2.2 Department of Conservation Outcome and Intermediate Outcomes, 2008.

Currently, no system exists for identifying and prioritizing work for objectives under each Intermediate Outcome, and any changes to Intermediate Outcome budgets are being made in the absence of an understanding of how much biodiversity values are being improved or reduced as a consequence. Sensible and sound monitoring and reporting practices that deliver cost-effective outcomes are also lacking. In summary, DOC has sound local procedures for managing natural heritage, but these have not been supported by national systems. There has not been consistency in the way DOC collects data, monitors biodiversity, prioritizes work, and measures and reports on the differences made. Because of this, DOC has been able to report only on activities and the results of a few individual projects, and has not been able to report adequately on the outcomes of its work across natural heritage management. A national Natural Heritage Management System (NHMS) is being instigated to help develop the processes that will allow DOC to address these shortcomings.

2.3.2 Building NHMS

The objective of NHMS is to provide an integrated and scientifically sound suite of tools for supporting New Zealand's natural heritage managers to make more consistent decisions and monitor their progress to national outcomes.

This objective applies to all of the work on ecosystems and threatened species in all environments: terrestrial, fresh water and marine. Currently, a third of DOC's annual budget is spent in this work area (over NZ$100 million). The development of NHMS represents one of the biggest challenges currently facing DOC. It is a complex task on which intensive development began in July 2006. It is estimated that it will take up to five more years to complete development work. Products are being completed and implemented progressively, providing information and tools for use not only by DOC staff, but also by the wider community and other stakeholders in DOC's biodiversity work, so all groups can work together for New Zealand's benefit.

Figure 2.3 gives an overview of the NHMS work programme. The basic building blocks are:

- Set goals: Clarify and define natural heritage goals. Goals will be specified and linked to DOC intermediate outcomes. The goals will recognize that resources are limited and will allow work to be ordered to achieve the most cost-effective results.
- Inventory: Collate data and develop classification systems to create a national assessment of natural heritage elements. Provide a good picture of biodiversity condition and trend both locally and at a national level. Classification products are used as the base blocks for prioritization work.
- Prioritization: Develop a transparent, objective and consistent process for ranking ecosystems and threatened species for conservation work based upon getting the greatest benefit for the least cost and with an emphasis on undertaking feasible actions.
- Planning: Planning local work within a national context and aligned with national systems.
- Doing the work: Plans implemented to a prescribed standard and at prescribed places, consistent

Figure 2.3 Overview of the Department of Conservation's Natural Heritage Management System. All photos Crown Copyright DOC N.Z.

with the national goals. Local work plans informed by better and more accessible data, and nationally consistent approaches and techniques.

- Measure: Develop a national monitoring system for biodiversity and introduce standard measurement processes. Ensure that the right amount of measurement is undertaken to determine that milestones and goals are being achieved, and that the general state of the condition of the environment and its trend is tracked.
- Report: Develop and standardize input, output and outcome data to ensure that work towards each goal, and combined across goals, is consistently and transparently reported, alongside the overall condition and trend information.

Underlying all is Database Application. This involves developing a database and software tools capable of storing and processing natural heritage data, and linking up with externally held data. NHMS will involve strong linkages with other agencies. The intention is that NHMS data systems and other tools will help and will be used by other agencies and community groups that carry out conservation work.

The remainder of this chapter we will focus on the prioritization component of the NHMS work. This work is separated into ecosystem and threatened species objectives: work on threatened species is well advanced, but that on understanding and developing wider ecosystem priorities is at an earlier stage. Consequently, the prioritization approach being taken will be illustrated by describing the Optimizing Threatened Species Recovery tool, which can be used to assign priorities across securing threatened species from extinction, and ensuring their long-term recovery.

2.4 Developing the Optimizing Threatened Species Recovery tool

Species managers in DOC face a dilemma. With so many species at risk of, or threatened with extinction (more than 2,700—see Hitchmough *et al.*, 2007), how do they decide which should be managed first? How do they know they are getting the best results for the funding available for threatened species recovery? And how can they demonstrate what could be achieved with more resources, or what species may be lost if there were fewer resources?

These are complex questions that lie at the core of the prioritization work. In part, the complexity arises because DOC manages species for different reasons. Sometimes it is because a local community feels strongly about a species in its area; or a species is managed as part of an ecosystem that is being

Plate 2.3 Whio/blue duck (*Hymenolaimus malacorhynchos*). A. Reith. Crown Copyright. DOC. N.Z. 1992

Plate 2.4 Rock wren (*Xenicus gilviventris*). R. Morris. Crown Copyright DOC N.Z. 1975

Plate 2.5 Maud Island frog (*Leiopelma pakeka*). R. Morris. Crown Copyright DOC N.Z. 1974

restored; or it is a charismatic icon that attracts public support for conservation; or it has a high risk of extinction. The first objective under the Optimizing Threatened Species Recovery Project is about that fourth reason – securing species from extinction. The full objective is to improve security of the greatest possible number of threatened species that are unique to New Zealand and that have the highest risk of loss.

This objective has been adopted as one of DOC's three Natural Heritage Intermediate Outcomes (Figure 2.2), thus providing a direct link between NHMS and DOC's higher level strategic directives (as expressed in the Statement of Intent, DOC, 2008 a).

Security is defined as security from extinction in the wild, which is achieved when available evidence indicates that there is at least one viable population that is stable, where the key threats are understood and can be managed, and future recovery is likely if additional resources are provided.

A population is considered as being *viable* when it is predicted to have a 95% probability of survival where:

- there is an intrinsic ability to increase given additional management because the population is large, or because recruitment exceeds mortality, and
- there is resilience against low- and moderate-level stochastic or environmental events over a 50-year time frame.

Threatened species are those that have a negative population trajectory, i.e. they are in the threatened categories (listed as Nationally Critical, Nationally Endangered, or Nationally Vulnerable) or in the at risk categories "Declining" or "Recovering" (where recovery is dependent on management), using the New Zealand Threat Classification System (see Figure 2.1).

Unique to New Zealand is judged by applying a weighting to reflect the relative contribution each species makes to global species diversity determined by its endemicity (i.e. what proportion of its breeding distribution is found within New Zealand?).

Risk of loss provides a measure of urgency of the management needed to secure the species: what difference can be made to the probability of a species' survival in 50 years if management action is taken, as opposed to no action at all (Joseph *et al.*, 2009).

Species experts have now identified actions required to secure over 2,100 species. Each species has its own *prescription*—a set of actions necessary to ensure its security. As part of this exercise, experts were asked to assess the costs, benefits, chance of success and value (uniqueness weighting) of implementing these prescriptions. From such assessments, a Conservation Outcome (CO) score was calculated for each species where:

$$CO = \frac{(B \times S \times W)}{C}$$

B = Benefits: probability of the species being secure if the chosen prescription is implemented minus the probability of the species being secure if no action is taken.

S = Success: combined probabilities of appraisals of whether a prescription can be implemented and, if so, will it work?

W = Uniqueness Weighting ('value'): a measure of a species' endemicity.

C = Cost: total annual cost of all management actions needed to achieve security (prescription), spread over 50 years.

See Joseph *et al.* (2009) for an illustration of how the CO score index is worked through on a case study of 32 New Zealand species from a range of taxonomic groups.

Note that the above equation and functions are expressed in a 'language' suitable to the DOC, an operational delivery-focused management agency. Elsewhere (e.g. Joseph *et al.,* 2009) the equation is expressed in an academic context and language: $E = W*B*S/C$ where E is the 'project efficiency' score.

A total of 578 of New Zealand's most threatened species have now been ranked under the security objective based upon their Conservation Outcome score. The order of the ranked list represents the most cost-effective method of achieving the security of the greatest number of threatened species on the basis of doing first, the best combination of what is most feasible, most urgent, cheapest, and most unique. When DOC senior managers allocate resources to DOC's Intermediate Outcome relating to threatened species (see Figure 2.2), they will be able to see how far the funding they make available will stretch down the list of species prescriptions ranked by Conservation Outcome scores.

Species recovery programmes are often continued after the prescribed security point has been reached. For example, considerable resources continue to be allocated to the management of the North Island brown kiwi (*Apteryx mantelli*), a species with an estimated total population of about 25,000 individuals and a threat ranking of "At Risk: Declining" (Miskelly *et al.*, 2008). It can be argued that species such as this are being funded at a disproportionate level, to the detriment of other more threatened species. But as already noted, work is done on a species for reasons other than just preventing its imminent extinction; for example, Maori and community partnerships, ecosystem restoration, or perhaps because it is an icon attracting sponsorships. Species are thus worked on under a range of ecological and socio-cultural objectives.

Such work should not necessarily stop, but the reason for doing it must be clearly stated so that it can be resourced from the most appropriate DOC Intermediate Outcome. In the case of the North Island brown kiwi, this may be the Intermediate Outcome relating to ecological restoration, or to increasing the engagement of New Zealanders in conservation, or even to enable business opportunities consistent with conservation outcomes; but for reporting and transparency it should not be placed in the Intermediate Outcome concerned with improving the security of species most at risk of extinction (see Figure 2.2).

Securing species from extinction is the first step in a much longer pathway of recovery. The long term recovery and maintenance of a species buffered against longer-term threats is a concurrent development step in this process, and constitutes the second objective of Optimizing Threatened Species Recovery. The intent for long-term recovery is that several populations of a species may be managed at several

Plate 2.6 Land snail (*Powelliphanta hochstetteri*). K. Walker. Crown Copyright DOC N.Z.

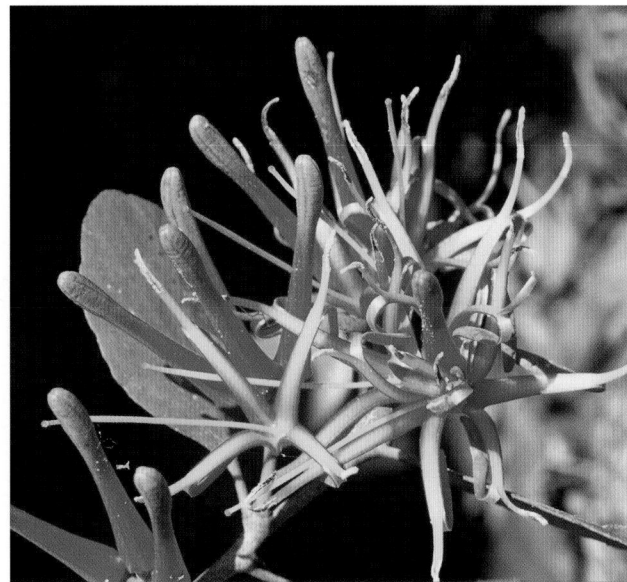

Plate 2.7 Mistletoe (*Peraxilla colensoi*). T. Johnston. Crown Copyright DOC N.Z. 1999

sites, with the aim of recovering and maintaining a species at a level of genetic variation and resilience that ensures it is buffered against the types of threats that are likely to occur on 100–300-year horizons. Later steps aim to restore natural heritage values related to ecosystem level biodiversity values and community aspirations.

2.5 Challenges in building and implementing the Optimizing Threatened Species Recovery tool

While the build of a national Natural Heritage Management System (NHMS) is seen as complex and difficult from a technical viewpoint, it is becoming apparent that the socialization and implementation of some of its component prioritization tools is even more challenging. These prioritization tools have yet to be fully built and adopted. Implementation of such tools requires a degree of change in and alignment of DOC's strategy, business systems, work structures and culture. Socializing and implementing these tools within DOC, let alone promoting their use for coherent inter-agency collaboration, has some big challenges. In countries unlike New Zealand that have multi-lateral (federal) government systems (New Zealand has a unilateral government system) no doubt these challenges would be compounded further. What have some of the challenges been so far?

2.5.1 Building the tool

A key requisite for developing the tool has been a foundation of stable and specific strategy within DOC. Priority setting needs this 'anchor'. Past high level strategic statements have been 'visionary', allowing relatively easy justification of a wide range of work nationwide, rather than strategically directing priority work in a focused and systematic way. Regular change in high level outcome statements, and the objectives that follow them, can undermine prioritization processes, and increasingly disconnects strategy and work delivery over time. DOC has been increasingly moving towards stability in the wording of its intermediate outcome statements and the specific objectives underneath them – statements, and key words within them, that facilitate relative ordering (prioritization) of work. Ideally this is completed as a 'top down' process in advance, before building prioritization tools, however, we have found that there is often a co-evolution between the bottom tier of strategy statements and the top tier of prioritization tools. This connection will cement as part of the development process.

Selected groups of experts were used to develop management prescriptions that would achieve security for species. Different experts were brought together for different taxonomic groups (plants, reptiles, terrestrial invertebrates, etc.). Expertise reflects science, technical and operational management disciplines relevant to the taxonomic group of species, their threats and mitigation actions. A key question is how accurate can experts be in terms of the level of precision in the data and information they provide to populate the optimization model? Knowledge of various species and different taxonomic groups varied considerably; similarly for the effectiveness of proposed management actions, many of which are experimental. Identifying an appropriate management scale or a minimum viable population size for hundreds of threatened species is not easily determined without extensive research. While different actions have different levels of confidence attached to them, arguments were advanced that many prescriptions should not have been prepared until more data are available.

However, with such a large number of threatened species facing extinction, it was reasoned that New Zealand does not have the time or resources to wait until a more data rich, scientific approach is possible. Furthermore, experimental research and adaptive management targeted at the most common management actions or the least feasible actions or the highest cost actions across the optimized list of species, could potentially provide quantum efficiency or effectiveness gains, compared to more species specific research and data collection.

One way of increasing precision around estimated data for cost, feasibility and scale of management is to further validate it with local field programme managers who would deliver each management prescription. This validation exercise is currently underway.

While development of the first objective of optimizing threatened species recovery (security from extinction) is largely completed, work on the second objective (long term recovery) is in progress, and building prioritization for ecosystem management has just commenced. Integrating prioritization tools by identifying rank ordered management actions across multiple (species and ecosystem) natural heritage objectives is an upcoming challenge for the development team. Optimizing multiple objectives is mathematically difficult if not impossible currently and informed national level judgements are likely to be necessary to achieve integration.

2.5.2 Socializing and implementing the tool

Acceptance of the optimization concept (doing first the best combination of what is most urgent, most feasible, cheapest, and most distinctive) has been good – people intuitively understand the logic. However, the first sight of a rank ordered list of species and their associated management prescriptions generally draws an emotional response, especially from those whose 'favourite' species are not highly ranked. For such people, the presence of obscure or unfamiliar species near the top (such as bryophytes, invertebrates, or fungi), with familiar iconic species (e.g. birds) further down may lead to their discarding the approach, or worse, looking for ways to undermine it. Notions of priority, degree of funding level, and 'iconic status' are emotional issues for many people – across a range of science, technical and management disciplines, and across both internal and external stakeholders. People employed in conservation generally have a strong passion for their chosen career and work and this needs to be recognized in development and communication around decision tools. The psychology associated with socialising the conceptual approach and the resulting list, is as much emotional as it is rational, and presents a significant challenge for DOC. A solution here is to separate out these various "motives" into different objectives. This will have two effects: it will make funding decisions between motives more transparent, and it will avoid the desire to create exceptions to doing priority work within an objective in order to continue to work on favoured things.

Plate 2.8 Tuatara (*Sphenodon punctatus*). P. Morrison. Crown Copyright DOC N.Z. 1965

Stakeholders should be kept informed from the outset, but to what extent? While an inclusive approach is best, there is a risk of spending too much time talking and not enough time building and testing the tool. Communications expertise is important and can help target and share the communication task during development, however, care must be taken not to oversell the tool as a 'silver bullet' as this can lead to unrealistic expectations, setting the tool up to under-deliver and promoting cynicism amongst its potential users. We have found that "evolution is better than revolution" – accepting faults and continuous improvement in early iterations of development. There will often not be a single right answer to prioritization problems and presenting a new tool as the perfect answer will take developers down a fraught and intractable road.

The application of optimization models does not fit comfortably with some more ideological or conservative viewpoints in the conservation community. There is much tradition around conventional approaches to conservation work to which the application of business tools is seen as radical, unscientific or threatening, particularly if it results in change to long standing work practices or specialist expertise needs within the organization. The hard pragmatism of the approach can 'test' people's core personal values and belief systems. The thought of planned extinctions is intolerable for some (a likely consequence of not funding costly programmes that have little chance of success), but we assert that the failure to take account of real world practicalities like cost and feasibility will result in unplanned extinctions. The consequences of more conventional approaches to priority setting are generally not transparent.

Transparency is a key attribute of the tool that helps demonstrate its utility in terms of return on investment, and makes a compelling case. Regular exposure to the logic of the tools approach is useful, as people do not necessarily get it first time and may need time and exposure to understand it more fully, comparing it to their traditional viewpoints and first reactions.

Prior to implementation, agreement must be reached on whether the prioritization tool is a decision maker, or decision supporter. Coupled with this, is the need to be explicitly clear who the 'end-user' of the tool is. The current species security tool is targeted at the senior management tier of DOC, to be used as an agreed collaborative national approach to get the best species security outcome for a given resourcing level. However, DOC has a devolved decision making structure, and the 'decision maker versus supporter' issue has been particularly vexed for middle managers who direct conservation work at a local or regional level. Applying such a tool nationally could remove local discretion and judgement, yet it provides a better means of obtaining a consistent national approach to maximizing return on investment.

Senior managers of DOC have signalled a desire to avoid a culture of compliance and place greater emphasis on community aspirations and individual accountability for professional judgement. At the same time they have also asked for focused national strategy and prioritization to achieve the best net conservation return for the increasingly scarce conservation dollar. We believe that both approaches can be applied, but in different circumstances. For example, optimizing species security could be directed nationally to minimize extinctions, whereas work under community engagement outcomes (see Figure 2.2) could be decided locally, based upon an operational manager's local knowledge and judgement of what a particular community's values are.

We think one solution lies in developing an agreed decision making spectrum that identifies when to make the decision locally, regionally or nationally. The spectrum could be expressed as a series of 'business rules', identifying what set of circumstances and how much discretion for each 'rule'. The most appropriate business rule could then be selected for each objective under intermediate outcome statements, as an agreed collective approach and collaboration between senior and middle management, which would then be applied nationwide.

Concern has been expressed that completion of the first species prioritization tool (aimed at security) will capture resources at the expense of other tools under species-based objectives aimed at long term recovery or community aspirations. DOC has a wide mandate and it is valid to work on species under a range of biodiversity protection and community aspiration objectives. We believe the allocation of funds amongst the three species objectives for example, is best decided on a national basis by the Department's senior managers. Therefore, prioritization tools such as the one we describe here, rank the best mix of species to manage first, but should leave the decision on how much to invest under each objective to the judgement of senior management.

Where an optimization approach is not used under an objective, the 'bulk-funded' investment decision could again be made by senior management; however local managers could then decide how to best

Plate 2.9 Kokako (*Callaeas cinerea wilsoni*). R. Colbourne. Crown Copyright DOC N.Z. 1980

Plate 2.10 Chevron skink (*Oligosoma homalonotum*). H. Aviss. Crown Copyright DOC N.Z. 1995

Plate 2.11 Takahe (*Porphyrio hochstetteri*). Crown Copyright DOC N.Z.

meet the national objective locally. Our point here is that it is important to separate work by objective to obtain maximum transparency and consistency. The choice of whether to apply a directed optimization model or a more discretionary prioritization method to a particular objective remains a choice that the organization's leadership should collectively determine. Again, the type of prioritization approach applied to a particular objective needs to be declared and systematically applied to obtain transparency and consistency.

Alignment of corporate systems (particularly resource allocation, business planning and reporting systems) is fundamental to enabling decision tools to link priority setting with planning, doing the work and reporting on the outcomes achieved (see Figure 2.3). The data used to populate each system and step must be in a 'common currency' form, compatible and designed for this integration in advance rather than having tool development in isolation, with connectivity only considered later.

Roll out of prioritization tools to managers, and any associated management of change needs to be carefully considered in advance, and planned for as a systematic sequence of support actions prior to and during roll out of tools. Likewise separate or concurrent roll out of prioritization tools across several objectives needs careful consideration. Should tools be provided as each is completed with consequent incremental gain, or should they be released together once all are finished, an approach that could result in 'organizational shock'? Each particular recipe for rollout needs to be matched to the organizations leadership model, structure, capability, capacity, degree of business system sophistication and culture. There is not, and should not be, a single generic blue print for this.

Despite these significant challenges, we should not loose sight of the potential returns from applying an integrated approach to natural heritage management and the potential quantum benefits of optimizing resources to maximize return. A transparent, objective, consistent and systematically applied approach with the right balance of compliance and discretion is a sound set of working principles. The 'counter-balancing' effect of the key functions in the optimization process that identifies the 'best mix' of work, offers strong potential for maximizing return against stated objectives. Optimizing threatened species recovery will not be perfect, but the logic of focusing species recovery on the combination of species projects which best represents the most urgent, most feasible, most affordable and most distinctive species, is strong. New Zealand has achieved much success with species that are actively managed, but active management targets little more than 10% of the total threatened (DOC, 2007) given available resources. We must look to smarter strategy and resource allocation to get the best species recovery and natural heritage outcome for our scarce resources.

2.6 Acknowledgments

We are most grateful for the continuing contributions and support of our colleagues Ana Cotter, Allan Ross, Jodie Davis, Theo Stephens, Benno Kappers and Elaine Wright in the development and reporting of our optimization model. Figures were prepared by Tom Lind-Jackson and Joanne Aitken. and valuable comments on the draft manuscript were provided by Lynette Clelland.

References

Cooper, A., Lalueza-Fox, C., Anderson, S., Rambaut, A., Austin, J. & Ward, R. (2001). Complete mitochondrial genome sequences of two extinct moas clarify ratite evolution. *Nature* **409**: 704-707.

de Lange, P.J. & Norton, D.A. (1998). Revisiting rarity: a botanical perspective on the meanings of rarity and the classification of New Zealand's uncommon plants. In *Ecosystems, entomology and plants*, Ed. by R. Lynch. *The Royal Society of New Zealand Miscellaneous Series* **48**: 145-160.

DOC (Department of Conservation). (2007). *Department of Conservation Annual Report for the year ended 30 June 2007*. Department of Conservation, Wellington. 200 pp.

DOC (Department of Conservation). (2008 a). *Department of Conservation Statement of Intent 2008-2011*. Department of Conservation, Wellington. 64 pp.

DOC (Department of Conservation). (2008 b). *Department of Conservation Annual Report for the year ended 30 June 2008*. Department of Conservation, Wellington. 152 pp.

DOC (Department of Conservation) & MfE (Ministry for the Environment). (2000). *The New Zealand Biodiveristy Strategy: Our Chance to Turn the Tide*. Department of Conservation and Ministry for the Environment, Wellington, New Zealand. 144 pp.

Ericson, P.G.P., Christidis, L., Cooper, A., Irestedt, M., Jackson, J., Johansson, U.S. & Norman, J.A. (2002). A Gondwanan origin of passerine birds supported by DNA sequences of the endemic New Zealand wrens. *Proceedings of the Royal Society of London B* **269**: 235-241.

Farber, S.C., Costanza, R. & Wilson, M.A. (2002). Economic and ecological concepts for valuing ecosystem services. *Ecological Economics* **41:** *(3: Special Issue: The Dynamics and Value of Ecosystem Services: Integrating Economic and Ecological Perspectives)*, 375-392.

Hitchmough, R., Bull, L. & Cromarty, P. (2007). *New Zealand Threat Classification System lists – 2005*. Department of Conservation, Wellington. 194 pp.

Holdaway, R.N. (1989). New Zealand's pre-human avifauna and its vulnerability. *New Zealand Journal of Ecology* **12** *(Supplement):* 11-25.

Joseph, L.N., Maloney, R.F., O'Connor, S.M., Cromarty, P., Jansen, P., Stephens, T. & Possingham, H.P. (2008). Improving resource allocation methods for threatened species: the case for a new national approach in New Zealand. *Pacific Conservation Biology* **14**:154-158.

Joseph, L.N., Maloney, R.F. & Possingham, H.P. (2009). Optimal allocation of resources among threatened species: a project prioritisation protocol. *Conservation Biology* **23**:328-338.

Mace, G.M., Possingham, H.P. & Leader-Williams, N. (2006). Prioritizing choices in conservation. In *Key topics in conservation biology,* Ed. by D.W. Macdonald and K. Service. Wiley - Blackwell. pp. 17-34.

McGlone, M.S., Duncan, R.P. & Heenan, P.B. (2001). Endemism, species selection and the origin and distribution of the vascular plant flora of New Zealand. *Journal of Biogeography* **28**(2): 199-216.

Miskelly, C.M., Dowding, J.E., Elliott, G.P., Powlesland, R.G., Robertson, H.A., Sagar, P.M., Scofield, R.P. & Taylor, G.A. (2008). Conservation status of New Zealand birds. *Notornis* **55**: 117-135.

Saunders, A. & Norton, D.A. (2001). Ecological restoration at Mainland Islands in New Zealand. *Biological Conservation* **99**(1): 109-119.

Townsend, A.J., de Lange, P.J., Duffy, C.A.J., Miskelly, C.M., Molloy, J. & Norton, D.A. (2008). *New Zealand Threat Classification System manual*. Department of Conservation, Wellington. 35 pp.

O'Connor, S.M., Maloney, R.F., Newman, D.G., Joseph, L.N. and Possingham, H.P. (2010). Development of a new approach to threatened species management in New Zealand. In: *Species Management: Challenges and Solutions for the 21st Century*, ed. by J.M. Baxter and C.A. Galbraith. TSO Scotland. Edinburgh. pp. 21-41

41

Chapter 3

Challenges and innovations in species management: a Norwegian perspective

Øystein Størkersen[1], Des B.A. Thompson[2] and John M. Baxter[2]

Summary

1. In Norway, the Directorate for Nature Management (DNM) is the national focal point for policy and information on biological diversity. It is engaged in a wide array of issues, spanning impacts on wildlife of fisheries, hunting, agriculture, forestry, amenity interests and climate change.
2. Species management in Norway often requires innovative approaches. The import or keeping of wildlife is prohibited, except under approved licences; new legislation is being taken forward on this matter.
3. Hunters in Norway are obliged to report the numbers of animals taken, giving near 100% reporting. National statistical reports based on these data are used to underpin the development and implementation of hunting policies.
4. Protected areas are selected using national inventories of important cultural landscapes with high value for biodiversity. Recently, cooperation over management of biodiversity in the cultural landscape has involved farmers in developing management strategies. A network of protected watercourses and salmon-fjords, are managed to prevent damaging activities affecting local Atlantic salmon (*Salmo salar*) populations.
5. Revitalization of nationwide monitoring of seabirds, and mapping of marine biodiversity has been given new impetus, as well as increasing inputs to the development of new renewable wind, tidal and wave energy technologies.
6. Nature conservation non-governmental organizations (NGOs) have been important for many years in collecting data and information; they continue to play a vital role in supporting policy development, and many receive core funding from the Norwegian government.

[1] Principal Adviser, Directorate for Nature Management, Tungasletta 2, 7485 Trondheim, Norway
[2] Scottish Natural Heritage, Silvan House, 231 Corstorphine Road, Edinburgh, EH12 7AT, UK

3.1 Introduction

Wolverine (*Gulo gulo*). © Lars Gangås

Norway has an internationally important range of natural and cultural maritime, land and freshwater habitats, with significant European and global populations of some species (e.g. Hallanaro and Pylvänäinen, 2001). The Ministry of the Environment in Norway, established in 1971, is one of the country's 17 Ministries. In addition to initiating, developing and carrying out its own measures, through its own instruments, the Ministry has an important role in influencing sectoral Ministries at the national level. It is responsible for coordinating the environmental policy objectives of the Government, ensuring follow-up actions, and monitoring the outcomes of environmental policies. There is an increasing local commitment in its work, which is of basic importance for creating legitimacy. This contributes to improving the overall work of the Ministry in the Norwegian environment. There is active work to continue

Plate 3.1 The populations of seabirds in the North Atlantic and North Sea such as northern gannets (*Morus bassanus*) run into millions, reflecting the high productivity of the area. Commercial fisheries on species such as herring, capelin and sandeel have reduced the availability of these prey species for birds which has had an impact on chick survival rates. © Lorne Gill/SNH

cooperation and dialogue with industry. International cooperation is a high profile feature of the Ministry (the joint authorship of this chapter relects this cooperation), and indeed is central to the Norwegian government's ethos, in order to meet the regional and global environmental challenges.

The Directorate for Nature Management (DNM) is a subsidiary body to the Ministry (see Boxes 3.1 and 3.2); it gives advice to the Ministry, and has been given powers to issue and enact national legislation and guidelines. With 280 employees the DNM handles a wide range of issues, including terrestrial wildlife management (protection, hunting, import regulations, etc.), freshwater fish management (including anadromous fish), marine species other than commercial species, establishing and managing protected areas, operation of a nationwide ranger system, buying areas for leisure activities, management of threatened species and alien species, Genetically Modified Organisms (GMO) issues, planning and building issues, international agreements and EU-directives.

Box 3.1 The principal agencies withn the Norwegian Ministry for the Environment (2009).

The Directorate for Nature Management

The Ministry of the Environment's advisory and executive body in the area of nature management.

The Norwegian Polar Institute

The central state institution for mapping and scientific investigations in polar regions.

The Directorate for Cultural Heritage

Responsible for the management of cultural heritage and is the advisory and executive body for the management of architectural and archeological monuments and sites, and cultural environments.

The Norwegian Pollution Control Authority

Responsible for providing the professional basis for decisions in connection with pollution issues.

The Norwegian Mapping Authority

Responsible for providing nationwide geographic information and services to private and public users. It also serves as the central government's professional body in the area of maps and geodata and handles the administrative tasks associated with this.

The research department of the DNM has been placed within an independent unit. The 19 County Governors represent the Government in the districts, and each has a department for environmental issues. The DNM issues policies, instructions and budgets to the County Governor (including the

Box 3.2 The Directorate for Nature Management (DNM), Norway.

The DNM is one of five central government agencies under the Ministry of Environment. The head office is located in Trondheim and has a staff of approximately 280 employees. It has national management and advisory responsibilities for several global and regional conventions and serves as an adviser to the Norwegian Directorate for Development Cooperation (Norad), and cooperates with national agencies in several developing countries. Activities related to the Arctic include: regional cooperation in the Arctic Council; the Barents Euro-Arctic Council and bilateral cooperation with Russia; and national policy and legislation related to Svalbard, Jan Mayen and the Barents Sea.

The DNM's main areas of responsibility lie within the conservation of biological diversity and insuring sustainable use of Norway's natural environment. These include a wide array of themes:

- environmental impact assessments
- spatial planning
- national parks and other protected areas
- outdoor recreation
- nature inspection and ranger services
- wildlife management
- invasive and endangered species
- salmonoids and freshwater fish
- environmental aspects of biotechnology
- motorized traffic
- the Svalbard environment.

Examples of recent reports are:

- 'Management plan for the Norwegian Sea' (draft 2008),
- 'Management plan for the Barents Sea' (2008),
- 'Surveilance of marine diversity at sea and in the Arctic' (2008),
- 'Population monitoring of salmon' (2007),
- 'Effects of climate change on ecosystems and diversity' (2006),
- 'Effects on the marine system of ocean acidification resulting from elevated levels of CO_2' (2006),
- 'Satelite images for mapping of changes in vegetation cover: test of methodology' (2005),
- 'Changes in Norwegian flora' (2005),
- 'Effects of liming on diversity' (2005),
- 'Mosses in the cultural landscape' (2004).

Governor of Svalbard) on environmental issues. The municipalities (450) are obliged to follow national guidelines on species management. There is a strong political will to delegate more tasks and powers to the municipalities. Curently, delegation trials include management of protected sites and leisure areas, and handling of grazing conflicts with wildlife . Handbooks and regulations have been issued by the Directorate to support its work. On issues where there are national laws, legally binding national guidelines exist, which tend to be handled by the municipalities.

Threatened species in Norway are not well protected outwith protected areas. Under a new Act on Biodiversity, it is anticipated that there will be a shift in government policy; this will replace the Nature Conservation Act (1971). The Impact Assessment Regulation (IAR) gives legal protection to sites hosting species in the categories: Critical (CR), Endangered (EN) and Vulnerable (VU) of the National Red List (Anon, 2006; see Box 3.3). For these species it is possible for the County Governors to oppose applications for construction or any other impact (e.g. a proposed site for a golf course was abandoned due to it having a nesting site for white-tailed eagle (*Haliaeetus albicilla*)).

An important function for the DMN is to

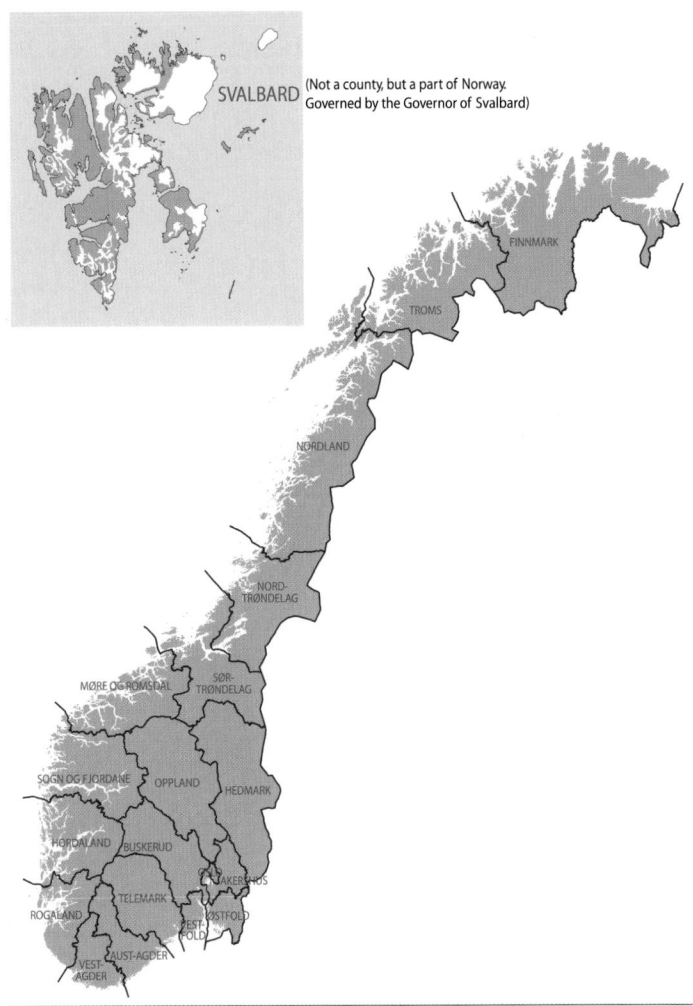

Plate 3.2 Map of Norway with Spitsbergen. Norway has been divided into 19 Counties which are further divided into around 460 local municipalities. Source: DNM

supply data and information for national policy decisions. Besides establishing data collections and a wide array of monitoring systems, effort is put into producing plans and reports on different issues (see list in Box 3.2). The DMN is the national focal point for policy and information on biological diversity. Essentially, it is an information centre on biodiversity, and supplies the evidence base and supporting data for informing management and decision making. The collection and collation of data are undertaken through cooperation across a range of research institutions, with increasing efforts being put into making the data and associated information more accessible to the public through reports, portals and interactive databases.

Box 3.3 Details of the Norwegian Red List.

The Norwegian 2006 Red List contains 3886 species. The evaluated area is mainland Norway, Norwegian oceans and Svalbard.

Species in the three categories Critically Endangered (CR), Endangered (EN) and Vulnerable (VU) together are described as threatened. In the Norwegian 2006 Red List, 1988 species are classified as threatened.

The highest occurrence of Red List species is in forest and woodland with 1,827 species, which is 48% of the Red List species. Agricultural landscapes have 1,330 Red List species, which is 35% of the Red List species.

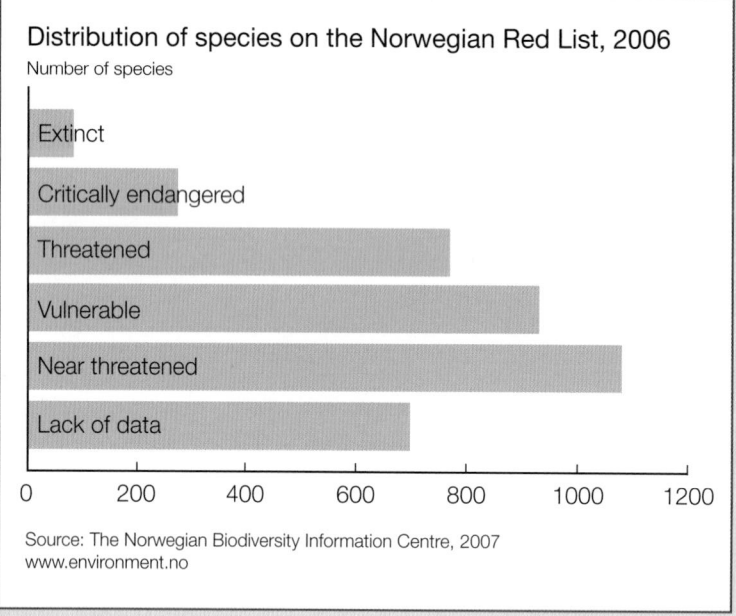

Distribution of species on the Norwegian Red List, 2006

Number of species

Source: The Norwegian Biodiversity Information Centre, 2007
www.environment.no

The majority of species on the Red List are in the following main groups:

- beetles: 802 species
- fungi: 744 species
- butterflies and moths: 430 species
- vascular plants: 384 species

Of the more widely known groups, the distribution of Red List species is:

- birds: 78 species
- fish: 44 species
- mammals: 31 species
- amphibians and reptiles: 5 species

Management principles that have proven to be successful include:

* prohibition to import and keep fauna unless this has been approved, cf. positive lists;
* obligatory reporting of hunters catches is near 100%; and
* revitalization of seabird monitoring and research started in 2006, and increased focus on marine biodiversity other than commercial species.

A dramatic change in the cultural landscape over the last 100 years or so has had a huge impact on wildlife. To mitigate this a 'bottom up' approach has been successful through close cooperation with farmers to link subsidies to contracts for producing and maintaining valuable cultural landscapes. A new, national unit for the collection and presentation of biodiversity information was established in 2005, which has developed a national reporting system open to the public. This has been a huge success, with the public encouraged to report any observations on flora and fauna; with critical observations being assessed and followed-up by expert groups. A new initiative, begun in 2009, aims to strengthen the search for new and rare species. Norway has established a system of protected watercourses and fjords aiming to prevent damaging activities affecting local Atlantic salmon populations, as well as establishing gene banks. A new unit for GMO studies which disseminates information on these was established in 2005. Since national NGOs have a limited membership, over the past 30 years the Parliament has approved funding without any restrictions to support NGO activities.

Plate 3.3 Arctic tern (*Sterna paradisaea*). A dramatic decline in breeding success of a number of seabirds has been observed in recent years. Some species like the Arctic tern, have in the southern regions of Norway in some years failed to produce any young. A rise in sea temperature seems to be the main driver, however, unsustainable fisheries have also had an impact. © Lorne Gill/SNH

3.2 Wildlife management: hunting and controls

Over the centuries the principles of wildlife management adopted in Norway have been copied from elsewhere and typically have focused on game management (grouse and ungulates), and included persecution of most birds of prey and mammal predators (large and small). A broader understanding of the ecosystems over the last 50 years has slowly changed this view and with new generations of managers the situation for predators has also changed for the better. Many predators were regarded as 'game' all year round until *c.*1970; the white-tailed eagle being one of these. This raptor has slowly recovered from *c.*1,000 pairs in the 1970s to the present 3,000 pairs as a result of the protected status it now enjoys. Indeed, chicks have been donated to Scotland for its reintroduction programme. At the same time the perception of this species as a threat to livestock has changed, with growing numbers of people understanding it to be primarily a scavenging species. The large carnivores, like Eurasian lynx (*Lynx lynx*), wolverine (*Gulo gulo*), wolf (*Canis lupus*), bear (*Ursus arctos*) and golden eagle (*Aquila chrysaetos*) still pose a threat to livestock in Norway. To mitigate this the Government has in place a nationwide system of rangers documenting all incidents of predation, which forms the basis for financial compensation. Due to the high political interest in this matter, the financial allocation for compensation payments is between £10-20 million per annum. At the same time there are on-going efforts to develop and trial new systems to reduce the levels of conflict, so that compensation payments can be reduced or avoided.

Plate 3.4 The wolverine (*Gulo gulo*) is a representative of the intact alpine ecosystem in Norway. Other important elements of this ecosystem are the wild reindeer (*Rangifer tarandus*) and the Arctic fox (*Alopex lagupus*). © Lars Gangås

Table 3.1 Example of hunting statistics provided in Norway (1995/96–2006/07).

Year / Species	1995/96	1996/97	1997/98	1998/99	1999/2000	2000/01	2001/02	2002/03	2003/04	2004/05	2005/06	2006/07
Roe deer	40,200	40,100	34,300	37,900	36,900	31,300	28,900	30,600	28,500	29,000	29,900	25,100
Moose	33,955	34,141	36,059	37,957	39,423	38,000	37,300	37,892	38,564	38,770	36,026	34,978
Red deer	17,855	18,043	21,226	21,638	22,063	22,534	23,599	24,533	25,194	25,896	27,635	29,173
Wild reindeer		9,395	9,179	9,761	8,992	7,631	6,976	6,617	44,17	3,895	4,817	5,091
Grouse	387,500	358,500	441,300	511,900	551,600	489,900	482,000	414,900	443,900	450,300	364,300	312,200
Capercaillie	12,100	10,800	13,800	12,900	14,700	13,600	10,600	10,100	9,900	10,500	7,200	10,500
Black grouse	26,000	23,600	31,200	32,500	35,600	31,300	27,200	27,400	28,200	23,400	16,900	21,900
Wood pigeon	56,400	41,800	47,400	48,800	47,200	43,100	44,700	53,600	58,600	61,700	56,500	49,300
Crow	50,500	45,100	49,700	55,800	50,000	43,200	40,900	45,600	47,800	46,200	42,300	40,800
Magpie and jay	36,500	34,100	36,600	36,600	40,200	34,100	30,200	35,600	34,400	31,900	33,100	29,900
Mallard	35,000	25,400	25,300	26,600	27,100	22,600	21,400	25,200	22,200	20,800	18,500	15,600
Other ducks	22,200	22,700	27,600	32,200	32,100	26,900	28,000	32,200	35,100	34,600	26,800	21,900
Geese	14,600	12,100	12,500	12,600	12,200	12,700	14,800	13,900	14,500	14,900	15,500	14,800
Seagull	27,700	19,300	17,900	31,700	18,400	18,200	17,100	18,000	20,700	19,500	16,500	16,100
Cormorant	10,300	9,800	9,300	10,200	11,600	11,100	11,100	13,900	15,000	12,700	9,700	9,500
Hare	51,000	43,200	43,100	38,600	42,600	32,800	28,600	24,200	28,500	29,400	25,000	22,900
Fox	15,100	15,600	16,600	16,400	17,900	16,800	16,200	19,300	18,300	19,600	21,100	18,200
Beaver							2,600	2,700	2,700	2,300	2,300	2,200

Large ungulates are very popular as game and the annual culls of different species are shown along with a range of other small game species (Table 3.1).

The allocation of how many ungulates can be culled is based on national densities of animals, with numbers in excess of these being culled. The culls are motivated to reduce damage to woodlands/forestry, livestock and to reduce collisons with traffic (in the case of moose). A group of experts has been commissioned to develop scenarios for these culls, and to focus on modernizing ungulate management in Norway.

Bird hunting is mainly focused on grouse, but also ducks and geese. There has been a continous decline in the number of huntable bird species in Norway, where the idea is that species must be of value for consumption or because some species are considered as pests (e.g. carrion crow). The DNM issues a list of huntable species every five years based on national and international evaluation of bird populations. International advice from Wetlands International and the African Eurasian Waterbirds Agreement (AEWA) on bird populations is increasingly important.

Plate 3.5 The moose (*Alces alces*) population in Norway has shown a remarkable and steady increase due to specific management. The annual take is now *c.*45000 individuals and the growth in the population has also led to thousands being killed in collisions with cars or trains. © Reidar Hindrum

Bag 'limits' have not yet been issued nationally; currently, local landowners (be they State or private) can decide on limits, and sell a given number of hunting permits. Hunters in Norway must undertake obligatory training and pass a hunting standards exam; for large animals it is necessary to pass a shooting test every year. All hunters are obliged to report their catches (including zero catch), either by mail or the internet. Failure to do so will incur a fine equivalent to £50.

3. 3 Monitoring of wildlife

Along with new computer technologies interactive systems have proliferated. The public can access the information through portals or databases. Many databases are also linked to a map-system, where a record can be located down to a resolution of 10m or better. For protection reasons the distribution of a few species can only be viewed at a much lower resolution or are not accessible at all. It is, however, a national policy to give access to the planning authorities at the municipality level, so as to reduce conflicts with planning issues. Linking together different databases has been a major task. One of the first initiatives was the digitizing of museum specimen records, and linking all the collections together into one searchable database at the threatened species unit (www.biodiversity.no). The national terrestrial monitoring programme also generates huge amounts of data including bird populations and sites, all of which can be accessed by planners from a database called the naturebase. All activities connected with culling large carnivores and damage to live stock, linked to maps, can be accessed at www.rovviltportalen.no. A similar system exists for ungulates at www.hjorteviltregisteret.no. Furthermore, it is obligatory for hunters to report on observations (sex, age) of ungulates which are used to analyse populations and fecundity.

National red lists of species are produced (see www.biodiversity.no). In relation to this, several independent expert groups have been established for different species groups. Important progress has been made in listing non-native species (see Box 3.4), and this is receiving a lot of national attention, not least because it guides policy and regulation decisions on import, trade and eradication programmes (Gederaas *et al.*, 2007; Ministry of the Environment, 2007).

Box 3.4 The 2007 Norwegian Black List.

The Black List is the first official ecological risk analysis of alien species, and so far the most complete overview of such species in Norway. The survey includes 2,483 alien species, of which risk analysis has been carried out for 217. A total of 93 species was found to represent a high risk to Norwegian ecosystems.

The dispersal of alien species is regarded as one of the greatest threats to biological diversity on the global scale. Alien species significantly damage natural biological diversity and have negative economic consequences for the business activities and basis for life for many people. They also constitute a health hazard for people, particularly in poor parts of the world.

The spread of alien species has major ecological and economic impacts in Norway, too. These effects will probably increase with the growing degree of globalization and a future warmer climate. Society will therefore also have a greater need for information on alien species.

NBIC hope that the 2007 Norwegian Black List can be an instrument for management authorities and a source of information on alien species for relevant parties in society and the public at large. We also hope that it will help to place focus on the need for information that should be acquired in the years to come and that the Norwegian Biodiversity Information Centre can continue to assist society in acquiring more knowledge about alien species.

NBIC's work with alien species

The role of the Norwegian Biodiversity Information Centre is to help to feed Norwegian society with up-to-date and easily available information on species and habitats, including alien species. The Centre is engaged in providing scientific knowledge and evaluations associated with the ecological consequences of alien species.

Box 3.4 The 2007 Norwegian Black List (continued).

The work of the Norwegian Biodiversity Information Centre in 2005-2007 has had two main objectives:

- To compile a survey of alien species that have been recorded in Norway, that is as up to date as possible.
- To develop a means of undertaking ecological risk analysis for a selection of alien species that have been recorded in Norway. The results of these risk analyses are gathered in the 2007 Norwegian Black List.

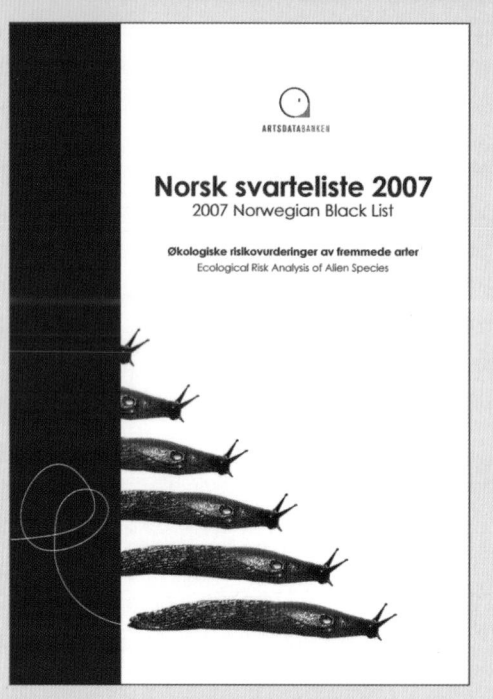

ARTSDATABANKEN

Norsk svarteliste 2007
2007 Norwegian Black List

Økologiske risikovurderinger av fremmede arter
Ecological Risk Analysis of Alien Species

The Team of Experts

The work has been carried out by a team of experts from relevant scientific institutions, and has taken place since autumn 2005.

As of May 2007, 2,483 alien species have been recorded in Norway. Many of these have not become established in large populations or spread to any great extent, whereas others have been successful in a biological sense, often at the cost of indigenous species and habitats.

Risk Analysis

When assessing the risk of extinction (Red Listing) of species that belong naturally in Norway, we have relied on internationally accepted methodology developed by the World Conservation Union (IUCN) over many years. Similar internationally standardized methodology has still not been established to evaluate ecological risks linked with alien species (Black Listing). A common set of criteria has been developed to standardize the assessments of ecological impacts across the groups of species. This should be further developed with regard to national requirements and be coordinated and standardized relative to international initiatives in this sphere.

The IUCN has, however, drawn up "Guidelines to avoid loss of biological diversity caused by alien species". They include recommendations for measures that should be prioritized in research and generation of knowledge, one of which is the preparation of Black Lists.

In 2009, the Government began a new national biodiversity programme, linking data collections and publication to the Swedish species programme. A new programme on seabird monitoring (www.seapop.no) is to extend the monitoring to cover annually the entire coastal areas, instead of only selected parts. The relationships between wind turbines and wildlife impacts are being mapped as part of a four year programme (2007-2011) with a budget of £2 million. The Government has also instructed the DNM to devote more resources to monitoring and mapping of marine biodiversity, in relation to planned protection of marine sites and the management of marine biodiversity.

3.4 National species action plans

Increased political interest in rare species has triggered work on action plans for selected species. A programme for a species implies that this species will be guaranteed funding for the period of the action plan. Typically this is c.£50,000 per annum for a five year period. So far 17 species action plans have been issued, and 30 more are planned for 2009. Two special cases are the Arctic fox (*Alopex lagupus*) and the lesser white-fronted goose (*Anser erythropus*), both near extinction in Scandinavia. The Arctic fox has a breeding programme costing annually £1 million, which includes activities to strengthen the reproductive success of the wild population, such as the removal of red foxes (*Vulpes vulpes*). The lesser white-fronted goose has been subject to monitoring and research for more than 20 years, and with a new action plan it is expected that national and international activities will cost £500,000 annually. Examples of action plans are the ones for red helleborine (*Cephalanthera rubra*), freshwater pearl mussel (*Margaritifera margaritifera*) (Norway hosts the largest European population with more than 300 million individuals), butterflies, beetles, corncrake (*Crex crex*), and great created newt (*Triturus cristatus*). The number of species in need of an action plan is probably more than 300. On the same basis, new action

Plate 3.6 Few invertebrate species in Norway have received more attention than the freshwater pearl mussel (*Margaritifera margaritifera*). Both research and monitoring play a vital role in the ongoing national action plan (DNM, 2006). © Sue Scott/SNH

Plate 3.7 The corncrake (*Crex crex*) was once a common species in Norway. Today the number of singing males rarely exceeds 200 in any year. A revised action plan for this species was published in 2008 (DNM). © Lorne Gill/SNH

Plate 3.8 Giant hogweed (*Heracleum mantegazzianum*) is quite widespread in Norway and it is still spreading. Concern has been raised due to its habit of outcompeting other species and due to its toxicity. As a priority species, a campaign has been started to reduce or eradicate it. © Lorne Gill/SNH

plans are being produced for habitats. The first four action plans comprise hay meadows (areas that have been managed using traditional tachniques over a long period), hollow oaks, chara lakes and limestone–linden forests. There is also a programme of action plans on non-native species. Hitherto three plans have been issued: racoon dog (*Nyctereutes procyonoides*), *Gyrodactylus* and salmon, and the North-American crayfish (*Pacifastacus leniusculus*). A number of species will be subject to different nationwide initiatives, e.g. the mink (*Neovison vison*), giant hogweed (*Heracleum mantegazzianum*) and Japanese rose (*Rosa rugosa*). A new nature conservation act (2009) strengthens the protection of rare and endangered species and habitats by offering automatic protection of identified species and habitats.

3.5 The cultural landscape

After the industrial revolution and the introduction of chemical fertilizers and pesticides, a dramatic change in the use of agricultural fields occurred at the beginning of the 20th century. A steady reduction of livestock grazing in the fields above 'in-bye' and mountain areas has also contributed to rapid changes in ecosystems which had been more or less stable for several thousand years. In Norway, the number of red listed species linked to the cultural landscape now comprises 35% of all the listed species (3,799). With changing agricultural practices and more focus on maintaining the landscape for tourism and biodiversity, a close collaboration between agriculture and environment authorities is gaining momentum.

A system of voluntary contracts with interested farmers is being developed, with subsidies for farming in these areas linked to management programmes and guidelines issued by the environment authorities. So far, 20 large sites have been selected for the initial programme. Looking ahead, there may be more focus on bioenergy/biofuel, and this may have impacts on the use of woods and plantations which may provide benefits for wildlife and the cultural landscape. Extensive studies of former use of the cultural landscape has resulted in several guidlines on how to manage old traditional cultural landscapes and how to maintain biodiversity, e.g. Norderhaug (1999).

3.6 Non-native species initiative

In 2007 the first inter-sectorial plan on non-native species was published by the Ministry of the Environment. The strategy was signed by ten different Ministries, with instructions that sectors each produce their own strategy and make their own analysis of activities in relation to the risk of non-native species spread. The main principle in the legal management of non-native species in Norway is to ban all import and trade in these species, unless they have been approved. The Wildlife Act (1981) was the first regulation that gave the directorate authority to ban the import and keeping of terrestrial vertebrates unless they have been approved. The scope of the list has been expanded to include terrestrial invertebrates and all freshwater flora and fauna. Close collaboration with traders unions (e.g. pet traders) is important in spreading information and taking informed decisions on new regulations. A further expansion of the initiative in the coming years will include regulations on flora imports. The first ban on import, sale and growing of particular flora has already been issued by the directorate.

3.7 Atlanitc salmon (*Salmo* salar) management

Norway is a stronghold for Atlantic salmon. The populations of wild salmon have been steadily declining due to acidification of river courses and impacts from the fish-farming industry (e.g. Costello, 2009). Established gene banks with both live fish (3) and semen (1) have been used to restock extinct populations and to strengthen existing populations. To reduce impacts from fish-farming, 52 rivers and 29 fjords have been designated by the Government as protected national salmon-watercourses and salmon-fjords. The fish-farming industry continues to expand and the spread of diseases and parasites (e.g. sea lice) are of major concern. The in-breeding between wild salmon and farmed salmon is also a major contributer to the decline of the wild salmon. The spread of the parasite *Gyrodactylus* and the cost of removing it from watercourses is among the most expensive species management tasks undertaken in Norway. Despite extensive research Rotenone is still deemed to be the most effective compound for eradicating *Gyrodactylus* from river courses. At present the directorate has identified 46 watercourses with *Gyrodactylus* and has managed to eradicate it from more than half of these. Liming of acidic watercourses in the south of Norway continues, even although the situation has significantly improved as a result of the liming and the fact that acidic rain is less frequent. The cost of liming is high and annually requires between £5-10 million.

3.8 Genetically Modified Organisms (GMOs)

In line with European policies on GMOs, Norway has established a precautionary approach to applications relating to GMOs. The Norwegian act on GMOs focuses on three different principles: 1) benefit for society, 2) sustainability and 3) ethics. To establish and disseminate this knowledge a new centre, Genøk (www.genok.no) with 30 employees was established recently. This centre focuses on research and capacity building and Genøk offers annually an international training seminar over two weeks for 50-60 participants.

3.9 Challenges and cooperation with NGOs

Through the inter-sectoral strategy on non-native species much more resources have been put into this theme, and it will be important to develop the capacity to activate national guidelines on handling alien species (see Chapter 12, Salvesen *et al.*). This is a major challenge for nature conservation and the need for broad scale action among all stakeholders is becoming more obvious. It is a concern that the access to qualified personnel is a limiting factor in implementing action for both threatened species and non-native species. International cooperation may alleviate this?

   International cooperation is surely needed for implementation of action plans for some threatened species. It is anticipated that the lesser white-fronted goose will be a major task for Norway and other partners in Europe in the coming years, in particular concerning management issues along the flyways and on the wintering grounds. Cooperation wth the NGO community has for many years been regarded as vital, and this looks set to continue with the Parliament's commitment to allocate funds, with no restrictions, for many nature conservation NGOs.

This is a positive note on which to end a brief overview of the Norwegian Governments work in support of wildlife species management. The growing threats posed by non-native invasive species are clearly a particular concern, and here work is likley to develop rapidly, involving the DNM, other government sectors in Norway, the NGOs and international cooperation.

References

Anon. (2006). *The Norwegian Red List 2006.* Norwegian Biodiversity Information Centre, Tronheim.

Costello, M.J. (2009). How sea lice from salmon farms may cause wild salmonid declines in Europe and North America and be a threat to fishes elsewhere. *Proceedings of the Royal Society, Series B.* **276**: 3385-3394.

Directorate for Nature Management (DNM). (2006). Action plan for the pearly mussel, *Margaritifera margaritifera*. Report 2006-3. 26pp.

Directorate for Nature Management (DNM). (2008). Action plan for the corncrake, *Crex crex*. Report 2008-3. 42pp.

Gederaas, L., Salvesen, I. & Viken, Å. (eds). (2007). Norweigian Black List – Ecological Risk Analysis of Alien Species. Artsdatabanken. Norway. 151pp.

Hallanaro, E-L. & Pylvänäinen, M. (2001). *Nature in Northern Europe. Biodiversity in a changing environment.* Nordic Council of Ministers, Helsinki.

Ministry of Environment. (2007). National cross-sectional strategy and action against invasive alien species. Oslo. 27pp.

Norderhang, A. (ed.). (1999). Guidlines for management of cultural landscapes. Landsbruksforlaget. 252pp.

Størkersen, Ø., Thompson, D.B.A. and Baxter, J.M. (2010). Challenges and innovations in species management: a Norwegian perspective. In: *Species Management: Challenges and Solutions for the 21st Century*, ed. by J.M. Baxter and C.A. Galbraith. TSO Scotland, Edinburgh. pp. 43-59.

Part 2

Species management for conservation

With changing land management practices across Europe, and with the challenge of adapting to climate change, it is increasingly difficult for the managers of species populations to get it "right". Indeed, it is becoming important to define what is "right", and to be clear how to deal with such multifaceted change. The management of species has never been easy, and different people have widely differing views on how abundant a particular species population should be, or on how best to manage habitats for species. Over the past few years, however, considerable common ground has developed on how to tackle some of the long running problems, such as habitat fragmentation or the ecological needs of individual species. Much of this progress relates to the implementation of the UK and Scottish Biodiversity Action Plans; and to the consequent focus on species recovery, rather than just maintaining present population levels or even worse, simply observing species decline without taking action to remedy the situation. The new challenge is, of course, to join-up all the planning for species and habitat conservation into a holistic and integrated ecosystem approach.

This section of the book begins to review some of the key issues in the conservation of species, focusing on Scotland and the UK, but drawing out some underlying wider issues and problems. Roy Dennis begins by encouraging us to be ambitious in what we do; to ensure the viability of the populations of native species; to have larger protected areas that are better managed, with funds provided for action. In developing this view, he urges that we mix a scientific approach with field knowledge, collected by workers over many years, to produce a robust and practical approach to the management of species. He acknowledges that risks will have to be taken by working in this way, but suggests that managers should not be afraid of failure. Better to have tried and failed than never to have tried at all.

Peter Brotherton and Jon Webb consider the important question, whether it is possible to manage species by habitat conservation alone. If the habitat is suitable then will the species be OK? Their fascinating study focused on Biodiversity Action Plan species and concluded that in most cases a detailed understanding of the species requirements was needed before it was possible to be sure that

Opposite – Chequered skipper (*Carterocephalus palaemon*). © David Whitaker the populations could thrive. Once the detail was known, then particular niches could be created in the habitat to assist particular species or in some cases groups of species. This is an important conclusion and its implications underpin much of species conservation practice.

Next, Steve Hawkins and colleagues review some of the issues of species management in the marine environment. Issues such as scale and complexity really come to the fore when considering conservation management in the sea. Importantly, they note that significant change has already occurred in the marine environment. Such an observation is only made possible due to the presence of long-running monitoring programmes, each measuring changes in species distribution or abundance over many years. With the changes now being detected by these schemes it is imperative that they continue to be funded, as they are a unique window into the past and into the present state of the ocean. Looking ahead, this chapter supports the development of models that reveal a range of possible scenarios for species populations. These will increasingly guide the choices we will have to make about the environment in the years to come. Many of these choices will, of necessity have to influence large areas of the sea, and in many cases will require a new level of international agreement and action.

Simon Milne and David Windmill then review some of the practical techniques used in the management of species, drawing on case studies and best practice from around the world. The chapter looks at how some of the most iconic species have been managed in recent years, concentrating on the role of reintroduction programmes and on the role of captive breeding and release, as an integral part of a renewed focus on action. They stress the increasingly important link from these programmes to the economic benefits they bring to the areas where the work takes place. The case of the reintroduction of the white-tailed sea eagle (Haliaeetus albicilla) to Scotland is used to make the point that local "buy-in" is needed to make a success of these schemes, and to show how the economy of rural areas can benefit. The importance of captive breeding in terms of maintaining the genetic resource, especially for very rare species, and as a practical tool in reintroductions is discussed. Similarly, its role in the wider education of the public about the need for an active approach to conservation is highlighted.

Whilst much of the conservation literature on the management of species relates to birds, Martin Gaywood, Mairi Cole and Rob Raynor consider the conservation of mammals at the present time. Mammal conservation has progressed hugely over the past decade, with effective monitoring schemes in place and innovative conservation techniques being tried. Indeed, the scientific, trial reintroduction of the European beaver (Castor fiber) to Scotland is perhaps the single most dramatic event in the conservation of mammals in the UK over the past 20, if not 50 years. The chapter notes, that in terms of the number of species, Scotland's mammal fauna is relatively impoverished, yet mammals are key to the ecology of the countryside and their presence figures largely in our culture and history. The threats to our mammal fauna are considerable, with the arrival of alien species such as the sika deer (Cervus nippon) and the grey squirrel (Sciurus carolinensis), as well as the dangers of hybridization between our native Scottish wild cat (Felis silvestris) and feral or domestic cats being a real problem. Managing land for the conservation of mammals will not be easy in years to come. How can we ensure sufficient habitat is available for bats? How do we conserve the native red squirrel (*Sciurus vulgaris*), so beloved by many, and will beavers be allowed, in time, to return to habitats across the country? These and many, even more difficult questions will need to be discussed and resolved in the years ahead.

Finally in this section, Martin Warren and his colleagues look at what lessons can be learned from the conservation actions taken to help conserve butterflies and moths. There is enormous public interest in these beautiful insects, yet they are some of the most rapidly declining species in the country. Habitat loss and fragmentation is at least part of the reason for these changes, and detailed studies have shown that positive management, at a landscape scale, will be required if populations are to be maintained at present levels, let alone fully recovered. The challenges here are daunting, yet these species have real value to us, not just because of their beauty, but because they are such effective indicators of environmental change. Would a coal miner in days gone by ever have killed the canary that had the potential to save his life? Well, perhaps that is what we are allowing to happen here.

Chapter 4

Bigger, better – it's when, not if

Roy Dennis[1]

Summary

1. What is needed is greater understanding and solutions to a range of issues that will influence the challenges for the 21st century. The long-term aim for all species management must be for thriving, and where possible self-sustaining or self-regulating populations of native species distributed throughout their natural range.
2. If we are to have an immediate effect on wildlife then we must create far larger protected areas, better managed and funded, with innovative and proactive management of species.
3. We need urgent acceptance that good nature conservation is not solely based on research but rather it is a pragmatic mix of scientific and field knowledge, experience and hard work
4. There is a great deal to be done. We must not be afraid of failure. The real failure is never to have tried at all.

[1] Honorary Director, Highland Foundation for Wildlife, Middle Lodge, Dunphail, Forres, Moray, IV36 2QQ, UK

4.1 Introduction

Much encouraging work has been carried out in Scotland for nature conservation in recent years, covering a wide range of species and habitats, and carried out by a whole range of government, NGOs and private businesses and individuals. Of particular note is the long awaited beaver reintroduction to Knapdale in 2009 and the release of young sea eagles that has taken place in Fife. Furthermore, breeding seabirds on Canna have benefited greatly from the eradication of rats from the island, and there is the opportunity to repeat this success elsewhere such as Rum. In addition, the Forestry Commission have continued with large scale restoration of native woodlands.

But there is so much more to do, so many exciting projects to carry out, and always a feeling that there is no time to waste. Wildlife management must be more proactive and must be more entrepreneurial. We are in difficult times and it is wrong that entrepreneurs are only normally associated with business and money: they should be in nature conservation as well.

We also live in strange times. Over the last 60 years the numbers of people working in natural heritage and biodiversity have increased massively, yet most wildlife species and natural habitats are in decline. In the United Kingdom, which has probably the biggest public interest in birds of any country in the world, there are serious declines in bird numbers. According to the latest report on the State of the UK's Birds 2007, lapwings (*Vanellus vanellus*) declined by 47% between 1970 and 2006, turtledove (*Streptopelia turtur*) by 60% between 1994 and 2007, grey partridge (*Perdix perdix*) by 47% between 1994 and 2007 and spotted flycatcher (*Muscicapa striata*) by 85% between 1970 and 2006.

Globally it is the same situation. Birdlife International reported in 2008 that the state of the world's biodiversity, as reflected by its 9,856 living bird species, continued to worsen, with many

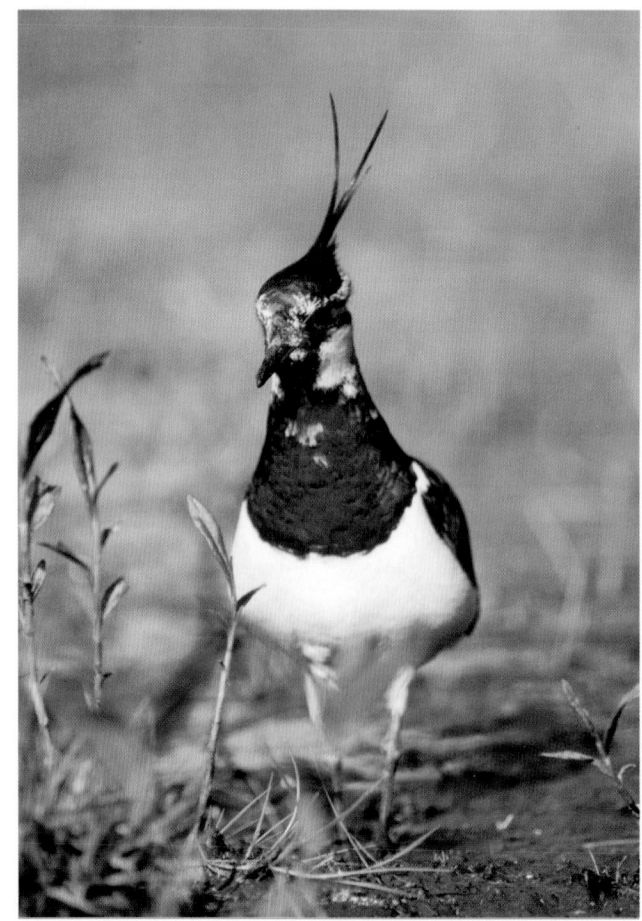

Plate 4.1 Lapwing (*Vanellus vanellus*). © Benoit Renevey/SNH

species in crisis due to human impacts. At the IUCN meeting in Barcelona (2008), it was reported that the most comprehensive assessment of the world's mammals confirmed an extinction crisis, with almost one in four species at risk of extinction. This is despite the world's governments taking the unprecedented step in 2002 of committing themselves to achieving a significant reduction in the rate of biodiversity loss by 2010. The evidence suggests that this will not be achieved and while governments have made verbal commitments to conserving biodiversity, the resources available fall far short of what are needed.

It is strange that despite being thought of as a nation of nature lovers, we still nearly always put the needs of humans first. There is no doubt that the amount of our land and seas set aside for nature is not fit for purpose. This is particularly damning when looked at in comparison with what some financially poor countries attempt to do. Some of them have declared one third of their land as protected zones. On a global scale, the UK implores countries to protect rainforests and iconic species, like orang utan and gorilla, but why should countries like Indonesia and the Congo listen to pleas of rich nations, when we have only 1% of our native forests remaining, and there is little progress in reversing this statistic. How much is enough is a question that continues to exercise many people, but my view is for 30% of land and sea to be protected, where long-term management for nature is the principal aim.

The Scottish Environment Minister, Michael Russell, demonstrated real enthusiasm and commitment to nature conservation in Scotland. But the fact remains that, both in Scotland and the United Kingdom, there is insufficient funding for, and political commitment to, proactive nature conservation. In my view, the Board of Scottish Natural Heritage should prepare a report detailing the funding requirements to ensure that Scotland's nature was in the best conservation state.

What is needed is greater understanding, discussion and solutions to a range of issues that will influence the challenges and solutions for the 21st century. The long-term aim for all species management must be for thriving, and where possible self-sustaining and self regulating populations of native species distributed throughout their natural range.

4.2 What are the challenges and problems involved? What is stopping progress?

Firstly, there is some fundamental confusion about what we are about. I know what I mean by nature conservation or wildlife management; it's to do with trying to conserve species and habitats for their own sake. Humans have a moral responsibility to care for all the other species on the planet. It is clear that this is what the early conservation pioneers believed, when they forged the government Nature Conservancy in the late 1940s and started the conservation bodies, like the RSPB, Wildfowl Trust, WWF and Wildlife Trusts.

In recent years, the term "nature conservation" has been changed or even subsumed by new terms including, "natural heritage" and "biodiversity", and often even further by concerns of green living for ourselves. The present aim of the Scottish Biodiversity Strategy is 'to conserve biodiversity for the health, enjoyment and well-being of the people of Scotland'. To me this is too human-centric. What is needed is to get back to true nature conservation and restore the altruistic benefits for all species. As the most influential species on the planet, we have a guardianship responsibility to conserve species for their own or the Earth's benefit, rather than for our own good.

The people of Ecuador have recently decided that nature should have rights of its own. The Rights of Nature section in the new Ecuadorian constitution, which recently became law, states that an ecosystem has the right to exist and to persist, has the right to maintain and regenerate its vital cycles, structure and functions, and has the right to its evolutionary processes. It also provides in law for any person, people or community to take legal action to defend those rights without the need to show personal harm or loss. This new law should provide a legal balance to the generally accepted view that nature is only a resource for humans. I would be proud if our Scottish Government were also to enact a Rights of Nature law. I would welcome the principle that rivers, forests, eagles and wildcats in Scotland have legal rights, not just legal protection. Too often, the conservation of species or sustainability is about what is in it for us.

So why is it proving so difficult to maintain most species in Scotland in favourable conservation status? Is it solely to do with pressures from intensive farming, forestry and fishing, or from human over-exploitation, contamination, industrialization and other problems of the past, and from new threats such as climate change? Or is it that we are failing to carry out good nature conservation and wildlife management? In fact, the array of negatives can be so great that there is a tendency to feel that nothing can be done, but it is imperative that we stay positive and endeavour to reverse the trends.

The relationship between climate change and nature conservation has become confused in people's minds and requires urgent clarification. They are distinct issues. There is no doubt that climate change is crucially important and that every effort must be made to reduce the human impacts that are causing our climate to change. It is important, however, also to recognize that its effect will probably be greatest on the human species and that the immediate problem for biodiversity is excessive human activity affecting natural habitats and species.

If we wish to have an immediate effect on wildlife, both in terms of biodiversity and long term sustainability, then we must create far larger protected areas, better managed and funded, with innovative and proactive management of species. There is no doubt that larger populations of species within larger more robust ecosystems will have a greater chance of adapting to the challenges of a changing climate. This will also demonstrate to people that there is something to be done in the face of a problem which can seem insurmountable.

Furthermore, remedies to combat climate change, even if they work, will take decades to show results. By which time, if we fail to take bold nature conservation actions, many species may be extinct and ecosystems lost. Many of these natural habitats and species are also likely to be important in maintaining the health and functioning of the planet. Although very important, climate change work is also presently very fashionable and attracts government funds, almost certainly to the detriment of nature conservation when these funds come from environmental departments and organizations. Lastly, the doom around climate change encourages a view that there is little we can usefully do to conserve nature

Plate 4.2 Over-fishing is a major contributor to the decline in many seabird populations. © Chris Martin/SNH

and obscures the obvious human impacts. For example, the seabird breeding failures which are now increasingly being put down to climate change. Whilst climate change may be a contributing factor in the continuing recent declines, it is over-fishing, discards, mechanical damage to the sea bed and chemical pollutants that are the main factors involved.

Looking at Scotland and the effort that has been put into proactive nature conservation, I believe that a higher proportion of the staff of the NGOs and Scottish Natural Heritage should spend more time in the field working in practical nature conservation rather than in offices responding to other people's agendas. More of the most senior people should be regularly visiting and working with people in the countryside in order to break down the barriers and mistrust which have grown up between town and country. This is having a severe impact on species conservation: one only has to consider the conflicts over raptors and

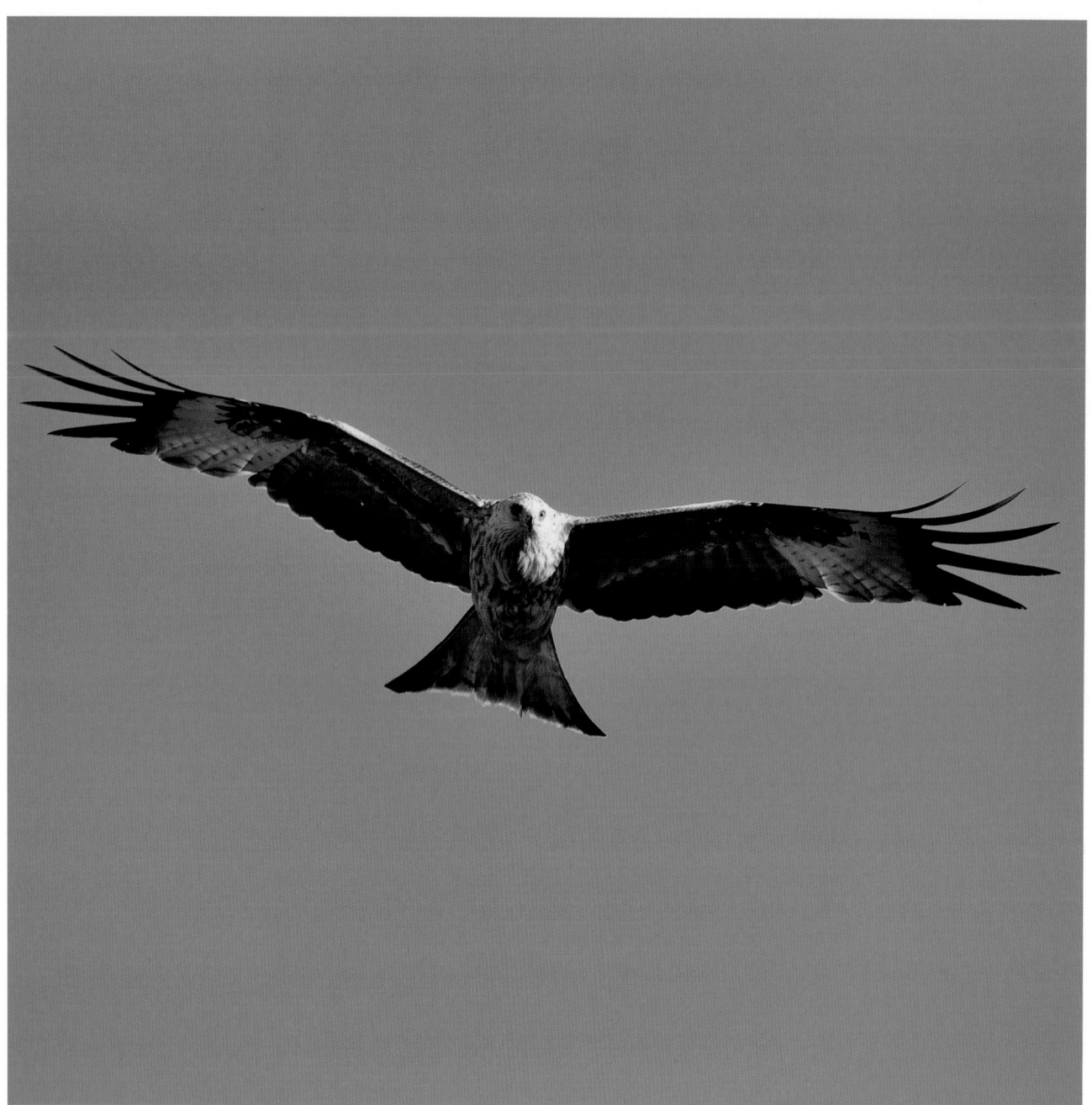

Plate 4.3 Red kite (*Milvus milvus*). © Lorne Gill/SNH

illegal persecution. It is difficult to reconcile these problems when the two sides tend to meet at official gatherings, often in offices, when battle lines are already drawn. It is so much better to discuss difficult issues over a cup of tea in a kitchen or in the countryside.

Nowadays, too many projects fail to move forward quickly enough because of excessive obstacles. Biological research often fails to address conservation needs, because many research programmes lack the necessary long-term vision and organizational structures for useful applied research. It's not only a question of short term research versus long-term management, but the fact that research cannot answer all the questions, many of which are often of a social or political nature. We need urgent acceptance that good nature conservation is not solely based on research, it is a pragmatic mix of scientific and field knowledge, experience and hard work – often it's more like farming and animal husbandry than scientific research. It is also important not to turn what should be simple management projects into complicated and expensive research.

Let us all be more honest about the roles of ecology and politics. For example in the case of the debate around the reintroduction of Eurasian lynx (*Lynx lynx*) to Scotland, some senior people who should know better say that it's not possible to have the lynx back in Scotland until there has been a hundred years of forest restoration; yet others, including experts on lynx in Europe, know that the reintroduction of the lynx to Scotland is nothing to do with quality of habitat or the amount of food (both of which are plentiful), but is solely social and political – a hot potato nobody wants to hold.

A further problem is that the IUCN guidelines, which are necessary to prevent inappropriate introductions and translocations, have become interpreted as laws to prevent things happening, rather than guidelines to help make decisions. As the years have gone by the list of guidelines has grown ever longer and stricter, to the point that they now unnecessarily delay or reject good projects. Every delay is another year lost and every year lost is another opportunity for detractors to prevent a project going ahead. We need to identify good projects and take them forward. The public are excited by these projects and they give hope to people who worry that there is no future for wildlife. We must not make projects too expensive and over complicated with undue levels of control. We also need to widen the range of groups and individuals that can make these projects happen; it doesn't just have to be Scottish Natural Heritage or the big Non-governmental Organizations. Reintroduction and translocation projects should be standard tools in our tool bag; instead they are often treated as difficult, expensive and very complicated, and in reality it is nearly impossible to get permission to carry them out. What is needed is a working group that draws on all relevant expertise to identify and encourage reintroduction and translocation projects within a proactive atmosphere.

There are the problems of rarity. Rare birds, rare flowers, rare fish, rare anything in the UK are usually rare due to persecution or loss of habitat, rather than inherent rarity, and, as such are a sign of failure. Our aim should be to make the rare as common as it naturally should be - to remove its listing as specially protected. But rarity can mean status, it means money, it can even mean someone's special project – I remember the first time I asked for some red kite eggs for translocation from Wales and was

Plate 4.4 Glen Quoich, Cairngorm National Park. © Lorne Gill/SNH

told firmly by a colleague that "kites belong to Wales, not Scotland". So let us try our best to reverse the trends and cause the rare to be commoner.

As an example, I carefully read the recent SNH commissioned report 'A Conservation Framework for Golden Eagles: implications for their conservation and management in Scotland', and agreed with much in this excellent report, although my vision for the species would be greater. The public debate it provoked mainly concentrated on the concluding emphasis on illegal persecution. That has been and remains, a big issue, which needs a rapid solution, but there is so much more we could do with golden eagle conservation to be proactive.

The big challenges revolve around how to restore breeding golden eagles to land where they have been persecuted for decades. How can we restore the prey base in so many home ranges, where there is no longer enough food to rear young? How do we utilize eggs and young from nests where we know the adults will not rear viable young? How do we change their cultural behaviour so that they can nest successfully in busy places like the Cairngorms National Park, where human access is so dominant? How do we translocate sub-adult golden eagles to distant home ranges as a mate for a single isolated adult? How do we change their choice of habitat, so that instead of being a species we think requires mountains and moorlands, it could again be a species of open lowland forests? Some of us could have a good try at doing most of those things, but I know how very difficult it would be to get the necessary permissions and licences to even try. This is what we need to change.

So, will the Eurasian lynx be restored to Scotland? We know our countryside holds large areas of suitable woodland habitats and high levels of food, but sadly, being pragmatic, I know it will take years, even decades, of debate and argument. Ecologically, it could happen next year but social and political issues will prevail and it may even never happen at all.

Those in favour will be asked to research and demonstrate every single issue. It seems to involve an inequality of control, not evident in other areas of human endeavour. At this time, a topical example would be the crisis in world banking, which can be placed at the door of a relatively small number of very rich people who were clearly acting recklessly, yet the control mechanisms of major governments were able neither to identify the looming crisis nor control it. It's worrying that a lynx proposal would be subject to much greater control and scrutiny, but would have minimal impact on anyone's interest let alone their financial security. If lynx are never restored to Scotland it will be a tragic failure.

So let's stop spending so much time talking about what we might do and start trying to do it. Let's be more ambitious, entrepreneurial and proactive. Let's get more staff into the field, breaking down the barriers which have grown up while we were at our desks, writing up our mission statements and putting reports on shelves. Let's challenge our politicians to take braver decisions, recognizing that social and political considerations are often the biggest obstacles to the conservation of nature. Let's embrace reintroduction and translocation projects, rather than treating them as tricky, expensive and terribly complicated - they're not, and they can work. And let's be positive, excited, inspirational and prepared for, but not frightened of, failure. The real failure is never to have tried at all.

Dennis, R. (2010). Bigger, better – it's when, not if. In: *Species Management: Challenges and Solutions for the 21st Century*, ed. by J.M. Baxter and C.A. Galbraith. TSO Scotland, Edinburgh. pp. 65-73

Chapter 5

Achieving species conservation through habitat-based approaches

Peter Brotherton[1] and Jon Webb[1]

Summary

1. New approaches to BAP delivery across the UK are placing greater emphasis on achieving our biodiversity targets through habitat-based delivery. But if we look after habitats, will species look after themselves?
2. We investigated this by analysing the relationship between the trends of UK BAP priority habitats and their associated species, and found no significant tendency for species associated with increasing habitats to also be increasing, or for those associated with declining habitats to also be in decline.
3. The findings suggest that for species conservation to be properly integrated into habitat-based approaches we need to place much greater emphasis on creating the component niches and resources required by species, rather than treating a "habitat" as a conservation end-point in itself.
4. Taking heathland species as an example, we demonstrate how such an approach could operate in practice.

[1] Natural England, Northminster House, Northminster Road, Peterborough, PE11UA, UK

A Surrey heathland. © Natural England

5.1 Introduction

The approach to biodiversity conservation in the UK is changing. Conservation effort for much of the 20th century was directed towards protecting our remaining wildlife, in particular through designating special sites and by protecting certain species from harm (e.g. National Parks & Access to the Countryside Act, 1949; Wildlife and Countryside Act, 1981). In 1994, the UK Biodiversity Action Plan (BAP) brought an additional focus on restoration, through 45 habitat action plans and 391 species action plans which aimed to achieve the recovery of the UK's most threatened biodiversity. We are now seeing a further shift to an integrated approach that aims to achieve the recovery of both habitats and species, and secure the ecosystem services they underpin (Natural England, 2008a).

There are two main reasons for this change. First, the biodiversity action plan approach has generally been most successful at recovering species that have already declined sufficiently to benefit from targeted recovery efforts, and least successful at achieving the recovery of habitats and widespread species (Defra, 2006). Placing a greater emphasis on habitat-based work will, it is hoped, enhance the delivery of habitat targets with associated benefits for species less suited to targeted recovery work.

Second, the first review of the UK BAP priority list led to a large increase in the number of habitats and species qualifying for priority listing: the new list contains 65 habitats (up from 47) and 1,149 species (up from 475). A habitat-based approach may allow this revised list to be incorporated into broader plans without significantly adding to the BAP bureaucracy and being a greater strain on limited resources available for coordinating activity.

If we look after habitats, however, will species look after themselves? In this chapter we explore this question by presenting two related analyses. First, we analyse UK BAP reporting data to investigate the relationship between the trends of priority habitats and their associated species. Our null hypothesis was that there should be an association between these two parameters, i.e. species that are increasing should tend to be associated with increasing habitats, while those that are declining should tend to be associated with habitats that are also in decline.

We go on to analyse the niche requirements of the new UK BAP list of priority species to assess what habitat features they are likely to need. We describe the general approach and then present a detailed analysis of species associated with heathlands and make recommendations for heathland management that is required for a habitat-based approach to secure the conservation of this group of species.

5.2 Methods and data sets

5.2.1 Species and habitat trend analysis

UK trend information for UK BAP priority habitats and species collected during the 2005 UK BAP reporting round (Defra, 2006) was used. In these triennial reporting rounds, lead partners (i.e. those organizations responsible for coordinating action and reporting progress) are asked to assess progress with action plans including the latest direction of change ('trend') for each priority habitat and species. Each species and habitat is assigned to a trend category by the lead partner, and for the purposes of this analysis, these were simplified as follows:

(i)   Species and habitats assessed as *declining continuing/accelerating, declining slowing,* or *fluctuating (probably declining)* were classified as 'declining'.

(ii) Species and habitats assessed as *stable,* or *fluctuating (probably stable)* were classified as 'stable'.

(iii) Species and habitats assessed as *increasing* or *fluctuating (probably increasing)* were classified as 'increasing'.

Species assessed as any other trend category (including *unknown* and *extinct*) were excluded from the analysis.

To establish associations between the species and habitats we used the publication 'Biodiversity - Making the Links' (English Nature, 1999), which identifies 'primary' and 'subsidiary' associations between UK BAP priority species and priority habitats. For the purpose of this analysis we only used 'primary' associations.

Species were included in the analysis if their trend was declining, stable or increasing and they had a primary association with a habitat that was also assessed as declining stable or increasing. Some species have a 'primary' association with more than one habitat, and these were excluded from the analysis unless the trends of the habitats were the same (e.g. all associated habitats were assessed as 'declining').

We assessed whether there was a relationship between the trends of habitats and the trends of their associated species using a chi-square goodness of fit test.

5.2.2 Species' habitat requirements analysis

The species and habitats selected for the habitat requirements analysis were those on the list of species and habitats of principle importance in England, published under s41 of the NERC Act (2006); in essence these are the English species on the UK BAP list. This list contains more species than were used in the trend analysis because the UK BAP list was reviewed in 2007 (see www.ukbap.org.uk). For this reason, the species-habitat association analysis described in this section depended upon a review of primary literature, rather than using the 'Biodiversity - Making the Links' report (English Nature, 1999) which was based on the original UK BAP list.

We split the list into broad taxonomic groupings consisting of mammals, birds, invertebrates, herpetiles (reptiles and amphibians), vascular plants, lower plants and fungi, and each one was analysed separately within spreadsheets in Microsoft Excel. Initially, a data trawl was undertaken to determine the species niche and resource requirements by referring to published atlases, primary data used in the latest UK BAP review, and a series of reference texts (Shirt, 1987; Hill *et al.*, 1994; Stewart *et al.*, 1994; UK Biodiversity Group, 1998, 1999a-e; Paton, 1999; Wiggington, 1999; Kirby *et al.*, 2000; Asher *et al.*,

2001; Brown and Grice, 2005; Cheffings and Farrell, 2005; Falk and Crossley, 2005; Preston *et al.*, 2002; Porley and Hodgetts, 2005; UK BAP review – unpublished information notes collated by JNCC, 2007; www.bwars.com; www.britishspiders.org.uk).

We followed this by consultations with experts in Natural England, specialist NGOs and other expert organizations. From this review and consultation the following two types of data were derived:

(i) A list of species associated with Heathland

For many species the association to heathland was not a simple one, e.g. Does the presence of a species in a few heathlands mean that it is associated with the it? Bats utilize heathlands for feeding but may not be inherently reliant on these habitats - should they be included? As a general rule, species associated only by transient and/or occasional association were not included. For most species, the final decision for inclusion or omission was made in accordance to the views of the experts.

(ii) A pen-picture of Niche/Habitat Requirements

We drafted a pen-picture of the requirements for each species. The available data to do this varied considerably between species:

- Where there was plenty of autecological information the drafting of the pen-picture was relatively simple (e.g. many vertebrate species).
- Where data were lacking the pen picture was greatly informed by expert opinion.
- There were only a few species for which their requirements were completely unknown.

It was also often possible to infer further niche/habitat requirements from data; as an example, many species require bare mud, which is also almost exclusively associated with drawdown zones from seasonal inundation by water (contributing to understanding how hydrological regimes are important).

To achieve an overall answer as to the question of what 'BAP species-friendly' habitats may look like a method was devised for pooling species requirements to produce a combined result. We identified stand-alone requirements within the pen-picture, creating fields for each one. Wherever possible, these fields were defined by simple yes/no answers (e.g. Does the species require bare ground?). Where this was not possible multiple-entry fields were used (e.g. what critical species does the organism live on?). It was not always possible to provide a pooled answer for multiple-entry fields.

This methodology is based on designs originally trialled for devising the Invertebrate Species-habitat Information System: ISIS (Webb and Lott, 2006). Within this system, invertebrate assemblages were, wherever possible, based on process (e.g. fluctuating water levels, grazing, etc.) and resource (e.g. nectar, pollen and seeds from flowers, heartwood from veteran trees, etc.).

Plate 5.1 Even-age heather stand in Surrey – does this provide suitable habitat for UK BAP species? © Natural England

Many species were associated with more than one component field (e.g. the flower bee (*Anthophora retusa*), requires both bare ground for nesting and grasslands for nectar and pollen resources).

The component fields were identified as follows:

- *Early successional habitat including bare ground and ruderal plants* – Bare, loosely friable soils on freely draining soils where repeated disturbance removes vegetation to create areas of bare and sparsely vegetated ground. The juxtaposition of disturbed areas of bare ground with other structural types of vegetation is often important.

- *Scrub and trees* – Vegetation dominated by woody plants which typically form an intermediate community between heath and high forest. Scrub that is structurally rich, containing gaps and different-sized shrubs is of much greater value than scrub forming large, homogenous blocks. The presence of occasional trees is beneficial as they provide further structural diversity. Species utilize scrub for many reasons including shelter, feeding, roosting and nesting.

- *Heathland* – Classed as either wet or dry heathland. Species in this category are identified as requiring the presence of ericaceous scrub to complete their life cycles.

- *Grassland* – Both the flowers (producing nectar and pollen) and the structural component (for example, tussocks) are utilized and many species require these resources to be present all or most of the year around. This type of grassland is extensively managed and, wherever possible, flower-rich throughout the spring and summer.

- *Seasonal Inundation* – Areas of land covered by water in the autumn and winter months, receding throughout the spring and summer.

- *Shelter* – This represents habitats open to direct sunlight but protected from excess wind by topography or vegetation. Species requiring shelter are often found in bays of scrub or against a woodland edge, cliff face or sloping ground.

- *Large-scale habitats* – This refers to the juxtaposition of different habitats at the landscape scale, such as heathlands adjacent to woodland or a complex of wetland habitats. Such mosaics are required largely by highly mobile terrestrial species.

Plate 5.2 Structurally complex heathland in Lincolnshire – bare ground, heather and scrub. © Natural England

5.3 Results

5.3.1 Species and habitat trend analysis

A total of 129 species were assessed in this analysis and there was no significant association between their trend and those of their habitats (n= 129, χ^2 = 8.9, d.f. = 4, p= N.S. Figure 5.1). To investigate whether this result was an artefact due to many UK BAP species being very rare, we used BAP species distribution data (available at www.searchnbn.org.uk) to restrict this analysis to species occurring in more than 15 10-km squares. This also showed no significant association (n= 47, χ^2 = 5.4, d.f. = 4, p= N.S.).

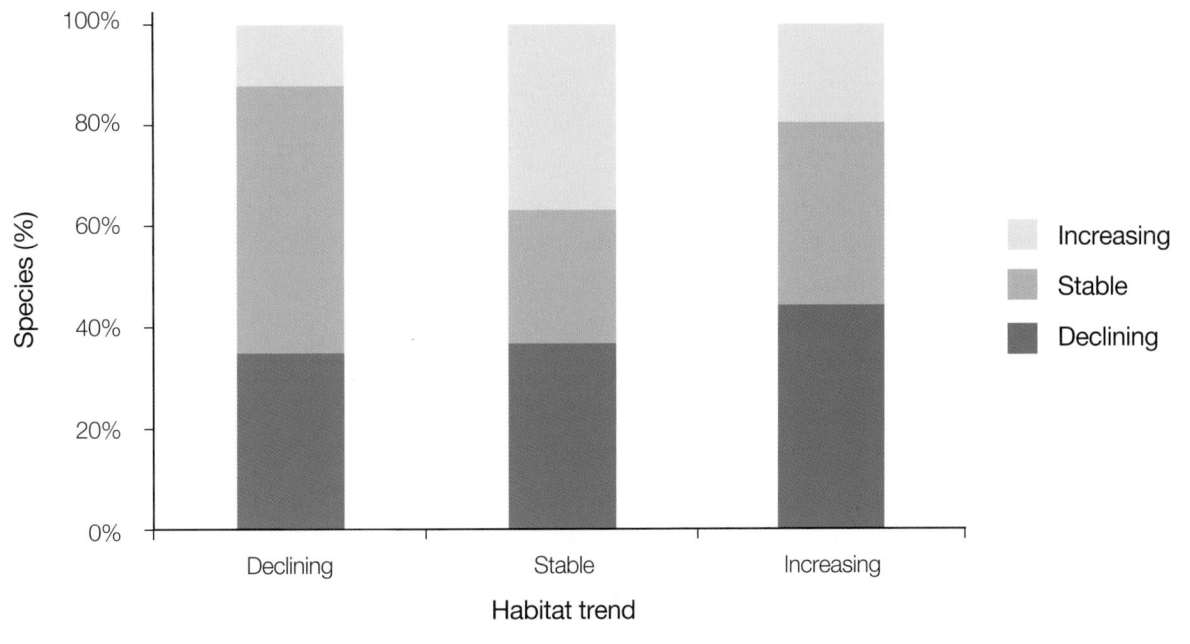

Figure 5.1 Relationship between trend of habitats and associated species.

5.3.2 Species' habitat requirements analysis

110 UK BAP species are associated with heathlands in England (see Table 5.1). These species are referred to in the literature as either being found exclusively on heathland sites or a significant proportion of records come from heathlands. Many of these species are also associated with other habitats, including woodlands, grasslands, uplands and wetlands.

Table 5.1 Types of UK BAP species associated with heathlands by taxonomic group.	
Taxonomic Group	**Number of Species**
Invertebrates	64
Vascular Plants	20
Lower Plants	9
Birds	8
Herpetofauna	6
Fungi	3
Total	110

A variety of niches were identified for UK BAP species associated with heathlands (Figure 5.2). Many species occur in more than one niche as they have multiple requirements:

- Over 60% of species require some form of shelter on heathlands.
- 56% of all species require early successional habitats. They require exposed sand and ruderal rather than being associated with any particular heathland stage (they are not dependent on pioneer *Calluna vulgaris*, for example). As many of these species also require shelter they go hand in hand with mosaics of taller vegetation, such as heather and scrub that form sheltered bays within the heathland.
- Over 30% of species require grasslands or grass-heath matrices. A further analysis showed that 56% of these species are associated with structure whereas 39% are associated with specific foodplants or a nectar resource (often all year round).
- 29% of species are associated with woody growth in the form of scattered scrub, woodland edge or individual trees. Large blocks of scrub and trees will, for the most, only be utilized along their edges.
- Seasonal inundation is a pre-requisite for 14% of species. The majority of these species utilize drawdown zones, mainly bare mud. Some also require the temporary water bodies, which are often shallow, fish free and of high water quality. Many of these seasonal pools are found on tracks where water collects in the winter.
- 12% of species are associated with the juxtaposition of different habitats at the landscape scale.
- Only 9% of species are associated with wet heathland (usually permanently wet or damp) and 6% are associated with dry heathland. This is suggests that heathlands dominated by even-age ericaceous scrub will support a very depauperate fauna and flora.

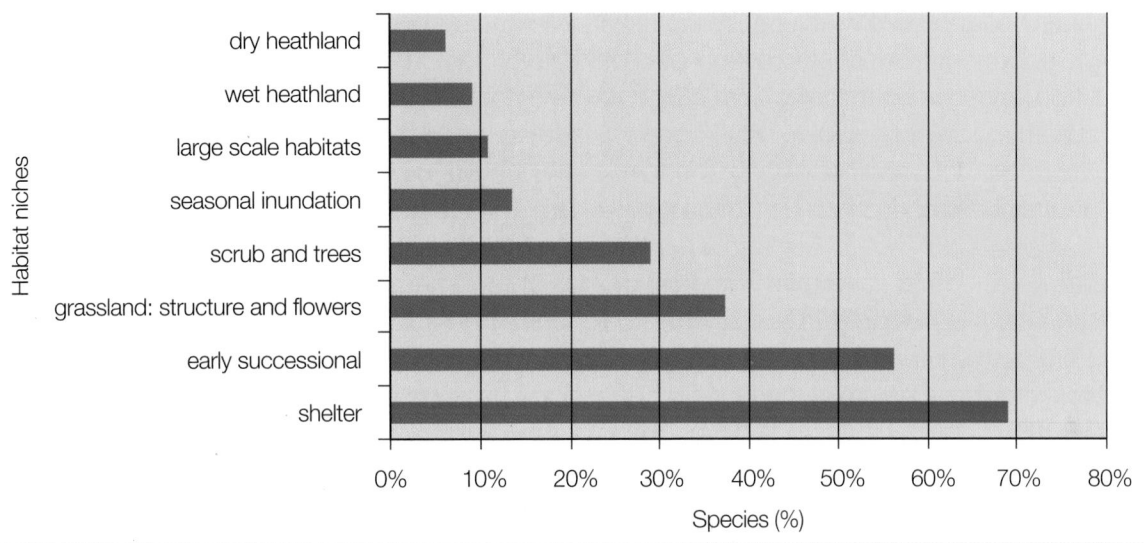

Figure 5.2 Niches/Habitats Requirements for UK BAP Species Associated with heathland.

5.4 Discussion

5.4.1 Species and habitat trend analysis

Our results demonstrate that there is currently no association between the trends of UK BAP habitats and their associated BAP species. One possible explanation for this surprising result is that recent improvements in habitats have not yet been reflected in species populations due to the time needed for species to recover. Similarly, there may be a considerable time lag before species recolonize sites from which they have been completely lost. This may be part of the answer, it does not, however, account for recent declines of species in particular habitat types. For example, the extent of woodlands has been steadily increasing in recent years, while many woodland species (including birds and butterflies) are currently in decline (Natural England, 2008b). In cases such as this, the lack of association may be because the trend assessments for most BAP habitats are based on extent, not on their suitability for meeting species' conservation requirements.

5.4.2 Species' habitat requirements for lowland heathland

There are very few 'true' heathland species, i.e. those strongly associated with heather. In fact, most species inhabiting heathland sites do not require ericaceous scrub to complete their life cycles.

For species requirements to be fully incorporated into heathlands a large number of niches and resources need to be made available. Heathland ecosystems will require dynamic processes that

Plate 5.3 *Poecilus (Pterostichus) kugelanni*, a species of beetle requiring sheltered bare ground. © Natural England.

Plate 5.4 *Meloe violaceus*, a species whose larvae live in solitary bees' nests. The bees require bare ground and plenty of flowering plants for nectar and pollen. © Natural England

Plate 5.5 The burrows of solitary bees and wasps within bare ground. © Natural England

Plate 5.6 Nightjar (*Caprimulgus europaeus*), requires a mosaic of bare ground and scrub vegetation. © Allan Drewitt.

encourage scrub matrices, seasonal inundation, patches of flowers and tall herbs - all of which provide valuable resources. These 'disturbance' processes are beneficial although they may not, historically, have been seen as such. There are no data to suggest how intimate the mix of structures need to be and there is a danger that very small, poorly-shaped or too fragmented habitats will still not deliver appropriate niches. As many of the species utilizing these habitats are small (invertebrates and plants) it is expected that the intimacy of the niche mosaic should be scaled appropriately i.e. any given hectare should have a number of different niches represented.

Examples include:

- Management that leads to small patches of herbs, such as umbellifers, yellow composites and legumes.
- Dynamic scrub that develops throughout the site, in particular species such as birch, willow, gorse and hawthorn. Scrub should not dominate a heathland or be present in large blocks. Often, a scatter of individual plants along with a few small blocks (represented by a small number of plants) should be seen as appropriate.
- Areas devoid of vegetation, in particular where this is in a tight mosaic with other habitat types. Bare sand and ruderal habitats were required by over half of all species under investigation. Temporary pools on un-surfaced paths, depressions and muddy/peaty areas are also of high importance.
- Mosaics of habitats, such as woodland-heathland and grassland-heathland, are of high importance both for the shelter they provide and the extra resources on offer for species.

This analysis has revealed the habitat features that will benefit heathland species, but it is important to remember that there are other factors that can affect the conservation status of species which have not been considered here. For example, the effect of air pollution, predation, disease or competition from other species. In addition, if the management recommendations made here were carried out everywhere, without any consideration of inter-site differences, some species could be detrimentally affected, in particular, species that require large areas of structurally poor habitats or whose requirements run contrary to most other species.

5.4.3 Issues arising from the analysis

When most specialists were asked if the heathland species habitat requirements results were as they had expected the response was generally: "yes" . The strength of the analysis is that it backs up expert opinion with strong evidence. Although the analysis was restricted to UK BAP species, we undertook further follow-up analysis on non-UK BAP invertebrates using the ISIS database (Webb and Lott, 2006), which summarizes the relationship between invertebrate species and habitats by assigning scores to catches of invertebrates sampled using standardized techniques (Drake *et al.*, 2007). This analysis indicated that our results apply widely across all invertebrate species.

Plate 5.7 Heathland scrub and trees in Lincolnshire. © Natural England   Plate 5.8 Sheltered bare ground on a south facing slope in Yorkshire. © Natural England

This, however, begs a further question: if experts generally did accept that species requirements are best served through structural diversity then why is this not put into practice more often? The answer is complex, but likely reasons include:

- Incompatibility/conflict between the needs of species groups
- A focus on a few species of perceived importance whose requirements do not necessarily marry up with other species.
- The focus of statutory site management on site 'features' (that focuses conservation effort on biological targets (population numbers) for specific features based on a static paradigm rather than allowing for flux and change).
- Action may already have been taken, but issues of time lag, fragmentation and/or isolation prevent results being realized.
- On-site issues which do not readily allow for changes in management regimes, including lack of resources.
- The classification of many habitats by their vegetation types, which fails to take into account structure.

Overall the results indicate that increased conservation effort to meet BAP habitat expansion targets, may not also benefit species in the ways that might be expected. To conserve species, we need an increased emphasis on increasing habitat heterogeneity, between sites, within sites and over time. We suggest that this more dynamic approach to managing our habitats has the potential to support the recovery of most species. This approach is also likely to be beneficial as our climate changes, by increasing the opportunities for species to persist within their existing habitats, and to colonize new sites.

Plate 5.9 Structurally complex wet heathland in southern England. © Natural England

5.5 Acknowledgements

The authors would like to thank all contributors and participants at the SNH species management conference, in particular John Baxter for his invitation and support. We are also grateful for the expert contributions of John Baker, Jeremy Biggs, Nigel Bourn, Andy Brown, John Buckley, Ian Carter, Stewart Clarke, Allan Drewitt, Alastair Driver, Mike Edgington, Jim Foster, Phil Grice, Dave Goulson, Vicky Kindemba, David Heaver, Nicola Hutchinson, Simon Leach, Chris Mainstone, Ant Maddock, Louise Mapstone, Gavin Measures, Stephen Miles, Tony Mitchell-Jones, Nick Moulton, Jill Nelson, Mark

Parsons, Henry Schofield, David Sheppard, Sue Tatman, Pam Taylor, Alan Stewart, Mike Sutcliffe, Ian Taylor, Andrew Whitehouse, John Wilkinson, Dorothy Wright, Robin Wynde and Derek Yalden. Finally, we thank Duncan Stone for his helpful comments on this paper.

References and selected bibliography

Asher, J., Warren, M., Fox, R., Harding, P., Jeffcoate, G. & Jeffcoate, S. (2001). *The Millennium Atlas of Butterflies in Britain and Ireland*. Oxford University Press.

Brown, A. & Grice, P. (2005). *Birds in England*. T & A D Poyser.

Cheffings, C. & Farrell, L. (Eds). (2005). *The Vascular Plant Red Data List for Great Britain*. JNCC, Peterborough, UK.

Defra. (2006.) The UK Biodiversity Action Plan: highlights from the 2005 reporting round. Defra, London. Full data set available from http://www.ukbap.org.uk/GenPageText.aspx?id=105

Drake, C.M., Lott, D.A., Alexander, K.N.A. & Webb, J.R. (2007). *Natural England Research Report NERR005:* Surveying terrestrial and freshwater invertebrates for conservation evaluation. Natural England, Sheffield, UK.

English Nature. (1999). Biodiversity – Making the Links. English Nature, Peterborough, UK.

Falk, S.J. & Crossley, R. (2005). *A Review of the scarce and threatened flies of Great Britain*. JNCC.

Hill, M. O., Preston, C. D. & Smith, A.J.E. (1994). *Atlas of the Bryophytes of Britain and Ireland: Volume 3 Mosses (Diplolepideae).* Harley Books.

Kirby, J., Drewitt, A., Chivers, L. & Saunders, R. (2000). *English Nature Research Report No.359:* Key Habitat Attributes for birds and bird assemblages in England. English Nature, Peterborough, UK.

Natural England. (2008a). Securing biodiversity – a new framework for delivering priority habitats and species in England. Natural England, Sheffield, UK.

Natural England. (2008b). The State of the Natural Environment 2008. Natural England, Sheffield, UK.

NERC Act: Natural Environment and Communities Act. (2006). HMSO.

Paton, J.A. (1999). *The Liverwort Flora of the British Isles*. Harley Books.

Porley, R. & Hodgetts, N. (2005). *Mosses & Liverworts*. Collins.

Preston, C.D., Pearman, D.A. & Dines, T. D. (2002). *New Atlas of the British & Irish Flora*. Oxford University Press.

Shirt, D.B. (Ed.). (1987). *British Red Data Books: 2.Insects*. Nature Conservancy Council.

Stewart, A., Pearman, D. A. & Preston, C. D. (Eds). (1994). *Scarce Plants in Britain*. JNCC, Peterborough, UK.

UK BAP review. (2007). – unpublished information notes by various authors.

UK BIODIVERSITY GROUP. (1998). *Tranche 2 Action Plans. Volume I Vertebrates and vascular plants.* UKBG/English Nature, Peterborough.

UK BIODIVERSITY GROUP. (1999a). *Tranche 2 Action Plans. Volume III Plants and fungi.* UKBG/English Nature, Peterborough.

UK BIODIVERSITY GROUP. (1999b). *Tranche 2 Action Plans. Volume IV Invertebrates*. UKBG/English Nature, Peterborough.

UK BIODIVERSITY GROUP. (1999c). *Tranche 2 Action Plans. Volume V Maritime habitats and species*. UKBG/English Nature, Peterborough.

UK BIODIVERSITY GROUP. (1999d). *Tranche 2 Action Plans. Volume VI Terrestrial habitats and species*. UKBG/English Nature, Peterborough.

UK BIODIVERSITY GROUP. (1999e). *Tranche 2 Action Plans. Volume VII Index*. UKBG/English Nature, Peterborough.

Webb, J.R. & Lott, D.L. (2006). The Development of ISIS: a habitat-based invertebrate assembale classification system for assessing conservation interest in England. *Journal of Insect Conservation* **10**:179-188.

Wigginton, M. J. (1999). *British Red Data Books 1: Vascular Plants* 3rd Edition. JNCC, Peterborough, UK.

Brotherton, P. and Webb, J. (2010). Achieving species conservation through habitat-based approaches. In: *Species Management: Challenges and Solutions for the 21st Century*, ed. by J.M. Baxter and C.A. Galbraith. TSO Scotland, Edinburgh. pp. 75-89

89

Chapter 6

Managing marine species in a rapidly changing world

Steve J. Hawkins[1], Heather E. Sugden[1], Nova Mieszkowska[2], Mike T. Burrows[3], and John M. Baxter[4]

Summary

1. Increases in human populations and accelerating climate change due to greenhouse gas emissions, are exerting increased pressure on our seas and coasts at both local and regional scales. Marine species and ecosystems are already responding to these drivers.
2. Examples are given of broadscale latitudinal and bathymetric shifts of planktonic, fish and benthic species northwards and into deeper water. In this chapter the focus is on the responses of well-studied intertidal indicator species using long-term data, with case studies of important species at their range edges in UK and Scottish waters.
3. By coupling long-term monitoring programmes with shorter term process-oriented studies it is possible to interpret past changes and to forecast future studies via modelling.
4. Sustained monitoring enables moving baselines to be established helping to solve contempory environmental management problems such as separation of climate driven change from local and regional scale impacts, as well as informing environmental status reporting. Modelling enables forecasts to be made of future states thereby anticipating change. Such contextual information is essential for nature conservation: species, biotopes, habitats and sites can only be rationally managed if globally driven changes can be separated from more manageable local and regional activities likely to cause impacts.
5. Adaptational strategies are required to manage the interactions of climate change operating on large spatial and temporal scales with more regional and localized impacts in order to conserve the role of biodiversity in ecosystem functioning. Global change necessitates a broad-scale approach transcending national boundaries. It also emphasizes the need for networks of Marine Protected Areas so that conservation is implemented against the backdrop of shifting distributions.

[1] School of Ocean Sciences, Bangor University, Menai Bridge, Anglesey, LL59 5AB, UK
[2] The Marine Biological Association of the UK, The Laboratory, Citadel Hill, Plymouth, PL1 2PB, UK
[3] Scottish Association for Marine Science, Dunstaffnage Marine Laboratory, Oban, Argyll, PA37 1QA, UK
[4] Scottish Natural Heritage, Silvan House, 231 Corstorphine Road, Edinburgh, EH12 7AT, UK

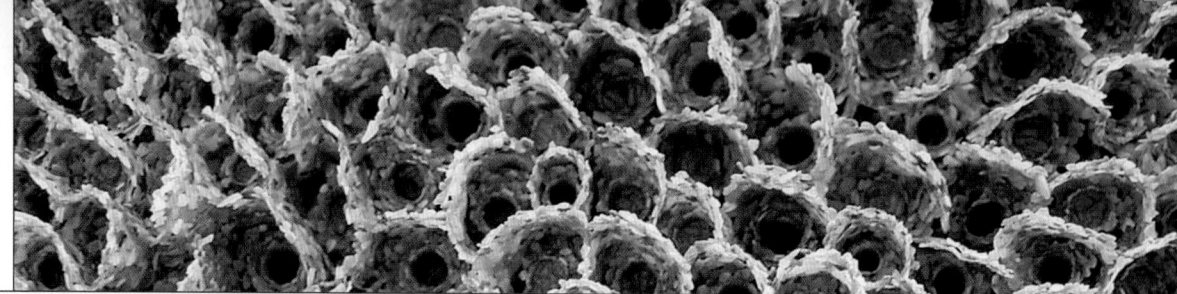

6.1 Introduction

We live in a rapidly changing world (IPCC, 2007). Marine ecosystems have been shown to rapidly respond to climate change, in part due to their open nature and high connectivity (Parmesan and Yohe, 2003; Stenseth *et al.,* 2003; Parmesan *et al.,* 2005). The marine natural heritage of Scotland is being altered through global environmental change and its interaction with regional and local scale impacts due to human activities. These themes are explored in this chapter to provide a framework for protection of marine species and their habitats through management of a range of human activities. Such management on a variety of spatial scales is essential to ensure that the goods and services provided by marine biodiversity and ecosystems can be maintained.

Inertia in the climate system means that temperatures are extremely likely to continue to rise – even if greenhouse gas emissions were to be drastically cut. Thus, over the next 50-100 years society has to adapt to climate change whilst it awaits the outcomes of current mitigation measures and the eventual switch from carbon-based to renewable or nuclear energy sources. The reduction in the pH of the ocean (so-called ocean acidification), as the result of the increased dissolution of carbon dioxide in sea water to form carbonic acid is also a serious concern and has the potential to severely affect marine organisms, food webs and fisheries within decades, but is not considered here as it is worth a chapter in its own right (but see the excellent summary by the Royal Society, 2005, and other recent reviews Caldeira and Wickett, 2003; Feely *et al.,* 2004; Sabine *et al.,* 2004; Orr *et al.,* 2005; Turley, 2008). Perhaps an even more pressing issue over the next 50-100 years will be the possible impacts of mitigation measures on marine biodiversity, particularly from construction, related to renewable energy generation through wind, wave and tidal power. Such impacts need to be evaluated and considered against the gains in provision of clean energy.

This chapter provides a summary of the likely changes to the physical environment and highlights the broadscale responses of plankton and fish to climate change in European, British and Scottish waters, drawing on information from long-term data sets. Changes in intertidal indicator species are then outlined, exemplifying the importance of broadscale and long-term data sets. Such changes are extrapolated to offshore benthos. The role of modelling in forecasting the future distribution and abundance of species and consequent changes in ecosystem functioning under different climate change scenarios is then discussed.

The need to manage the interactions of climate change with other regional (e.g. fishing) and local (e.g. habitat loss or damage) scale impacts is emphasized. Finally consideration is given to the legislative tools and instruments needed to manage Scottish marine species and especially their habitats. The importance of factoring connectivity into marine spatial planning and Marine Protected Area design is emphasized. Thereby we set the scene for the Marine Strategy Framework Directive and the Scottish Marine Bill, currently at the consultation stage at the time of writing this chapter.

6.2 Past baselines, present and future trends

There is now widespread acceptance that the planet is warming due to human activities that have led to an increase in greenhouse gas emissions (IPCC, 2007). These trends are not smooth, however, and historical instrumental data for sea surface temperature (SST) stretching back over 150 years shows both warm (1880s) and cold periods (either side of the First World War). There was a steady warming of the waters of the North-east Atlantic from the 1920s to the 1950s, before a cold spell from the mid 1960s to 1980s was heralded in by the extreme winter of 1962/1963 (Figure 6.1). Regional climatic conditions have fluctuated markedly throughout the last 60 years. Thus care must be taken in comparing data from the trough of the cold period of the 1960s and 1970s with today. A more suitable baseline would be the warmer decade of the 1950s. It is also very important not to confuse weather with climate (Helmuth et al., 2006). Long-term data are essential for segregation of inter-annual fluctuations from longer-term decadal scales change.

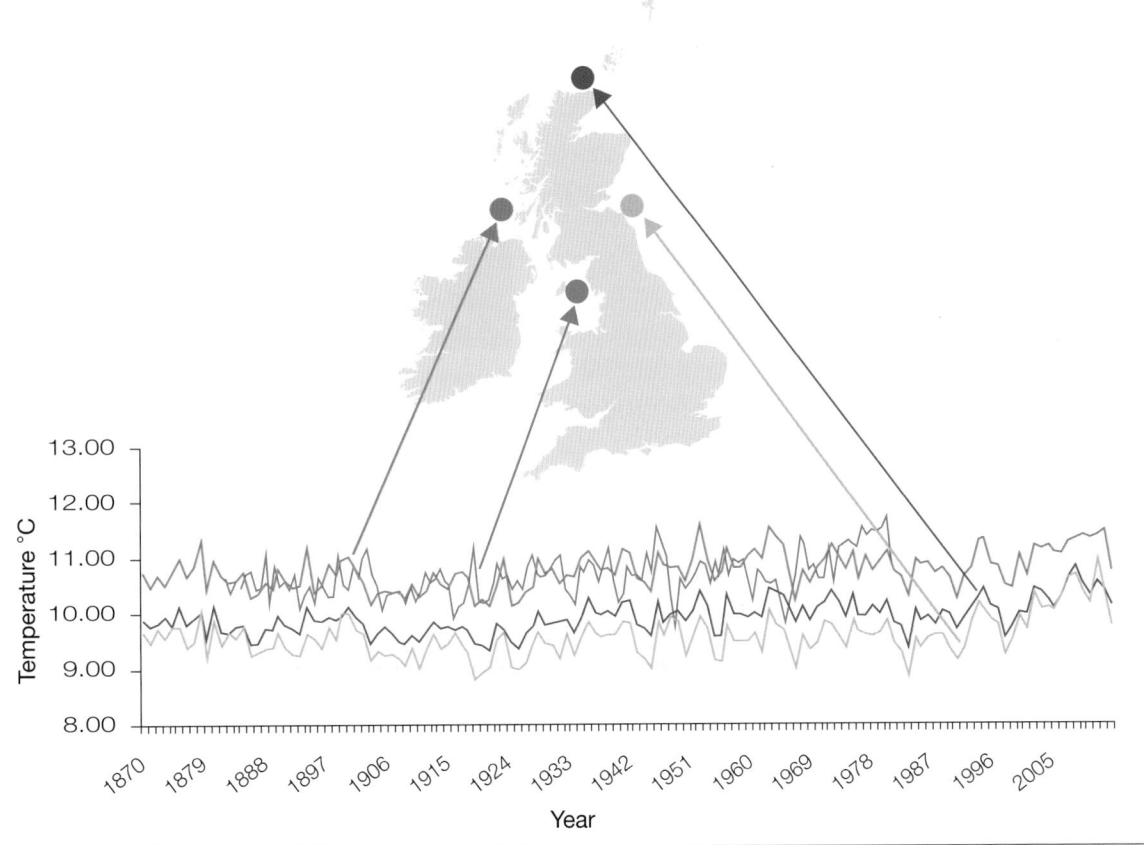

Figure 6.1 Average yearly sea surface temperature (SST) from 1870-2008 at four locations in the UK: Isle of Man (blue), South-west Scotland (green), North Scotland (purple), South-east Scotland (gold), using data from Hadley Centre SST data set (HadSST2: Rayner et al., 2006).

The Scottish coastline is influenced in the west and north by warm water from the North Atlantic Drift, which penetrates into the cooler northern North Sea (Figure 6.2). Scotland divides oceanic warmer west coast water derived from the Gulf Stream from the continentally influenced North Sea, which is cooler in the winter. During the winter, there is an inversion in the latitudinal temperature gradient whereby the south-north temperature trend is reversed.

The enclosed Irish Sea can also be much colder in the winter. Since the late 1980s the climate of north-west Europe in general and Scotland in particular has markedly warmed (Sheppard, 2004). Much of the change in annual temperatures is due to milder, shorter winters. These have led to much milder conditions in the North Sea (MacKenzie and Schiedek, 2007). The milder, shorter winters were thought to be due to a higher frequency of North Atlantic Oscillation (NAO) Index positive years leading to wetter more westerly winter weather, although the increasing winter seasonal temperature trend has diverged from the NAO index during recent years, illustrating the complexity of the atmospheric-oceanic climate system (Hulme et al., 2002).

Future projections of sea temperatures all point to rises of between 1.1 and 6.4°C around Scotland depending on emissions scenarios over the next 100 years (Hulme et al., 2002). NAO positive years are likely to become more frequent. Extreme precipitation events (both drought and flood) will occur more often affecting inshore waters and semi-enclosed sea lochs and estuaries. The frequency of severe storms is expected to increase and sea levels continue to rise (IPCC, 2007). In Scotland, isostatic rebound following the last Ice-Age has reduced the impact of rising sea levels up until recently, but isostatic rebound is now negligible, increasing the impact of continuing sea-level rise (Shennan et al., 2006a, b).

In the more distant future the possibility of slow down of the thermohaline circulation of the Atlantic looms (Hansen et al., 2001; Bryden et al., 2005). This has, however, happened rapidly once before 12,000-14,000 years ago. As the north-east Atlantic warmed after the last ice age, a rapid switch (<100 years) to much colder conditions occurred - the Younger Dryas cold event, which lasted for 1,300 years before warming resumed (Alley et al., 1993; Taylor et al., 1997; Bradley and England, 2008).

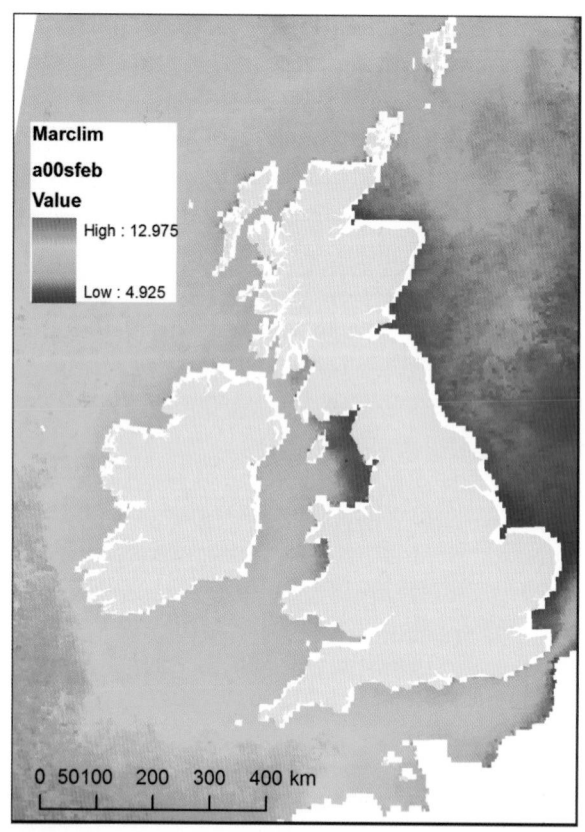

Figure 6.2 Averaged sea surface temperature (SST) for February 2001-06 projected using NASA 4 km resolution AVHRR Pathfinder Data. The AVHRR Pathfinder SST Data were obtained from the Physical Oceanography Distributed Data Active Archive Centre (PO.DAAC) at the NASA Jet Propulsion Laboratory, Pasadena, CA. http://podaac.jpl.nasa.gov (Burrows, unpublished).

6.3 Responses of marine biodiversity and ecosystems

Fluctuations in pelagic ecosystems in relation to climate have been long-known with switches in zooplankton assemblages and pelagic fish occurring between warm and cold periods (e.g. Russell, 1973; Southward, 1980). For example, in the English Channel, switches between pilchards (also called sardine – *Sardina pilchardus*) during warm periods and herring (*Clupea harengus*) in cold periods have been known to occur since the Middle Ages (Southward, 1988; Southward *et al.*, 2005). The Continuous Plankton Recorder (CPR) survey operated by the Sir Alastair Hardy Foundation for Ocean Science (SAHFOS) has shown rapid changes in response to accelerated warming. Zooplankton assemblages have shifted northwards by more than 1,000 km during the second half of the 20th century (Beaugrand *et al.*, 2001; Beaugrand and Reid, 2003). The plankton off Scotland now was once typical of the Bay of Biscay, Celtic Sea and western approaches to the English Channel (Beaugrand and Ibanez, 2004; Ibanez and Beaugrand, 2008). Northern assemblages that were once typical of the offshore waters to the west of Scotland and in the northern North Sea and are now restricted to Iceland and northern Norway.

Similar changes have also occurred in fish assemblages. Pelagic fish are particularly sensitive to climate change: anchovies and sardines are now common in much of the English Channel and southern North Sea (Enghoff *et al.*, 2007). Similar changes have occurred in demersal fish. In south-west England, warm water species, such as red mullet (*Mullus barbatus*) and sea breams (Family Sparidae), are now more common (Genner *et al.*, 2004) and as shown by Beare *et al.* (2003) *"the northern North Sea is experiencing waves of immigration by exotic southern species (e.g. red mullet, anchovy and pilchard) which are unprecedented in the context of the 79 year history of our extensive databases"*. In the North Sea shifts both northwards and into deeper water have been recorded for northern species such as eelpout (*Zoarces viviparus*), blue whiting (*Micromesistius poutassou*) and redfishes (*Sebastes* spp. Perry *et al.*, 2005; Dulvy *et al.*, 2008). Phenological changes have also been found in planktonic species (Edwards and Richardson, 2004). These shifts in timing of appearance of species in the spring phytoplankton bloom, have major implications for the recruitment of commercial fish due to a mismatch between larval output and food supply. Changes in the composition of the plankton can also reduce recruitment success: the shift from *Calanus finmarchicus* to *Calanus helgolandicus* has been implicated in reduced recruitment of cod (Beaugrand and Ibanez, 2004) already at risk from reduced spawning stock biomass due to overfishing (Holmes *et al.*, 2008).

Fishing pressure interacts with climate to shape fish assemblages. Many target species in Scottish and British waters are northern species (e.g. cod, haddock). Reduced stock sizes have long been known to increase the probability of mismatch (Cushing, 1961, 1975) with larval food availability which can be made worse due to climate change (see above). Evidence from the English Channel suggests that abundances of smaller non-commercial fish track climate, but that a clear signal cannot be determined for larger fish since fishing pressure appears to over-ride climate drivers (Genner *et al.*, 2009).

Similar changes are likely to occur in subtidal and offshore benthos but the lack of broadscale surveys and time series means that few trends have been detected. There are many anecdotal shifts recorded in the grey literature (e.g. spider crabs) but as yet there are no peer-reviewed published studies in this area. Predictions of likely range edge shifts under different climate scenarios are summarized in Hiscock *et al.* (2004).

Shifts in space and time in lower trophic levels (i.e. plankton) and intermediate levels (e.g. fish) are likely to have consequences for top predators such as birds and marine mammals. There is convincing evidence that reductions in sandeels have had detrimental consequences for seabird populations, particularly black-legged kittiwakes (*Rissa tridactyla*) and northern gannets (*Morus bassanus*) (Wanless *et al.*, 2005; Harris *et al.*, 2008; Furness, this volume). Although it is difficult to completely separate the effects of climate change and over-fishing it is likely that their interactions will amplify negative effects (Harley *et al.*, 2006; Day *et al.*, 2008). Thus a precautionary approach to managing fisheries is needed, especially for northern species.

6.4 Rocky intertidal species

There have been extensive broadscale surveys of a broad suite of rocky intertidal species for much of Great Britain and Ireland (Southward and Crisp, 1954; Crisp and Southward, 1958) and continental Europe (Fischer-Piette, 1936, 1955) that provide a baseline from the warm spell of the 1950s. There are more scattered but largely unpublished records for the decades since those publications, including observations following the extremely cold winter of 1962/1963 (Crisp, 1964). For barnacles there are extensive time-series recording the fluctuations of northern (*Semibalanus balanoides:* Figure 6.3) and southern (*Chthamalus montagui* and *Chthamalus stellatus*) species. These extend over 50 years at multiple sites in south-west England (Southward, 1991; Southward *et al.*, 2005).

In recent years range extensions have occurred in many southern species: these have been manifested both northwards and eastwards along the Welsh and Scottish coastlines and also eastwards into the colder eastern English Channel basin (Figure 6.4). Many species have now extended further east beyond the Isle of Wight which was the range edge of many species in the 1950s and 1980s. The barnacle *Perforatus (Balanus) perforatus* (Figure 6.5) has penetrated to Kent in the English Channel (Herbert *et al.*, 2003; S.J. Hawkins unpublished observations). The limpet *Patella ulyssiponensis* (*Patella aspera*), has reached Beachy Head. The high shore gastropod *Melarhaphe neritoides* has not only reached Kent, but it is also now found on artificial habitats such as

Figure 6.3 *Semibalanus balanoides* – a northern, cold-water species. © Nova Mieszkowska

breakwaters and low-crested structures in East Anglia (Norfolk). *Patella depressa* (Figure 6.6) has only made a very small hop from the Isle of Wight to sea defences on Hayling Island. The warm water topshell *Gibbula umbilicalis* (Figure 6.7) has been very successful – rapidly expanding in recent years being found round to Kent with breeding populations being established at Folkstone since 2005. Sea defences and other artificial structures (piers, breakwaters, Brighton Marina) have probably acted as stepping stones aiding expansion.

Similar range extensions have been observed in the Irish Sea. The topshell *Osilinus lineatus* (Figure 6.8) has now recovered all the ground lost after the cold winter of 1962/1963, when its range was trimmed back from Anglesey to the south side of the Lleyn Peninsula (Crisp, 1964). It is present in large numbers on Anglesey with rapid increases in the last 3-4 years (Mieszkowska *et al.*, 2007). In 2007 and 2008 it was found beyond its previously known range on the east of the Orme at Llandudno. *Gibbula umbilicalis* has also been recorded along the North Wales

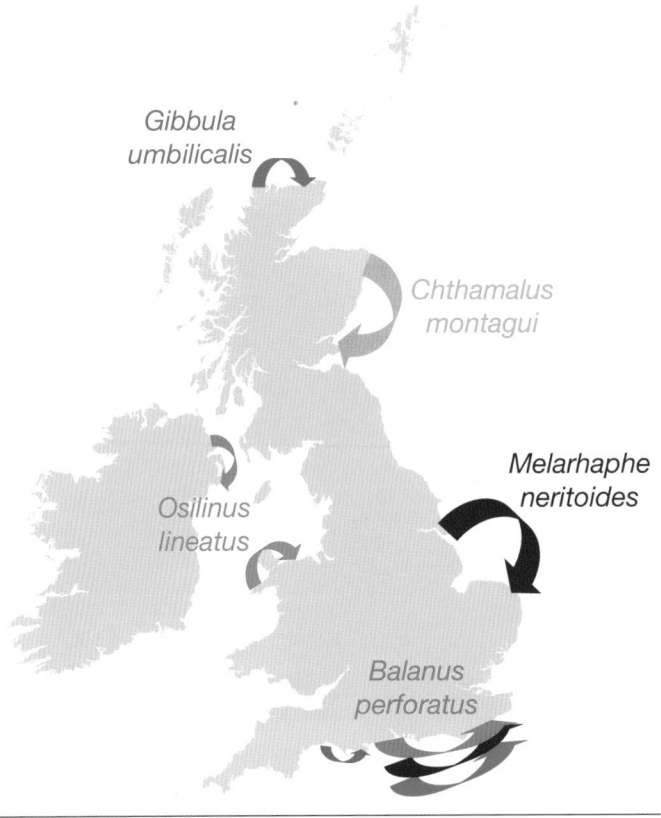

Figure 6.4 Some examples of range extensions of rocky intertidal species, arrows indicate the limit to which each of the species have reached and the direction from which they have extended their range. For further details see Mieszkowska *et al.* (2007) and Herbert *et al.* (2003).

coast beyond Anglesey and the Orme where it has not previously been recorded. The warm water barnacle *Chthamalus montagui* has been found on the Orme and on sea defences at Llandulas, the Wirral and at Hilbre, infilling a section of the biogeographic distribution where it has previously been largely absent other than occasional specimens found on Hilbre and the Wirral in the 1950s. The BAP species, the honeycomb worm *Sabellaria alveolata* (Figure 6.9) has recolonized Hilbre Island and occurs on sea defences on the Wirral. It has also recolonized the North Wales coast at Llandulas and the Little Orme. *S. alveolata* probably recolonized from the north: it has always been present at Heysham and on the Cumbrian coast. *C. stellatus* which had not been previously found in the northern Irish Sea basin was recorded for the first time in 2005 on the Isle of Man; although a large old individual found in 2008 suggests it had been there for some time but had been missed in earlier surveys. *P. depressa* has markedly increased in abundance in northern Cardigan Bay; but has made little recovery on the north side of the Lleyn and the west coast of Anglesey, where it once occurred quite commonly (Crisp and Knight-

Jones, 1954). This species seems to disperse poorly and the Lleyn Peninsula appears to still present a major barrier to recruitment and spread. In Northern Ireland *O. lineatus* has spread further along the Antrim coast, south-westerly into the northern Irish Sea basin.

Figure 6.5 *Perforatus (Balanus) perforatus.* © Nova Mieszkowska

Figure 6.6 *Patella depressa.* © Nova Mieszkowska

Figure 6.7 *Gibbula umbilicalis.* © Nova Mieszkowska

Figure 6.8 *Osilinus lineatus.* © Nova Mieszkowska

Due to the late opening of the English Channel and Irish Sea following the last Ice Age most marine species recolonized Scottish waters from the south and west, often being recruited via refugia populations on the west coast of Ireland. Penetration of these species into the North Sea occurred around the north-east tip of Scotland resulting in some paradoxical consequences, including the advance southwards into the North Sea of warm water species.

In Scotland, *G. umbilicalis* has extended further along the north coast (Figure 6.4). In contrast to the surveys in the 1980s when recruitment was rare and populations were dominated by old individuals (Kendall and Lewis, 1986), new recruits were present in 2002, 2003, 2004 (Mieszkowska *et al.*, 2006). *C. montagui* was recently found in Fife (at Pittenweem: M. T. Burrows, personal observation), an extension further south into the North Sea from its previous limit in Aberdeenshire (Crisp *et al.*, 1981).

Fewer retreats of northern species have been found although the relative abundance of the cold water limpet *Patella vulgata* and barnacle *S. balanoides* has decreased in south-west England. The kelp, *Alaria esculenta*, retracted in the English Channel during the warm period of the 1950s. It did not recover during the subsequent cooler period of the 1960s and 1970s. More recently it has further decreased in abundance around its southern limits in both south-west and north-east England (Mieszkowska *et al.*, 2005) as well as in Ireland (Simkanin *et al.*, 2005). *Testudinalis testudinalis* (Figure 6.10), the tortoiseshell limpet, was once quite common on the south coast of the Isle of Man, but has not been seen in recent years despite much searching. This species is towards its extreme southern limit in the Irish Sea, with confirmed specimens having been recently found in Northern Ireland and also on the north coast of Anglesey.

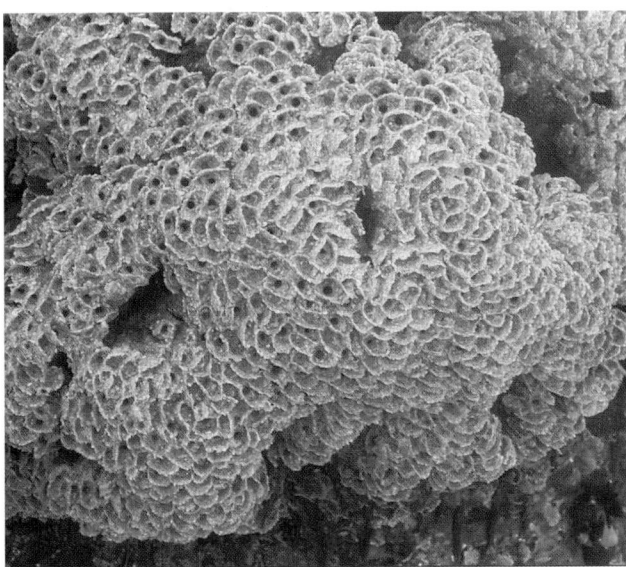

Figure 6.9 *Sabellaria alveolata.* © Nova Mieszkowska

Figure 6.10 *Testudinalis testudinalis.* © Nova Mieszkowska

In summary, although many changes in geographical distribution and abundance of intertidal organisms have occurred they are very species specific, depending upon life history and ecological traits. Therefore unlike in the plankton where assemblages are likely to shift in phase polewards, responses will be idiosyncratic leading to changes in assemblage composition, community structuring and hence ecosystem functioning (Hawkins *et al.,* 2008).

6.5 Predicting future states

Predicting future ecosystem states and rates of change in abundance and extent of species is essential in planned adaptational management of climate change impacts. A variety of approaches are available to make such predictions. Our first approach involved statistical modelling of bioclimatic envelopes to predict the potential future ranges of species, based on their current distributions. Wave action and minimum February sea surface temperatures have been used as predictors derived from known ranges of species. Wave exposure (as total wave fetch) has been estimated for the north-western European coast using an algorithm based on Thomas (1986) adapted by Burrows *et al.* (2008). Modelled distributions can then be tested against broadscale surveys made as part of the MarClim project (Mieszkowska *et al.,* 2005). Then various UKCIP scenarios can be used to predict future distributions under different greenhouse gas emission regimes.

The bioclimatic envelope approach has someshort comings and has attracted some criticism (Thompson *et al.*, 2004; Heikkinen *et al.,* 2006; Poyry *et al.,* 2008), but it does provide a robust first approximation of where species could potentially occur in the future (e.g. Davies *et al.*, 1998). Differences between actual distributions today and modelled contemporary distributions also help to pinpoint other factors determining geographic ranges such as barriers to dispersal and lack of suitable habitat influencing connectivity at range edges. *C. montagui* has yet to extend beyond the Isle of Wight, unlike some other species (e.g. *G. umbilicalis, P. depressa, P. ulyssiponensis, M. neritoides,* and *P. perforatus* see Figure 6.4). This is probably due to offshore dispersal and lack of suitable habitat. Interestingly, *C. montagui* is yet to be found on artificial habitats such as sea defences and harbours on the south coast. This contrasts with the east coast of Scotland, where a considerable expansion has been recorded.

A second approach has involved process-based models using barnacles as test species (e.g. Poloczanska *et al.*, 2008). More data are required for such models and it is fortunate that both extensive time-series and considerable ecological background knowledge on interactions are available for cold and warm water barnacles. The long-term data sets have revealed through path analysis that the cold water species *S. balanoides* is negatively affected by warm springs, presumably increasing juvenile mortality. In contrast, the warm water *C. montagui* is not directly influenced by temperature, but by release from competition with *S. balanoides* during warm years. This matches what has long-been known from field surveys (Southward and Crisp, 1954) and experiments (Connell, 1961). A two-species, space-limited model was developed (based in part on Alexander and Roughgarden, 1996; Shkedy and Roughgarden, 1997) into which variable recruitment due to climate was incorporated. The outputs from this model were tested against the long-term data sets of A.J. Southward; a reasonable fit occurred. This approach was then projected into the future using UKCIP02 climate scenarios. The results unequivocally show that even under low emission scenarios that *S. balanoides,* the dominant barnacle on English Channel coasts in the 1930s (Moore, 1936) will go largely locally extinct in south-western Britain in the next 25-30 years. There is growing evidence of more frequent failure years of *S. balanoides* towards its southern limit (Svensson *et al.,* 2005). The invasive species, *Elminius modestus*, dominates much of the lower estuarine refuge occupied by *S. balanoides* throughout Europe. Thus prospects for *S. balanoides* in southern Britain and Ireland are poor and further south in its range in Spain it has already contracted much with local extinction of many populations leading to a small remaining toe hold in Galicia (Wethey and Woodin, 2008). Both modelling approaches need refinement, but even in their current form they could be used and adapted for a range of species including offshore benthos.

6.6 Implications for management and conservation

The pace of future change in our physical environment is uncertain but reasonable climatic scenarios can be considered. Human responses to climate change are more predictable. Around Britain, the generation of electricity from offshore renewables will increase. For wind power this is already well underway. Offshore wave and tidal energy will follow as pilot projects such as the Wave Hub off Cornwall and the EMEC test facility in Orkney, plus the instream turbine in Strangford Lough result in commercial arrays of turbines being located in various areas (e.g. the recently proposed scheme on Islay). Tidal barrages are also being strongly advocated. A Severn Estuary barrage would make a large contribution to clean energy provision, but would inevitably affect the ecology of the largest estuary and catchment in England and Wales due to the alteration of water flow. Similar schemes are likely to be proposed for Scotland.

Nuclear power generation is now fashionable again with the UK government and is likely to lead to re-commissioning of existing sites or even the building of new ones in England. The value of intake screens as monitoring tools must not be forgotten and analyses of data from Hinckley Point in the Bristol Channel has been extremely valuable in generating data showing the influence of climate on fish assemblage structure (i.e. Genner *et al.*, 2004) plus showing species in decline in need of management action such as eels (*Anguilla anguilla*) and shad (*Alosa alosa* and *Alosa fallax:* Henderson, 2007).

Offshore structures will influence connectivity and act as stepping stones by providing more hard substratum. Wave and tidal devices will remove significant amounts of energy from the water column. Transmission of electricity could also influence species sensitive to perturbations in electromagnetic fields, such as elasmobranchs with well developed electroreceptive organs (Gill, 2005). Offshore wind farms have been shown to have some impacts on seabirds but these are generally not severe. They also exclude areas of sea bed from towed-gear fishing which could reduce impacts on benthic communities and may provide refugia for exploited fish.

Condition status of Special Areas of Conservation (SACs) needs to be judged in the context of the moving baseline caused by climate change. Thus broadscale contextual monitoring on an annual basis in sensitive regions is essential to segregate the noise of inter-annual variability from the signal of climate change. Changes may occur which have nothing to do with the internal state of an SAC but which are merely responses to climate.

All Marine Protected Areas (MPAs) need to be extensive and networked if they are to accommodate shifts in distribution and abundance and provide avenues for advance and retreat of species whose ranges are being driven by climate change. More work is needed on connectivity to ensure that MPAs are effectively sited and ecologically coherent. For many benthic species there will be idiosyncratic responses depending on life history and ecological traits – so there will be no simple answers (Kinlan and Gaines, 2003). Other protection measures need to be afforded to the areas between MPAs to enable species to move. A rolling system of management would allow for the re-assessment of MPAs should plans made during the current climate state fail to protect ecosystems with respect to future environmental change.

Climate change also emphasizes the need for a precautionary approach: little can be done about climate change for the next 50 years but society can manage the interactions of globally driven change with regional (e.g. fishing, eutrophication) and local (e.g. habitat degradation and loss due to inappropriate development, aquaculture and pollution) impacts that can be managed by legislation and voluntary guidelines. Climate change generally exacerbates the impacts of over-fishing and other anthropogenic activities and certainly should not be an excuse for inaction. Difficult decisions are also required to deal with sea-level rise – particularly in England and Wales. Human adaptation to rising and stormier seas will lead to a proliferation of sea defences to prevent flooding. These must be designed in an environmentally sensitive manner (Airoldi et al., 2005; Moschella et al., 2005).

Marine spatial planning will increasingly become an essential tool in enabling adaptation to climate change and in the management of human activities that may adversely affect marine species and habitats in a rapidly changing world. Such an approach features strongly in the new European Marine Strategy Framework Directive and the Marine Bills under consultation for England and Wales and for Scotland. The most difficult ethical dilemma will be in balancing the gains from mitigation of greenhouse gas emissions by renewable energy generation against the pain of localized impacts on naturalness and on the biological character of habitats associated with the proliferation of such installations.

6.7 Acknowledgements

The research summarized in this chapter was gathered as part of the MarCLIM project (www.mba.ac.uk/marclim) which was funded by The Countryside Council for Wales, The Crown Estate, Department for Environment and Rural Affairs, English Nature, Environment Agency, Joint Nature Conservation Committee, Scottish Executive, Scottish Natural Heritage, States of Jersey and the Worldwide Wildlife Foundation. We would like to thank all those who assisted with the fieldwork, especially Pippa Moore and Roger Herbert as well as Keith Hiscock for his unpublished observations and comments on the manuscript.

References

Airoldi, L., Abbiati, M., Beck, M.W., Hawkins, S.J., Jonsson, P.R., Martin, D., Moschella, P.S., Sundelof, A., Thompson, R.C. & Aberg, P. (2005). An ecological perspective on the deployment and design of low-crested and other hard coastal defence structures. *Coastal Engineering* **52**:1073-1087.

Alexander, S.E. & Roughgarden, J. (1996). Larval transport and population dynamics of intertidal barnacles: A coupled benthic/oceanic model. *Ecological Monographs* **66**:259-275.

Alley, R.B., Meese, D.A., Shuman, C.A., Gow, A.J., Taylor, K.C., Groates, P.M., White, J.W.C., Ram, M., Waddington, E.D., Mayewski, P.A. & Zielinski, G.A. (1993). Abrupt increase in Greenland snow accumulation at the end of the Younder Dryas event. *Nature* **362**:527-529.

Beare, D.J., Reid, D.G. & McKenzie, E. (2003). Fish schooling behaviour in the northwest North Sea: interspecific associations measured by acoustic survey. *Aquatic Living Resources* **16**: 307-312.

Beaugrand, G. & Ibanez, F. (2004). Monitoring marine plankton ecosystems. II: Long-term changes in North Sea calanoid copepods in relation to hydro-climatic variability. *Marine Ecology Progress Series* **284**:35-47.

Beaugrand, G. & Reid, P.C. (2003). Long-term changes in phytoplankton, zooplankton and salmon related to climate. *Global Change Biology* **9**:801-817.

Beaugrand, G., Ibanez, F. & Lindley, J.A. (2001). Geographical distribution and seasonal diel changes in the diversity of calanoid copepods in the North Atlantic and North Sea. *Marine Ecology-Progress Series* **219**:189-203.

Bradley, R.S. & England, J.H. (2008). The Younger Dryas and the Sea of Ancient Ice. *Quaternary Research* **70**:1-10.

Bryden, H.L., Longworth, H.R. & Cunningham, S.A. (2005). Slowing of the Atlantic meridional overturning circulation at 25°N. *Nature* **438**:655-657.

Burrows, M.T., Harvey, R. & Robb, L. (2008). Wave exposure indices from digital coastlines and the prediction of rocky shore community structure. *Marine Ecology Progress Series* **353**:1-12.

Caldeira, K. & Wickett, M.E. (2003). Anthropogenic carbon and ocean pH. *Nature* **425**:365-365.

Connell, J.H. (1961). The influence of interspecific competition and other factors on the distribution of the barnacle *Chthamalus stellatus*. *Ecology* **42**:710-723.

Crisp, D.J. (1964). The effects of the severe winter of 1962-63 on marine life in Britain. *Journal of Animal Ecology* **33**:179-210.

Crisp, D.J. & Knight-Jones, E.W. (1954). Discontinuities in the distribution of shore animals in North Wales. *Report of the Bardsey Observatory* **2**:29-34.

Crisp, D.J. & Southward, A.J. (1958). The distribution of intertidal organisms along the coasts of the English Channel. *Journal of the Marine Biological Association of the UK* **37**:157-208.

Crisp, D.J., Southward, A.J. & Southward, E.C. (1981). On the distribution of the inter-tidal barnacles *Chthamalus-stellatus, Chthamalus-montagui* and *Euraphia-depressa*. *Journal of the Marine Biological Association of the UK* **61**:359-380.

Cushing, D.H. (1961). On the failure of the Plymouth herring fishery. *Journal of the Marine Biological Association of the UK* **41**:799-816.

Cushing, D.H. (1975). *Marine Ecology and Fisheries*. Cambridge University Press, Cambridge.

Davies, A.J., Jenkinson, L.S., Lawton, J.H., Shorrocks, B. & Wood, S. (1998). Making mistakes when predicting shifts in species range in response to global warming. *Nature* **391**:783-786.

Day, J.W., Christian, R.R., Boesch, D.M., Yanez-Arancibia, A., Morris, J., Twilley, R.R., Naylor, L., Schaffner, L. & Stevenson, C. (2008). Consequences of climte change on the ecogeomorphology of coastal wetlands. *Estuaries and Coasts* **31**:477-491.

Dulvy, N.K., Rogers, S.I., Jennings, S., Stelzenmuller, V., Dye, S.R. & Skjoldal, H.R. (2008). Climate change and deepening of North Sea fish assemblage: a biotic ndicator of warming seas. *Journal of Applied Ecology* **45**:1029-1039.

Edwards, M. & Richardson, A.J. (2004). Impact of climate change on marine pelagic phenology and trophic mismatch. *Nature* **430**:881-884.

Enghoff, I.B., MacKenzie, B.R. & Nielsen, E.E. (2007). The Danish fish fauna during the warm Atlantic period (ca. 7000-3900 BC): Forerunner of future changes? *Fisheries Research* **87**:167-180.

Feely, R.A., Sabine, C.L., Lee, K., Berelson, W., Kleypas, J., Fabry, V.J. & Millero, F.J. (2004). Impact of anthropogenic CO_2 on the $CaCO_3$ system in the oceans. *Science* **305**:362-366.

Fischer-Piette, E. (1936). Etudes sur la biogeographie intercotidale des deux rives de la Manche. *Journal of the Linnean Society, Zoology* **40**:181-272.

Fischer-Piette, E. (1955). Repartition, le long des cotes septentrionales de l'Espagne, des principales especes peuplant les rochers intercotidaux. *Annual Insitutional Ocenaographique Monaco* **31**:37-124.

Furness, R.W. (2010). Scottish seabird predator-prey relationships. In: Species Management: Challenges and Solutions for the 21st Century, Ed. by J.M. Baxter and C.A. Galbraith. TSO Scotland, Edinburgh.

Genner, M.J., Sims, D.W., Wearmouth, V.J., Southall, E.J., Southward, A.J., Henderson P.A. & Hawkins, S.J. (2004). Regional climatic warming drives long-term community changes of British marine fish. *Proceedings of the Royal Society of London Series B-Biological Sciences* **271**:655-661.

Genner, M.J., Sims, D.W., Southward, A.J., Budd, G.C., Masterson, P., McHugh, M., Rendle, P., Southward, E.J., Wearmouth, V.J. & Hawkins, S.J. (2009). Body size–dependent response of a marine fish assemblage to climate change and fishing over a century-long scale. *Global Change Biology* DOI 10.1111/j.1365-2486.2009.02027.x

Gill, A. (2005). Offshore renewable energy: ecological implications of generating electricity in the coastal zone. *Journal of Applied Ecology* **42**:605-615.

Hansen, B., Turrell, W.R. & Osterhus, S. (2001). Decreasing overflow from the Nordic seas into the Atlantic Ocean through the Faroe Bank channel since 1950. *Nature* **411**:927-930.

Harley, C.D.G., Hughes, A.R., Hultgren, K.M., Miner, B.G., Sorte, C.J.B., Thornber, C.S., Rodriguez, L.F., Tomanek, L. & Williams, S.L. (2006). The impacts of climate change in coastal marine systems. *Ecology Letters* **9**:228-241.

Harris, M.P., Newell, M., Daunt, F., Speakman, J.R. & Wanless, S. (2008). Snake pipefish *Entelurus aequoreus* are poor food for seabirds. *IBIS* **150**:413-415.

Hawkins, S.J., Moore, P.J., Burrows, M.T., Poloczanska, E., Mieszkowska, N., Herbert, R.J.H., Jenkins, S.R., Thompson, R.C., Genner, M.J. & Southward, A.J. (2008). Complex interactions in a rapidly changing world: responses of rocky shore communities to recent climate change. *Climate Research* **37**:123-133.

Heikkinen, R.K., Luoto, M., Araujo, M.B., Virkkala, R., Thuiller, W. & Syke, M.Y. (2006). Methods and uncertainties in bioclimatic envelope modelling under climate change. *Progress in Physical Geography* **30**:751-777.

Helmuth, B., Mieszkowska, N., Moore, P. & Hawkins, S.J. (2006). Living on the edge of two changing worlds: forecasting responses of rocky intertidal ecosystems to climate change. *Annual Review of Ecology, Evolution & Systematics* **37**:373-404.

Henderson, P.A. (2007). Discrete and continuous change in the fish community of the Bristol Channel in response to climate change. *Journal of the Marine Biological Association of the UK* **87**:589-598.

Herbert, R.J., Hawkins, S.J., Sheader, M. & Southward, A.J. (2003). Range extension and reproduction of the barnacle *Balanus perforatus* in the eastern English channel. *Journal of the Marine Biological Association of the UK* **83**:73-82.

Hiscock, K., Southward, A.J., Tittley, I. & Hawkins, S.J. (2004). Effects of changing temperature on benthic marine life in Britain and Ireland. *Aquatic Conservation: Marine and Freshwater Ecosystems* **14**:333-362.

Holmes, S.J., Wright, P.J. & Fryer, R.J. (2008). Evidence from survey data for regional variability in cod dynamics in the North Sea and west of Scotland. *ICES Journal of Marine Science* **65**:206-215.

Hulme, M., Jenkins, G.J., Lu, X., Turnpenny, J.R., Mitchell, T.D., Jones, R.G., Lowe, J., Murphy, J.M., Hassell, D., Boorman, P., McDonald, R. & Hill, S. (2002). Climate change scenarios for the United Kingdom: The UKCIP02 Scientific Report, Tyndall Centre for Climate Research, School of Environmental Science, University of East Anglia, Norwich, UK. 120pp.

Ibanez, F. & Beaugrand, G. (2008). Monitoring marine plankton ecosystems: Identification of the most relevant indicators of the state of an ecosystem. *Journal of Marine Systems* **73**:138-154.

Intergovernmental Panel on Climate Change. (2007). Climate Change 2007: The Physical Science Basis. Contribution of Working Group I to the Fourth Assessment Report of the Intergovernmental Panel on Climate Change, Vol. Cambridge University Press, Cambridge.

Kendall, M.A. & Lewis, J.R. (1986). Temporal and spatial patterns in the recruitment of *Gibbula umbilicalis*. *Hydrobiologia* **142**:15-22.

Kinlan, B.P. & Gaines, S.D. (2003). Propagule dispersal in marine and terrestrial environments: a community perspective. *Ecology* **84**:2007-2020.

MacKenzie, B.R. & Schiedek, D. (2007). Long-term sea surface temperature baselines – time series, spatial covariation and implications for biological processes. *Journal of Marine Systems* **68**:405-420.

Mieszkowska, N., Hawkins, S.J., Burrows, M.T. & Kendall, M.A. (2007). Long-term changes in the geographic distribution and population structures of *Osilinus lineatus* (Gastropoda : Trochidae) in Britain and Ireland. *Journal of the Marine Biological Association of the UK* **87**:537-545.

Mieszkowska, N., Leaper, R., Moore, P., Kendall, M.A., Burrows, M.T., Lear, D., Poloczanska, E., Hiscock, K., Moschella, P.S., Thompson, R.C., Herbert, R.J., Laffoley, D., Baxter, J., Southward, A.J. & Hawkins, S.J. (2005). Assessing and Predicting the Influence of Climate Change Challenging Intertidal Rocky Shore Biota: Final Report for United Kingdom Funders. Report No. 20, Marine Biological Association of the UK.

Mieszkowska, N., Kendall, M.A., Hawkins, S.J., Leaper, R., Williamson, P., Hardman-Mountford, N.J. & Southward, A.J. (2006). Changes in the range of some common rocky shore species in Britain – a response to climate change? *Hydrobiologia* **555**:241–251.

Moore, H.B. (1936). The biology of *Balanus balanoides*. V. Distribution in the Plymouth area. *Journal of the Marine Biological Association of the UK* **20**:701-716.

Moschella, P.S., Abbiati, M., Aberg, P., Airoldi, L., Anderson, J.M., Bacchocchi, F., Bulleri, G., Dinesen, G.E., Frost, M., Gacia, E., Granhag, L., Jonsson, P.R., Satta, M.P., Sundelof, A., Thompson, R.C. & Hawkins, S.J. (2005). Low-crested coastal defence structures as artificial habitats for marine life: using ecological criteria in design. *Coastal Engineering* **52**:1053-1071.

Orr, J.C., Fabry, V.J., Aumont, O., Bopp, L., Doney, S.C., Feely, R.A., Gnanadesikan, A., Gruber, N., Ishida, A., Joos, F., Key, R.M., Lindsay, K., Maier-Reimer, E., Matear, R., Monfray, P., Mouchet, A., Najjar, R.G., Plattner, G.K,, Rodgers, K.B., Sabine, C.L., Sarmiento, J.L., Schlitzer, R., Slater, R.D., Totterdell, I.J., Weirig, M.F., Yamamaka, Y. & Yool, A. (2005). Anthropogenic ocean acidification over the twenty-first century and its impact on calcifying organisms. *Nature* **437**:681-686.

Parmesan, C. & Yohe, G. (2003). A globally coherent fingerprint of climate change impacts across natural systems. *Nature* **421**:37-42.

Parmesan, C., Gaines, S., Gonzalez, L., Kaufman, D.M., Kingslover, J., Townsend Peterson, A. & Sagarin, R. (2005). Empirical perspectives on species borders: from traditional biogeography to global change. *Oikos* **108**: 58-75.

Perry, A.L., Low, P.J., Ellis, J.R. & Reynolds, J.D. (2005). Climate change and distribution shifts in marine fishes. *Science* **308**:1912-1915.

Poloczanska, E., Hawkins, S.J., Southward, A.J. & Burrows, M.T. (2008). Modelling the response of populations of competing species to climate change. *Ecology* **89**: 3138-3149.

Poyry, J., Luoto, M., Heikkinen, R.K. & Saarinen, K. (2008). Species traits are associated with the quality of bioclimatic models. *Global Ecology and Biogeography* **17**:403-414.

Rayner, N.A., Brohan, P., Parker, D.E., Folland, C.K., Kennedy, J.J., Vanicek, M., Ansell, T. & Tett, S.F.B. (2006). Improved analyses of changes and uncertainties in sea surface temperature measured *in situ* since the mid-nineteenth century: the HadSST2 data set. *Journal of Climate* **19**:446-469.

Russell, F.S. (1973). Summary of observations on occurrence of planktonic stages of fish off Plymouth 1924-1972. *Journal of the Marine Biological Association of the UK* **53**:347-355.

Sabine, C.L., Feely, R.A., Gruber, N., Key, R.M., Lee, K., Billister, J.L., Wanninkhof, R., Wong, C.S., Wallace, D.W.R., Tilbrook, B., Millero, F.J., Peng, T.H., Kozyr, A., Ono, T. & Rios, A.F. (2004). The oceanic sink for anthropogenic CO_2. *Science* **305**:367-371.

Shennan, I., Bradley, S., Milne, G., Brooks, A., Bassett, S. & Hamilton, S. (2006a). Relative sea-level changes, glacial isostatic modelling and ice-sheet reconstructions from the British Isles since the Last Glacial Maximum. *Journal of Quaternary Science* **21**: 585-599.

Shennan, I., Hamilton, S., Hillier, C., Hunter, A., Woodall, R., Bradley, S., Milne, G., Brooks, A. & Bassett, S. (2006b). Releative sea-level observations in Western Scotland since the Last Galcial Maximum for the testing of models of glacial isostatic land movements and ice sheet reconstructions. *Journal of Quaternary Science* **21**: 601-613.

Sheppard, C. (2004). Sea surface temperature 1871-2099 in 14 cells around the United Kingdom. *Marine Pollution Bulletin* **49**: 12-16.

Shkedy, Y. & Roughgarden, J. (1997). Barnacle recruitment and population dynamics predicted from coastal upwelling. *Oikos* **80**:487.

Simkanin, C., Powers, A., Myers, A., McGrath, D., Southward, A.J., Mieszkowska, N., Leaper, R. & O'Riordan, R. (2005). Using historical data to detect temporal changes in the abundances of intertidal species on Irish shores. *Journal of the Marine Biological Association of the UK* **85**:1329-1340.

Southward, A.J. (1980). The western English-Channel - An inconsistent ecosystem. *Nature* **285**:361-366.

Southward, A.J. (1988). Fluctuations in the herring and pilchard fisheries of Devon and Cornwall linked to change in climate since the 16th century. *Journal of the Marine Biological Association of the UK* **68**:423-445.

Southward, A.J. (1991). 40 years of changes in species composition and population-density of barnacles on a rocky shore near Plymouth. *Journal of the Marine Biological Association of the UK* **71**:495-513.

Southward, A.J. & Crisp, D.J. (1954). The distribution of certain intertidal animals around the Irish coast. *Proceedings of the Royal Irish Academy* **57**:1-29.

Southward, A.J., Langmead, O., Hardman-Mountford, N.J., Aiken, J., Boalch, G.T., Dando, P.R., Genner, M.J., Joint, I., Kendall, M.A., Halliday, N.C., Harris, R.P., Leaper, R., Mieszkowska, N., Pingree, R.D., Richardson, A.J., Sims, D.W., Smith, T., Walne, A.W. & Hawkins, S.J. (2005). Long-term oceanographic and ecological research in the western English Channel. *Advances in Marine Biology* **47**:1-105.

Stenseth, N.C., Otterson, G., Hurrell, J.W., Mysterud, A., Lima, M., Chan, K.S., Yoccoz, N.G. & Adlandsvik, B. (2003). Studying climate effects on ecology through the use of climate indices: the North Atlantic Oscillation, El Nino Southern Oscillation and beyond. *Proceedings of the Royal Society London Series B* **270**:2087-2096.

Svensson, C.J., Jenkins, S.R., Hawkins, S.J. & Aberg, P. (2005). Population resistance to climate change: modelling the effects of low recruitment in open populations. *Oecologia* **142**:117-126.

Taylor, K.C., Mayewski, P.A., Alley, R.B., Brook, E.J., Gow, A.J., Grootes, P.M., Meese, D.A., Saltzman, E.S., Severinghaus, J.P., Twickler, M.S., White, J.W.C., Whitlow, S. & Zielinski, G.A. (1997). The Holocene Younger Dryas Transition recorded at Summit, Greenland. *Science* **278**:825-827.

The Royal Society. (2005). Ocean acidification due to increasing atmospheric carbon dioxide. Policy document 12/05. The Clyvedon Press Ltd, Cardiff, UK.

Thomas, M.L.H. (1986). A physically derived exposure index for marine shorelines. *Ophelia* **25**:1-13.

Thompson, R.C., Olsen, Y., Mitchell, R.P., Davis, A., Rowland, S.J., John, A.W.G., McGonagle, D. & Russell, A.E. (2004). Lost at sea: Where is all the plastic? *Science* **304**:838-838.

Turley, C. (2008). Impacts of changing ocean chemistry in a high-CO_2 world. *Mineralogical Magazine* **72**:359-362.

Wanless, S., Harris, M.P., Redman, P. & Speakman, J.R. (2005). Low energy values of fsh as probable cause of a major seabird breeding failure in the North Sea. *Marine Ecology-Progress Series* **294**:1-8.

Wethey, D.S. & Woodin, S.A. (2008). Ecological hindcasting of biogeographic responses to climate change in the European intertidal zone. *Hydrobiologia* **606**:139-151.

Hawkins, S.J., Sugden, H.E., Mieszkowska, N., Burrows, M.T. and Baxter, J.M. (2010). Managing marine species in a rapidly changing world. In: *Species Management: Challenges and Solutions for the 21st Century*, ed. by J.M. Baxter and C.A. Galbraith. TSO Scotland, Edinburgh, pp. 91-107.

Chapter 7

Perspectives on reintroductions:

The value of reintroductions – *Simon Milne MBE* [1]
Captive breeding, captivating people – *David Windmill* [2]

Summary

1. Many of the best known examples of successful reintroductions around the world have involved conspicuous, iconic species. More than ever, however, it is necessary to demonstrate the value of reintroductions in terms of both their human and ecological benefits.
2. Examples such as the reintroduction of *Erica verticillata* in South Africa, and the white-tailed eagle in Scotland demonstrate the community and financial benefits of reintroductions, as well as the biological ones.
3. The case for reintroductions is relatively straightforward, but needs to be communicated better.
4. Captive breeding is an essential tool in ensuring that some of the most endangered species can recover to such an extent that they have secure populations from both a demographic and genetic perspective.
5. Captive breeding serves other functions as well as assuring a species survival. It can provide a guaranteed stock for species reintroduction programmes, it can act as an education tool and as a source of revenue through fund raising.

[1] Scottish Wildlife Trust, Cramond House, 3 Kirk Cramond, Edinburgh, EH4 6HZ, UK
[2] The Royal Zoological Society of Scotland, Edinburgh Zoo, 134 Corstorphine Road, Edinburgh, EH12 6TS, UK

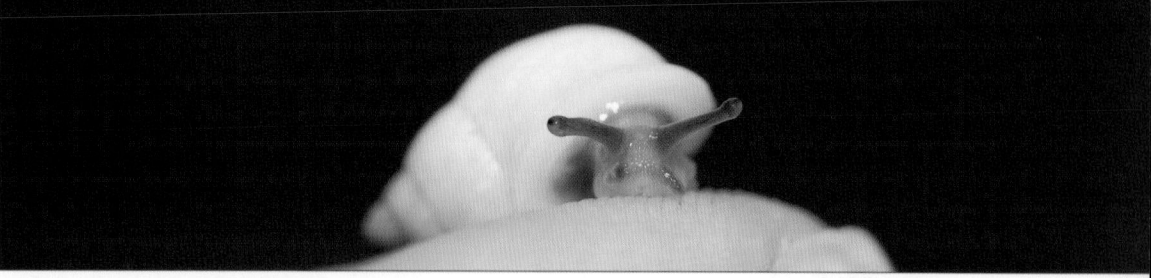

7.1 The value of reintroductions: Simon Milne MBE

Hebe bella. © Alan Thomson/RZS

There is a wide range of historical and contemporary examples from around the world of successful species reintroductions including Arabian oryx *(Oryx leucoryx)* to the Middle East, Miami blue *(Cyclargus thomasi bethunebaken)* to Florida, Cape Flats erica *(Erica verticillata)* to South Africa, European beaver *(Castor fiber)* to 24 European countries, grey wolf *(Canis lupus)* to Yellowstone National Park, and capercaillie *(Tetrao urogallus),* red kite *(Milvus milvus)* red squirrel *(Sciurus vulgaris)* and white-tailed eagle *(Haliaeetus albicilla)* to Great Britain.

It is no accident that these are some of the better known examples of reintroductions as they are conspicuous, impressive and, to employ that over-used word, "iconic" species. But there has to be much more to reintroductions than merely restoring charismatic species that look good in glossy magazines and on the cover of fundraising brochures. Whilst such images help to promote the conservation cause and engage people with biodiversity, we increasingly have to evaluate, justify and demonstrate the value of reintroductions in terms of their human and ecological benefit.

The public consultation in 2008 on a proposed reintroduction programme for the European beaver to Scotland demonstrated significant support for the proposal but it also indicated some perceived cultural barriers, mistrust and lack of public awareness of many of the important issues facing conservation in the 21st century. This reinforces the need for better engagement with the public, landowners and other stakeholders and demonstrates that we have some way to go in communicating messages relating to concepts such as natural processes, ecosystem resilience, keystone species, ecosystem services and the value of biodiversity to society and mankind.

At this stage I should point out that, at risk of upsetting the purists, I am going to blur the boundaries between translocation and reintroductions on the basis that the differences between the two are academic. One beaver's reintroduction in France is another beaver's translocation from Germany.

There are many who believe that there is a moral imperative to reintroducing species which have disappeared due to human persecution or anthropogenic habitat loss. This is reinforced by Annex IV of the European Habitats Directive (EU, 1992) which directs member states to study the desirability of reintroducing species which were native to their territory. Nonetheless, we need to be aware that the moral case for reintroductions, however laudable, can become somewhat arcane unless it is underpinned by tangible benefits and it is these benefits on which I will now focus.

The cultural value of restoring a species to one's country is hard to quantify – but should not and cannot be ignored. The Scottish Minister for the Environment, Michael Russell, said to me last year (2007) that he viewed the proposed return of the beaver as being of huge cultural significance; the same can be said of the Arabian oryx in Saudi Arabia or perhaps the great bustard *(Otis tarda)* on Salisbury Plain. Inevitably, species attracting the label of cultural significance are those that have the ability to inspire or evoke a strong sense of place. Their reintroduction not only helps to foster pride in our natural

110

Plate 7.1 Grey wolf (*Canis lupus*) – reintroduced to Yellowstone National Park, USA in 1995. © Peter Cairns

heritage and provide a feel-good factor but is also an important tool for promoting the engagement of people with the concept of rebuilding biodiversity in our landscapes – to the benefit of people as well as the environment. We cannot overlook or ignore public perception.

The simple message is that the loss of *any* species that occurs naturally in an ecosystem tends to reduce the resilience of that ecosystem and its ability to naturally function without human intervention. Often the greater the loss of species diversity, the more expensive and intensive is the subsequent conservation management action. With over a thousand species identified under the UK Biodiversity Action Plan (UK BAP) (DoE, 1994) as requiring conservation action, it is clear that the Plan cannot be achieved purely on a species-by-species basis, otherwise we may end up conserving or restoring iconic species at the expense of other less charismatic species which may have a more important keystone function. Where keystone species are lacking within the ecosystem, given the right conditions, they should be afforded the appropriate priority.

7.1.1 Let us consider some examples

Of all the above ground woodland invertebrates, wood ants are arguably one of the most important keystone species. When present in numbers, they influence profoundly the distribution and abundance of other invertebrates, disperse plant seeds, prey on herbivorous invertebrates thereby indirectly increasing tree growth rates, contribute to nutrient recycling in woodland soils, provide an important food source for woodland birds such as the *reintroduced* capercaillie, and even *create* habitat for a range of myrmecophilous species through nest mound building. The translocation of wood ant colonies would not only assist the conservation of rare UK BAP species such as *Formica exsecta* (a species for which Scottish Wildlife Trust is the lead partner) but would also have a positive effect on community ecology. This illustrates that keystone species come in all shapes and sizes; not all are charismatic mega-fauna like the European beaver.

The Scottish beaver trial reintroduction project involves a mammal which can bring significant ecological benefits to riparian ecosystems through the creation of ponds which act as sediment traps by reduced flooding, neutralizing acid run-off and providing additional niche habitats for aquatic species. In addition, beavers create valuable mosaics of riparian habitats, coppice trees, increase deadwood and prevent scrub invasion (Scott Porter Research and Marketing Ltd., 1998). The beaver is a fine example of a keystone species whose reintroduction provides a long-term, cost-effective conservation management tool; hence its inclusion in SNH's Species Action Framework (SNH, 2007) and the enormous effort made to achieve the licence for its trial reintroduction in Knapdale (mid-Argyll) in spring 2009. This trial should be a very useful vehicle for demonstrating the value of reintroducing keystone species and hopefully will help to further the case for other reintroductions.

Staying with mammals, populations of Eurasian lynx (*Lynx lynx*) were confined to pockets of Siberia and Eastern Europe until a number of European countries embarked on reintroduction programmes. Germany, Switzerland, Poland, Slovakia and France all now have populations of lynx (Hetherington,

Plate 7.2 Wood ants in pine needle litter. © Lorne Gill/SNH

2006). Spain has its own threatened population of the distinctly separate Iberian lynx (*Lynx pardinus*). Reintroductions of top predators such as lynx do meet with opposition particularly from farmers; yet the lynx is another keystone species and as a top predator it can control deer numbers where deer densities are high (the main predator has been man with a rifle since the lynx was extirpated (Hetherington, 2005)). The research on the Eurasian lynx (Hetherington, 2006) and associated publicity is not only taking us one important step further towards restoring a missing species to its natural range but is also highlighting the benefits of reintroductions to the restoration of ecosystem function.

Near Capetown, South Africa, in a small, new sanctuary (Bottom Road) *Erica verticillata*, the Cape flats erica, was planted. Once thought to be extinct, 10 living specimens were found and propagated at Kirstenbosch, with one of the "lost plants" coming from Kew Gardens. Effective cross pollination was achieved and progeny were planted and have thrived at the sanctuary. Quite apart from this being a success story for botanical biodiversity, the tale has an interesting human aspect. Bottom Road, once a place of rubbish, violence and prostitution, is now a clean and attractive sanctuary created by the community, and pride of place went to a reintroduced plant. Kirstenbosch curator Anthony Hitchcock calls *Erica verticillata* "a flagship for the conservation efforts to save other highly endangered indigenous plant species of lowland areas, like the Cape Flats"(Yeld, 2007).

Closer to home the Royal Botanic Garden, Edinburgh's (RBGE) programme to reintroduce the rare fern *Woodsia ilvensis* (oblong woodsia) to five sites is an excellent example of a well-conducted reintroduction programme which is, perhaps, the last chance to save this species in the wild.

In these days of the credit crunch and the unabated drive to place financial value on everyone and everything, consideration must also be given to the economic value of some reintroductions. There are the "difficult to quantify" ecosystem benefits such as lynx culling deer and beaver dams filtering acid run-off, but there are also more measurable benefits. The well-documented case of the reintroduction of the white-tailed eagle in Scotland indicates that these birds are worth between £1.4 and £1.69 million

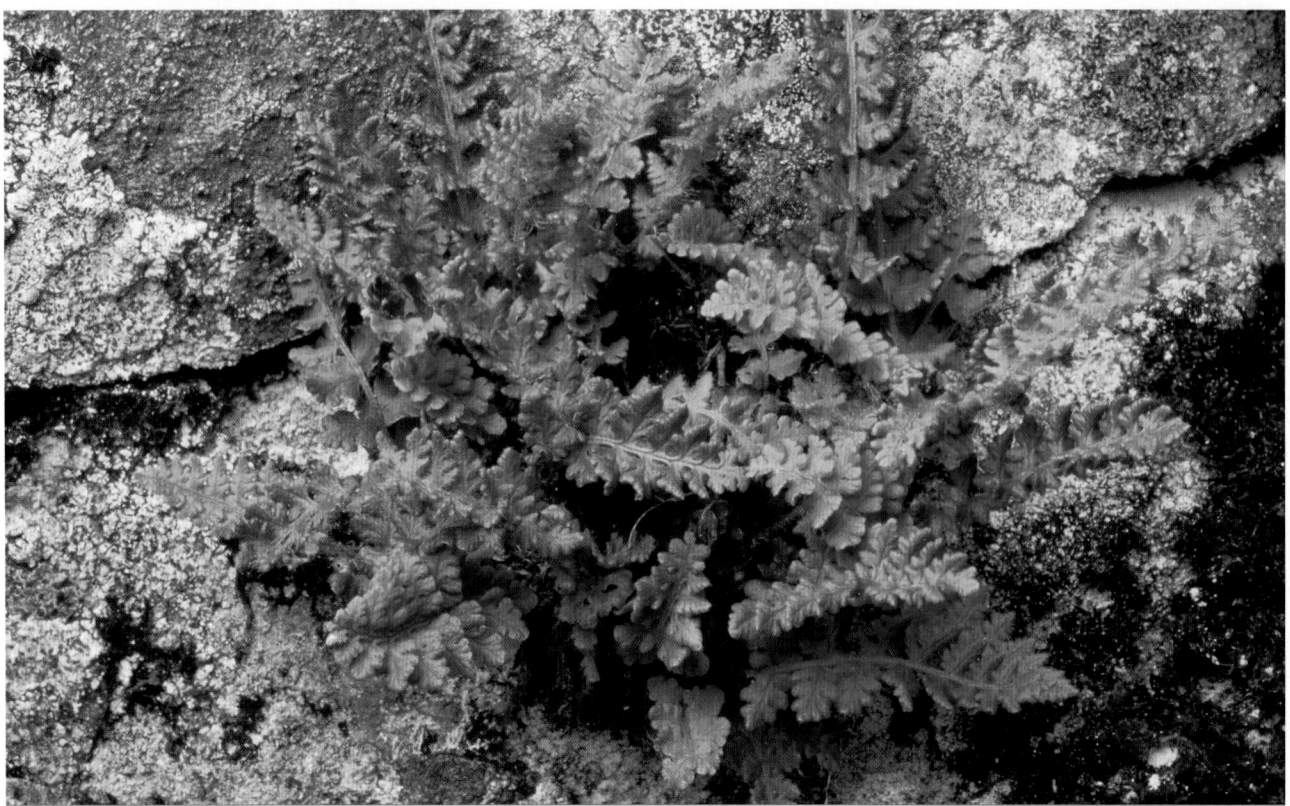

Plate 7.3 The rare fern – oblong woodsia (*Woodsia ilvensis*) – the subject of a reintroduction programme by Royal Botanic Garden, Edinburgh.
© Lorne Gill/SNH

Plate 7.4 Cape flats erica (*Erica verticillata*) – a reintroduction success story from South Africa. © San Marcos Growers

Plate 7.5 Red kite (*Milvus milvus*) – stimulating growth in local economies. © Darin Smith

annually to the local economy on Mull (RSPB, 2007), and there is a similar story with the very successful red kite trail in Dumfries and Galloway (http://www.wildlifeextra.com. 23 March 2007). In South Africa, an evaluation (Spenceley and Barnes, 2005) concluded that both black rhinoceros and white rhinoceros conservation projects involving reintroductions and translocations provided a net benefit to both state and private protected areas. The evaluation included such aspects as how rhinoceros might add value to existing wildlife operations, the extent to which their protection might confer blanket protection for other wildlife, their contribution to community-based tourism and how they impact on land-use change.

Although there will be no rhinos in Argyll, a study by Oxford University's Wildlife Conservation Research Unit (Campbell *et al.,* 2007) concluded that the financial benefits of a beaver reintroduction could be around 100 times greater than costs.

We have a tendency to be too introspective in the UK and sometimes forget, or choose to forget, what is being learnt and achieved elsewhere. This does not mean that we should throw open the back of a van and let beavers and lynx out in areas of suitable habitat within Scotland, but I believe we can benefit so much by learning from the successes and mistakes of others and communicating this information to stakeholders and the public. If we are to garner public support and achieve successful reintroductions, we must ensure that any project is supported by a thorough (but hopefully timely) scientific assessment which includes experiences of other countries and socio-economic evaluations; all in accordance with IUCN guidelines and procedures. We should stop spending so much time speculating about what we might do and start trying to do it. The case for many reintroductions is relatively straightforward – we just need to be better at communicating the messages.

7.2. Captive breeding, captivating people: David Windmill

Until recently the analogy used by *ex situ* conservationists was 'to have money in the bank' when describing the security and assurance proffered to populations faced with the threat of extinction. Given recent events in the banking world, this is perhaps not assurance enough, so the metaphor we should now adopt is one of life boats on a ship, essential to have them but in the hope that you never have to use them.

Simon Milne in considering the value of reintroductions mentioned specifically two species of plant that had been successfully reintroduced to the wild: *Woodsia ilvensis* and *Erica verticulatta*. It should be noted that in both cases the source populations were effectively captive bred, or in botanical terms 'propagated'. This followed the recommendation made in the Species Management and Protection Plan for *Woodsia* (UKBAP, 1998):

> '*Establish* ex-situ *collections of spores and sporophytes ensuring that collections do not further reduce likelihood of recruitment. If stocks permit, make spores and/or plants available to specialist horticultural outlets and fern enthusiasts to reduce any temptation to collect from the wild.'.*

The Royal Botanic Garden Edinburgh's (RBGE) excellent international conifer conservation programme (RBGE, 2007) that has been running for 17 years is another fine example of the role and value of *ex situ* species management. Project activities in Chile which also received Darwin Initiative funding have included the establishment of an arboretum and the training of key personnel.

The events in Rio de Janeiro in 1992 (CBD, 1992) provided for the first time a framework into which the contribution that *ex situ* species management and captive breeding could be formalized in global conservation terms.

Article 9 of the Convention on Biological Diversity states that Parties should:

- 'adopt measures for the *ex-situ* conservation of components of biological diversity, preferably in the country of origin of such components;'

The article continues:

- 'establish and maintain facilities for *ex-situ* conservation of and research on plants, animals and micro-organisms, preferably in the country of origin of genetic resources;
- cooperate in providing financial and other support for *ex-situ* conservation and in the establishment and maintenance of *ex- situ* conservation facilities in developing countries.'

This article of CBD provides a firm footing for *ex situ* conservation in theory but the reality remains that political will, infrastructure, skills and finances are still major limiting factors in the achievement of establishing such facilities in range countries, particularly where economies are weak.

In 2002 IUCN published its Technical Guidelines on the Management of *Ex-situ* Populations for Conservation (IUCN, 2002) with the purpose of ... maintain[ing] present biodiversity levels through all available and effective means including, where appropriate, *ex situ* propagation, translocation and other *ex situ* methodologies.

The guidelines included the warning: "If the decision to bring a taxon under *ex situ* management is left until extinction is imminent, it is frequently too late to effectively implement, thus risking permanent loss of the taxon."

Captive breeding programmes are initiated for a number of reasons including the production of individuals for reintroduction to the wild, supplementation of existing wild stocks or simply to maintain viable captive populations that provide assurance against gradual or catastrophic decline *in situ*.

But when is it appropriate to fit the life boats to the ship? There are strong arguments to suggest that such interventions should be initiated well before extinction is imminent given that each species will and does have particular husbandry requirements from housing to nutrition and veterinary care?

The guidelines also recommend that: "... effective integration between *in situ* and *ex situ* approaches should be sought wherever possible." This highlights the need for *ex situ* and *in situ* conservation practitioners (where they are separate entities) to work to a single species action plan.

IUCN also recognizes the considerable set of resources committed worldwide to *ex situ* conservation by the world's zoological and botanical gardens, gene banks and other *ex situ* facilities. The effective utilization of these resources represents an essential component of conservation strategies at all levels.

In 2005 the World Association of Zoos and Aquaria launched its second strategy (WAZA, 2005) providing clear guidance on how maximum conservation and education value can be attained by its worldwide member organizations. The cover page of the strategy itself depicts the release of captive bred Przewalski's horses (*Equus ferus przewalskii*) in Mongolia. It recognizes that to achieve this, *ex situ* populations need to be demographically stable, well-maintained and capable of self-sustaining reproduction. They should also be distributed among several institutions and of sufficient size to maintain high levels of genetic diversity.

The world's zoos and aquaria, like botanic gardens, are therefore well placed to provide the sort of facility described in Article 9 of CBD. Knowledge transfer and capacity building across this global

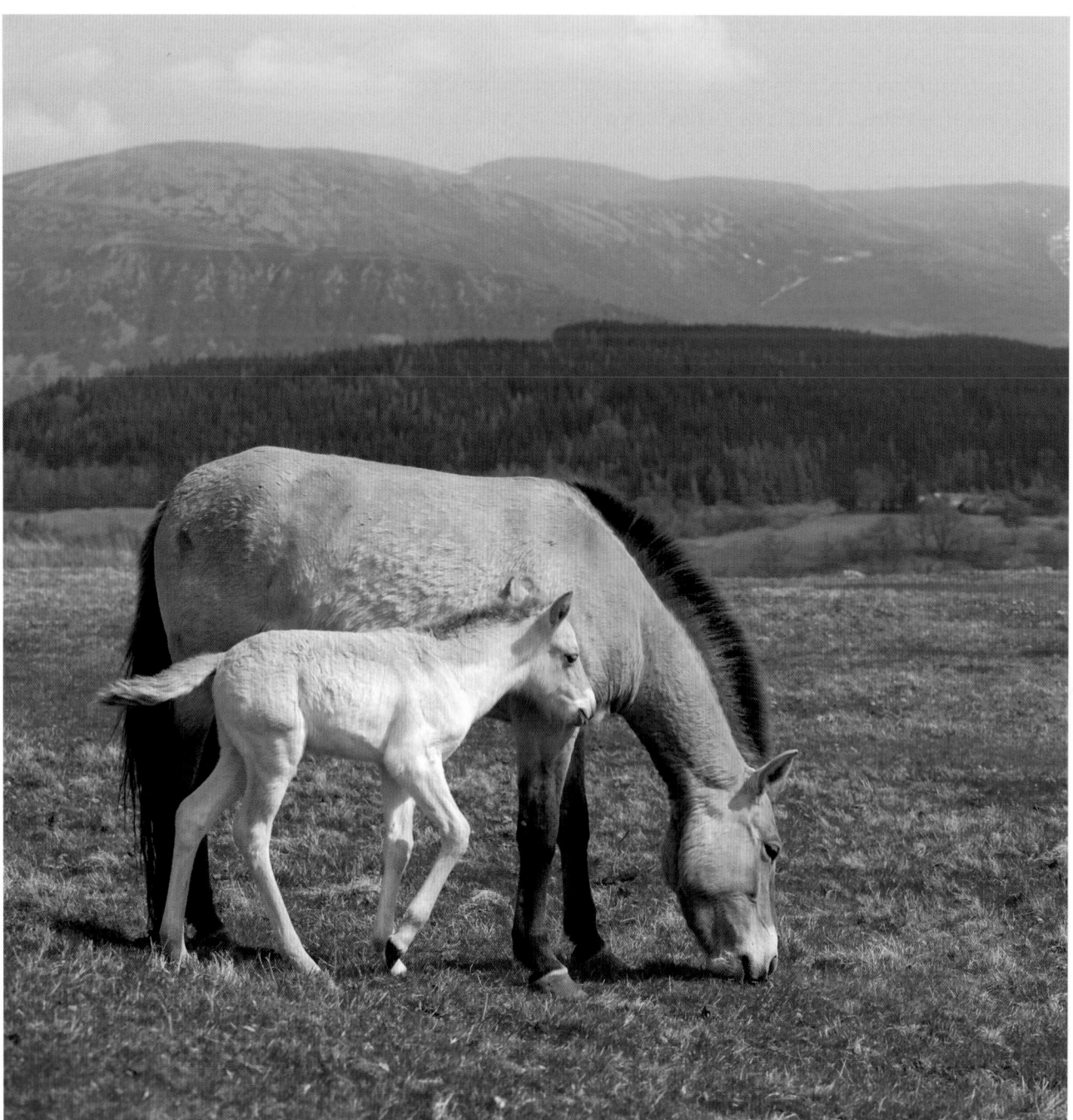

Plate 7.6 Przewalski's horses (*Equus ferus przewalskii*) an *ex situ* conservation success story. © Alan Thomson/RZSS

community are common practice and are increasingly capable of utilizing new tools and techniques in reproductive biology and wildlife veterinary medicine for the delivery of key conservation actions.

The two living animal collections that are operated by the Royal Zoological Society of Scotland (RZSS) in Edinburgh and Kincraig are not only good examples of the type of facility required by CBD but also offer an ideal platform for engaging with people. We recognize the value of positive attitudes to animals and the opportunity for us to promote animals as ambassadors for conservation both in Scotland and internationally.

This relationship between people and biodiversity is a key element of any conservation effort and the need to include, involve and accommodate the concerns, values and aspirations of all stakeholders is paramount.

Similarly the socio-economic aspects of any conservation initiative are gaining in importance and relevance. Whether these are through:

* income generation through wildlife tourism for example in the central Luangwa Valley in Eastern Zambia;
* direct benefit through employment in the project in Uganda, where the RZSS funds the Budongo Conservation Field Station. Although aimed primarily at the study of chimpanzee behaviour, the facility provides vital information on many aspects of forest ecology and the way local communities interact with it. The field station employs 26 people bringing considerable economic benefit to the area;
* or increasingly, by focusing on sustainable use of natural resources and encouraging sustainable landscape level practices such as in examples from the Brazilian Pantanal. Cattle ranching is a major and traditional industry and scientists are advising on optimum grazing practices to reduce the impact on natural vegetation and wild herbivores.

Biodiversity conservation, whether *in situ* or *ex situ*, home or abroad is a human activity that requires support at all levels, from political will to financial resourcing; from priority actions to society buy-in.

The continued existence of what I call 'Colonial Conservation' is not doing the world of conservation any favours. The arrival of well-funded conservationists carrying out projects in complete isolation from the local communities which are part of the same ecosystem as the wildlife they are studying, will not be well received. Local villagers will not appreciate all the attention and resources being given to local wildlife when they themselves have no access to clean drinking water, three meals a day or proper education for their children.

So what has captive animal breeding achieved to date? Are there many ships with many life boats? The number of species that now have secure populations from both a demographic and genetic perspective through sustained breeding success is substantial. There are currently 329 species across all animal taxa that are managed under cooperative breeding programmes in the European region alone

(EAZA, 2008) The network of zoological collections extend beyond Europe to North America, Australasia and increasingly, in the developing regions of South-east Asia, South America and Africa, providing holding and breeding space for a dispersed meta-population of threatened species. There are many examples of species that have larger, healthier *ex situ* populations than occur in the wild, from the northern bald ibis (*Geronticus eremita*) once widespread throughout Southern Europe and North Africa and now found at just three key sites (Birdlife International, 2008).

The Bali starling (*Leucopsar rothschildi*), that at one point was reduced to a wild population of just nine individuals, has so far been saved from extinction because of a large and extensive captive population.

The endemic snails of French Polynesia were decimated by an introduced predator in the 1970s Murray *et al*. (1988) with several species becoming extinct in the wild. However, due to their size it has been possible to maintain entire populations of *Partula* spp. by managing and distributing across 15 separate *ex situ* facilities.

Similarly the Socorro dove (*Zenaida graysoni*), an island endemic species extinct in the wild but about to be reintroduced using captive bred stock from the US and Europe.

One of the earliest examples of how an *ex situ* intervention can help to save a species is that of Pere Davids deer (*Elaphurus davidianus*), (Jiang Zhigang and Harris, 2008). Having been reduced to a single population on a private reserve in their native China they were eventually consumed by soldiers during the Boxer Rebellion. However, a small fragmented population from several European zoos was brought together in the early 20th century to establish what was the founding group of the current world population of several hundred individuals.

In 2008, The Year of the Frog, an initiative called Amphibian Ark was launched which was a global partnership between the Amphibian Specialist Group and the Conservation Breeding Specialist Group of IUCN together with the World Association of Zoos and Aquaria. This is another global response to a global problem, that of the catastrophic decline and loss of amphibian species in the wild due in the main to the spread of the Chytrid fungus. Amphibian Ark is an ambitious project aimed at securing the future of at least 500 species under threat of imminent extinction.

It is important to reiterate that captive reproduction, whether the propagation of plants or the breeding of endangered animals, is a tool within the wider sphere of *ex situ* management programmes. It is a tool that can be switched on and off and one that serves four major functions in conservation:

- the maintenance (over many decades and many generations) of assurance populations;
- the provision of stock for species reintroduction programmes;
- for education, animals as ambassadors;
- for fundraising.

Charismatic species have been used to market commercial products for many years. It's time they benefited from their own marketing value!

Plate 7.7 The northern bald ibis (*Geronticus eremita*), a species that may yet depend on the captive population for its survival.© Alan Thomson/RZSS

References

BirdLife International. (2008). Species factsheet: *Geronticus eremita*. Downloaded from http://www.birdlife.org on 22/8/2008.

Campbell, R., Dutton, A. & Hughes, J. (2007). *Economic Impacts of the Beaver.* Wildlife Conservation Research Unit, University of Oxford.

Convention on Biological Diversity. (1992). Convention on Biological Diversity, Rio de Janeiro, Brazil.

Department of Environment. (1994). Biodiversity: The UK Action Plan. HMSO.

European Association of Zoos and Aquaria. (2008). European Association of Zoos and Aquaria, Breeding Programme Statistics. Retrieved 24.08.08 from www.EAZA.net

European Union. (1992). Council Directive 92/43/EEC on the Conservation of natural habitats and of wild fauna and flora.

Hetherington, D.A. (2005). *The feasibility of reintroducing the Eurasian lynx* (Lynx lynx) *to Scotland.* PhD Thesis, University of Aberdeen.

Hetherington, D.A. (2006). The lynx in Britain's past, present and future. *ECOS* **27** (1): 66-74.

International Union for Conservation of Nature. (2002). Technical Guidelines on the Management of Ex Situ Populations for Conservation, approved at the 14th Meeting of the Programme Committee of Council, Gland Switzerland,

Jiang Zhigang & Harris, R.B. (2008). *Elaphurus davidianus, 2008 IUCN Red List of Threatened Species*. IUCN 2008. Retrieved on 7 January 2009.

Murray, J., Murray, E., Johnson, M.S. & Clarke, B. (1988). The extinction of Partula on Moorea, Pacific Science [PAC. SCI.]. Vol. 42, no. 3-4, pp. 150-153.

Royal Botanic Gardens, Edinburgh. (2007). downloaded August 2008, http://www.rbge.org.uk/science/genetics-and-conservation/international-conifer-conservation-programme/chile

Royal Society for the Protection of Birds. (2007). *A landmark in white-tailed eagle history.* http://www.rspb.org/news/details.asp

Scott Porter Research and Marketing Ltd. (1998). Reintroduction of the European Beaver to Scotland. SNH Research, Survey and Monitoring Report 153, Battleby.

Scottish Natural Heritage. (2007). A Five Year Species Action Framework: Making a difference for Scotland's Species. SNH. 80pp.

Spenceley, A. & Barnes, J. (2005). *Economic Analysis of Rhino Conservation in a Land-Use context within SADC region.* September 2005, SADC RPRC Task 6.3-1.2 (Phase II).

United Kingdom, Biodiversity Action Plan. (1998). http://www.ukbap.org.uk/UKPlans.aspx?ID=634 Downloaded August 2008, originally published in UK Biodiversity Group Tranche 2 Action Plans - Volume I: Vertebrates and vascular plants (June 1998, Tranche 2, Vol I, p261).

World Association of Zoos and Aquariums. (2005). Building a future for Wildlife – The World Zoo and Aquarium Conservation Strategy.

Yeld, J. (2007). *Extinct fynbos is pride of the Cape Flat*. Cape Argus 7 August 2007.

Milne, S. MBE, (2010). Perspectives on reintroductions: The value of reintroductions & Windmill, D. (2010). Perspectives on reintroductions: Captive breeding, captivating people. In: *Species Management: Challenges and Solutions for the 21st Century*, ed. by J.M. Baxter and C.A. Galbraith. TSO Scotland. Edinburgh. pp. 109-122

Chapter 8

Terrestrial mammal conservation in Scotland

Martin Gaywood[1], Mairi Cole[2] and Rob Raynor[1]

Summary

1.   Although the number of mammal species in Scotland is relatively small, there are a number of ecological reasons which give them particular significance, and there is widespread public support for their conservation. Consequently, considerable effort and resources have been targeted on maintaining or restoring the conservation status of Scottish mammals.
2.   Species management is the most important type of action within the species conservation toolkit, although it needs to be underpinned and supported by other actions such as research and communications.
3.   The threats faced by Scottish mammals, and the management actions required, are varied and challenging. Species management is often expensive so there is a need to prioritize and consider the wider benefits to biodiversity that such management can bring. Coordinated action by partnerships is essential and long term commitment to projects is often required.
4.   Species management may be specific and targeted, such as addressing the problems caused by particular invasive non-native species, namely niche competition (e.g. grey squirrel (*Sciurus carolinensis*) which has an impact on native red squirrel (*Sciurus vulgaris*)), hybridization (e.g. domestic feral cat (*Felis catus*) which has an impact on native Scottish wildcat (*Felis silvestris*)) and predation (e.g. American mink (*Neovison vison*) which preys on native water vole (*Arvicola terrestris*)). Other more specific, targeted management action includes ensuring any existing use is sustainable (e.g. for mountain hare (*Lepus timidus*)) and undertaking reintroduction in situations where a species is no longer found in Scotland (e.g. European beaver (*Castor fiber*)). Alternatively, management action may need to be far broader and at the wider countryside/ ecosystem level (for example ensuring suitable foraging habitat for bat species).

[1] Scottish Natural Heritage, Great Glen House, Leachkin Road, Inverness, IV3 8NW, UK
[2] Scottish Natural Heritage, Silvan House, 231 Corstorphine Road, Edinburgh, EH12 7AT, UK

8.1 Introduction

European beaver (*Castor fiber*). © Scottish Beaver Trial

The successful conservation of any species usually requires a range of different, interlinked, actions. These actions fall under the following broad headings:

- Policy and legislation.
- Designated site safeguard and management.
- Advice.
- Research and monitoring.
- Communications and publicity.
- Species protection.
- Species management.

The last type of action on the list, species management, is arguably the most important since it involves practical work on the ground. It can be undertaken for a variety of reasons, e.g. pest control or sustainable harvesting, however, this chapter concentrates on the species management needed to meet the conservation objectives of Scotland's mammal species, in particular those with priority conservation listing.

There are 31 mammal species native to Scotland (i.e. not introduced by humans) which represents 0.7% of the 4325 terrestrial mammal species in the world (Harris and Yalden, 2008). This relatively low diversity, even when compared to 147 species in Europe west of Russia, is largely a legacy of Britain's glacial history and separation from continental Europe at the end of the last ice age and the subsequent hunting to extinction of some species.

The conservation of Scotland's mammals is important for a number of strong ecological reasons including:

- Scotland represents the north-western edge of the range of some species, which could be of further significance if species' ranges alter as a result of climate change, e.g. red squirrel (*Sciurus vulgaris*);
- isolation has often resulted in unique specific variations, e.g. on islands such as the Orkney vole (*Microtus arvalis orcadensis*), or as a result of post-glacial patterns of colonization, such as the water vole (*Arvicola terrestris*) in Scotland (Piertney *et al.*, 2005);
- Scotland has acted as a significant British refuge for some species that have experienced more pronounced declines in England and Wales e.g. pine marten (*Martes martes*) and Eurasian otter (*Lutra lutra*);
- mammals often have influential and keystone roles within ecosystems, e.g. European beaver (*Castor fiber*); and
- management action targeted at the conservation of mammals may also benefit a wider range of other species, e.g. water vole.

Scotland's mammals also command strong public appeal and this was demonstrated when Scottish Ministers sought to produce a list of flora, fauna and habitats considered to be of principal importance in furthering the conservation of biodiversity. One of the criteria used identified those species judged to be most important by the Scottish public. Table 8.1 shows that, despite representing such a small proportion of Scotland's biodiversity (Usher, 1997), mammals were strongly represented in the top ten. This strong public interest in mammals carries an associated expectation that public and private resources should be invested in their conservation.

Table 8.1 Animal species judged to be most important by the Scottish public in ranked order (for production of the Scottish Biodiversity List under The Nature Conservation (Scotland) Act 2004).

Rank	Animal Species
1	**Red deer** or **roe deer**
2	**Red squirrel**
3	Golden eagle
4	**Dolphin, porpoise or whale**
5	Wild salmon
6	**Badger**
7	Osprey
8	**Otter**
9	Butterfly
10	Robin

Twenty-four terrestrial mammal species (Table 8.2) have been identified on three lists which have strongly influenced conservation activities in Scotland in recent years, namely: the UK Biodiversity Action Plan (UKBAP, 2007); the Scottish Biodiversity list (Biodiversity Scotland, 2005); and the Species Action Framework (Scottish Natural Heritage, 2007). The rest of this chapter focuses on some examples prioritized on these lists.

Plate 8.1 Eurasian otter (*Lutra lutra*). © Lorne Gill

Table 8.2 Scottish terrestrial mammal species on the UKBAP, Scottish Biodiversity List and Species Action Framework (cetaceans and seals are therefore not listed).

Taxonomic group	Common name	Scientific name	UKBAP priority species	Scottish Biodiversity List	Species Action Framework (Species conservation category)
Rodentia	Black rat	*Rattus rattus*		Yes	
Rodentia	Common vole (Orkney vole)	*Microtus arvalis*		Yes	
Rodentia	European beaver*	*Castor fiber*			Yes
Rodentia	Red squirrel	*Sciurus vulgaris*	Yes	Yes	Yes
Rodentia	Water vole	*Arvicola terrestris*	Yes	Yes	Yes
Lagomorpha	Brown hare	*Lepus europaeus*	Yes	Yes	
Lagomorpha	Mountain hare	*Lepus timidus*	Yes	Yes	
Insectivores	West European hedgehog	*Erinaceus europaeus*	Yes		
Chiroptera	Brandt's bat	*Myotis brandtii*		Yes	
Chiroptera	Brown long-eared bat	*Plecotus auritus*	Yes	Yes	
Chiroptera	Common pipistrelle	*Pipistrellus pipistrellus*		Yes	
Chiroptera	Daubenton's bat	*Myotis daubentonii*		Yes	
Chiroptera	Nathusius's pipistrelle	*Pipistrellus nathusii*		Yes	
Chiroptera	Natterer's bat	*Myotis nattereri*		Yes	
Chiroptera	Noctule	*Nyctalus noctula*	Yes	Yes	
Chiroptera	Soprano pipistrelle	*Pipistrellus pygmaeus*	Yes	Yes	
Chiroptera	Whiskered bat	*Myotis mystacinus*		Yes	
Carnivora	Scottish wildcat	*Felis silvestris*	Yes	Yes	Yes
Carnivora	Eurasian badger	*Meles meles*		Yes	
Carnivora	Eurasian otter	*Lutra lutra*	Yes	Yes	
Carnivora	Pine marten	*Martes martes*	Yes		
Carnivora	Polecat	*Mustela putorius*	Yes		
Ungulates	Red deer	*Cervus elaphus*		Yes	(No, but in 'Sustainable use' category)
Ungulates	Roe deer	*Capreolus capreolus*		Yes	(No, but in 'Sustainable use' category)

* Trial reintroduction for beaver commences spring 2009.

8.2 Conservation management themes

The range of threats some mammal species are exposed to, and the management action required, varies widely. Some types of management are relevant to all species, to a greater or lesser extent, such as ensuring suitable habitat exists to support viable populations. However, if one looks at some of the mammal species which have been given a particularly high priority for conservation action in Scotland in recent years, it is possible to identify four broad management issues that stand out :

- Invasive non-native species.
- Use.
- Wider countryside management.
- Species extinction and reintroduction.

8.2.1 Invasive non-native species

The majority of introduced, non-native species have little effect on the ecosystem or may even, in cases such as rabbit (*Oryctolagus cuniculus*), now be considered as 'naturalized' or 'long-established'. However, some introduced species are invasive and present novel challenges to native species which are not ecologically equipped to deal with them. Where this impact is substantial, intervention may be required to re-establish favourable conditions for the native fauna to thrive. Opportunities for this vary between situations, and sometimes considerable levels of long term commitment are required if such intervention is to work.

Invasive non-natives can impact on native species in a number of ways, such as through niche competition, hybridization and predation. The most cost-effective way of dealing with these problems is to prevent the arrival of non-natives in the first place but the following reviews a number of cases where, unfortunately, that is no longer an option.

8.2.1.1 Niche competition – red squirrel

The problem

The UK red squirrel (*Sciurus vulgaris*) population has declined dramatically within the last 100 years. Formerly widespread across Britain, the species is now largely confined to Scotland, north England and small pockets of Wales. There are estimated to be 161,000 red squirrels in Britain of which 121,000 are estimated to be resident in Scotland (Harris *et al.,* 1995). Scotland, therefore, provides a stronghold for the UK population.

The UKBAP recognized two significant threats to red squirrels - grey squirrels, and habitat loss/ fragmentation. These threats are faced by red squirrels across their geographic range and, consequently, action to address them within the Scottish population is set out in both the *Scottish Strategy for Red Squirrel Conservation* (SNH, 2004) and, most recently, the *Scottish Red Squirrel Action Plan 2006-2011*

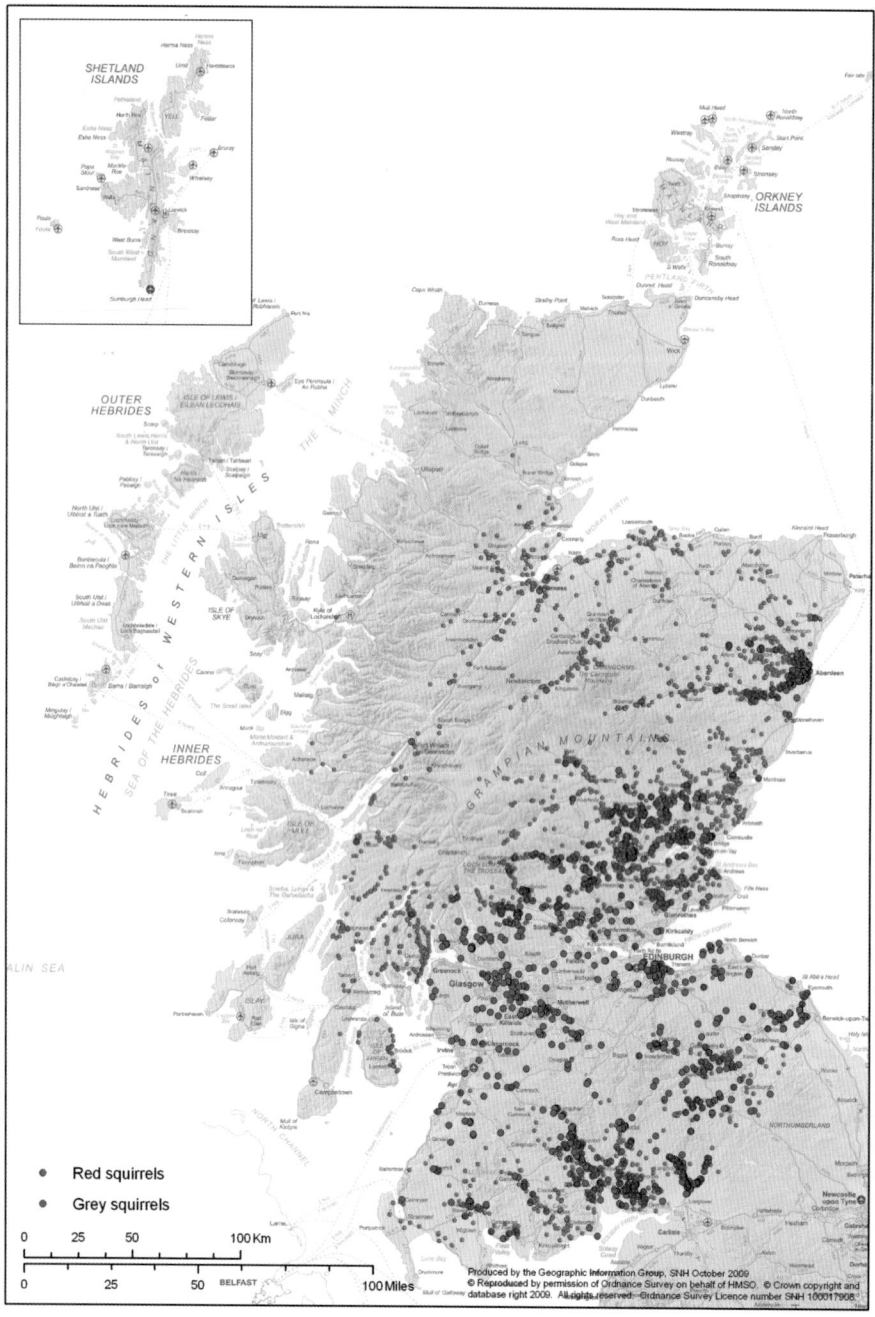

Figure 8.1 Red squirrel and grey squirrel records from Scotland 2000-2008 (map prepared from Scottish Squirrel Database records).

(SNH, 2006). These set out principles and targets which aim to establish favourable conditions for long-term red squirrel conservation and which form the basis of policy for those statutory bodies which deal with wildlife conservation.

Grey squirrels (*Sciurus carolinensis*) present the main threat to red squirrels, through ecological displacement and disease:

Ecological displacement - Although the mechanism for this remains undefined, red and grey squirrels occupy similar ecological niches in places where they both occur, and evidence suggests that displacement occurs through niche competition, i.e. competition for food resources, rather than direct aggression. Although there are situations where red squirrels appear to remain even when grey squirrels are present, red squirrels are generally displaced within 15 years of the first record of grey squirrel occupation in an area (Shorten, 1957).

Disease - Grey squirrels are also known to carry the squirrelpox virus. This virus is believed to have been introduced from North America with grey squirrels and, whilst the host species appears to remain asymptomatic, it is fatal in red squirrels (Sainsbury *et al.*, 2000; Tomkins *et al.*, 2003). Cases have been reported in England, most notably in Norfolk and Cumbria, and it is thought that this disease may have played a role in the disappearance of red squirrels across much of its range in England and Wales (Tompkins *et al.*, 2003).

Scotland was squirrelpox-free until May 2007 when the first case was detected at Newcastleton in the Scottish Borders (McInnes *et al.,* in prep). Despite extensive trapping to remove the source of the infection, there have been subsequent cases from Lockerbie (September 2007) and Drumlanrig (April 2008). Red squirrel populations exposed to the virus may be lost 18-25 times faster than those populations exposed only to ecological competition with grey squirrels (Rushton *et al.*, 2006). This illustrates the scale and immediacy of the action required to support the red squirrel population.

The action
A programme of action to support the long-term conservation of red squirrel in Scotland can be divided into two main elements:

Habitat management to favour red squirrels – This is based on maintaining or improving habitat to sustain viable populations of red squirrels and minimizing the competition from grey squirrels (Pepper and Patterson, 1998). The former may be tackled by creating woodland of appropriate size and composition to provide continuous food supplies and places for red squirrels to construct shelters. Diversification of coniferous woodlands will often satisfy this requirement, although the inclusion of large-seeded broadleaves also provides opportunities for grey squirrels to colonize. The challenge for red squirrel conservation is to come up with suitable management advice, and then implement action, which favours red squirrels and does not encourage grey squirrels.

The red squirrel is one of the most widespread species of conservation concern and therefore may have to compete with other management objectives in many woodland management plans. Action through the *Scottish Red Squirrel Action Plan 2006-2011* (SNH, 2006) will identify a suite of 20 red squirrel stronghold sites managed to maintain the current geographic range of the species and provide the basis for its long-term conservation. Although wide scale action will also continue, a specific objective in the design and management plans of these 20 sites will be the conservation of red squirrels, thereby providing refuge sites at which to retain red squirrels even in the face of further grey squirrel spread.

Reduction of the threat posed by grey squirrels - Red and grey squirrels occupy very similar niches. Habitat management can create conditions that discourage grey squirrels but species control is also essential to reduce the ecological pressure on red squirrels. Grey squirrels have established widely across the country and, as such, total eradication is not a viable option at the present time. The *Scottish Grey*

Squirrel Control Strategy is currently being developed by SNH and aims to capitalize on natural landscape barriers and pinch-points, coordinating effort to benefit red squirrels where possible. It aims to deliver a strategic approach in grey squirrel control towards preventing further spread of the squirrelpox virus, constraining natural dispersal of the grey squirrel and protecting red squirrel stronghold sites. It is anticipated that this *Strategy* will be available publicly in early 2010.

8.2.1.2. Hybridization – Scottish wildcat

The problem

The Scottish wildcat (*Felis sylvestris*) is the only native species of felid in the UK. Once widespread, the wildcat began to decline in the 1800s and was lost from England by 1862. The decline continued in Scotland and, despite a small increase in range post-1920, has been relatively stable since the 1940s. Harris *et al.* (1995) estimated there to be approximately 3,500 animals in Scotland, although Macdonald *et al.* (2004) speculated that there may be as few as 400 true wildcat left. The species is now largely confined to north-east Scotland and a small pocket in Argyll, although there have recently been unconfirmed reports in the Borders.

The wildcat faces four conservation challenges:

Plate 8.2 Scotland remains a British stronghold for the red squirrel (*Sciurus vulgaris*). © Lorne Gill/SNH

Hybridization with feral domestic cats - This is the greatest threat and is not restricted to Britain but has been recorded across the European range of the wildcat. Domestic cats were introduced to Britain with the Romans, approximately 2,000 years ago and rapidly became widespread. Although it is unknown when hybridization first occurred, the phenomenon was first noted between the species 200 years ago.

The debate over identification of the Scottish wildcat was raised in 1990 when an expert witness in a court case queried whether pelage markings were indicative of the species. The Scottish wildcat receives full protection under domestic legislation but the court case raised uncertainties about traditional methods of species identification, undermining the ability to enforce the legal protection. Furthermore, although no unique genetic marker could be identified which correlated with the traditional pelage markings, Beaumont *et al.* (1999) were able to segregate three groups of cats on the basis of their genetics: domestic cats, cats with 'wildcat' morphology and a group of hybrids which included genotypes from both domestic and 'wildcat' groups. Their results inferred that introgression was advanced and conservation efforts should focus on 'wild-living' cats which filled the ecological niche for the species.

Work has continued to clarify the morphometric and pelage characteristics of Scottish animals in a European context, with Kitchener *et al.* (2005) proposing a scoring system of pelage markings by which to identify wildcat. In addition, the species' genetics have also continued to raise interest and Driscoll *et al.* (2007) set out results which infer a series of nuclear and mitochondrial markers indicative of the species. This has yet to be tested against the characteristics set out by Kitchener *et al.* (2005) to enable any genetic distinctions to be applied under field conditions.

Predator control and incidental capture - The confusion over wildcat identification has undermined the ability to carry out positive conservation action or enforce the legislation. More practically, the absence of a definitive description of the species has damaged the ability of land managers to avoid incidental killing of protected wildcat when undertaking legal control of pest feral cats. Land managers have continued to use the advice available (Kitchener *et al.*, 2005) but clarity is required urgently.

Habitat loss and fragmentation - This has proven to be a problem for wildcat in the past (Langley and Yalden, 1977). There appears to be a difference in habitat preferences across its range, with animals in the east of the country selecting marginal agricultural areas with moorland, pastureland and woodland, in contrast with animals in the west that favour rough grazing and moorland with limited pastureland.

Wildcats are generally solitary animals, interacting only during the breeding season. They occur at relatively low densities, inhabiting consistent territories and are susceptible to any changes in the resources available to them within these. Although development controls and Structural Plans help prevent widespread change in land use, small-scale changes in habitats in the core areas may pose threats to individual animals (Easterbee *et al.*, 1991). Action is required to maintain the quality and quantity of habitat available to the wildcat to avoid wider impacts on the population.

Disease - Scottish wildcat, in common with most mammal species, is susceptible to a number of pathogens. The greatest threat is from the introduction of novel pathogens against which wildcat have no natural defence, and exposure to feral domestic cats raises the likelihood of this. This includes the Feline Leukemia Virus (FeLV) which appears to be present as a sustained infection in some populations rather than an occasional event (McOrist *et al.*,1991). Although recognized as a problem, the role of disease in wildcat population ecology requires further investigation to identify actions to counter potential impacts.

The action

There are several core actions for Scottish wildcat:

Evaluation of the Scottish population - The Scottish Wildcat Survey was commissioned in 2007 to clarify the current known range of the species. This involved collating historic records and recent sightings from both experienced land managers and members of the public using traditional methods of identifying a wildcat from pelage markings (Kitchener *et al.*, 2005) in order to prepare a map identifying hot spots of wildcat activity. The survey was closed in December 2008 and is expected to be reported by 2010. The results will help to target future conservation action for the species.

Clarification of the genetic integrity of the species + identification in the field - Further work is needed to confirm the genetic identity of the wildcat and resolve the outstanding questions of taxonomic identification. An immediate priority is to evaluate the level of agreement between the work published by Driscoll *et al.* (2007) and the field key provided by Kitchener *et al.* (2005). Once resolved, this will provide a definitive description of the species on which to base subsequent management advice and action. Providing a genetic description of the species is crucial to evaluating the process of hybridization, contributing to an understanding of where the current wildcat population is in this process. This will help to identify the greatest threats to the species, such as hybridization with feral cats or back-crossing between wildcats and first generation hybrids, which in turn will enable species management priorities to be tailored accordingly, e.g. prioritizing removal of hybrids rather than feral cats.

Provision of management guidance to aid conservation action - An immediate priority is to provide advice on management methods and practices to land managers to maximize opportunities for wildcats in their area. A partnership of organizations is currently preparing to evaluate the methods and effectiveness of wildcat conservation methods in the Cairngorms National Park, integrating legal feral cat control with monitoring of wildcat populations to assess the level of commitment and action required to deliver conservation effectively. In addition, raising public awareness, and the promotion of responsible domestic cat ownership to help minimize the risk of hybridization between wildcats and pet domestic cats, will be undertaken.

8.2.1.3 Predation – water vole

The problem

The American mink (*Neovison vison*) is an adaptable opportunist predator that has become established over most of the Scottish mainland and some of the Hebridean islands as a result of escapes and releases from fur farms from the 1930s onwards (Sigfússon and MacLeod, this volume). Mink have had a devastating effect on a range of native vertebrates, notably seabirds and the water vole. Although water voles had been declining in Britain throughout the 20th century, initially as a result of sheep over-grazing of the vole's riparian habitat, this trend has accelerated in recent decades. In the 1990s it was cited as our most rapidly declining mammal (Harris *et al.*, 1995). This decline has been attributed to a combination of pressures including predation from mink and the fragmentation and degradation of habitats resulting from detrimental riparian management. In most areas where water voles survive, numbers are low and their metapopulation structure is compromised as individual colonies become more isolated.

A wide range of native predators, including otters, stoats and herons, prey on water voles but none appear to impact on them at the population level. However, there is abundant evidence of mink predation being a major cause of water vole mortality in many areas (Macdonald and Strachan, 1999; Harris and Yalden, 2008). The threat is considered to be greatest from breeding female mink, which are smaller than males and capable of following the voles into their burrows.

The threat posed by mink applies over most of the water vole's range, although in the uplands, where many of Scotland's water voles now find refuge, mink are often scarce or absent. This scarcity of mink is attributed to the restricted availability of prey and suitable denning sites, when compared with the lower reaches of river systems. However, the establishment of mink can occur in upland areas where there are resident rabbit populations, with detrimental implications for any nearby water voles (Aars *et al.*, 2001). In these cases, the presence of an established rabbit population is thought to increase the likelihood of mink also becoming established rather than transient in the area, in what is otherwise sub-optimal habitat for the species. The result of this predation and the effects of habitat loss/degradation, particularly in lowland areas, is the fragmentation of water vole populations. Consequently, for many river systems, water voles may be absent from most of the main stem and the larger tributaries, and restricted to the headwaters and smaller tributaries in the upper or peripheral parts of the catchment.

The action

Mink predation is only one of several pressures acting on water voles, but strategically targeted mink control undertaken on a suitably large scale is now considered to be the single most effective management tool for reversing the water vole decline in Scotland. Water vole conservation in Scotland is therefore based around local mink eradication programmes.

There are many examples of mink control schemes in England and Wales (see Strachan and Moorhouse, 2006). Many of them operate at a relatively small scale, and are not part of a larger regional control strategy. However, in Scotland the scale of some schemes is much larger, with mink control increasingly being implemented at a large multi-catchment scale.

On the mainland, mink rafts developed by the Game & Wildlife Conservation Trust (Reynolds, 2003) are extensively used, with the emphasis placed on building and maintaining a network of participating gamekeepers, fishing ghillies and other local volunteers to operate the rafts, overseen by a professional coordinator. There are currently two such projects operating in North-east Scotland:

Plate 8.3 A mink raft set in trapping mode. A cage trap is placed within the tunnel only after evidence of mink has been confirmed on the clay tracking pad which is located beneath. When set in monitoring mode the raft only needs to be checked every two weeks, whereas in trapping mode it must be checked every 24 hours. © Llinos Davies

The Cairngorms Water Vole Conservation Project - This operates throughout the Cairngorms National Park, over 5,500 km², and has focused effort on removing mink from areas where the species is well established such as Speyside and Deeside. It has the overall aim of preventing further mink incursion into the main Cairngorm massif – a vast area supporting one of Scotland's most important water vole metapopulations.

The North-east Water Vole Project - This covers the entire River Ythan Catchment and parts of neighbouring river systems in Aberdeenshire. It has gradually increased its coverage from 30 km² to 1,000 km² in four years during which time it has successfully removed mink from the entire river system.

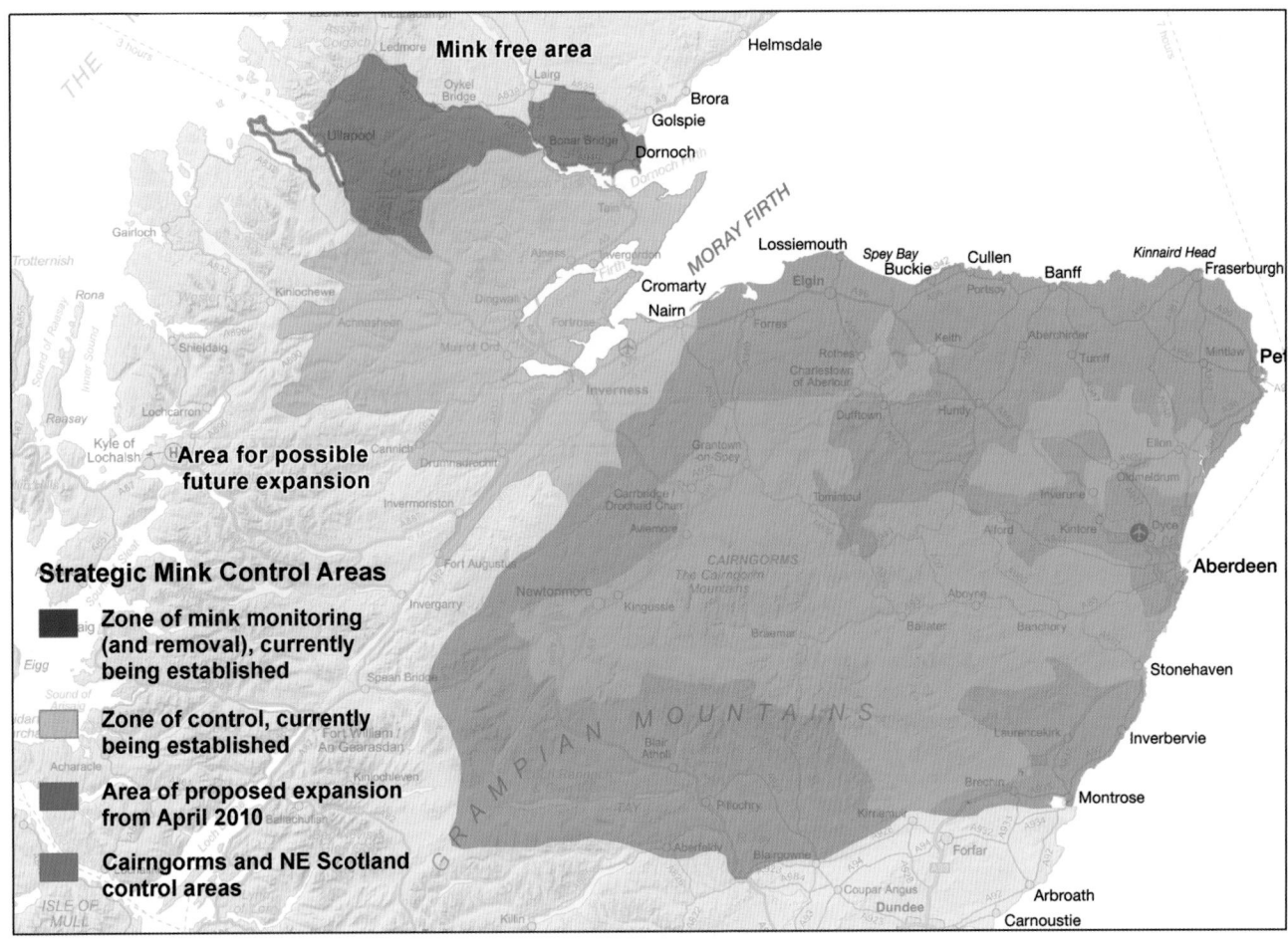

Figure 8.2 Existing and proposed areas of strategic mink control in northern Scotland. A study of mink dispersal is underway in part of the area marked for possible future expansion and the findings will help inform further management. Crown Copyright and database right 2009. All rights reserved. Ordnance Survey Licence number SNH 100017808.

The intention is to merge and expand the geographical coverage of these projects, with the longer term aim of building a very extensive control network across the whole of North-east Scotland and westwards into the North-west Highlands, where mink are currently at the northern edge of their range in the UK. This will secure, expand and reconnect remnant lowland water vole populations and, in the process, preclude reinvasion of the Cairngorms. It will also halt, reverse and preclude the spread of mink in northern Scotland, thereby contributing to achieving targets outlined in the UKBAP for water voles, i.e. to maintain the species' current range (730 occupied 10km squares) in the UK, and achieve an increase in range by 50 new occupied 10km squares in the UK by 2010.

Other conservation measures include riparian habitat management, for which landowners can receive financial assistance through the Scottish Rural Development Programme (SRDP), and a reintroduction project of the water vole in the Loch Lomond & Trossachs National Park. The first of its kind in Scotland, this project is regarded as a pilot. There has been considerable initial investment in habitat creation and an ongoing commitment to mink control and the monitoring of voles and mink at the reintroduction site, all considered as prerequisites for gaining the formal approval of Scottish Natural Heritage (SNH).

8.2.2 Use – mountain hare

The problem

European legislation requires that any exploitation of certain species, such as mountain hare (*Lepus timidus*), must be sustainable. It has been suggested that mountain hares may have declined in recent years (e.g. Battersby [ed.] & Tracking Mammals Partnership, 2005; Newey *et al.*, 2008), although the data from the National Game Census do not reveal any significant long-term trends (Davey and Aebischer, 2008). The vast majority of hare control is currently unregulated and there are concerns about the species' conservation status. Kinrade *et al.*

Plate 8.4 Mountain hare (*Lepus timidus*). © Lorne Gill

(2008) report that a minimum of around 25,000 mountain hares are killed on Scottish estates annually, although this may be an underestimate as it reflects the number of hares *reported* to have been killed by the respondents to a questionnaire survey. The majority (79%) of this unregulated cull comprises hares shot by day; the rest were snared. The largest proportion of culled mountain hares within the sample (50%) were taken for the purposes of tick control. A further 40% of hares were shot primarily for sport and the remaining 10% were killed specifically to protect growing trees.

The action

In order to better inform future mountain hare management, a partnership of bodies developed a programme of research and surveillance to address the deficiencies in our knowledge. As a result, Newey *et al.* (2008) recommended the need to develop and validate a survey methodology that can be used to provide reliable abundance estimates, but does not require specialist technical expertise. There are limitations on the data generated by current methods of counting mountain hares (e.g. distance sampling, daytime transect counts) since they cannot be used to provide reliable estimates of absolute abundance. This level of information is needed to inform decisions on the sustainable management of the species. The methods commonly used in demographic studies such as capture-mark-recapture are resource-intensive and not generally applicable to management situations in which an estimate of the mountain hare population within a defined area is required to inform bag limits on licences (No licences for the control of mountain hares have been issued by Scottish Government since December 2005). Alternative methods of estimating abundance such as pellet counts, are therefore being investigated as a more cost effective surrogate.

8.2.3 Wider countryside management – bats

The problem

Bat conservation issues, in particular of bat roosts in houses, are covered in detail by Mitchell-Jones (this volume). However, although important, the protection of the places of shelter for mobile and wide-ranging species such as bats, is insufficient by itself to ensure the maintenance or improvement of their

Plate 8.5 Pipistrelle bat (*Pipistrellus pipistrellus*). © Pete Moore/SNH

conservation status. Conservation strategies are also required at the wider countryside scale. Such wider management includes the need to sympathetically manage critical foraging areas and connecting habitat to aid movement, and to reduce pollutants.

In Scotland there are no designated sites (such as SSSIs or SACs) which have been set up for any bat species. This means the role of the wider countryside in providing suitable bat habitat is particularly important for them.

Habitat connectivity - The need for maintaining habitat connectivity is identified in Article 10 of the EC 'Habitats Directive' which obliges member states to improve the ecological coherence of the Natura 2000 site network. All British bats make use of landscape features to navigate from the roost to their foraging area. The distance bats travel to forage varies greatly, often less than 2km, but up to 20km or more, for some of the larger species (Entwistle *et al.*, 2001). Linear landscape features can be important foraging areas in their own right, but are often used primarily as navigational cues. Therefore the removal of hedgerows, tree lines or the unmitigated construction of a new transport link bisecting important linear features can have serious consequences for the local bat population. Some species, notably brown long-eared bats, are particularly vulnerable in this respect, as they are very reluctant to cross large gaps between areas of cover and will therefore, either make extensive detours to avoid such crossings, or attempt to find alternative foraging areas elsewhere.

Pesticides - Bats have also suffered from the use of pesticides, notably lindane (or gamma-HCH), widely used to treat infestations of wood-boring insects in the roof timbers of buildings which often harboured bat colonies (Mitchell-Jones *et al.*, 1989). The effects of pesticides, both within roosts and in the wider countryside, contributed significantly to the general decline in bat populations throughout much of the 20th century.

The action

In terms of wider countryside management, bat conservation relies heavily on the following:

Promoting appropriate management of bat habitats - This can be achieved through, firstly, agri-environment incentive schemes such as the Scottish Rural Development Programme (SRDP) through which land managers can receive payments for management practices designed to enhance the local environment for bats, and secondly, the promotion of best practice guidance designed to help land managers create optimum foraging, commuting and roosting conditions for bats.

Sympathetic development - Effective influencing of the planning process and the provision of advice on how best to integrate the requirements of bats within proposed developments, amongst developers and building professionals, can play an important role in bat conservation.

Control of pesticides - Over the past two decades, a range of less toxic timber treatment compounds has been developed, suitable for use in bat roosts and this threat to bat populations has largely been eliminated. Evidence from the National Bat Monitoring Programme suggests that since 1997 populations of some species are now either stable, or on the increase (Battersby, 2005).

8.2.4 Extinction and reintroduction

The problem

Mammal populations have sometimes disappeared at local levels and so there is the potential to reintroduce animals from one part of their British or Scottish range to another. An example of this is the reintroduction of water vole to parts of the Loch Lomond and Trossachs National Park referred to above.

However, Scotland has also lost a number of mammal species which no longer occur anywhere in Britain, in some cases as a direct result of human actions. Beaver, wild boar, brown bear, wolf and lynx have all become extinct as a result of human activities over the last 2,000 years. For these species, there is

Plate 8.6 One of the first European beavers (*Castor fiber*) released in May 2009 as part of the Scottish Beaver Trial. © Scottish Beaver Trial

no likelihood of natural recolonization and so the only way they could be restored to Scotland is through reintroduction from sources outwith Britain. The big question is which species to reintroduce?

Reintroductions are specifically referred to in the EC 'Habitats Directive', Article 22(a) of which states that EU Member States are required to "study the desirability of reintroducing species in Annex IV that are native to their territory…". The species listed in Annex IV which are relevant to Scotland are wolf, lynx, bear and European beaver. Of these, the only mammal reintroduction which has so far received sufficient public and government support to proceed, at least to an initial trial phase, has been for the only non-predator on this list, European beaver.

Such reintroductions are usually high profile projects which generate a lot of public interest and can be used to raise the profile of bigger issues relating to the overall restoration of wider ecosystems. However, they tend to be controversial, expensive and time consuming, so the costs and benefits of a reintroduction have to be carefully considered. Beaver has scored relatively well so far because of the expected benefits it could bring to other Scottish biodiversity, but it remains to be seen what level of support there will be once the 'Scottish Beaver Trial' finishes (also see Milne and Windmill, this volume).

The action

In assessing any mammal reintroduction, it is essential that it addresses the IUCN Guidelines on Reintroductions (IUCN, 1995) which provide a simple and pragmatic approach, and which have been adopted by all the GB countryside agencies. The Guidelines can, very broadly, be divided into two over-arching elements - the ecological feasibility of a reintroduction, and the public desirability.

In the case of the European beaver, these two broad elements have passed the first hurdle, but concerns have continued to be raised over precisely what effects beaver may have on the Scottish environment (Gaywood et al., 2008). Therefore, following the inclusion of beaver on the Species Action Framework (SAF, see Scottish Natural Heritage, 2007), a carefully managed trial reintroduction project was proposed and given Ministerial approval in May 2008. The Scottish Beaver Trial is being managed by the Royal Zoological Society of Scotland and the Scottish Wildlife Trust with the stated aim of undertaking "a scientifically monitored trial reintroduction of the European beaver to Knapdale, mid-Argyll, over a five year period in order to:

- study the ecology and biology of the European beaver in the Scottish environment;
- assess the effects of beaver activities on the natural and socio-economic environment;
- generate information during the proposed trial release that will inform a potential further release of beavers at other sites with different habitat characteristics;
- determine the extent and impact of any increased tourism generated through the presence of beaver;
- explore the environmental education opportunities that may arise from the trial itself and the scope for a wider programme should the trial be successful."

Success and failure criteria for the trial have also been set out in the licence application. The trial involved the release of three families of beavers in spring 2009 to Knapdale Forest, a site owned by Forestry Commission Scotland, with SNH providing independent coordination of the research, survey and monitoring and reporting to the Scottish Government. At the end of the trial a decision will then be made on the future of the Knapdale beavers, and beaver reintroduction in Scotland as a whole.

The reintroduction of beaver to Scotland has been criticized as being a step too far by some, too slow by others. The trial approach is therefore a compromise that provides a practical means of testing some of the concerns and the potential benefits on the ground.

8.3 Implementation of conservation management

The prioritization of species and resources, and the need for partnership working are all key considerations in implementing management actions. Over the last decade, species conservation in the UK has been largely driven by the UKBAP process and this has helped to prioritize species for conservation (including the 12 UKBAP priority species of Scottish terrestrial mammal, Table 8.2), identify actions, and encourage local delivery through LBAPs (Local Biodiversity Action Plans), supported by national groups of specialists. Scotland also has its own 'Scottish Biodiversity List', linked to the UKBAP, which identifies species considered to be of principal importance for the purpose of biodiversity conservation under the Nature Conservation (Scotland) Act 2004.

The SAF has a relatively short list of 32 species, although targeted specifically at management action in Scotland from 2007-2012 (SNH, 2007), with four mammals on the list for species conservation purposes (Table 8.2). The emphasis of the SAF is on management on the ground and partnership delivery. Resources come from SNH and partner organizations, although SAF is also a national priority of the SRDP, thereby influencing the delivery of species management through appropriate agri-environment packages. The SAF also sets out five general principles to guide all species management:

- Species management is a shared responsibility.
- There are ecological and socio-economic aspects to species management decisions.
- Species management benefits from a strategic approach.
- Species management needs an adaptive approach.
- Management activity should have regard to animal welfare.

Species conservation programmes are often criticized as an inefficient use of resources which could otherwise be spent on management targeted at the habitat/ecosystem level. However, management action targeted at certain species can also benefit a range of other species, and at the wider ecosystem scale. Such species were specifically selected for inclusion within the SAF – for example the removal of the opportunist predator America mink for water vole conservation will also benefit many other species, such a ground nesting birds (and also species of commercial value). High profile species management can also be used to highlight wider ecosystem management requirements to the general public, and individual invasive species management projects can be used as opportunities for increasing awareness of the wider problems associated with invasive species.

The coordination of work between partners is always essential for the successful implementation of most mammal conservation projects. Public bodies, NGOs and private individuals can contribute different and complementary expertise and guidance. Large-scale invasive species management projects in Scotland, such as the Cairngorms Water Vole Project, have involved local volunteers, professionals and groups which in turn have helped empower communities to implement the work. Such projects need very long term commitments to ensure invasive species do not recolonize areas they have been removed from. Partnerships can help provide the necessary resources, and increase the likelihood of accessing funds from major funding sources (e.g. European sources such as LIFE funds).

Although research, communications and similar underpinning types of actions are vital in mammal conservation, it is the practical management on the ground that ultimately gets the important work done. The threats faced by Scottish mammals are diverse and challenging and therefore the management actions required are similarly varied, ranging from the very specific, targeted work associated with some invasive species control and reintroductions, to the much broader work associated with wider countryside management to improve foraging habitat quality. In all cases though, mammal conservation can only work with the active involvement and input of partners, and the support of the public.

References

Aars, J., Lambin, X., Denny, R. & Griffin, C. (2001). Water vole in the Scottish uplands: distribution patterns of disturbed and pristine populations ahead and behind the American mink invasion front. *Animal Conservation* **4**: 187-194.

Battersby, J. [ed.] & Tracking Mammals Partnership. (2005). *UK Mammals: Species Status and Population Trends*. First report by the Tracking Mammals Partnership. JNCC/Tracking Mammals Partnership, Peterborough.

Beaumont, M., Barratt, E.M., Gotelli, D. & Bruford, M.W. (1999). *An anaysis of genetic differentiation in the wild-living cat population of Scotland*. Scottish Natural Heritage Commissioned report F96AC305. Battleby, Perth.

Biodiversity Scotland. (2005). The Scottish Biodiversity List. http://www.biodiversityscotland.gov.uk/pageType2.php?id=35&type=2&navID=92

Davey, P.A. & Aebischer, N.J. (2008). Participation of the National Gamebag Census in the mammal surveillance network. A report to JNCC for the year 2007/08.

Driscoll, C.A., Menotti-Raymond, M., Roca, A.L., Hupe, K., Johnson, W.E., Geffen, E., Harley, E.H., Delibes, M., Pontier, D., Kitchener, A.C., Yamaguchi, N., O'Brien, S.J. & Macdonald, D.W. (2007). The near eastern origin of cat domestication. *Science* **317**: 519-523.

Easterbee, N., Hepburn, L.V. & Jeffries, D.J. (1991). *Survey of the status and distribution of the wildcat in Scotland, 1983-1987*. Nature Conservancy Council for Scotland, Edinburgh.

Entwistle, A.C., Harris, S., Hutson, A.M., Racey, P.A., Walsh, A., Gibson, S.D., Hepburn, I. & Johnston, J. (2001). *Habitat management for bats. A guide for land managers, land owners and their advisors*. JNCC, Peterborough.

Gaywood, M., Batty, D. & Galbraith, C. (2008). Reintroducing the European Beaver in Britain. *British Wildlife* **19**: 381-391.

Harris, S. & Yalden, D. (2008). *Mammals of the British Isles.* Mammal Society, London.

Harris, S., Morris, P., Wray, S. & Yalden, D. (1995). *A review of British Mammals: population estimates and conservation status of British mammals other than cetaceans.* Joint Nature Conservation Committee, Peterborough.

International Union for Conservation of Nature. (1995). *IUCN Guidelines for Re-introductions.* IUCN, Gland.

Kinrade, V., Ewald, J., Smith, A., Newey, S., Iason, G., Thirgood, S. & Raynor, R. (2008). The distribution of Mountain Hare (*Lepus timidus*) in Scotland (2006/07). *Scottish Natural Heritage Commissioned Report* No 278 (ROAME No. R07AC308). Battleby, Perth.

Kitchener, A.C., Yamaguchi, N., Ward, J.M. & Macdonald, D.W. (2005). A diagnosis for the Scottish Wildcat (*Felis silvestris*): a tool for conservation action for a critically-endangered felid. *Animal Conservation* **8**: 223-237.

Langley, A.J.W. & Yalden, D.W. (1977). The decline of the rarer carnivores in Great Britain during the nineteenth century. *Mammal Review* **7**: 95-116.

Macdonald, D.W. & Strachan, R. (1999). *The mink and the water vole: analyses for conservation.* WildCru, Oxford.

Macdonald, D.W., Daniels, M.J., Driscoll, C., Kitchener, A. & Yamaguchi, N. (2004). *The Scottish Wildcat: analysis for conservation and an action plan.* WildCru, Oxford.

McOrist, S., Boid, R., Jones, T.W., Easterbee, N., Hubbard, A.L. & Jarrett, O. (1991). Some viral and protozool diseases in the wildcat (*Felis silvestris*). *Journal of Wildlife Diseases* **27(4)**: 693-696.

Mitchell-Jones, A.J. (2010). Bats in houses - the conservation challenge. In: Baxter, J.M. & Galbraith, C.A. (Eds). *Species Management: Challenges and Solutions for the 21st Century*. Edinburgh, TSO Scotland, pp. 365-378.

Mitchell-Jones, A.J., Cooke, A.S., Boyd, I.L. & Stebbings, R.E. (1989). Bats and remedial timber treatment chemicals – a review. *Mammal Review* **19**: 93-110.

Newey, S., Iason, G. & Raynor, R. (2008). The conservation status and management of mountain hares. *Scottish Natural Heritage Commissioned Report* No 287 (ROAME No. F05AC316). Battleby, Perth.

Pepper, H. & Patterson, G. (1998). *Red Squirrel Conservation.* Forestry Commission Practice Note No. 5, FC, Edinburgh.

Piertney, S.B., Stewart, W.A., Lambin, X., Telfer, S., Aars, J. & Dallas, J.F. (2005). Phylogeographic structure and post-glacial evolutionary history of water voles (*Arvicola terrestris*) in the United Kingdom. *Molecular Ecology* **14** (5): 1435-1444.

Reynolds, J.C. (2003). Mink control in conservation. *Game Conservancy Trust Review* **34**: 42-46.

Rushton, S.P., Lurz, P.W.W., Gurnell, J., Nettleton, P., Breummer, C., Shirley, M.D.F. & Sainsbury, A.W. (2006). Disease threats posed by alien species: the role of a poxvirus in the decline of the native red squirrel in Britain. *Epidemiology and Infection* **134**: 521-533.

Strachan, R. & Moorhouse, T. (2006). *Water Vole Conservation Handbook.* (Second edition). WildCru, Oxford.

Sainsbury, A.W., Nettleton, P., Gilray, J. & Gurnell, J. (2000). Grey squirrels have high seroprevalence to a parapoxvirus associated with deaths in red squirrels. *Animal Conservation* **3**: 229-233.

Scottish Natural Heritage. (2004). *Strategy for Red Squirrel Conservation*. SNH, Edinburgh.

Scottish Natural Heritage. (2006). *Scottish Red Squirrel Action Plan 2006-2011*. SNH, Perth.

Scottish Natural Heritage. (2007). *A Five Year Species Action Framework Making a difference for Scotland's Species*. SNH, Perth.

Shorten, M. (1957). Squirrels in England, Wales and Scotland, 1955. *Journal of Animal Ecology* **26**: 287-294.

Sigfússon A.P. & MacLeod, I. (2010). *Mink eradication – comparing Icelandic and Western Isles approaches.* In: Baxter, J.M. & Galbraith, C.A. (Eds) Species Management: Challenges and Solutions for the 21st Century. Edinburgh, TSO Scotland.

Tomkins, D.M., White, A.R. & Boots, M. (2003). Ecological replacement of native red squirrels by invasive greys driven by disease. *Ecology Letters* **6**: 189-196.

UKBAP. (2007). UK List of Priority Species and Habitats. http://www.ukbap.org.uk/NewPriorityList.aspx

Usher, M.B. (1997). Scotland's biodiversity: an overview. In *Biodiversity in Scotland: Status, Trends and Initiatives*, Eds. L.V. Fleming, A.C. Newton, J.A. Vickery & M.B. Usher. Edinburgh: The Stationery Office. pp. 5-20.

Gaywood, M., Cole, M. and Raynor, R. (2010). Terrestrial mammal conservation in Scotland. In: *Species Management: Challenges and Solutions for the 21st Century*, ed. by J.M. Baxter and C.A. Galbraith. TSO Scotland, Edinburgh. pp. 123-144

Chapter 9

Lessons from managing habitats for butterflies and moths

Martin S. Warren[1], Paul Kirkland[2] and Tom Prescott[2]

Summary

1. Butterflies and moths are one of the most rapidly declining groups of wildlife in the UK and over 170 species are listed as Priorities within the UK Biodiversity Action Plan (BAP).
2. The main causes of their decline have been severe habitat loss and changes in habitat management. These have led to long term threats due to habitat fragmentation.
3. Butterflies and moths often occupy specialized niches and are highly sensitive to micro-scale conditions such as vegetation structure and turf height. They are strongly affected by habitat management, e.g. the timing and density of grazing, and type of livestock.
4. Butterflies and moths are also strongly affected by macro-scale conditions, notably the extent and distribution of suitable habitats in the landscape. Many threatened species occur in discrete habitat patches and exist as metapopulations that depend on suites of connected sites across the landscape.
5. The conservation of many, perhaps most, species thus requires a landscape scale approach. The aim is to maintain or restore as much suitable habitat as possible to provide large patches (perhaps tens of hectares for some species), in close proximity, and over as wide an area as possible. Well designed and funded land management schemes are vital to implement such a landscape approach.
6. Butterfly Conservation has currently identified 76 landscapes upon which to focus our conservation work for threatened species in the UK. The growing threat of climate change gives further impetus to a landscape scale approach which increases the resilience of both species and ecosystems.
7. Efforts to conserve threatened butterflies and moths are known to help a wide range of other species, often because issues such as habitat scale and complexity are properly addressed.
8. Butterflies have been adopted as indicators of biodiversity at a UK level and for Scotland and England. They provide us with a cost-effective way of measuring the impact of environmental change, as well as the success or otherwise of conservation measures.

[1] Butterfly Conservation, Manor Yard, East Lulworth, Dorset, BH20 5QP, UK
[2] Butterfly Conservation, Balallan House, Allan Park, Stirling, FK8 2QG, UK

9.1 Introduction

Small pearl-bordered fritillary (*Boloria selene*). © Laurie Campbell/SN

Butterflies and moths together comprise the order Lepidoptera, which is known to be one of the most rapidly declining groups of wildlife (Thomas *et al.*, 2004). For butterflies, two surveys have been completed in Britain and Ireland during the last 30 years. They show that five of our 60 butterfly species have become extinct overall and 71% of the remainder have declined over the last 30 years, many of them severely (Asher *et al.*, 2001; Fox *et al.*, 2006a).

Data on moths show a similar downward trend: 62 species are known to have become extinct during the 20th century (Parsons, 2003) and trends for 337 common species show that a similar number, 70%, are declining (Fox *et al.*, 2006b). Moreover, overall moth numbers have declined by one-third over the last 35 years, raising concerns for species higher in the food chain, such as birds and bats, for which moths are important prey items. The results also show that many species have expanded their range significantly northwards, probably due to climate change.

Based on these data, many new species were added as Priorities in the UK Biodiversity Action Plan (BAP) in 2008 and the current list includes 24 butterflies (almost half of all UK species) and 81 moths. A further 71 widespread but rapidly declining moths are listed as Priorities for research because the causes for their decline are largely unknown.

Detailed autecological research has been conducted on many rare species (e.g. Thomas, 1991; Dennis, 1992) and has identified important lessons for conservation. Butterflies and moths are valuable indicators that help us understand changes in our fauna and flora, and help us predict the impact of environmental factors such as climate change.

9.2 Causes of decline: habitat loss and fragmentation

The causes of decline in butterflies and moths have been well documented and is largely attributable to two main factors: habitat loss and habitat change (including changing management and abandonment) (Asher *et al.*, 2001). The combined effect has exacerbated a third problem, habitat fragmentation, which is only now having a strong impact (see below).

9.3 Specialized niches and the importance of habitat management

9.3.1 Turf height

Butterflies and moths have evolved highly complex and specialized life cycles, and many species use a single or small number of host plants (Asher *et al.,* 2001; see section 9.4.1). However, it is not just the presence of the host plant but the size and surroundings of the host plant that are critical for survival. Some species require host plants growing in open sunny conditions, while others prefer more shaded or overgrown conditions (Thomas, 1991).

In grasslands, turf height is a key factor determining the breeding presence of several butterfly species (Butterflies Under Threat Team, 1986). Some species such as Adonis blue (*Polyommatus bellargus)* and slender Scotch burnet (*Zygaena loti*) require short vegetation, while others such as the Lulworth skipper (*Thymelicus acteon)* require taller vegetation. Other species such as chalkhill blue (*Polyommatus coridon)*, New Forest burnet (*Zygaena viciae*) and marsh fritillary (*Euphydryas aurinia*) require intermediate turf heights (Warren, 1991; Ravenscroft, 1994 a,b, 2003; Brereton *et al.*, 2008).

The preference for short vegetation often seems to be simply temperature related, with thermophilous species requiring shorter vegetation because this can be several degrees warmer than taller vegetation (Thomas, 1991). Some species such as silver-spotted skipper (*Hesperia comma*) go one step further and require patches of bare ground which provides even hotter conditions for larval development (Thomas *et al.*, 1986).

Plate 9.1 Marsh fritillary larval nest in well structured vegetation maintained by cattle grazing. © Paul Kirkland

9.3.2 Selection of other warm micro-habitats

Habitat selection for several threatened species is limited by larval requirements for particular thermal conditions. A major habitat of the heath fritillary (*Mellicta athalia*), a BAP Priority, is within coppiced woodland where it breeds in the early (warmer) stages after coppicing (Warren, 1987). However, adults are relatively sedentary and only colonize new sites if they are within around 600m from an existing colony. Successful conservation thus requires a regular coppice cycle with coupes cut in close proximity for the species to survive. Such conditions would have been provided widely under traditional coppice practice, which has occurred over many centuries in parts of Britain but has now been almost completely abandoned (Rackham, 1990; Warren and Key, 1991).

Two other fritillaries that are typically associated with coppiced woodland or woodland clearings also utilize grassland where *Viola* species grow beneath a canopy of light bracken (*Pteridium aquilinum*) rather than trees. Here the crucial factor is not just the presence of abundant *Viola* species but the presence of dead bracken litter which provides a warm substrate on which the larvae bask in the early spring (Warren, 1994; Bulman *et al.*, 2005). The larvae of the high brown fritillary (*Argynnis adippe*) (BAP Priority) are among the most selective and require a high cover of dead bracken in the spring when temperatures on the dead litter surface can reach almost 20°C above the ambient. The other species is the pearl-bordered fritillary (*Boloria euphrosyne*) which has similar requirements.

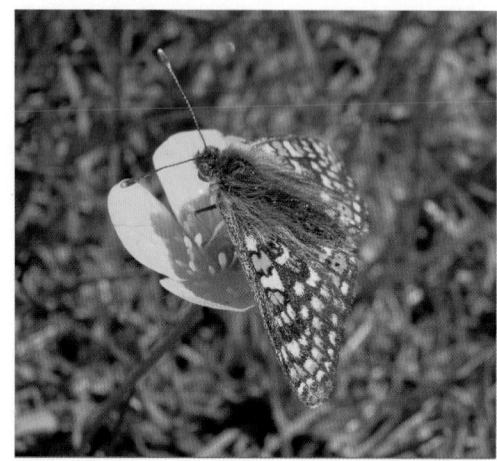

Plate 9.2 Marsh fritillary adult (*Euphydryas aurinia*).
© Paul Kirkland

9.3.3 Plant nutrition and feeding specialization

The nutrient content of the host plant is another factor that can limit a species' breeding niche, with some species selecting hosts growing in slightly more nutrient rich conditions. For example, in Scotland, the chequered skipper (*Carterocephalus palaemon*) (BAP Priority) is restricted to tall vegetation in nutrient-rich flushes where its sole host plant, purple moor-grass (*Molinia caerulea*), has a longer growing season than is typical, which permits full larval development (Ravenscroft, 1994a).

The larvae of the dark-bordered beauty moth (*Epione vespertaria*) (BAP Priority) have also been shown to feed on the fresh, bronzy leaves of short aspen (*Populus tremula*) suckers growing in sunny locations. As these young leaves slowly turn green they are ignored by the larvae in preference for newer fresh bronzy leaves (R. Leverton pers. comm.).

The caterpillars of an estimated 121 moth species feed on birch (*Betula* sp.), but some have very exacting requirements (Young, 1997). The micro-moth *Ancylis tineana* only utilizes very low stunted 'trees' normally less than 20cm tall, whereas the rare day-flying Kentish glory (*Endromis versicolora*) favours young trees up to 2m tall. In contrast the Rannoch sprawler (*Brachionycha nubeculosa*) only exploits old, veteran trees.

Plate 9.3 The dark-bordered beauty (*Epione vespertaria*) is an extremely rare moth whose larvae, in Scotland, feed on low aspen suckers.
© Roy Leverton

9.4 Landscape scale conservation

9.4.1 Habitat specialists vs generalists

Butterflies and moths fall into two very broad ecological groups: habitat specialists and habitat generalists (Asher *et al.*, 2001; Warren *et al.*, 2001). The former tend to be sedentary species that breed on discrete patches of habitat and live in more-or-less closed populations. In contrast, generalists tend to be more mobile species that can move freely through the countryside, exploiting a wider range of resources as they go. Not all species fit easily into these categories and in reality there is probably a continuum with species lying all along the range. However, it is the specialists that have declined most, whereas the generalists have remained stable or have even expanded their ranges.

9.4.2 Metapopulations and implications for conservation

The vast majority of threatened species in the UK are habitat specialists that depend on recognized "habitats" (biotopes) such as unimproved grassland or woodland. However, within these biotopes they typically occupy small breeding areas, which support their specialized life-cycles (e.g. Dennis, 1992). Smaller, more isolated populations that occur on discrete habitat islands are more prone to local extinction and their survival is directly related both to the area of suitable habitat and the proximity of habitats to neighbouring occupied habitats (Thomas *et al.*, 1992 ; Hanski, 1999). In fragmented habitats that predominate in the UK and much of Europe, such species occur as metapopulations whose survival at regional and national level depends on the amount of habitat in the landscape, its suitability and connectedness (Hanski, 1999; Thomas *et al.*, 2001).

9.4.3 Landscape scale conservation

The need to conserve whole metapopulations has important implications for conservation as it requires a landscape scale approach. Successful conservation requires the protection and proper management of suites of adjacent sites that are capable of supporting a metapopulation of a species in the long term.

Butterfly Conservation has developed a strategy that concentrates on 76 key landscapes across the UK, selected because they are national or regional strongholds of BAP Priority Species (Figure 9.1). A key feature of these projects is that they rely on the close cooperation of a wide consortium of conservation organizations, landowners, agencies and volunteers.

The minimum viable size of a suite of sites to support a metapopulation is poorly known and has only been estimated by careful observations and modelling in a small number of species. Bulman *et al.* (2007) have estimated that, in fragmented landscapes, the marsh fritillary may require a network of patches of

Key to Figure 9.1 map (opposite)

1 Moray Firth
2 Badenoch and Strathspey
3 Lochaber
4 Upper Deeside
5 Mull
6 Lorne
7 Highland Perthshire
8 Islay
9 Mid-Argyll and Knapdale
10 Solway Coast and Hinterland
11 County Fermanagh
12 County Down
13 Harlech
14 Clocaenog Forest
15 Oswestry Uplands
16 Mynydd Mawr
17 South Wales Coal Measures
18 High Brown Brackenlands
19 North Cumbria
20 Durham Coalfield Pennine Fringe
21 North East Brownfields
22 S. Cumbria Low Fells and Morecambe Bay Limestones
23 Yorkshire Dales
24 North York Moors
25 North Shropshire and Staffordshire Mosses
26 Notts/Derby Coalfields Brownfields
27 South Shropshire Metal Mines
28 Telford and Wrekin Brownfields
29 Cannock Chase
30 Ketton Limestone Area Brownfields
31 Norfolk Heaths
32 Norfolk Broads
33 South Shropshire Wet Flushes and Rush Pastures
34 S. Shropshire and N. Herefordshire Woodlands
35 Black Country Brownfields
36 Wyre Forest
37 North Warwickshire Brownfields
38 Princethorpe Woodlands
39 Peterborough Brownfields
40 Cut off Channel
41 The Brecks
42 Suffolk Coast and Heaths (inc Sandlings)
43 Herefordshire Commons
44 Herefordshire Woodlands
45 Malvern Hills
46 Southam Lias Grasslands
47 Cambridge Elm Belt
48 Cambs and Essex Chalk Grasslands
49 Forest of Dean
50 The Cotswolds
51 Bedfordshire Chilterns
52 Bedfordshire Brownfields
53 Hertfordshire Chalk Grassland
54 Hertfordshire Quarries
55 South Essex Woodlands
56 Langdon Hills, South Essex
57 North Cornwall Coast
58 Mid Cornwall Moors
59 Tamar Valley
60 Two Moors Project
61 Reconnecting the Culm
62 Blackdown Hills (Neroche Project)
63 Polden Hills
64 Cranborne Chase and Wessex Downs
65 Blackmoor Vale
66 Salisbury Plain
67 Tytherley Woods
68 New Forest
69 Thames Basin Heaths
70 Surrey/Sussex Woods West Weald
71 Ashdown Forest
72 Rother Woods
73 Dungeness/Romney Marsh
74 Blean Woods
75 Denge Woods
76 Sandwich Bay

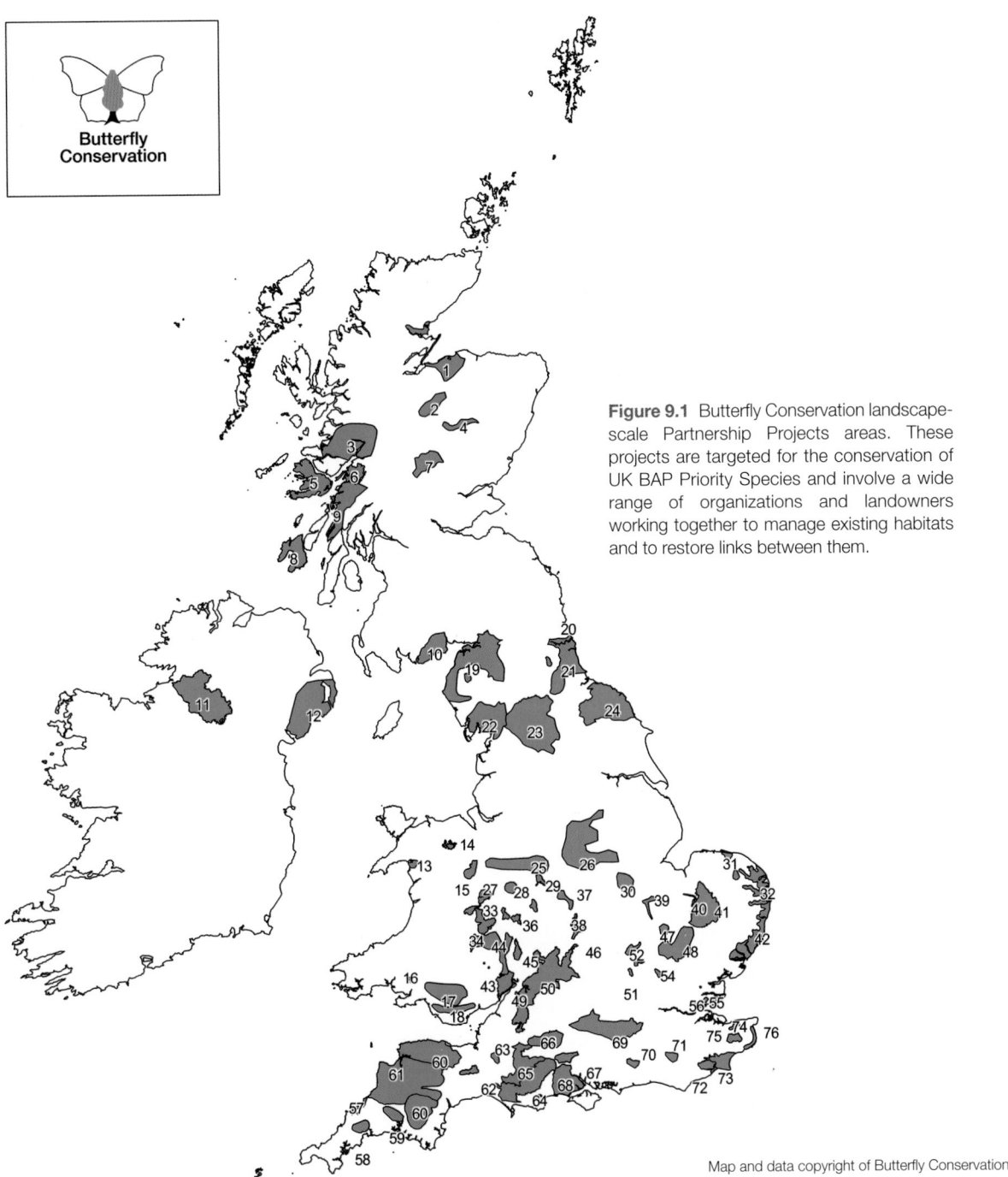

Figure 9.1 Butterfly Conservation landscape-scale Partnership Projects areas. These projects are targeted for the conservation of UK BAP Priority Species and involve a wide range of organizations and landowners working together to manage existing habitats and to restore links between them.

Map and data copyright of Butterfly Conservation 2009

collectively up to 70 ha of habitat to ensure long term survival, and that habitat patches must be within 5-10 km to allow successful recolonization. Such parameters are vital to understand how to target conservation effort and ensure that habitat restoration is aimed at recreating suitable links between nearby sites. Because information is lacking for most species, the general aim for now is to maintain or restore as much suitable habitat as possible, to provide large patches (perhaps tens of hectares for some species), in close proximity, and over as wide an area as possible.

The understanding of metapopulations brings a further dilemma for conservationists as many sites that are currently occupied by threatened species may be below the threshold of size and isolation for a species to survive in the long term. However, such sites probably contain important habitats for other species and could play a vital role in the future of the threatened species concerned (e.g. if conditions improve as a result of climate change). For these sites, habitat restoration becomes the priority to make the whole habitat network more viable for more species.

9.4.4 Understanding the matrix

Most metapopulation studies focus on the configuration of breeding habitat within the landscape and take little account of the nature of the intervening land; the matrix of the landscape. However, there is currently very little information on how the structure and composition of the matrix affects the movement of specialist butterflies and consequently the functioning of their metapopulations.

Although it is obvious that the nature of the matrix is important to some wildlife, evidence so far suggests that it has little effect on metapopulations of threatened butterflies. Some species seem to ignore linear features in the landscape and it is the proximity of habitats that is the key feature, rather than the nature of the matrix itself (Thomas and Jones, 1993; Ries and Debinski, 2001; Dover and Settele, 2009).

A key factor is how a species behaves when it leaves its original habitat patches. So far most studies have been done on mobile generalist butterflies but even here the picture is unclear as some species follow linear features such as hedges, while others ignore them (Dover and Settele, 2009). Recent reviews of the functioning of corridors for other insects have shown an equally variable response with some species benefitting and others not (e.g. Boitani et al., 2007; Ockinger and Smith, 2008). A better understanding of the matrix is thus an important area for future research.

9.5 Case studies in landscape scale conservation

9.5.1 Marsh fritillary on Islay

The marsh fritillary is a BAP Priority Species that is threatened across Europe (Van Swaay and Warren, 1999), and is listed on Annex II of the EU Habitats and Species Directive. One of its UK strongholds is on Islay, one of the larger Argyll Islands, characterized by large areas of moorland, pasture, dunes and coastal heath. The sole butterfly host-plant, devil's-bit scabious (*Succisa pratensis*), is widespread and abundant in a variety of semi-natural habitats across the island, but the butterfly is associated with areas

Plate 9.4 Butterfly Conservation is targeting effort at key landscapes for Lepidoptera, such as this extensive marsh fritillary habitat on Islay.
© Paul Kirkland

that are extensively grazed by cattle and sheep with a turf height of 5-20 cm (Ravenscroft, 2003). Marsh fritillary populations on Islay are highly volatile, with explosions in some years when it is found in abundance across the island, and contractions to apparent core areas in others (Ravenscroft, 2003).

Butterfly Conservation has been working to raise the profile of the butterfly on the island (and elsewhere in Argyll), primarily through habitat management workshops for farmers and countryside staff, and survey and monitoring days for volunteers. We are now working with Scottish Agricultural College staff and others to help farmers enter the new Scottish agri-environment scheme under the appropriate tiers. However, there seem to be problems with eligibility of sites submitted purely on biodiversity reasons because the scoring system makes it difficult for such sites to qualify.

9.5.2 Reconnecting the culm (Devon)

The culm grasslands of Devon are a series of damp grasslands and moors, bordered by thick hedgerows and sallow carr woodland. The habitat has been greatly reduced in extent over the last 100 years by agricultural intensification, so that only 20% of the original area of culm remains. Despite these losses, the region is another UK stronghold of the marsh fritillary and provides a test case of how to conserve the species in a highly fragmented landscape (Burgess et al., 2008).

Butterfly Conservation had a dedicated Project Officer in the region for three years, from 2005-8, providing advice on habitat management to land managers and landowners. Four areas were prioritized with concentrations of colonies and areas of potential habitat to link nearby key sites. Over the three years, 782 ha of culm grassland were brought into favourable condition for the marsh fritillary by entering land into the Environmental Stewardship Scheme (Burgess et al., 2008). A further 111 ha were restored to provide strategic links between key sites, and agreements covering a further 700 ha of land are currently being processed.

The project has led to a wide range of benefits including increased area of culm grassland habitat and better viability of the Culm Natural Network; improved chances of survival of BAP Priority Species; and recommendations for the refinement of Environmental Stewardship schemes. The response of the marsh fritillary will be closely monitored in coming years as the project is integrated into a wider project run by the Devon Wildlife Trust.

9.5.3 Dark-bordered beauty

Aspen is the main breeding habitat of many threatened species including three BAP Species that have very differing requirements; the dark-bordered beauty requires short aspen suckers; the aspen bristle moss (*Orthotricum obtusifolium*) favours mature trees; and the aspen hoverfly (*Hammerschmidtia ferruginea*) breeds under the bark of freshly dead aspen trees. The future of these three flagship species lies in increasing and linking the currently isolated small aspen stands in the Scottish Highlands (Cosgrove and Amphlett, 2002).

This is being achieved through a partnership overseen by the Highland Aspen Group that has brought together many individuals and organizations, including Butterfly Conservation, to promote aspen and its

Plate 9.5 Young, bronze coloured aspen growth used by larvae of dark-bordered beauty. © Paul Kirkland

Plate 9.6 Dark-bordered beauty larvae. © Roy Leverton

conservation (Cosgrove *et al.*, 2005). Aerial surveys have identified gaps in the network that need to be filled and an aspen tree nursery run by volunteers is now producing trees of local provenance to help bridge these gaps. The resulting formation of large ecological units means that each network can provide the necessary specialized requirements for each of the three BAP Species (Highland Aspen Group, in prep.).

9.5.4. Slender Scotch burnet

With funding from Scottish Natural Heritage's Species Action Framework, Butterfly Conservation Scotland is working with landowners to restore habitats for the slender Scotch burnet on Mull. Over many decades the intensity of land management on the Ardmeanach Peninsula has been declining, leading to widespread encroachment of scrub and bracken over former species-rich grassland that was once occupied by the moth.

The slender Scotch burnet now occupies about a dozen or so habitat patches with varying degrees of isolation from one another mainly along coastal undercliffs (Ravenscroft, 1994b). Most of these patches are very small, some just a few 100m^2. Coordinated work at all extant sites is currently underway in order to reconnect these sub-populations to increase their size and viability and to control invasive cotoneaster.

9.6 Links with other taxa

There is a legitimate concern amongst conservationists as to whether efforts to save one particular group of threatened species will help or hinder any others. Fortunately, there is a growing body of evidence that conservation measures for butterflies and moths are leading to the effective conservation of a wide range of other rare and threatened species.

A good example is the large blue (*Maculinea arion*), which has been the subject of a major re-establishment programme that includes the restoration of its unimproved grassland habitat in south-west England. Habitat restoration involves scrub and tree removal followed by grazing to restore flower-rich grassland with the larval host plant, wild thyme (*Thymus* sp.) and the correct host ant, *Myrmica sabuleti* (Thomas, 1999). The results have been impressive with over 15 large blue populations now established in three regions, with a total of over 10,000 adults. Other taxa have increased substantially in response to the new management, including other butterflies such as high brown and pearl-bordered fritillaries and invertebrates such as the hornet robber-fly (*Asilus crabroniformis*), green tiger-beetle (*Cicindela campestris*) and western bee-fly (*Bombylius canescens*). Birds such as the woodlark (*Lullula arborea*) and plants such as the pale dog-violet (*Viola lactea*) have also increased (J. A. Thomas, unpublished data).

In coppiced woodlands, management for the heath fritillary in Kent has helped the very rare cow-wheat shield bug (*Sehrius bigutatus*), while management for the pearl-bordered fritillary in Sussex has helped a suite of moths that utilize young and middle-aged coppice, including other UKBAP species such as the waved carpet moth (*Hydrelia sylvata*) (Clarke, 2003).

Several rare fritillaries require cattle and pony grazing in moorland fringe habitats on Dartmoor and Exmoor. The maintenance of such conditions is thought to be essential to conserve other Priority invertebrates such as the southern damselfly (*Coenagrion mercuriale*), blue ground beetle (*Carabus intricate*) and Kugelann's ground beetle (*Poecilus kugelanni*) (P. Boyd, pers.comm.).

The efforts to save the marsh fritillary on the Devon culm grasslands are also having a major impact not just on the conservation of this internationally rare habitat type but also a wide range of other UKBAP species such as double line moth (*Mythimna turca*), narrow-bordered bee hawk-moth (*Hemaris tityus*), southern damselfly (*Ceonagrion mercuriale*), dormouse *(Muscardinus avellanarius)* and otter (*Lutra lutra*).

In Scotland, the dark-bordered beauty is serving as a very useful flagship species for aspen woodland (see above). Management for the pearl-bordered fritillary and chequered skipper in Scotland will benefit many other species that require open clearings within woodland, including black grouse *(Tetrao tetrix)*, moths, wood ants, dragonflies, flowering plants and lichens. Such management can also be beneficial to archaeological sites and in the provision of access.

9.7 Butterflies and moths as indicators

Butterflies are widely regarded as good biodiversity indicators because they respond rapidly to changes in environment and habitat management, and because they occur in a wide range of habitats. They are also representative of many other insects, which collectively account for more than 50% of terrestrial UK wildlife species. Butterflies can play a complementary role to birds as an indicator, because they use the landscape at a far finer scale.

Butterflies have recently been adopted as indicators both at the UK level (www.jncc.gov.uk/page-4229) and within Scotland (www.snh.org.uk/trends) and England (www.defra.gov.uk/environment/statistics/wildlife/kf). The trends in butterfly abundance shown by the indicators make use of the UK Butterfly Monitoring Scheme which compiles trends from over 850 sites. Separate trends in butterfly abundance can also now be generated for different habitats, such as farmland and woodland. Butterflies thus provide a valuable way of measuring the impact of environmental change as well as the success of conservation measures in the future.

9.8 Conclusions

Studies on Lepidoptera have provided important lessons to conservation, mainly focused around the question of scale.

Lepidoptera are highly sensitive to habitat management on a fine scale, usually determined by their requirement for specific niches. They are especially sensitive to habitat structure often determined by grazing levels and type of grazing animal. Such factors need to be taken into account in the design of agri-environment schemes and forestry grant schemes as well as the management of reserves and Sites of Special Scientific Interest.

Lepidoptera also require conservation on a macro, or landscape, scale in order to survive in the long term. The science of metapopulation biology has taught us that the configuration of semi-natural habitats in the landscape is vital to the conservation of most threatened species. In general terms, we need habitats to be better managed and linked.

A major gap in our understanding is that of the importance of the precise structure and composition of the matrix of land between habitat patches. Further research is needed as to whether we should pay more attention to this in landscape scale projects.

Landscape scale conservation is vital for the survival of many species but is even more important as the climate changes and exacerbates the problems of habitat fragmentation facing many species. Landscape conservation will help buffer such adverse impacts and make habitats, and thus species, more resilient to change.

A vital question is how landscape conservation can be resourced on a sufficient scale to conserve species in the long term. The growing impact of climate change should make us renew our efforts for landscape-scale conservation, and ensure improved and carefully targeted agri-environment and other schemes are adequately funded through the Common Agricultural Policy or its successor.

9.9 Acknowledgements

We would like to thank our many funders especially Scottish Natural Heritage, Forestry Commission Scotland, Natural England, Countryside Council for Wales, the Northern Ireland Environment Agency, the Esmée Fairbairn Foundation, the Tubney Trust, and the Heritage Lottery Fund. We are also extremely grateful for the enthusiasm and support of our many volunteers and the cooperation of many landowners, and to Bernadette Noake and Amber Rosenthal for compiling the landscape map.

References

Asher, J., Warren, M., Fox, R., Harding, P., Jeffcoate, G. & Jeffcoate. S. (2001). *The Millennium Atlas of butterflies in Britain and Ireland*. Oxford University Press, Oxford.

Boitani, L., Falcucci, A., Maiorano, L. & Rondinini, C. (2007). Ecological networks as conceptual frameworks or operational tools in conservation. *Conservation Biology* **21**: 1414-1422.

Brereton, T. M., Warren, M. S., Roy, D. B. & Stewart, K. (2008). The changing status of the Chalkhill Blue butterfly *Polyommatus coridon* in the UK: the impacts of conservation policies and environmental factors. *Journal of Insect Conservation* **12**: 629-638.

Bulman, C., Joy, J. & Bourn, N. (2005). *Bracken for Butterflies*. Butterfly Conservation leaflet, Wareham.

Bulman, C.R., Wilson, R.J., Holt, A.R., Bravo, L.G., Early, R.I., Warren, M.S. & Thomas, C.D. (2007). Minimum viable metapopulation size, extinction debt, and the conservation of a declining species. *Ecological Applications* **17(5)**: 1460–1473.

Burgess, P., Bulman, C.R., Bourn N. & Warren M.S. (2008). The Re-Connecting the Culm Project: methods and achievements 2005 – 2008. Report No: S08-24, Butterfly Conservation, Wareham.

Butterflies Under Threat Team (BUTT). (1986). The management of chalk downland for butterflies. Focus on Nature Conservation series, No.17. Nature Conservancy Council, Peterborough.

Clarke, S. A. (2003). The Waved Carpet moth *Hydrelia sylvata*: Coppice woodland survey 2002. Report No. S03-15 Butterfly Conservation, Wareham.

Cosgrove, P. & Amphlett, A. (Eds). (2002). *The Biodiversity and Management of Aspen Woodlands*. Proceedings of a one-day conference held at Kingussie, Scotland on 25th May 2001.

Cosgrove, P., Amphlett, A., Elliott, A., Ellis, C., Emmett, E., Prescott, T. & Featherstone, A. (2005). Aspen – Britain's missing link with the boreal forest. *British Wildlife* **17** (No.2): 107-115.

Dennis, R.L.H. (Ed.). (1992). *The ecology of butterflies in Britain*. Oxford University Press.

Dover, J. & Settele, J. (2009). The influences of landscape structure on butterfly distribution and movement: a review. *Journal of Insect Conservation* **13**: 3-27.

Fox, R., Asher, J., Brereton, T., Roy, D. & Warren, M. (2006a). *The state of butterflies in Britain and Ireland*. Pisces Publications, Newbury.

Fox, R., Conrad, K.F., Parsons, M., Warren, M.S. & Woiwod, I.P. (2006b). *The state of Britain's larger moths*. Butterfly Conservation and Rothamsted Research, Wareham, Dorset.

Hanski, I. (1999). *Metapopulation ecology*. Oxford University Press, New York.

Highland Aspen Group. (in prep.). *Aspen in Scotland – Biodiversity and management. The second Scottish Aspen Conference.* Proceedings of a two-day conference held at Boat of Garten, Scotland, 3-4 October 2008.

Ockinger, E. O. & Smith, H. G. (2008). Do corridors promote dispersal in grassland butterflies and other insects? *Landscape Ecology* **23**: 27–40.

Parsons, M.S. (2003). The changing moth fauna of Britain during the twentieth century. *Entomologist's Record and Journal of Variation* **115**: 49-66.

Pollard, E. & Yates, T.J. (1993). *Monitoring butterflies for ecology and conservation*. Chapman and Hall, London.

Rackham, O. (1990). *Trees and woodlands in the British landscape* (revised edition). Dent, London.

Ravenscroft, N. O. M. (1994a). The ecology of the Chequered Skipper butterfly *Carterocephalus palaemon* Pallas in Scotland. *Journal of Applied Ecology* **31**: 613-630.

Ravenscroft, N. O. M. (1994b). The enigma of the burnet moths of Western Scotland. *British Wildlife* **5**: 222-228.

Ravenscroft, N. O. M. (2003). Marsh Fritillary Survey 2002 Final Report. Contract Report to Scottish Natural Heritage, Edinburgh.

Ries, L. & Debinski, D. M. (2001). Butterfly responses to habitat edges in the highly fragmented prairies of Central Iowa. *Journal of Animal Ecology* **70**: 840-852.

Thomas, C. D. & Jones, T. M. (1993). Partial recovery of a skipper butterfly (*Hesperia comma*) from a population refuge: lessons for conservation in a fragmented landscape. *Journal of Animal Ecology* **62**: 472-481.

Thomas, C. D., Thomas, J. A. & Warren, M. S. (1992). Distributions of occupied and vacant butterfly habitats in fragmented landscapes. *Oecologia* **92**: 563-567.

Thomas, J.A. (1991). Rare species conservation: butterfly case studies. In: *The scientific management of temperate communities for conservation*. Eds I.F. Spellerburg, F.B. Goldsmith and M.G. Morris. Blackwell Scientific, Oxford, pp149-198.

Thomas, J. A. (1999). The Large Blue butterfly – a decade of progress. *British Wildlife* **1**: 22-27.

Thomas, J.A. (2005). Monitoring change in the abundance and distribution of insects using butterflies and other indicator groups. *Philosophical Transactions of the Royal Society (B)* **360**: 339-357.

Thomas, J. A., Thomas, C. D., Simcox, D. J. & Clarke, R. T. (1986). The ecology and declining status of the silver-spotted skipper butterfly *(Hesperia comma)* in Britain. *Journal of Applied Ecology* **23**: 365-380.

Thomas, J. A, Bourn, N. A. D., Clarke, R. T., Stewart, K. E., Simcox, D. J., Pearman, G. S., Curtis, R. & Goodger, B. (2001). The quality and isolation of habitat patches both determine where butterflies persist in fragmented landscapes. *Proceedings of the Royal Society (B)* **268**: 1791-1796.

Thomas, J.A., Telfer, M.G., Roy, D.B., Preston, C.D., Greenwood, J.J.D., Asher, J., Fox, R., Clarke, R.T. & Lawton, J.H. (2004). Comparative losses of British butterflies, birds, and plants and the global extinction crisis. *Science* **303**:1879–1881.

Van Swaay, C.A.M. & Warren M.S. (1999). *Red Data Book of European Butterflies (Rhopalocera)*. Nature and Environment No. 99, Council of Europe Publishing, Strasbourg.

Warren, M. S. (1987). The ecology and conservation of the heath fritillary butterfly, *Mellicta athalia*. *Journal of Animal Ecology* **24**: 467-583.

Warren, M. S. (1991). The successful conservation of an endangered species, *Mellicta athalia* (the heath fritillary butterfly), in Britain. *Biological Conservation* **55**:37-56.

Warren, M. S. (1993). A review of butterfly conservation in central southern Britain. *Biological Conservation* **64**: 25-49.

Warren, M. S. (1994). The UK status and metapopulation structure of a threatened European butterfly, *Eurodryas aurinia* (the marsh fritillary). *Biological Conservation* **67**: 239-249.

Warren, M. S. & Key, R.S. (1991). Woodlands: past, present and potential for insects. In: Collins, N.M. and Thomas, J.A. (Eds). *The conservation of insects and their habitats.* Academic Press, London, pp155-211.

Warren, M.S., Hill, J.K., Thomas, J.A., Asher, J., Fox, R., Huntley, B., Roy, D.B., Telfer, M.G., Jeffcoate, S., Harding, P., Jeffcoate, G., Willis, S.G., Greatorex-Davies, J.N., Moss, D. & Thomas, C.D. (2001). Rapid responses of British butterflies to opposing forces of climate and habitat change. *Nature* **414**: 65–69.

Young, M.R. (1997). *The Natural History of Moths.* Poyser, London.

Warren, M.S., Kirkland, P. and Prescott, T. (2010). Lessons from managing habitats for butterflies and moths. In: *Species Management: Challenges and Solutions for the 21st Century*, ed. by J.M. Baxter and C.A. Galbraith. TSO Scotland, Edinburgh. pp. 145-160

Part 3

Dealing with invasive non-native species

The spread of invasive non-native species was identified by the Millennium Ecosystem Assessment, published in 2005, as one of the key threats to biodiversity worldwide. Many species, of both plant and animal, have been moved around the world by man, especially over recent decades, altering the balance of native biodiversity in numerous countries. The impact of invasive non-native species continues to increase, both in terms of the number of species involved and in the severity of the problems they are causing. The potential for serious economic impact in future years caused by the spread of alien species cannot be ignored. Indeed, there are already billions of US dollars being spent to control just one invasive non-native species, the zebra mussel (*Dreissena polymorpha)* that has invaded freshwater habitats in North America. Worryingly, the signs are that climate change has the potential to exacerbate such problems by allowing some species to spread in a more vigorous fashion than before.

This section of the book illustrates that the problem of alien species transcends many ecosystem types, and that it will require large scale, and expensive measures to control or eradicate even some of the species causing harm. Options for the management of alien species are reviewed, drawing out the principles involved, considering case studies and looking to future mechanisms for the control or eradication of invasive non-native species.

David Macdonald and his co-authors highlight the global nature of the problem, stressing the need for detailed studies into the ecology of the species involved. They argue that it is only with a detailed understanding of the issues involved, that long-lasting solutions can be developed. They categorize the impacts of these species as predating or grazing on native animals or plants, competition, spreading disease, or in some cases hybridization with native species. These are all important and complex problems, and with the added need for researchers to investigate solutions in the context of a changing climate and other land-use and management shifts, finding lasting solutions will be difficult. Whilst the problems are complex, solutions do need to be found and speed is of the essence.

As with much of science and ecology, not everyone agrees that invasive alien species are always a problem, highlighting that there may be regional and local variations around the world in terms of the severity of the problem. The impact may vary between species groups in some countries; hence developing a better understanding of their patterns of distribution becomes important in helping to focus effort and to give some context for any control programme. Chris Preston outlines his doubts about the degree of threat to global plant biodiversity, suggesting that specific assessments are needed to better quantify the problem. He suggests that there is, in fact, a lack of evidence to support ideas of native species loss due to invasive alien species. He suggests that efforts of control and eradication in Scotland should be concentrated on known problem issues such as the spread of *Rhododendron ponticum*.

One of the key themes of this book is to draw examples from a range of countries, and learn from what has been done elsewhere. Ingrid Salvesen and her co-authors, outline the situation in Norway, where 2485 alien species have been recorded. Of this staggering total, 70% are vascular plants. A risk assessment, reviewing the potential for the species to become invasive, has been completed for 215 species out of this total. In a novel development, since 2007 the Norwegian Government have published a "Black List" of alien species found in the country. This provides documentary evidence of what is happening and serves to highlight the changing pattern of invasion. Studies have revealed that many of the alien species concerned have reached Norway via land-based industry, mainly by the import of plants or plant material. Importantly, systematic study of the economic impact of invasive alien species has yet to be undertaken.

Phil Boon and Colin Bean then outline the key issues in relation to the freshwater environment. They suggest that the presence of invasive non-native species is a major problem and, as in previous chapters of this book, suggest that a detailed understanding is needed of the species and habitats involved. They record that a variety of techniques have been tried in order to control or eradicate species, although none have been completely successful; and suggest that it would be much more effective to prevent the introduction of the species in the first place, rather than to spend large sums of money in partially successful control measures after the species has become established. They conclude by noting the enormous scale of the task ahead if the problem of invasive non-native species is to be tackled in a coordinated and effective way.

The damage to our native biodiversity from predation by the North American mink (*Neovison vison*) is perhaps one of the most widely publicized problems caused by alien species. This species has escaped from "fur farms" in many parts of the world, and has proved itself to be an adaptable and resourceful species, establishing populations in many areas. Arnór Sigfússon and Iain Macleod discuss the effectiveness of mink control programmes in Iceland and in Scotland. Work in Scotland has concentrated on controlling mink on the Western Isles, with excellent progress being made in the complete eradication of the species from some of the islands concerned. This has been achieved after considerable effort and a high degree of commitment from the field-workers involved. Given these early successes it now appears possible to eradicate mink from the whole island chain. This would be a huge achievement, illustrating the value of a coordinated, holistic and determined approach. Work in Iceland is focusing on a five year experiment to compare trapping techniques in order to evaluate the costs and techniques that would be involved in any wider control programme. The chapter illustrates the real value of cooperation between these two projects and serves to highlight how effective control activity can be.

Finally in this section David Donnan and Fiona Manson review the threats caused by invasive non-native species in the marine environment. This environment really is very vulnerable to invasion by such species, and, given its scale, it is daunting to consider what could happen in the future and to see how any problems could be tackled. Significantly, many of the introductions appear to have arrived here as a result of human activity, mainly by shipping, carrying species over huge distances around the world. The chapter notes that much of the impact so far has been on biodiversity, rather than having any major economic impact. It is important to view this in the context of climate change, however, where different climate regimes may, in the future, allow greater spread and impact of species. The chapter focuses on the arrival of the wireweed (*Sargassum muticum)* to Scotland, and suggests that high profile public awareness and education campaigns are needed to alert people to the spread of this and other invasive non-native species.

Chapter 10

Invasives: global lessons and local perspectives

David W. Macdonald[1], Rosalind F. Shaw[1] & Tom P. Moorhouse[1]

Summary

1. Malign invasive species are found across the globe and in a huge range of habitats, making them one of the great threats to biodiversity today. Efforts to deal with invasive species can be hampered by differences in the terminology used to describe them, and inconsistencies in the attitudes and ideologies of varying groups and institutions towards different invasive species.
2. Understanding the characteristics of invasive species is crucial for both predicting which introduced species are likely to become invasive and their possible impacts. While the impacts of invasive species are specific to each habitat, their general impacts can be divided into: i) effects of predation or herbivory; ii) effects of competition; iii) effects of disease and; iv) effects of hybridization. Finally, invasive species may cause cascading chain effects or result in the loss of a keystone species, leading to ecosystem level impacts.
3. Neither the issues raised by invasive species, nor solutions to the problems they pose are straightforward. Curative approaches can be prohibitively expensive and need to consider not only the cost and feasibility of their objectives, but also the likely ecological outcome. This is further complicated by a human dimension to removing species which, in some cases, may form an important part of peoples' enjoyment of nature. Prevention of the establishment of invasive species is an ongoing challenge and needs to be considered within the context of curative approaches.
4. The need for understanding the possible impacts of invasive species is likely to increase due to the potential for future climate change. Climate change will probably not only alter the interactions between established, introduced and invasive species but will increase the number of colonizers, leading to further ethical conundrums concerning how to deal with species taking advantage of a human-induced process.

[1] Wildlife Conservation Research Unit, Recanati-Kaplan Centre, University of Oxford, Department of Zoology, Tubney House, Tubney, Oxfordshire, OX13 5QL, UK

American signal crayfish (*Pasifastacus leniusculus*). © Astrid Willer

10.1 Introduction

The introduction, by humans, of species to areas beyond their geographical range has consequences ranging from minor to major impacts on ecosystems, economics and even human health. Non-native species have been transported to every continent on the globe, including Antarctica (Frenot *et al.*, 2005). The majority of introduced species may simply be imported, never to become established (Williamson, 1996). A rule of thumb is that 10% of introduced species will become established, and of those 10%, a further 10% will become a pest ('the tens rule', Williamson, 1993).

The terms used to refer to introduced and invasive species vary from author to author. Indeed, not only is the language used to describe these species frequently inconsistent, and therefore potentially misleading, but also the core ideology surrounding treatment of invasives can differ, depending upon the species, authors and institutions involved. For the purposes of this paper, the word 'invasive' is used to describe those introduced species that have colonised large areas, or reached large numbers in areas other than their original habitats or range. Our use of the word 'invasive' contains no implication regarding whether the effects of those species are positive or negative: invasive species do not necessarily have a negative impact, but those which do ('malign invasives', or 'invasive alien species' in the language of the Convention on Biological Diversity; Secretariat of the Convention on Biological Diversity, 2007) can have dramatic effects, resulting in the loss of native species or alteration to ecosystem function. The extent of these impacts is such that invasive species are considered one of the greatest threats to biodiversity (Vitousek *et al.*, 1997; Chapin *et al.*, 2000), although measuring both the extent of a threat and its relative importance (commonly by assessing the number of vulnerable species at risk from a particular threat) is a process also hampered by both lack of data and inconsistency in terminology (for example, Coutts-Smith *et al.*, 2007).

10.2 What makes a successful invasive species?

The science behind understanding what causes a species to be invasive, and the impacts that invasives have on their host community, are likely to become increasingly important in the light of increased human movements around the globe. Given that many species do not become established (a self-sustaining population), or become established but not invasive (a self-sustaining population, but one which is not spreading and colonising new areas), what is different about the ones that do? This question has prompted several decades of research, leading to a few general rules. A successful malign invasive is likely to have an r-selected life strategy (including characteristics such as the ability to use pioneer habitats, short generation time, high fecundity, environmental tolerance and dietary plasticity) or the ability to switch between r and k strategies (Kolar and Lodge, 2001). For an invasive to become established also requires its new habitat to be susceptible to invasion. Habitats which are in early successional stages, disturbed or which contain low biodiversity are thought to be more vulnerable to invasion

(Diamond and Case, 1986; Lodge, 1993). If an introduced species has come from a climate similar to that of their new habitat they are also more likely to thrive (Diamond and Case, 1986; Lodge, 1993). The presence of species which occupy similar ecological niches may prevent invasion by a species (Lack, 1947) but possibly only if the native species has a competitive advantage, as the widespread decline of the European mink in the presence of the very similar, but slightly larger, introduced American mink has shown (Macdonald *et al.*, 2002a). Release from their native predators and diseases may allow introduced species to reproduce more successfully than similar native species in a new area (Maron and Vila, 2001), but in turn, encountering novel diseases and predators may have severe negative impacts (Moyle, 1986; Newsome and Noble, 1986). One of the most important factors in a successful invasion appears to be the number of individuals introduced; the more individuals and incidences of introduction there are, the more likely it is that the introduced species will find a toehold in a new environment (Forsyth and Duncan, 2001; Forsyth *et al.*, 2004). In some cases the establishment of an introduced species is seen as a desirable outcome: classical biological control programmes, which involve introducing a non-native species to control pest species (Eilenberg *et al.*, 2001), are sometimes considered a favourable option by environmentalists, when compared to the application of polluting chemicals.

Plate 10.1 American mink (*Neovison vison*) which has been introduced to Europe. © Sugoto Roy

Plate 10.2 European mink (*Mustela lutreola*) is in decline in areas where American mink has colonized. © Antti Below

10.3 Ecological effects of endangered species

The ecological effects of invasive species can be complex, and generalizations beyond those listed above can be difficult to draw (Macdonald et al., 2007). In general, however, the negative impacts on native flora and fauna can be classified into: 1) effects from predation and herbivory; 2) effects from competition; 3) effects of associated novel pathogens and parasites and; 4) effects of hybridizations. We describe these effects on a case-by-case basis, below.

10.3.1 Effects of predation/herbivory

Predation is the cause of approximately one third of the documented negative impacts of invasive animals (Macdonald and Thom, 2001). However, it is worth noting that predation is also relatively easy to detect and quantify, compared to the more insidious effects of competition and hybridization (below), which can take place over a much longer time scale.

Carnivores comprise 19% of mammalian introductions, a large proportion considering that they comprise 5% of the total number of mammalian species (Macdonald and Thom, 2001). The impacts of predators on native populations vary greatly, dependent upon the characteristics of the prey, the predator and the other biotic and abiotic conditions that form the species' habitat. For example, a large, high altitude breeding colony of Hutton's shearwaters (*Puffinus huttoni*) in New Zealand has survived the presence of stoats (*Mustela ermina*) for over 100 years, when they have had a devastating impact on smaller, low altitude colonies (Holdaway, 1999). At high altitude, stoat populations remain relatively small due to the lack of food outside the shearwater breeding season (Cuthbert and Davis, 2002). The relatively low numbers of stoats, combined with the large size of the shearwater colony results in the stoats reducing the annual productivity by less than 1% a year, allowing the population to persist (Cuthbert and Davis, 2002).

Where habitats are degraded, the effects of predators may be more pronounced. For example, the quantity of riparian vegetation available is the major determinant of a number of demographic factors in populations of water voles (*Arvicola terrestris*) - a UK small mammal species - including growth rates, survival rates, population densities and range sizes (Moorhouse et al., 2008; Moorhouse and Macdonald, 2008). Previously such vegetation has offered a refuge from predators, allowing water voles to remain concealed in tall grasses, swim away or hide in their burrows. The invasive American mink (*Neovison vison*), however, can hunt them in all of these refuges, and the reduction of lowland riparian habitat to narrow riverside strips by agricultural conversion enhanced the susceptibility of water voles to predation, leading to a drastic decline in numbers across the UK (Macdonald and Strachan, 1999). The individual effects of mink predation and habitat loss are difficult to separate. A recent study investigating the impact of habitat quality upon reintroduction success in water voles concluded that the primary determinant of reintroduction success was sufficient mink control to prevent contact between the released populations and dispersing mink (Table 10.1, Moorhouse et al., 2009). Where mink control was successful (in seven of 12 releases), the survival rates and population densities of the reintroduced populations were

Table 10.1 Causes of population extinction in a water vole reintroduction programme during the first year post release (from Moorhouse *et al.*, 2009).

Stage of reintroduction	End of month	Number of extant populations	Reason for loss of population(s)
Initial release	May	12	
Establishment	June	9	Flooding post release (1) Failure of mink control (2)
Survival to end of breeding season	October	8	Failure of mink control (1)
Successful overwintering of population	April	7	Failure of mink control (1)

determined by habitat quality (Figure 10.1, Moorhouse *et al.*, 2009). Macdonald *et al.* (2002b) demonstrate, for extant populations of water voles in Belarus, that the configuration and dispersion of available habitat can mitigate the impact of American mink, and Carter and Bright (2003) demonstrate that British reed beds can act as refuges from mink predation. Although these studies suggest that effects of invasives can be mitigated on a local scale by good quality habitats, even pristine habitats are unlikely to afford complete protection from predation (Macdonald *et al.*, 2002b).

The effects of introduced predators are complicated by interactions within the predator community. A top predator (introduced or not) may prevent less competitive (generally smaller) predators (which also may be introduced or native) from having a more damaging effect on vulnerable prey species, through intra-guild competition and predation (mesopredator effects). Mesopredator release has been demonstrated in the sage-scrub habitat of California, where the absence of the coyote in some habitat fragments has led to an increase in smaller predators (including both the native grey fox and the introduced domestic cat) and a decrease in the diversity of scrub breeding birds (Crooks and Soule, 1999).

Introduction of new prey species may have indirect impacts on native prey species via a shared predator, a process known as

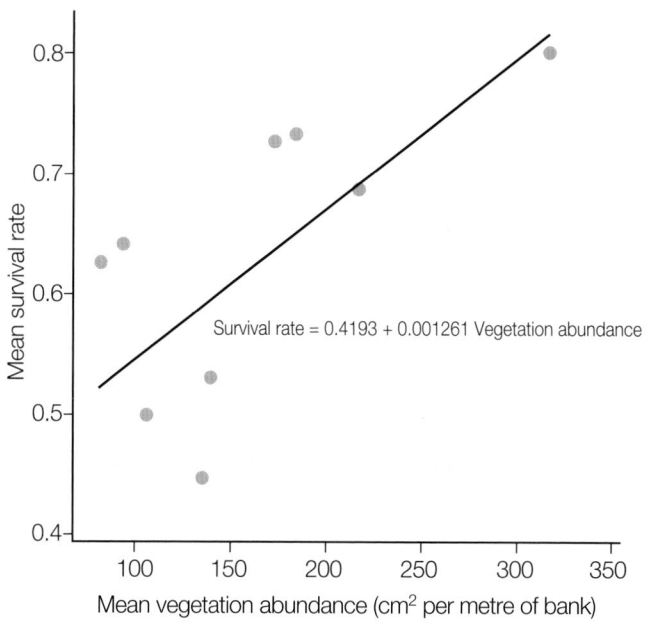

Survival rate = 0.4193 + 0.001261 Vegetation abundance

Figure 10.1 The relationship between water vole survival rate and the 'quality' of the habitat in terms of vegetation abundance (from Moorhouse *et al.*, 2009).

Plate 10.3 The arctic fox (*Vulpes lagopus*) has been introduced to the Aleutian Islands causing a cascade of effects resulting in altered vegetation communities. © Mikhail Gottsman

hyperpredation (Smith and Quin, 1996; Courchamp *et al.*, 1999). For example, in California the cascades frog (*Rana cascadae*) is preyed upon opportunistically by the Pacific coast aquatic garter snake (*Thamnophis atratus*). The introduction of non-native fish species (mainly *Oncorhynchus*, *Salmo* and *Salvelinus* spp.) has led to an expansion of *T. atratus* and a concomitant decline in the abundance of *R. cascadae*. Introduced fish also prey upon *R. cascadae*, complicating the case of hyperpredation with intraguild predation, however, the indirect impacts of introduced fish via *T. atratus* appear to cause significant additional declines (Pope *et al.*, 2008).

Herbivory by introduced species can cause changes to vegetation communities and soil characteristics, which in turn impact on the native species which depend on them. Plant communities in both north-east Russia and Finland have been altered by the arrival of the North American muskrat (*Ondatra zibethicus*), resulting in increased dominance of aquatic plant species that are resistant to muskrat grazing (Smirnov and Tretyakov, 1998). In Finland, muskrat introduction also resulted in a switch in the dominant shoreline species from *Equisetum* and *Schoenoplectus* to *Phragmites* and *Typha* (Nummi, 1996). Reindeer grazing on South Georgia resulted in the native grass *Parodiochola flabellata* and dwarf shrub *Acaena magellanica* being replaced by *Poa annua* in grassland communities (Leader-Williams *et al.*, 1987), which in turn caused a

Plate 10.4 Red deer (*Cervus elaphus*) introduced into New Zealand where its grazing activities result in degredation of native grasslands. © Joelene Hughes

decline in an indigenous beetle (*Hydromedion sparsatum*) by slowing larval growth rates (Chown and Block, 1997). Herbivores do not only impact upon plants but also upon soils, as has been demonstrated by a reduction of soil stability and increased erosion on islands with introduced sheep, goats and rabbits (Coblentz, 1978; Van Vuren and Coblentz, 1987; North *et al.*, 1994).

10.3.2 Effects of competition

Extinctions entirely, and indisputably, attributed to competition by introduced species are rare (Mooney and Cleland, 2001; Sax *et al.*, 2002). There is difficulty in interpreting the impacts of invasives via competition: shared resource use does not necessarily constitute evidence for competition as the resource may not be limiting for the species involved (Sale, 1974) and the extent of overlap may not represent the intensity of competition (Colwell and Futuyma, 1971). There are, however, some obvious examples from invasive plant species: in the UK exotic species such as *Rhododendron ponticum* on land, and water primrose (*Ludwigia* sp.) in waterways shade out the rest of the plant community; dense mats of New Zealand pygmy weed (*Crassula helmsii*) in British pools destroy the habitat of native invertebrates, amphibians and fish (Dawson and Warman, 1987).

Competition may take two forms; direct 'interference' competition and indirect 'exploitation' competition. Interference competition occurs through individuals interacting with each other, resulting in one species having reduced survival and/or reproductive rates. Exploitation competition occurs when species' interactions are mediated via another species, for example a preferred food species. In some cases the form of competition is relatively easy to discern, such as the indirect interaction between the introduced red deer (*Cervus elaphus*) and the rare, flightless takahe (*Porphyrio hochstetteri*) in New Zealand. Red deer grazing upon subalpine tussock grassland, the last remaining habitat of the takahe, results in it becoming degraded and less suitable for the birds (Lee and Jamieson, 2001). In other cases careful experimentation is required to disentangle the two forms of competition. One such example is that of the endemic Galápagos rice rats, where the loss of up to eight species may have been due to competition from the invasive black rat, (*Rattus rattus*) (Patton *et al.*, 1975; Steadman and Ray, 1982; Clark, 1984; Steadman *et al.*, 1991; Hutterer and Oromi, 1993; Dowler *et al.*, 2000). The recent rediscovery of the Santiago rice rat (*Nesoryzomys swarthi*), not only surviving despite the introduction of *R. rattus* up to 400 years ago (Patton *et al.*, 1975; Dowler *et al.*, 2000), but overlapping with the latter in habitat use in both space and time (Harris *et al.*, 2006), provided the opportunity to investigate in detail the mechanisms of competition and coexistence. Black rat removal experiments and resource supplementation experiments ruled out exploitation competition as a factor and supported interference competition (Harris *et al.*, 2006; Harris and Macdonald, 2007). A comparison of the preferred and selected diets of the two species suggests that *N. swarthi* utilized less preferred foods to avoid encounters with *R. rattus* (Gregory and Macdonald, 2009). Although *N. swarthi* appears to be the poorer competitor (Figure 10.2), populations of *R. rattus* crash during the dry season, whereas *N. swarthi* populations are less affected (Figure 10.3, Harris and Macdonald, 2007), probably due to their ability to utilize the fruit of *Opuntia* cacti. It is thought that this provides a competition refuge for *N. swarthi* (Harris and Macdonald, 2007; Gregory and Macdonald, 2009).

Coexistence between a native and invasive species is often complex. The invasive American mink colonized the UK at a time when both otters (*Lutra lutra*), a larger native aquatic predator from the same guild, and polecats (*Mustela putorius*), a similarly sized but more terrestrial predator, were largely absent due to river pollution and hunting (Chanin and Jefferies, 1978), and persecution (Birks and Kitchener, 1999), respectively. Both species are now recovering in the UK (Birks, 2000; Crawford, 2003) and early research showing that otters may out-compete mink (Bonesi and Macdonald, 2004b) led to optimism that the recovery of the otter would result in a widespread decline in American mink numbers. Research has shown, though, that the reality is more complex. Indeed the degree of coexistence between these two species appears to depend both on the ability of mink to adapt behaviourally and on the specific kind of habitat where the two competitors are found. In the presence of otters, mink seem to shift the timing of their activities so that it does not coincide with that of the otters (Harrington *et al.*, in 2009b). A similar mutual temporal avoidance appears to facilitate the coexistence of mink and recovering populations of polecats (Harrington and Macdonald, 2008). Mink also modify their diet to include more

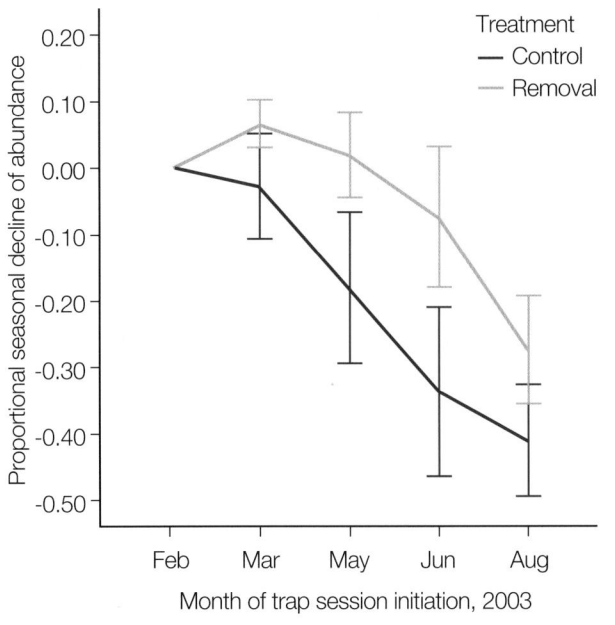

Figure 10.2 The proportional seasonal decline of Santiago rice rats (*Nesoryzomys swarthi*) in plots from which black rats had been experimentally removed (removal) compared to control plots (from Harris and Macdonald, 2007).

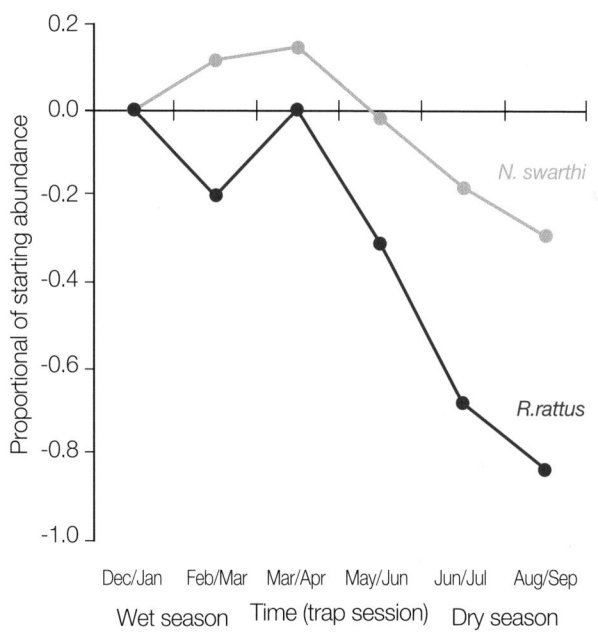

Figure 10.3 The seasonal declines in the abundance of both Santiago rice rats (*N. swarthi*) and black rats (*R. rattus*). Note the relatively steeper decline of *R. rattus* during the dry season (from Harris and Macdonald, 2007).

terrestrial items and fewer fish, suggesting competitive exclusion (Clode and Macdonald, 1995; Bonesi *et al.*, 2004b). How much these adaptations influence the American mink's fitness in the presence of its competitors is likely to be determined by extrinsic factors that may favour or disfavour coexistence. In particular, it has been shown that the type of habitat where otter and mink are found when sympatric may influence the duration of coexistence, with riparian habitats surrounded by areas with abundant terrestrial prey being the most likely to promote coexistence (Bonesi and Macdonald, 2004a). The interplay between the mink's adaptations to the arrival of otter and polecat and to extrinsic factors that may act locally, are likely to determine the degree of coexistence between these three mustelids. While it is highly unlikely that recovering native carnivores will lead to the extirpation of mink, local conditions may influence the relative abundance of these three species or the rate of spread of invasive mink into new areas, as also shown by Ruiz-Olmo *et al.* (1997) in Spain, where the colonization rate of mink was slower where otters were present. The problem of mink invasions occurs in widely spread parts of the world (Fasola *et al.*, 2009; Ibarra, 2009), but the impacts and rate of its spread are likely to be strongly locally influenced.

10.3.3 Effects of disease

While the impacts of diseases (both native and introduced) are considered, in general, to stop short of species-level extinctions, due to reduced transmission between hosts as they become rarer (Anderson and May, 1979), the presence of invasive species provides one of the conditions under which pathogens may cause extinction: they may act as a biotic reservoir for disease (McCallum and Dobson, 1995). The grey squirrel (*Sciurus carolinensis*) was introduced to the UK in 1876 (Shorten, 1954) and is thought to be responsible for the decline of the native red squirrels (*Sciurus vulgaris*). The similarity in resources used by red and grey squirrels has been compared at a number of locations in the UK and in Italy. Niche overlap has been estimated to be between 70 and 77% (Wauters *et al.*, 2000, 2002a, 2002b; Bryce *et al.*, 2002), leading to the conclusion that where they overlap, competition for food or space will occur when resources become limited. Coexistence for extended periods of time has been demonstrated in areas containing a relatively high proportion of habitat favoured by red squirrels (conifer woodlands) compared to that favoured by grey squirrels (mixed broadleaf woodlands, Bryce *et al.*, 2002), but in many parts of the UK greys have come to dominate even in coniferous woodland. Where coexistence occurs it may be due to a reduction in the greys' competitive advantage in areas with only isolated patches of their favoured habitat and a lack of nearby source populations (Bryce *et al.*, 2002). Competition, however, is not the only ecological effect at work. Sainsbury and Ward (1996) demonstrated that the grey squirrel is also the carrier of the squirrel pox virus, a disease which causes significant mortality in red squirrel populations. A similar example is the story of *Rhododendron ponticum* brought to the UK in the late 18th century: in addition to shading out other plants and producing chemicals to prevent regeneration of competitors, this species now also hosts an introduced plant disease, *Phytophthora ramorum*, found in the UK in 2002, which can be fatal not only to rhododendrons but also to nearby native trees and shrubs. As yet, there have been relatively few native trees with lethal canker outbreaks in the UK, however, *P. ramorum* has reached epidemic proportions in California (Defra, 2008b).

The American signal crayfish (*Pasifastacus leniusculus*) is endemic to North America, but has been introduced into over 20 countries in Europe since the 1960s. Signal crayfish were introduced to Britain in 1976, and had colonized more than 250 British waters by 1988 (Lowery and Holdich, 1988). They frequently carry crayfish plague (*Aphanomyces astaci*), a fungal infection to which they are highly resistant (Alderman *et al.*, 1990) but which is lethal for many native European species, including the British white-clawed crayfish (*Austropotamobius pallipes*). The British population of white-clawed crayfish has been devastated by the arrival of signal crayfish, mainly due to the effects of crayfish plague (Holdich and Rogers, 1997; Lozan, 2000). In the absence of crayfish plague, the

Plate 10.5 Signal crayfish (*Pasifastacus leniusculus*), introduced to Britain in 1976. © Astrid Willener

displacement of white-clawed crayfish by signal crayfish takes place over several years (Bubb *et al.*, 2005), probably via aggressive interspecific competition for in-stream refuges from predation (such as large cobbles and boulders) (Bubb *et al.*, 2006). In this case, the effect of signal crayfish upon native fauna as a vector for disease appears to be stronger than their effect as a direct competitor for resources.

The effects of introduced pathogens can be catastrophic when the reservoir effect is combined with small, vulnerable populations. Recent evidence for the extinction of a mammalian species due to an introduced pathogen has been obtained for the extinct endemic Christmas Island rat (*Rattus macleari*) (Wyatt *et al.*, 2008). Two endemic species of rat were recorded from Christmas Island in the late 1800s (*R. macleari* and *R. nativitatis*) but within 10 years of the introduction of *R. rattus* to the island by settlers, both species were extinct. Ancient DNA analysis confirmed that the suspected pathogen (a trypanosome) was absent from specimens of native rats collected prior to the introduction of *R. rattus* but was present following the introduction of *R. rattus*, during the period in which the native rat populations declined. Modern *R. rattus* infected with *Trypanosoma lewisi* – the trypanosome confirmed from some Christmas Island samples - commonly survive unless infected when pregnant (Shaw and Dusanic, 1973). If the *R. rattus* introduced to Christmas Island responded in the same way they will have provided a biotic reservoir of the disease, resulting in the extinction of the susceptible native rats (Wyatt *et al.*, 2008).

10.3.4 Effects of hybridization

The overcoming of natural barriers by humans can remove reproductive isolation between species, allowing populations of native species to be overwhelmed by introduced species. For example, the construction of five bridges across the Chamkhar River in Bhutan has allowed the capped langur (*Trachypithecus pileata*) to traverse what was previously a geographical barrier. Hybrid offspring between the endangered golden langur (*T. geei*) and the capped langur are now common (Wangchuk, 2005). This illustrates one of the difficult questions in relation to what, precisely, is an introduced species. While the mechanism of expansion was human induced (equivalent in a sense, albeit on a much more local scale, to climate change), the langurs traversed the bridge themselves and so could be considered to have arrived 'naturally'. Are the hybrid offspring therefore also 'natural'? Or should they be destroyed to preserve the golden langur?

The wildcat (*Felis silvestris*) in Scotland is at risk from hybridization with feral domestic cats. Genetic analysis has shown that domestic cat genes have introgressed into the Scottish wildcat genome but that the wild cat is still genetically distinct (Daniels *et al.*, 1998; Beaumont *et al.*, 2001). The wildcat genes are now packaged as part of the wild cat hybrids, leading to the question of how they figure in the policy of shooting feral cats, aimed at reducing the threat to the wild cat population (Macdonald *et al.*, 2004; Macdonald *et al.*, in press). This problem is exacerbated by the difficulty of distinguishing between wild cats, hybrids and feral cats, and the fact that individuals that look like domestic cats may in fact be closely related to wild cats and vice versa (Figure 10.4, Kitchener *et al.*, 2005). Domestic cats and dogs,

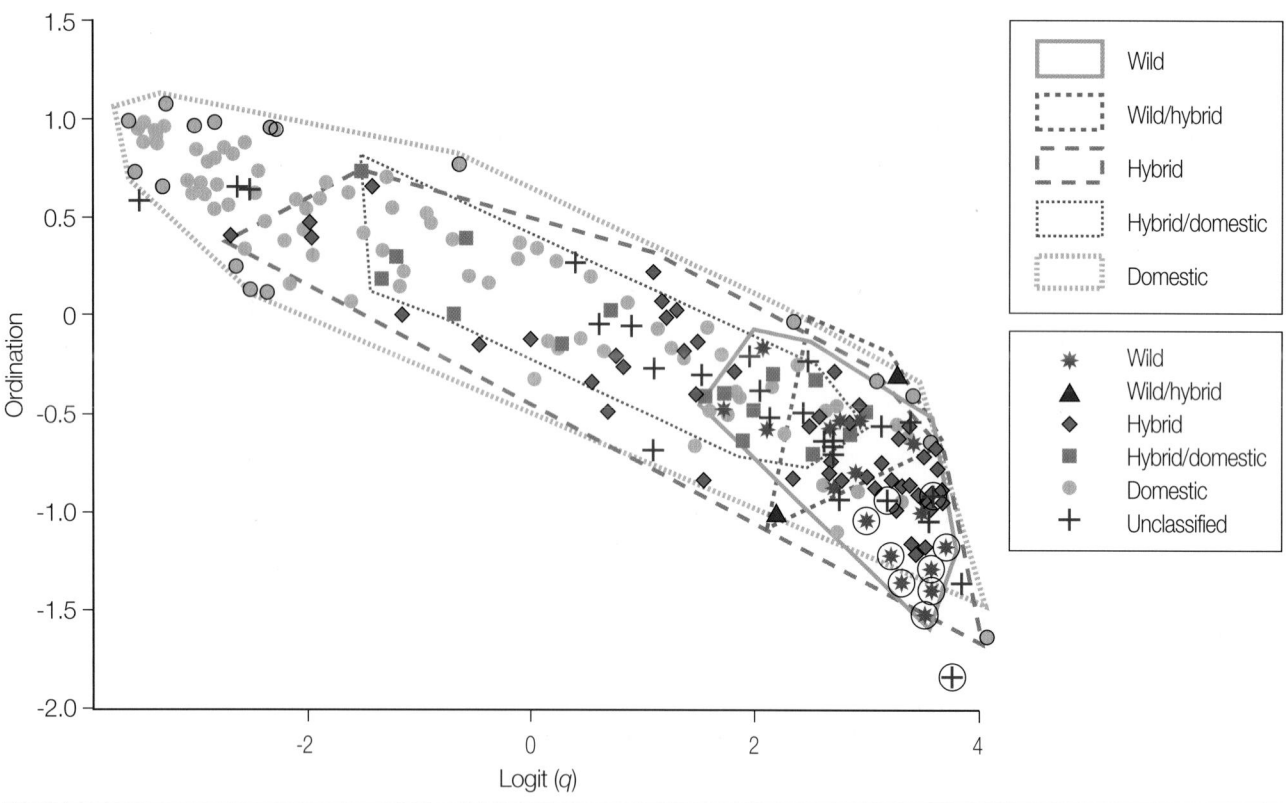

Figure 10.4 The relationship between the genetic classification of cats as 'wild cats', those genetically most different from domestic cats (q value), compared to the classification of wild cats based on pelage characteristics. Note that all 'wild' cats possess high q values, but other categories, even 'domestic', include many cats with similar q values (from Beaumont *et al.*, 2001).

while not released purposefully into the wild, have had dramatic consequences in terms not only of hybridization but also predation and disease, and may affect wild populations by several mechanisms. For example the Ethiopian wolf (*Canis simensis*) is threatened by rabies, transmitted by domestic dogs, as well as hybridization (Sillero-Zubiri and Macdonald, 1997; Sillero-Zubiri *et al.*, 2004)

10.3.5 Ecosystem effects

Impacts caused by the interactions of invasives with native species potentially cause ecological 'chain reactions' with varying and often unpredictable consequences (Towns *et al.*, 1997; Zavaleta *et al.*, 2001). For example, the introduction of a carnivorous mammal can alter vegetation community structure and soil nutrient dynamics, as was the case in the Aleutian archipelago, where the introduction of arctic foxes reduced seabird populations and thus nutrient input. The resulting changes in soil nutrient dynamics caused the vegetation community to change from grassland to tundra (Croll *et al.*, 2005).

Ecosystem effects are particularly likely if invasive species affect species which play a key role within the invaded community without replacing their function. The invasive pathogen *Cronartium ribicola*, which causes mortality in the whitebark pine (*Pinus albicaulis*), may have a large impact on the functioning of treeline communities because the whitebark pine facilitates community development as well as producing large, nutritious seeds of importance to native bird species (Tomback and Resler, 2007). The impacts of invasive species may be even more complex when more than one species is introduced and when the introductions occur in degraded or fragmented habitats (Smith and Quin, 1996; Macdonald and Strachan, 1999; Zavaleta *et al.*, 2001). The kaka (*Nestor meridionalis*), an endemic forest parrot in New Zealand, is affected by competition with introduced possums (*Trichosurus vulpecula*) for fruit and with introduced Vespulid wasps for honeydew produced by scale insects (*Ultracoelostoma* spp. - Beggs and Wilson, 1991; Wilson *et al.*, 1998). While kaka populations persist, albeit in reduced numbers, in the presence of possums, predation by stoats is thought to lead to decline and local extinctions (Wilson *et al.*, 1998).

10.4 Discussion

10.4.1 Managing invasive species

It is clear that invasive species can result in a number of undesirable ecological and economic impacts. This leads to the question of what to do about them. Management of already established invasive species (the 'curative' approach) is a time-consuming and expensive business. To remove *Rhododendron ponticum* from the UK region of Argyll and Bute alone is likely to cost £9.6 million (Edwards and Taylor, 2008) and there is the permanent possibility of reinvasion. Successful eradications of invasive species are possible as has been demonstrated by the removal of pigs (*Sus scrofa*) and feral goats (*Capra hircus*) from San Fernadino in the Galapagos, and the subsequent recovery of the Galapagos rail (*Laterallus spilonotus*; Donlan *et al.*, 2007). In the UK there have been several examples of success in the islands off the north-west coast of Scotland, including the removal of brown rats from Canna, the removal of American mink from the Hebrides and the removal of hedgehogs (*Erinaceus europaeus*) from North Uist (Anon, 2006; SNH, 2008; Tayton, 2008), but there is still the risk of reinvasion if preventative measures are not put in place. The majority of success stories have come from island areas. Removing invasive species from large inland bodies may prove more difficult, although the eradication of coypu (*Myocastor coypus*) from England has demonstrated that this is possible (Gosling and Baker, 1989). In areas where eradication is not possible, long-term, sustained, control is the only option. While it is possible to remove mink from small (20 km) stretches of waterway, to maintain those stretches at a mink density sufficiently low to permit the survival of water vole populations, requires continual monitoring and immediate response to new mink incursions (Harrington *et al.*, 2009a).

When considering the removal of invasive species, it is important to anticipate the impacts of removal. Once an ecosystem or community has been altered it may not simply revert to its previous state once the initial cause of the problem has been removed. This is even more likely to be the case when multiple introductions have occurred, or if an invasive species now functions as an ecosystem engineer or keystone species (Crooks, 2002). The challenge is perhaps to consider dealing with invasive species as part of a programme of ecosystem restoration, which may include considering the removal of several introduced species and also the re-establishment of native species (Zavaleta *et al.*, 2001). In the case of the Santiago rice rat, removing black rats may benefit the population by reducing direct competition but it may also lead to an increase in another species suppressed by black rats, the introduced house mouse (*Mus musculus*) (Harris and Macdonald, 2007). Increases in *M. musculus* may be detrimental to *N. swarthi* as they cause mortality in the important *Opuntia* cacti, thus removing one of the key species that may allow *N. swarthi* to survive periods of low resource availability (Snell *et al.*, 1994; Gregory and Macdonald, 2009). The removal of invasive herbivores may result in an increase in invasive plant species, rather than native species, as has occurred in the Kerguelen archipelago on the removal of rabbits (Chapuis *et al.*, 2004). The effects of this may be exacerbated by the loss of native herbivores, as is suggested on the Mascarene island of Ile Aux Aigrettes, where Aldabran tortoises (*Geocholone gigantia*)

Plate 10.6 A water vole (*Arvicola terrestris*) being placed into a soft holding pen prior to full release as part of a reintroduction programme. © Amy Isherwood

Plate 10.7 The Santiago rice rat (*Nesoryzomys swarthi*), an endemic island species which currently coexists with the invasive black rat. © Donna Harris

have been introduced to suppress non-native vegetation and carry out the functional role of the now extinct endemic giant tortoises (*G. triserrata* and *G. inepta*) after the removal of goats and rabbits (Zavaleta *et al.*, 2001). While ecosystem restoration is the ideal, it may not be practical or feasible. Safford and Jones (1998) found that restoring native vegetation did not halt the decline of Mauritian land birds unless combined with the control of introduced predators; furthermore it was more cost-effective to enhance degraded habitats using introduced plant species which provided nesting sites with some protection from predation.

Management of invasive species includes an important human dimension. While some invasives can be unequivocally defined as malign - due to their negative impacts on agricultural crops, public health or native biota - and general agreement for their management obtained, for others it is not so simple. Conservationists may argue that any introduced species interferes with natural processes and should therefore be removed. This argument, however, may be opposed by those who enjoy seeing an introduced species, such as the wild mustang (*Equus caballus*) or grey squirrel. In the case of the mustang this is complicated by the indirect impacts it has on native fauna and conflicts with commercial interests. Mustangs can cause overgrazing and erosion in waterholes, competing with cattle (another introduced species) leading to ranchers to call for their control (Beever and Brussard, 2000; Beever, 2003; Abella, 2008). Furthermore there is concern that, along with other livestock, they may compete with the desert tortoise (but see Boarman, 2002), leading conservationists to call for their removal or cull, while animal welfare rights charities campaign to prevent culls from happening (Williams, 2006). Not ensuring the agreement of all interested parties may lead to the failure of management projects, even in what may appear (to a biologist) to be relatively open-and-shut cases. For example the eradication of the grey squirrel from Italy was halted by a series of court cases brought by animal rights protesters (Genovesi and Bertolino, 2001). The delay of three years resulted in the spread of the grey squirrel from patchy habitat in central Piedmont to contiguous favourable habitats in the Alps, and any future eradication programmes are now considered infeasible without significant additional resources and political commitment (Bertolino and Genovesi, 2003).

Given the difficulties of removing an invasive species once it has become established, a 'preventative' approach is clearly useful; the focus of the recent Invasive Non-Native Species Strategy for Great Britain has been on prevention rather than cure (Defra, 2008a). The eradication of the creeping water primrose (*Ludwigia peploides*) in France, where it has become established, is costing several million Euros per year, whereas a research project into eradicating it from the few affected UK sites cost £10,000 and resulted in nearly complete eradication (Defra, 2007). Preventing the entry of new species is a daunting task and in some cases may conflict with free trade: two of the common entry methods for invasive species are through the horticultural trade or ballast water used by the shipping industry. UK legislation is already in place to prevent the release of non-native organisms into the wild (Section 14 of the Wildlife and Countryside Act 1981) and the amendments proposed in the Nature Conservation (Scotland) Act 2004 and the Natural Environment and Rural Communities (NERC) Act 2006 give the government the power to prevent the sale of malign invasive species. A problem with prevention is that introduced species may become established in small numbers, and only become invasive beyond the point for effective early intervention. There are ongoing activities in both the UK and Europe to set up centralized information points (for example DAISIE http://www.europe-aliens.org/ and the UK Non Native Species Secretariat site http://www.nonnativespecies.org/) to collate information on the distribution of invasive species and to eventually provide an 'alert' early warning system to allow action to be taken against newly arrived invasive species.

Not all invasive species will be detrimental. The raccoon dog (*Nyctereutes procyonoides ussuriensis*) has colonized Finland from populations introduced into the Soviet Union for fur trade, with apparently little ill effect on native carnivores of a similar size (red foxes and badgers). The raccoon dog appears to have taken advantage of a vacant niche: while the diets of all three carnivores overlap, the red fox specializes on small mammals, badgers on invertebrates and raccoon dogs on plant material (Kauhala, 1994). Introduced species may even have positive impacts. For example, there are no modern records of a rare native beetle, the noble chafer (*Gnorimus nobilis*) in wild trees; it is now thought to be exclusively confined to decaying fruit trees in old, planted orchards (Green, 2004). Assessing the likely impacts of introduced species involves high levels of uncertainty and general rules do not always apply. The highly invasive Japanese knotweed (*Fallopia japonica* var. *japonica*) consists of a single female which has vegetatively spread across Europe and the UK. Introducing a female individual of a functionally dioecious plant (Pysek, 2006) would not normally be expected to have such dramatic consequences. Any risk assessment and management needs to operate on precautionary principles, given the difficulties of establishing both the impacts and invasiveness of introduced species.

10.4.2 Challenges ahead

In the future we are likely to be faced with further challenges from species that have arrived and are established but may only become malign under climate change. Climate change may also change the balance between well-established malign invasives and native species. In the case of *N. swathi*, the predicted increase in the frequency and intensity of warm, wet El Niño years may cause the *R. rattus* population to boom and will reduce *Opuntia* populations (Hamann, 2004; Harris and Macdonald, 2007), removing the competitive refuge that appears to be allowing coexistence of the two species. Changes in climate and increased stress in native species may result in communities that are more susceptible to invasive species.

Human induced climate change that aids the establishment of new species blurs the boundaries of what is an introduced species and what has arrived naturally and further confuses the question of what to do about them. The movement of native species northwards may result in vacant niches for colonisers from the south. The small red-eyed damselfly (*Erythromma viridulum*) is the first migrant damselfly that has been recorded as establishing itself in Britain (Keat *et al.*, 2005). One of the most obvious effects of climate change on insects has been their north-westerly range expansion, and small red-eyed damselfly

Plate 10.8 The small red-eyed damsel fly (*Erythromma viridulum*), previously a migrant species in the south of Britain but which has recently been recorded as established. © Steve Cham

has followed this pattern. It arrived in Essex in 1999 and it has now colonized most of the south-east of England, reaching as far as the Midlands at a rate of expansion of 32 km per year. Negative consequences of this damselfly, if any, on native species that share habitat and seasonal niches are currently unknown. However, in this case it could be argued that since the small red-eyed damsel fly has reached the UK by itself and has been able to settle by its own merits, it is not an invasive species but a product of natural colonization processes. Of course, if a future invasion and settlement involves a territorial species the effects could be detrimental on native odonates.

The development and use of genetically modified organisms (GMOs) is likely to add another level of complexity, and also lexicon, to invasive species issues. In common with other introduced domestic species, there is the possibility that GMOs may escape into the wild and become invasive, but there is also the risk that transgenes will 'escape' into native species via processes such as hybridisation (Craig *et al.*, 2008). This may alter the invasiveness ('weediness' in an agricultural context) of native species and lead to a problem of native species containing an 'invasive' gene. Some lessons do appear to have been learnt: GMOs are trialled and risk-assessed prior to release and while in the some cases the risks of gene transfer have been under-estimated and transgenes have escaped (for examples see Andow and

Zwahlen, 2006), this is a very different attitude to that of the generation which introduced numerous species to places such as Australia and New Zealand with such dramatic consequences.

The decisions regarding whether to remove invasive species should not only consider the practical issues, ecological and social dimensions, but also the ethics of such programmes. Eventually many invasive species become 'naturalised' and considered as a native species, for example the rabbit and fallow deer (*Dama dama*) in the UK. It is difficult to see why the fallow deer should be accepted as native and the muntjac (*Muntiacus reevsii*) not, aside from the fact that fallow deer arrived some nine centuries earlier. In the case of another introduced deer in the UK, the Chinese water deer (*Hydropotes inermis*), removing it would also result in the destruction of around 10% of its global population, something that might be hard to justify given the lack of established negative impacts. The ethical considerations become even more murky when one considers the case of commensal rodents, such as rats, which have evolved the ability to maintain populations on ships and to utilize humans as dispersers; in some sense then, a natural colonizer. The label of 'invasive' species should not be used as an excuse for fruitless killings. The blame for the detrimental effects lies with people rather than the individuals themselves. When the negative effects of some invasives are such that we are put in the unfortunate ethical position of having to remove one species to save another, at the very least we should ensure that any removals are carried out as humanely as possible (Macdonald *et al.*, 2007).

10.5 Conclusions

The challenges posed by malign invasives are not going to go away. The examples presented here demonstrate the vast array of potential consequences, both anticipated and unanticipated, of the worldwide translocation of both animals and plants. While we have attempted to draw generalizations in this overview, the ecological, economical and social impacts of invasive species, the ideology surrounding their treatment, and the potential for their amelioration or the restoration of affected ecosystems, are so diverse as to require that each species and habitat is dealt with on a case-by-case basis whilst trying to avoid inconsistent ethics and double standards. While, therefore, the lessons from invasion events across the globe have provided a general framework in which to consider the risks and consequences of the process of invasion, the sobering truth appears to be that each invasion requires a detailed knowledge of all of the components - the habitat, predators, prey, competitors, economic consequences and public opinion - before any decision as to whether to attempt restoration can be made.

References

Abella, S. R. (2008). A systematic review of wild burro grazing effects on Mojave Desert vegetation, USA. *Environmental Management* **41**: 809-819.

Alderman, D. J., Holdich, D. M. & Reeve, I. (1990). Signal crayfish as vectors in crayfish plague in Britain. *Aquaculture* **86**: 3-6.

Anderson, R. M. & May, R. M. (1979). Population biology of infectious diseases. 1. *Nature* **280**: 361-367.

Andow, D. A. & Zwahlen, C. (2006). Assessing environmental risks of transgenic plants. *Ecology Letters* **9**: 196-214.

Anon. (2006). Mink control to protect the important birds in the SPA's in the Western Isles - Technical final report EU Life Project no. LIFE00 NAT/UK/007073. Scottish Natural Heritage, Inverness.

Beaumont, M., Barratt, E.M., Gottelli, D., Kitchener, A.C., Daniels, M.J., Pritchard, J.K. & Bruford, M.W. (2001). Genetic diversity and introgression in the Scottish wildcat. *Molecular Ecology* **10**: 319-336.

Beever, E. (2003). Management implications of the ecology of free-roaming horses in semi-arid ecosystems of the western United States. *Wildlife Society Bulletin* **31**: 887-895.

Beever, E.A. & Brussard, P.F. (2000). Charismatic megafauna or exotic pest? Interactions between popular perceptions of feral horses (*Equus caballus*) and their management and research. In *Nineteenth Vertebrate Pest Conference, Proceedings* ed. by T. P. Salmon & A. C. Crabb. University of California, Davis. pp. 413-418.

Beggs, J.R. & Wilson, P.R. (1991). The kaka *Nestor meridionalis*, a New Zealand parrot endangered by introduced wasps and mammals. *Biological Conservation* **56**: 23-38.

Bertolino, S. & Genovesi, P. (2003). Spread and attempted eradication of the grey squirrel (*Sciurus carolinensis*) in Italy, and consequences for the red squirrel (*Sciurus vulgaris*) in Eurasia. *Biological Conservation* **109**: 351-358.

Birks, J.D.S. (2000). The recovery of the polecat, *Mustela putorius*, in Britain. In *Mustelids in a modern world* Ed. by H. I. Griffiths. Backhuys Publishers, Netherlands. pp. 141-152.

Birks, J.D.S. & Kitchener, A.C. (1999). *The distribution and status of the polecat Mustela putorius in Britain in the 1990s.* The Vincent Wildlife Trust, London.

Boarman, W.I. (2002). Threats to desert tortoise populations: a critical review of the literature. U.S.Geological Survey Western Ecological Research Centre, San Diego.

Bonesi, L. & Macdonald, D.W. (2004a). Differential habitat use promotes sustainable coexistence between the specialist otter and the generalist mink. *Oikos* **106**: 509-519.

Bonesi, L. & Macdonald, D.W. (2004b). Impact of released Eurasian otters on a population of American mink: a test using an experimental approach. *Oikos* **106**: 9-18.

Bonesi, L., Chanin, P. & Macdonald, D.W. (2004). Competition between Eurasian otter *Lutra lutra* and American mink *Mustela vison* probed by niche shift. *Oikos* **106**: 19-26.

Bryce, J., Johnson, P. J. & Macdonald, D.W. (2002). Can niche use in red and grey squirrels offer clues for their apparent coexistence? *Journal of Applied Ecology* **39**: 875-887.

Bubb, D.H., Thom, T.J. & Lucas, M. C. (2005). The within catchment invasion of the non-indigenous signal crayfish *Pacifastacus leniusculus* (Dana) in upland rivers. *Bulletin Francais de Peche et de Pisciculture* **376–377**: 665–673.

Bubb, D.H., Thom, T.J. & Lucas, M.J. (2006). Movement, dispersal and refuge use of co-occurring introduced and native crayfish. *Freshwater Biology* **51**: 1359-1368.

Carter, S.P. & Bright, P.W. (2003). Reedbeds as refuges for water voles (*Arvicola terrestris*) from predation by introduced mink (*Mustela vison*). *Biological Conservation* **111:** 371-376.

Chanin, P.R.F. & Jefferies, D.J. (1978). Decline of the otter *Lutra lutra* in Britain - analysis of hunting records and discussion of causes. *Biological Journal of the Linnean Society* **10**: 305-328.

Chapin, F.S., Zavaleta, E.S., Eviner, V.T., Naylor, R.L., Vitousek, P.M., Reynolds, H.L., Hooper, D.U., Lavorel, S., Sala, O.E., Hobbie, S.E., Mack, M.C. & Diaz, S. (2000). Consequences of changing biodiversity. *Nature* **405**: 234-242.

Chapuis, J.L., Frenot, Y. & Lebouvier, M. (2004). Recovery of native plant communities after eradication of rabbits from the subantarctic Kerguelen Islands, and influence of climate change. *Biological Conservation* **117**: 167-179.

Chown, S.L. & Block, W. (1997). Comparative nutritional ecology of grass-feeding in a sub-Antarctic beetle: the impact of introduced species on *Hydromedion sparsutum* from South Georgia. *Oecologia* **111**: 216-224.

Clark, D.A. (1984). Native land mammals. In *Key environments: Galapagos*, Ed. by R. Perry). Pergamon, Oxford. pp. 225-231.

Clode, D. & Macdonald, D.W. (1995). Evidence for food competition between mink (*Mustela vison*) and otter (*Lutra lutra*) on Scottish islands. *Journal of Zoology* **237**: 435-444.

Coblentz, B.E. (1978). Effects of feral goats (*Capra hircus*) on island ecosystems. *Biological Conservation* **13**: 279-286.

Colwell, R.K. & Futuyma, D.J. (1971). Measurement of niche breadth and overlap. *Ecology* **52**: 567-576.

Courchamp, F., Langlais, M. & Sugihara, G. (1999). Control of rabbits to protect island birds from cat predation. *Biological Conservation* **89**: 219-225.

Coutts-Smith, A.J., Mahon, P.S., Letnic, M. & Downey, P.O. (2007). *The threat posed by pest animals to biodiversity in New South Wales*. Invasive Animals Cooperative Research Centre, Canberra.

Craig, W., Tepfer, M., Degrassi, G. & Ripandelli, D. (2008). An overview of general features of risk assessments of genetically modified crops. *Euphytica* **164**: 853-880.

Crawford, A. (2003). *Fourth otter survey of England 2000-02*. Environment Agency, Bristol.

Croll, D.A., Maron, J.L., Estes, J.A., Danner, E.M. & Byrd, G.V. (2005). Introduced predators transform subarctic islands from grassland to tundra. *Science* **307**: 1959-1961.

Crooks, J.A. (2002). Characterizing ecosystem-level consequences of biological invasions: the role of ecosystem engineers. *Oikos* **97**: 153-166.

Crooks, K.R. & Soule, M.E. (1999). Mesopredator release and avifaunal extinctions in a fragmented system. *Nature* **400**: 563-566.

Cuthbert, R. & Davis, L.S. (2002). The impact of predation by introduced stoats on Hutton's shearwaters, New Zealand. *Biological Conservation* **108**: 79-92.

Daniels, M.J., Balharry, D., Hirst, D., Kitchener, A.C. & Aspinall, R.J. (1998). Morphological and pelage characteristics of wild living cats in Scotland: implications for defining the 'wildcat'. *Journal of Zoology* **244**: 231-247.

Dawson, F.H. & Warman, E.A. (1987). *Crassula helmsii* (T-Kirk) Cockayne - is it an aggressive alien aquatic plant in Britain? *Biological Conservation* **42**: 247-272.

Department for Environment, Food and Rural Affairs. (2007). *Alien "nuisance" plant almost eradicated in the UK*. Department of the Environment, Farming and Rural Affairs, London.

Department for Environment, Food and Rural Affairs. (2008a). *The Invasive Non-Native Species Framework Strategy for Great Britain*. Department for the Environment, Farming and Rural Affairs, London.

Department for Environment, Food and Rural Affairs. (2008b). *Phytophthora ramorum* - Why the concern & what is being done? http://www.defra.gov.uk/planth/pramorum1.htm Accessed 8/12/08

Diamond, J.M. & Case, T.J. (1986). *Community Ecology*. Haper and Row, New York.

Donlan, C.J., Campbell, K., Cabrera, W., Lavoie, C., Carrion, V. & Cruz, F. (2007). Recovery of the Galapagos rail (*Laterallus spilonotus*) following the removal of invasive mammals. *Biological Conservation* **138**: 520-524.

Dowler, R.C., Carroll, D.S. & Edwards, C.W. (2000). Rediscovery of rodents (Genus *Nesoryzomys*) considered extinct in the Galapagos Islands. *Oryx* **34**: 109-117.

Edwards, C. & Taylor, S. L. (2008). *A survey and strategic appraisal of rhododendron invasion and control in woodland areas in Argyll and Bute*. Forestry Commission, Scotland, Perth.

Eilenberg, J., Hajek, A. & Lomer, C. (2001). Suggestions for unifying the terminology in biological control. *BioControl* **46**: 387-400.

Fasola, L., Chehebar, C., Macdonald, D.W., Porro, G. & Cassini, M.H. (2009). Do alien North American mink compete for resources with native South American river otter in Argentinean Patagonia? *Journal of Zoology* **277**: 187-195.

Forsyth, D.M. & Duncan, R. P. (2001). Propagule size and the relative success of exotic ungulate and bird introductions to New Zealand. *American Naturalist* **157**: 583-595.

Forsyth, D.M., Duncan, R.P., Bomford, M. & Moore, G. (2004). Climatic suitability, life-history traits, introduction effort, and the establishment and spread of introduced mammals in Australia. *Conservation Biology* **18**: 557-569.

Frenot, Y., Chown, S.L., Whinam, J., Selkirk, P.M., Convey, P., Skotnicki, M. & Bergstrom, D.M. (2005). Biological invasions in the Antarctic: extent, impacts and implications. *Biological Reviews* **80**: 45-72.

Genovesi, P. & Bertolino, S. (2001). Human dimension aspects in invasive species issues: the case of the failure of the grey squirrel eradication project in Italy. *The great reshuffling: human dimensions of invasive alien species,* Ed. J. A. McNeely. IUCN, Gland. pp. 113-120.

Gosling, L.M. & Baker, S. J. (1989). The eradication of muskrats and coypus from Britain. *Biological Journal of the Linnean Society* **38**: 39-51.

Green, H. (2004). The noble chafer *Gnorimus nobilis*. Records needed. Worcestershire Record No. 16, pages 10-11. Accessed online 10/12/08 http://wbrc.org.uk/WorcRecd/Issue%2016/noble_chafer.htm

Gregory, S.D. & Macdonald, D.W. (2009). Prickly coexistence or blunt competition? *Opuntia* refugia in an invaded rodent community. *Oecologia* **159**: 225-236.

Hamann, O. (2004). Vegetation changes over three decades on Santa Fe Island, Galapagos, Ecuador. *Nordic Journal of Botany* **23**: 143-152.

Harrington, L.A. & Macdonald, D.W. (2008). Spatial and temporal relationships between invasive American mink and native European polecats in the southern United Kingdom. *Journal of Mammalogy* **89**: 991-1000.

Harrington, L.A., Harrington, A.L., Moorhouse, T.P., Gelling, M., Bonesi, L. & Macdonald, D.W. (2009a). American mink control on inland rivers in southern England: an experimental test of a model strategy. *Biological Conservation* **142**: 839-849.

Harrington, L.A., Harrington, A.L., Yamaguchi, N., Thom, M.D., Ferreras, P., Windham, T.R. & Macdonald, D.W. (2009b). The impact of native competitors on an alien invasive: temporal niche shifts to avoid inter-specific aggression? *Ecology* **90**(5): 1207-1216.

Harris, D.B. & Macdonald, D.W. (2007). Interference competition between introduced black rats and endemic Galapagos rice rats. *Ecology* **88**: 2330-2344.

Harris, D.B., Gregory, S.D. & Macdonald, D.W. (2006). Space invaders? A search for patterns underlying the coexistence of alien black rats and Galapagos rice rats. *Oecologia* **149**: 276-288.

Holdaway, R.N. (1999). Introduced predators and avifaunal extinction in New Zealand. In *Extinctions in near time* Ed. R. D. E. MacPhee. Kluwer Academic/Plenum Publishers, New York. pp. 189-238.

Holdich, D.M. & Rogers, W.D. (1997). The white-clawed crayfish, *Austropotamobius pallipes*, in Great Britain and Ireland with particular reference to its conservation in Great Britain. *Bulletin Francais de la Peche et de la Pisciculture* **347**: 597-616.

Hutterer, R. & Oromi, P. (1993). La rata gigante de la Isla Santa Cruz, Galápagos: algunos datos y problemas. Resultados científicos del proyecto Galápagos: patrimonio de la humanidad. *Museo de Ciencias Naturales, Tenerife* **4**: 63-76.

Ibarra, J.T., Fasola, L., Macdonald, D.W., Rozzi, R. & Bonacic, C. (2009). Invasive American mink (*Mustela vison*) in wetlands of the Cape Horn Biosphere Reserve, southern Chile: what are they eating? *Oryx* **43**: 87-90.

Kauhala, K. (1994). The raccoon dog: a successful canid. *Canid News* **2**: 37-40.

Keat, S., Thompson, D.J., Kemp, S.J. & Watts, P.C. (2005). Ten microsatellite loci for the small red-eyed damselfly *Erythromma viridulum* (Charpentier). *Molecular Ecology Notes* **5**: 788-790.

Kitchener, A.C., Yamaguchi, N., Ward, J.M. & Macdonald, D.W. (2005). A diagnosis for the Scottish wildcat (*Felis silvestris*): a tool for conservation action for a critically-endangered felid. *Animal Conservation* **8**: 223-237.

Kolar, C.S. & Lodge, D.M. (2001). Progress in invasion biology: predicting invaders. *Trends in Ecology & Evolution* **16**: 199-204.

Lack, D. (1947). *Darwin's Finches*. Cambridge University Press, Cambridge.

Leader-Williams, N., Smith, R.I.L. & Rothery, P. (1987). Influence of introduced reindeer on the vegetation of South Georgia – results from a long-term exclusion experiment. *Journal of Applied Ecology* **24**: 801-822.

Lee, W.G. & Jamieson, I.G. (2001). *The Takahe: Fifty years of conservation management and research*. University of Otago Press, Dunedin.

Lodge, D.M. (1993). Species invasions and deletions: community effects and responses to climate and habitat change. In *Biotic interactions and global change*, Eds P. M. Kareiva, J. G. Kingsolver & R. B. Huey. Sinnauer Associates, Sunderland, MA. pp. 367-387.

Lowery, R.S. & Holdich, D.M. (1988). *Pacifastacus leniusculus* in North America and Europe, with details of the distribution of induced and native crayfish species in Europe. In *Freshwater crayfish: biology, management and exploitation*, Eds D. M. Holdich & R. S. Lowery. Croom Helm Ltd., London. pp. 283-308.

Lozan, J.L. (2000). On the threat to the European crayfish: A contribution with the study of the activity behaviour of four crayfish species (Decapoda: Astacidae)*. *Limnologica* **30**: 156-161.

Macdonald, D.W. & Strachan, R. (1999). *The mink and the water vole: analyses for conservation*. Wildlife Conservation Research Unit, Oxford.

Macdonald, D.W. & Thom, M.D. (2001). Alien carnivores: unwelcome experiments in ecological theory. In *Carnivore Conservation* Eds J. L. Gittleman, S. M. Funk, D. W. Macdonald & R. K. Wayne. Cambridge University Press, Cambridge. pp. 93-122.

Macdonald, D.W., Sidorovich, V.E., Maran, T. & Kruuk, H. (2002a). *European mink, Mustela lutreola: Analyses for conservation*. Wildlife Conservation Research Unit, Oxford.

Macdonald, D.W., Sidorovich, V., Anisomova, E.I., Sidorovich, N.V. & Johnson, P.J. (2002b). The impact of American mink *Mustela vison* and European mink *Mustela lutreola* on water voles *Arvicola terrestris* in Belarus. *Ecography* **25:** 295-302.

Macdonald, D.W., Daniels, M.J., Driscoll, C.A., Kitchener, A.C. & Yamaguchi, N. (2004). *The Scottish wildcat: analyses for conservation and an action plan*. Wildlife Conservation Research Unit, Oxford, UK.

Macdonald, D.W., King, C.M. & Strachan, R. (2007). Introduced species and the line between biodiversity conservation and naturalistic eugenics. In *Key Topics in Conservation Biology* Eds D.W. Macdonald & K. Service. Blackwell Publishing Ltd, Oxford. pp 186-205.

Macdonald, D.W., Yamaguchi, N., Kitchener, A.C., Daniels, M.J., Kilshaw, K. & Driscoll, C. A. (in press). Reversing cryptic extinction: the history, present and future of the Scottish wildcat. In *Biology and Conservation of Wild Felids* Eds D. W. Macdonald & A. J. Loveridge). Oxford University Press, Oxford.

Maron, J.L. & Vila, M. (2001). When do herbivores affect plant invasion? Evidence for the natural enemies and biotic resistance hypotheses. *Oikos* **5**: 361-373.

McCallum, H. & Dobson, A. (1995). Detecting disease and parasite threats to endangered species and ecosystems. *Trends in Ecology & Evolution* **10**: 190-194.

Mooney, H.A. & Cleland, E.E. (2001). The evolutionary impact of invasive species. *Proceedings of the National Academy of Sciences of the United States of America* **98**: 5446-5451.

Moorhouse, T.P. & Macdonald, D.W. (2008). What limits male range sizes at different population densities? Evidence from three populations of water voles. *Journal of Zoology* **274**: 395-402.

Moorhouse, T.P., Gelling, M. & Macdonald, D.W. (2008). Effects of forage availability on growth and maturation rates in water voles. *Journal of Animal Ecology* **77**: 1288-1295.

Moorhouse, T.P., Gelling, M. & Macdonald, D.W. (2009). Effects of habitat quality upon reintroduction success in water voles: Evidence from a replicated experiment. *Biological Conservation* **142:** 53-60.

Moyle, P.B. (1986). Fish introductions into North America: Patterns and ecological impact. In *Ecology of biological invasions of North America and Hawaii* Eds H. A. Mooney & J. A. Drake. Springer-Verlag, New York. pp. 27-43.

Newsome, A.E. & Noble, I.R. (1986). Ecological and physiological characteristics of invading species. In *Ecology of Biological Invasions* Eds R. H. Groves & J. J. Burdon. Cambridge University Press, Cambridge. pp. 1-20.

North, S.G., Bullock, D.J. & Dulloo, M.E. (1994). Changes in the vegetation and reptile populations on Round Island, Mauritius, following eradication of rabbits. *Biological Conservation* **67**: 21-28.

Nummi, P. (1996). Wildlife introductions to mammal deficient areas: the Nordic countries. *Wildlife Biology* **2**: 221-226.

Patton, J.L., Yang, S.Y. & Myers, P. (1975). Genetic and morphological divergence among introduced rat populations (*Rattus rattus*) of the Galapagos Archipelago, Ecuador. *Systematic Zoology* **24**: 296-310.

Pope, K.L., Garwood, J.M., Welsh, H.H. & Lawler, S.P. (2008). Evidence of indirect impacts of introduced trout on native amphibians via facilitation of a shared predator. *Biological Conservation* **141**: 1321-1331.

Pysek, P. (2006). *Fallopia japonica* http://www.europe-aliens.org/pdf/Fallopia_japonica.pdf Accessed online 12/12/08

Ruiz-Olmo, J., Palazon, S., Bueno, F., Bravo, C., Munilla, I. & Romero, R. (1997). Distribution, status and colonization of the American mink. *Journal of Wildlife Research* **2**: 30-36.

Safford, R.J. & Jones, C.G. (1998). Strategies for land-bird conservation on Mauritius. *Conservation Biology* **12**: 169-176.

Sainsbury, T. & Ward, L. (1996). Parapoxvirus infection in red squirrels. *Veterinary Record* **138**: 400.

Sale, P. F. (1974). Overlap in resource use and interspecific competition. *Oecologia* **17**: 245-256.

Sax, D.F., Gaines, S.D. & Brown, J.H. (2002). Species invasions exceed extinctions on islands worldwide: A comparative study of plants and birds. *American Naturalist* **160**: 766-783.

Secretariat of the Convention on Biological Diversity. (2007). *What are invasive alien species?* http://www.cbd.int/invasive/WhatareIAS.shtml. Accessed online 26th September 2008.

Shaw, G.L. & Dusanic, D.G. (1973). *Trypanosoma lewisi* - termination of preganancy in infected rat. *Experimental Parasitology* **33**: 46-55.

Shorten, M. (1954). *Squirrels*. Collins, London.

Sillero-Zubiri, C. & Macdonald, D.W. (1997). The *Ethiopian wolf - status survey and conservation action plan*. IUCN, Gland, Switzerland.

Sillero-Zubiri, C., Marino, J., Gottelli, D. & Macdonald. D.W. (2004). Ethiopian wolves. In *Biology and conservation of wild canids* Eds D.W. Macdonald & C. Sillero-Zubiri. Oxford University Press, Oxford. pp 311-322.

Smirnov, V.V. & Tretyakov, K. (1998). Changes in aquatic plant communities on the island of Valaam due to invasion by the muskrat *Ondatra zibethicus* L. (Rodentia, Mammalia). *Biodiversity and Conservation* **7**: 673-690.

Smith, A.P. & Quin, D.G. (1996). Patterns and causes of extinction and decline in Australian conilurine rodents. *Biological Conservation* **77**: 243-267.

Snell, H.L., Snell, H.M. & Stone, P.A. (1994). Accelerated mortality of *Opuntia* on Isla Plaza Sur: another threat from an introduced vertebrate? *Noticias de Galápagos* **53**: 19-20.

Scottish Natural Heritage. (2008). The Uist Wader Project - Historical Digest. http://www.snh.org.uk/scottish/wisles/waders/. Accessed online 26th September 2008.

Steadman, D.W. & Ray, C.E. (1982). The relationships of *Megaoryzomys curiori*, an extinct Cricetine rodent (Muroidea: Muridae) from the Galapagos Islands, Ecuador. *Smithsonian Contributions to Paleobiology* **I-IV**: 1-23.

Steadman, D.W., Stafford, T. W., Donahue, D.J. & Jull, A.J.T. (1991). Chronology of holocene vertebrate extinction in the Galapagos Islands. *Quaternary Research* **36**: 126-133.

Tayton, J. (2008). Canna seabird recovery project progress report 53. National Trust for Scotland, Edinburgh.

Tomback, D.F. & Resler, L.M. (2007). Invasive pathogens at alpine treeline: consequences for treeline dynamics. *Physical Geography* **28**: 397-418.

Towns, D.R., Simberloff, D. & Atkinson, I.A.E. (1997). Restoration of New Zealand islands: redressing the effects of introduced species. *Pacific Conservation Biology* **3**: 99-124.

Van Vuren, D. & Coblentz, B.E. (1987). Some ecological effects of feral sheep on Santa Cruz Island, California, USA. *Biological Conservation* **41**: 253-268.

Vitousek, P.M., Mooney, H.A., Lubchenco, J. & Melillo, J.M. (1997). Human domination of Earth's ecosystems. *Science* **277**: 494-499.

Wangchuk, T. (2005). The evolution, phylogeography, and conservation of the golden langur (*Trachypithecus geei*) in Bhutan. PhD, University of Maryland.

Wauters, L.A., Lurz, P.W.W. & Gurnell, J. (2000). Interspecific effects of grey squirrels (*Sciurus carolinensis*) on the space use and population demography of red squirrels (*Sciurus vulgaris*) in conifer plantations. *Ecological Research* **15**: 271-284.

Wauters, L.A., Gurnell, J., Martinoli, A. & Tosi, G. (2002a). Interspecific competition between native Eurasian red squirrels and alien grey squirrels: does resource partitioning occur? *Behavioral Ecology and Sociobiology* **52**: 332-341.

Wauters, L.A., Tosi, G. & Gurnell, J. (2002b). Interspecific competition in tree squirrels: do introduced grey squirrels (*Sciurus carolinensis*) deplete tree seeds hoarded by red squirrels (*S. vulgaris*)? *Behavioral Ecology and Sociobiology* **51**: 360-367.

Williams, E. (2006). Horse sense. *Audubon*, **Sept-Oct**.

Williamson, M. (1993). Invaders, weeds and the risk from genetically manipulated organisms. *Experientia* **49**: 219-224.

Williamson, M. (1996). *Biological Invasions*. Chapman & Hall, London.

Wilson, P.R., Karl, B.J., Toft, R.J., Beggs, J.R. & Taylor, R.H. (1998). The role of introduced predators and competitors in the decline of kaka (*Nestor meridionalis*) populations in New Zealand. *Biological Conservation* **83**: 175-185.

Wyatt, K.B., Campos, P.F., Gilbert, M.T.P., Kolokotronis, S.-O., Hynes, W.H., DeSalle, R., Daszak, P., MacPhee, R.D.E. & Greenwood, A.D. (2008). Historical mammal extinction on Christmas Island (Indian Ocean) correlates with introduced infectious disease. *PLoS ONE*, 3, e3602.

Zavaleta, E.S., Hobbs, R.J. & Mooney, H.A. (2001). Viewing invasive species removal in a whole-ecosystem context. *Trends in Ecology & Evolution* **16**: 454-459.

Macdonald, D.W., Shaw, R.F. & Moorhouse, T.P. (2010). Invasives: global lessons and local perspectives. In: *Species Management: Challenges and Solutions for the 21st Century*, ed. by J.M. Baxter and C.A. Galbraith. TSO Scotland, Edinburgh. pp. 167-191

Chapter 11

Alien plants in Scotland – is there a problem?

Chris D. Preston[1]

Summary

1. The very frequent assertion that invasive alien species are the second greatest threat to biodiversity is very doubtfully true at the global scale.
2. There is no justification for applying this global generalization to invasive plants in Scotland, where the northerly vegetation is relatively resistant to invasion and the native species are almost all wide-ranging rather than narrowly endemic.
3. Studies of species' loss in Britain highlight habitat destruction, agricultural intensification, the polarization of arable and pastoral agricultural systems with consequent under- or over-grazing, and eutrophication as the main causal factors; there is little evidence of the adverse effect of alien plant species.
4. In Scotland there are strong gradients in the density of alien species, with species concentrated in the lowlands of the south and east.
5. Efforts to control invasive aliens need to be concentrated on those few that have a seriously adverse effect on the native flora, of which the most troublesome is *Rhododendron ponticum*.
6. The spread of invasive species, especially in response to climate change, raises philosophical questions to which we currently have no convincing answers.

11.1 Introduction

Rhododendron (*Rhododendron ponticum*). © Lorne Gill/SN

As the terminology relating to alien species proliferates almost as rapidly as some of the species, and at least some of the arguments in this field are apparently based on misunderstandings of the nature and purpose of the classification of species as alien, it seems best to start with some definitions. I use the following definitions:

- A *native* species is one which arrived in the study area without human intervention, having come from an area in which it is native, *or* one which has arisen *de novo* in the study area.
- An *alien* species is one which was brought to the study area by humans, intentionally or unintentionally, even if native to the source area *or* one which has come into the area without human intervention, but from an area in which it is alien.

The definitions therefore apply only to a defined study area, in this case Scotland. Examples of the many species with well-documented fossil histories which show that they arrived in Scotland without human intervention are hazel (*Corylus avellana*), Scots pine (*Pinus sylvestris*), broad-leaved pondweed (*Potamogeton natans*) and Alpine meadow-rue (*Thalictrum alpinum*). Few species are thought to have arisen *de novo* in Scotland. The recently described (*Sorbus pseudomeinichii*) is an example of a taxon which has clearly evolved by *in situ* hybridization in Scotland, in this case between rowan (*S. aucuparia*) and Arran service-tree (*S. pseudofennica*) (Robertson and Sydes, 2006). Many species which are alien in Scotland have been brought directly from the areas where they are native, such as New Zealand willowherb (*Epilobium brunnescens*) and few-flowered garlic (*Allium paradoxum*), both garden escapes which were first recorded in Britain in Midlothian. Unintentional introductions include many species introduced as propagules attached to imported wool; their identification provided good sport for early 20th century botanists in places such as Galashiels (Hayward and Druce, 1919). The second alien criterion, covering species which have come into the area without human intervention but from an area in which they are alien, is needed to cover plants such as American willowherb (*Epilobium ciliatum*), which clearly spread northwards into Scotland from the naturalized population in England (Preston, 1989). This is also true of the current Scottish populations of Oxford ragwort (*Senecio squalidus*), although there were earlier, non-persistent escapes from cultivation (Kent, 1955). Inevitably the history of some species is so complex that it does not fit easily into either the native or the alien category. The Welsh groundsel (*Senecio cambrensis*) has evolved (separately) in Wales and Scotland, but one of the two parents from which it has arisen is the introduced *S. squalidus* (Abbott *et al.*, 1997). Further species with complex histories can be expected as the native and alien floras interact.

The classification of species as native or alien is a single-character classification which distinguishes taxa by their method of arrival. It is *not* a value judgement on the species. Several authors, most recently

Plate 11.1 Indian balsam (*Impatiens glandulifera*) a relatively recent introduced species. © George Logan/SNH

Warren (2007), have criticized the distinction between native and alien species, and Warren supposes that it "seems destined for abandonment because its conceptual foundations are disintegrating". Such authors have failed to distinguish sufficiently clearly the biogeographical classification of species as native or alien from the common use of the terms to attach value judgements to species, with natives regarded as good and aliens as evil. It is difficult to know how the biogeography of Scotland could be understood if the native/alien distinction was somehow erased from the minds of biologists.

Alien species remain alien no matter how long they have been resident in the study area. In Britain we have recently begun to distinguish ancient introductions or *archaeophytes* (thought to have arrived before 1500) from more recent introductions or *neophytes* (Preston *et al*., 2004). Archaeophytes include many arable weeds, such as cornflower (*Centaurea cyanus*) and long-headed poppy (*Papaver dubium*), as well as some medicinal plants like elecampane (*Inula helenium*). Neophytes are more numerous, and include many European and Asian species imported by horticulturists (e.g. Norway maple (*Acer platanoides*), Himalayan cotoneaster (*Cotoneaster simonsii*), Indian balsam (*Impatiens glandulifera*)) as well, of course, as all established species from North and South America (e.g. Canadian waterweed (*Elodea canadensis*), fuchsia (*Fuchsia magellanica*), Sitka spruce (*Picea sitchensis*)) and Australasia (e.g. New Zealand pigmyweed (*Crassula helmsii*)). This chapter is solely concerned with neophytes.

11.2 Invasive alien species – the second greatest threat to biodiversity in Britain?

Globally, invasive alien species are very often cited as the second greatest threat to biodiversity after habitat destruction. This assertion appears in a range of contexts from the introductory sentence of many scientific papers to dramatic posters available from the Global Invasive Species Programme (www.gisp.org). Although originally applied to global biodiversity, it has also been applied to British biodiversity, as on the Plantlife UK website (www.plantlife.org.uk) which explicitly states that "Non-native invasive plants are the second most important threat to our native plants after habitat destruction".

Before considering whether it is valid to apply the global generalization to Britain, and to Scotland, and to plants, it is worth noting that even in the global context it must be regarded as unsubstantiated. Most authors making this claim either cite no source, or cite a source which is clearly secondary. In fact the claim appears to originate with E. O. Wilson (1992)[1] who lists "introduction of animals such as rats and goats, and diseases carried by these exotic animals" as two of the four "mindless horsemen of the environmental apocalypse" and says that "in recent centuries, and to an accelerating degree during our generation, habitat destruction is foremost among the lethal forces, followed by the invasion of exotic animals". Chew and Laubichler's (2003) criticism that Wilson's view represents "a vast intuitive extrapolation from unpublished data about North American fishes" is clearly unfair, as Wilson's view is based on a more general consideration of the literature, with Mooney and Drake (1986) cited as the main source and numerous examples provided. Data (published and unpublished) on fish do feature prominently in his discussion, as do the molluscs of oceanic islands; fish are perhaps singularly vulnerable to the deliberate introduction for economic reasons of alien species. It is, however, very clear that Wilson was primarily concentrating on animals. A further and more quantitative study of 2,490 "imperilled species", including both animals and plants, ranked alien species as the second of five threats, less than habitat degradation but more than pollution, over-exploitation and disease (Wilcove *et al.*, 1998). This study, which highlighted its conclusion that "Habitat loss is the single greatest threat to biodiversity, followed by the spread of alien species" in a prominent text-box, was doubtless influential in propagating the view and extending it from "animals" to "species". However, a later assessment of threats on a world-wide basis ranked biotic exchange as only the fourth of five threats, after land use change, climate change and nitrogen deposition but above changes in atmospheric CO_2 (Sala *et al.*,

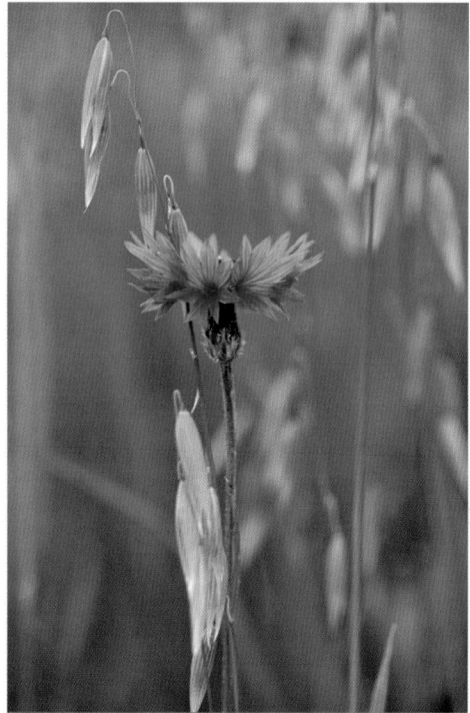

Plate 11.2 Cornflower (*Centaurea cyanus*). © Lorne Gill/SNH

[1] My quotations are taken from a copy of the first British printing, published in 1993 by Allen Lane The Penguin Press.

2000). The difference between the five threats chosen by these two groups of authors shows that there is considerable subjectivity in the way threats are grouped. Although Sala *et al.*'s paper is very widely quoted in other contexts, one rarely sees their conclusion about biotic exchange cited by authors writing about invasive species.

Almost all authors agree that there is widespread geographical variation in the effects of invasive species. The results obtained by Wilcove *et al.* (1998) show this, as the proportion of species that was threatened by invasives in Hawaii (included in their study) was much greater than that in the continental states. Hawaii has become a classic case of the impact of invasives on a species-rich and largely endemic biota (Loope, 1997). Sala *et al.* (2000) regard Mediterranean ecosystems and southern temperate forests as the major terrestrial biomes which are most susceptible to the impact of alien species, with Arctic, Alpine and Boreal biomes as the least susceptible. Within biomes, the flora of Europe seems to be more successful when transplanted to similar climatic areas ('neo-Europes') elsewhere than the flora of other continents is in Europe (Crosby, 1986); the British flora is more invasive than invaded. For all these reasons it is clear that Scotland is, as Jim Dickson (2001) has pointed out, no Hawaii, being much less susceptible to invasive species (Table 11.1). Even if invasive alien species are the second greatest threat to global biodiversity, this generalization cannot be applied to invasive plants in Britain.

Table 11.1 Differences between Hawaii and Scotland which may influence the effect of alien species on biodiversity.

	Hawaii	Scotland
Climate	Warm temperate/subtropical	Cool temperate
Isolated from other biota	For long periods	Never
Human occupation	Short (1,000 years)	Long (9,000 years)
Native biota	Species-rich; most species endemic	Species-poor; most species wide-ranging

Studies of historical vascular plant extinctions at the county level in Britain highlight land-use change (including building development, habitat destruction and modification resulting from agricultural intensification, and changing levels of grazing) and eutrophication as important causal factors, but there is little evidence for the effects of alien species even in SE England where they are most numerous (Preston, 2000; Walker and Preston, 2006). In NW Scotland it is difficult to identify major changes in native plant distribution in the last two centuries; the only marked losses appear to result from the disappearance of arable plots as a mixed farming economy has become overwhelmingly pastoral (Pearman and Preston, 2000; Pearman *et al.*, 2008). These studies support Manchester and Bullock's (2000) view that "there is little evidence that introductions to the UK have led to species extinctions" and the conclusion by Maskell *et al.* (2006) that alien species "are not a significant influence on vegetation change at the landscape scale". Even in the United States, "there is no evidence that even a single long-term resident has been driven to extinction, or even extirpated within a single US state, because of competition from an introduced plant species" (Davis, 2003). It may be that things will be different in future, but the paucity of 'cautionary tales' suggests that the direct impact of alien plants on their native counterparts is less great than is sometimes imagined.

11.3 Enumeration of the alien vascular plants of Scotland

Producing a comprehensive list of the alien vascular plants of Britain, or any of its component countries, is far from easy. Species range from casuals which have been recorded just once to species which are well-established and frequent. Even the standard British works (Clement and Foster, 1994; Ryves *et al.*, 1996) include many rather broad aggregate groups and do not specify which of the component segregates have been recorded in the British Isles. Table 11.2 enumerates those species which are mapped solely as aliens in Scotland in the *New Atlas of the British and Irish Flora* (Preston *et al.*, 2002). This atlas maps the species included in Stace's *New Flora* (1997), which aimed to include naturalized species but only the most frequent casuals. A detailed listing of alien vascular plants in Scotland is provided by Welch *et al.* (2001).

Table 11.2 The number of taxa mapped solely as aliens in Scotland by Preston *et al.* (2002). The status categories refer to the British Isles as a whole; taxa which are listed as established rather than casual are not necessarily established in Scotland.

Status	Recorded since 1970	Not seen since 1970	Total
Established neophyte species	673	92	765
Established neophyte hybrids	77	2	79
Casuals	78	72	150
Species native elsewhere in British Isles	103	29	132
Total	**931**	**195**	**1,126**

There is a clear gradient in the frequency of alien species from southern England to north-west Scotland (Figure 11.1). Alien species are more unevenly recorded than natives as recorders differ in the degree to which they record the less well naturalized taxa, but this does not obscure the overall gradient or the concentrations in urban areas, notably London. The number of alien species with latitude decreases more rapidly than the number of native species, so that the proportion of aliens as well as the number decreases northwards (Figure 11.2). This reflects the fact that in Britain alien species tend to come from more southern areas, and especially from areas further south in mainland Europe (Welch *et al.*, 2001; Hill *et al.*, 2005), as well as to be plants of disturbed and artificial habitats (Maskell *et al.*, 2006). There are strong local gradients as well: even on the island (and National Nature Reserve) of Rum, there is a strong concentration around the castle policies at Kinloch in the sheltered east of the island, but large areas on the exposed and uninhabited western side have no alien species (Pearman *et al.*, 2008). There is also a much stronger turnover of alien than of native species: 91% of the native species recorded on Rum have been refound since 2000 compared to only 54% of the aliens.

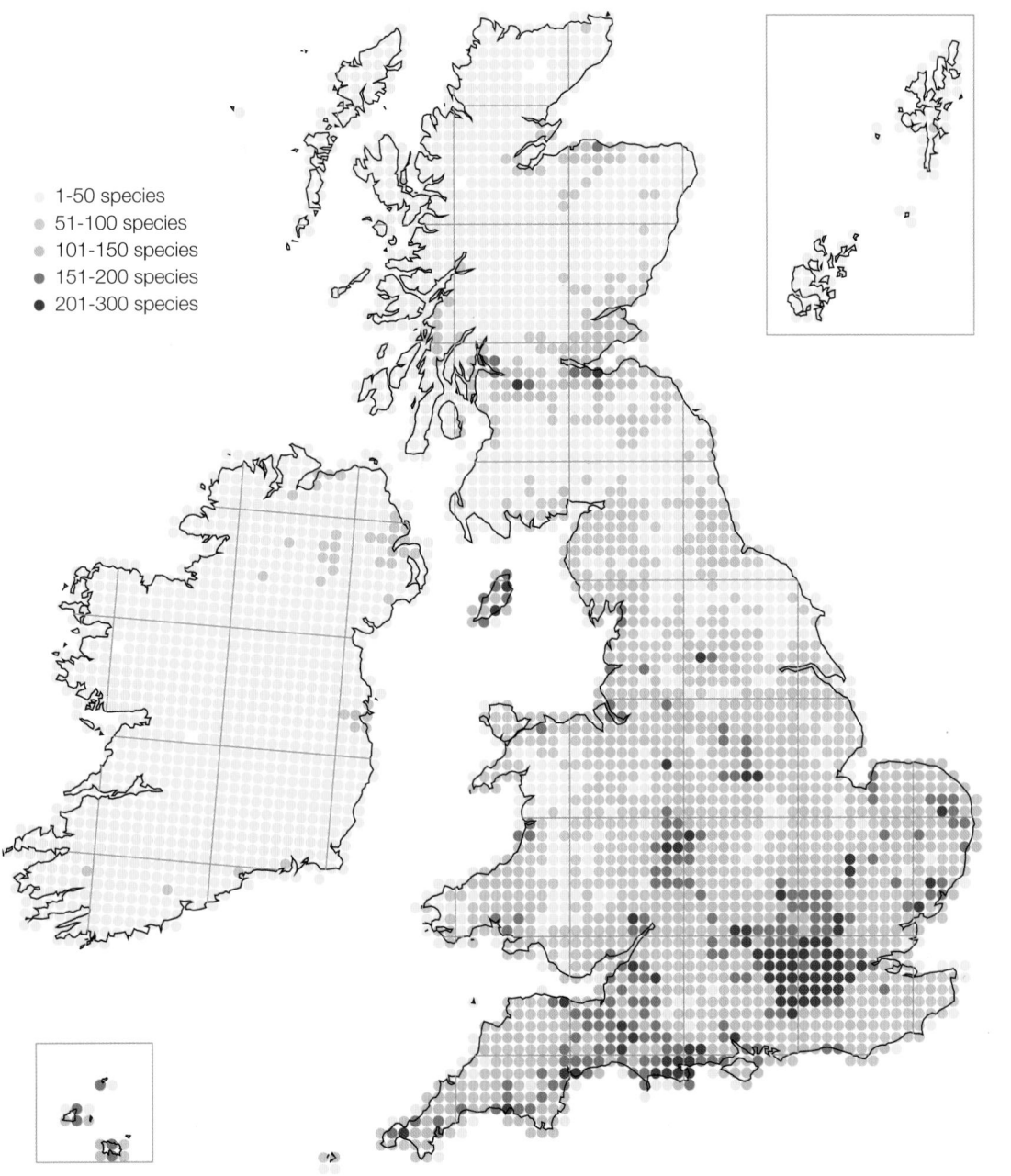

Figure 11.1 The number of neophyte species and hybrids established in the 10-km squares of the British Isles. Only species recorded from 1970 onwards are included. Species which are only casual in the British Isles are excluded.

○ 1-50 species
● 51-100 species
● 101-150 species
● 151-200 species
● 201-300 species

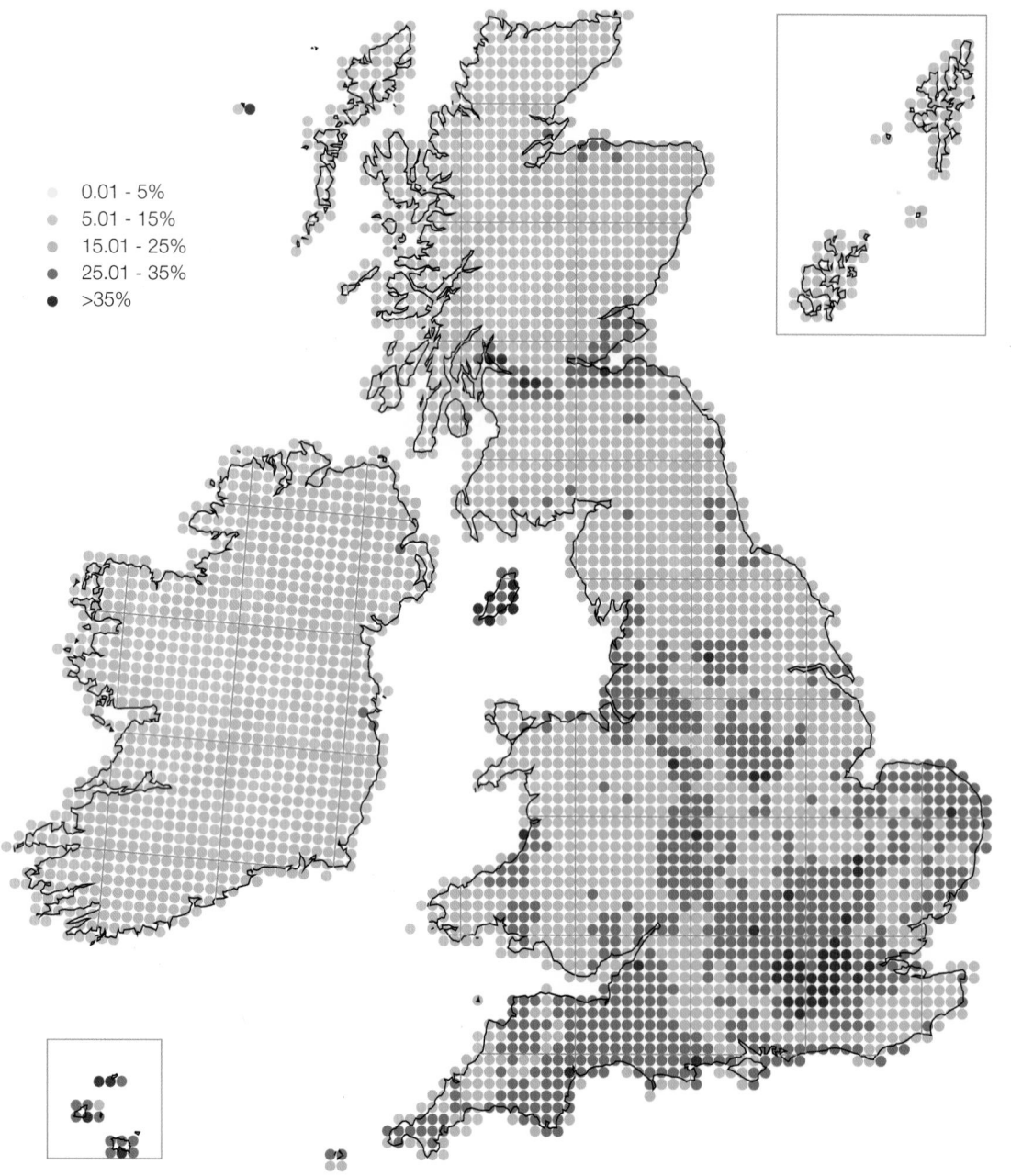

Figure 11.2 The neophyte species and hybrids established in the 10-km squares of the British Isles, shown as a proportion of the native species in that square.

11.4 The most frequent neophyte species and hybrids in Scotland

The most frequent neophytes in Scotland are listed in Table 11.3. All but two were deliberately introduced, most of them for horticultural purposes. The most widespread is pineappleweed (*Matricaria discoidea*), which in the mainland is only absent from the most montane 10-km squares, and which occurs throughout the Northern and Western Isles. It is typically found on trampled paths and in gateways, and has little or no impact on biodiversity. The next most frequent species is sycamore, a tree which is regarded favourably by some and unfavourably by other natural historians: even bryologists disagree about its impacts (Bates *et al.*, 1997). Some naturalists are so keen on the species that they have even tried to convince themselves that it is might be native in the north and west (Green, 2005). As Dickson (1998) points out, a scholarly account of the history of sycamore in Britain is badly needed, but if it is not an archaeophyte it must be a very early neophyte. Only two of the species listed in Table 11.3 are

Table 11.3 The neophytes in Scotland recorded from more than 400 10-km square squares (Preston *et al.*, 2002). The counts refer to the number of squares in which the species has been recorded since 1970; the total number of squares in Scotland is 1,117.

Species	English name	Square count	Life-form	Reason for introduction (if deliberate)
Matricaria discoidea	Pineappleweed	883	Annual herb	
Acer pseudoplatanus	Sycamore	806	Broad-leaved tree	Horticulture?
Epilobium brunnescens	New Zealand willowherb	667	Perennial herb	Horticulture
Rhododendron ponticum	Rhododendron	588	Ericaceous shrub	Horticulture
Mimulus	Monkeyflowers	587	Aggregate of related perennial herbaceous species and hybrids	Horticulture
Picea sitchensis	Sitka spruce	523	Coniferous tree	Forestry
Larix decidua	European larch	510	Coniferous tree	Horticulture and forestry
Aesculus hippocastanum	Horse-chestnut	477	Broad-leaved tree	Horticulture
Ribes uva-crispa	Gooseberry	467	Shrub	Culinary
Fallopia japonica	Japanese knotweed	453	Giant perennial herb	Horticulture
Claytonia sibirica	Pink purslane	440	Annual to perennial herb	Horticulture
Myrrhis odorata	Sweet cicely	436	Perennial herb	Culinary
Veronica filiformis	Slender speedwell	432	Perennial herb	Horticulture
Crocosmia aurea × pottsii (*C. × crocosmiiflora*)	Montbretia	420	Perennial herb	Horticulture
Symphoricarpos albus	Snowberry	418	Shrub	Horticulture
Picea abies	Norway spruce	412	Coniferous tree	Horticulture and forestry
Epilobium ciliatum	American willowherb	401	Perennial herb	

Plate 11.3 Sycamore (*Acer pseudoplatanus*), the second most frequent neophyte in Scotland. © John M. Baxter

widely regarded as having a seriously detrimental effect on native species. One is *Rhododendron 'ponticum'*, many populations of which appear not to be wild-type *R. ponticum* but to have become introgressed with other species in cultivation (Milne and Abbott, 2000). This spreads in dense thickets in habitats which include semi-natural oakwoods such as Ellary Wood SSSI (Figure 11.3), an Atlantic oakwood rich in hyperoceanic bryophytes which are of international importance in Scotland (Hodgetts, 1997). The other species which is widely perceived as detrimental is Japanese knotweed (*Fallopia japonica*), although even this divides opinion, with some experienced botanists arguing that it is starting to play a valuable role in urban habitats by providing a quasi-woodland cover which supports its own association of species (Gilbert, 1994, 2001; Hart *et al.*, 1997).

Figure 11.3 Rhododendron *'ponticum'* invading an Atlantic oakwood, Ellary Wood SSSI. © Gordon Rothero

Plate 11.4 Rhododendron (*Rhododendron ponticum*) which can be so appealing to the eye. © Lorne Gill/SNH

11.5 Attitudes to the presence and control of alien species

11.5.1 Are alien species intrinsically undesirable?

There appears to be little agreement amongst conservationists on one fundamental question. Is the presence of alien species in semi-natural habitats undesirable in itself, or is their presence only undesirable when they have adverse impacts on native species? The *Nature Conservation Review* (Ratcliffe, 1977, p. 7), normally a model of clear writing, gives uncharacteristically ambiguous guidance on this point:

> "An abundance or predominance of obviously introduced species usually, in fact, reduces the value of an area, though in moderation, non-indigenous species may add to diversity and interest".

Elsewhere (Ratcliffe, 1977, p. 352) the NCR suggests that the presence of introduced species "is not regarded as undesirable unless there is definite evidence of this in the form of competition with more highly valued natives" but I doubt if there is any consensus on this point. A request for participants in the SNH conference to say (by a show of hands) whether or not they regarded alien species as intrinsically undesirable showed no clear majority for one view or the other.

11.5.2 Alien species and climate change

Although I earlier indicated my fundamental disagreement with Warren (2007) over the division of species into natives and aliens, I do have much more sympathy with both him and earlier authors such as Peretti (1998) who question the blanket condemnation of alien species. If the environment changes, the spread of plant species is likely, in many cases, to be mediated by human dispersal; human beings are (in the modern landscape) much more effective than 'natural' dispersal agents (Wichmann et al., 2009). Changes in vegetation in response to climate change are therefore likely to involve the spread of species which will often be alien at least regionally, and perhaps sometimes nationally. Are we to continue to strive ever more frenetically to preserve the vegetation we inherited from a former climate? In Norway there are efforts to conserve the arctic fox (Alopex lagupus) by shooting the red foxes (Vulpes vulpes) which are spreading into areas where woodland is spreading uphill into hitherto open landscapes. Is this the right approach, or should we accept that in new environments, new species and communities will inevitably spread at the expense of those which are no longer adapted to the prevailing conditions?

11.5.3 Restricting the sale of alien plants: evidence-based conservation versus the precautionary principle

As Table 11.3, and the more comprehensive national inventories (Welch et al., 2001; Hill et al., 2005) demonstrate, horticultural imports have been the major source of established neophytes in Britain. This has not only led to attempts to restrict the sale of known nuisance species, but also to discussions of how future invasions will be prevented. It is extremely difficult to predict which species will become invasive (Williamson and Brown, 1986; Goodwin et al., 1999; Lambdon and Hulme, 2006; Wichmann et al., 2009). There must therefore be a conflict between the precautionary principle, which would suggest restricting the sale of large numbers of species, and the requirement for evidence-based conservation which would postpone restrictions until there is evidence that a species is problematical, and thus risk postponing action until the problem is out of control. There is even the view that gardeners should be encouraged to grow only native species. We should perhaps all in considering these matters give more prominence to the need to protect individual freedom – it is all too easy to be in favour of freedom in general, but to consider that one's own particular interests represent such an important special case that they justify restrictions. Thus liberty is squeezed on all sides by the relentless activities of pressure groups.

Plate 11.5 European larch (*Larix decidua*) create a striking contrast in mixed coniferous woodland. © Lorne Gill/SNH

11.6 Conclusions

Alien plants in Scotland – is there a problem? Yes, but not as great a problem as might be imagined. If we exaggerate the problem we risk distracting attention from the major threats to biodiversity, some of which might be much harder to tackle (both intellectually and politically). We also dilute the effort needed to tackle those few really problematic invasive plants, of which *Rhododendron* is surely the greatest problem in Scotland. These need to be tackled not by strategies, meetings or even conferences but by effective action in the field.

11.7 Acknowledgements

I am very grateful to SNH for the invitation to participate in what was a superbly organized and very stimulating conference. I thank Helen and David Roy for their help in the tracing the source of the belief that invasive species are the second greatest threat to biodiversity, Gordon Rothero for kindly providing the photograph of rhododendron invasion and Stephanie Ames for preparing the distribution maps. I should perhaps state that the views expressed in this chapter are entirely my own.

References

Abbott, R. J., Harris, S. A. & Lowe, A. J. (1997). Interspecific hybridization and the origin of new plant taxa in Scotland. *Botanical Journal of Scotland* **49:** 247-256.

Bates, J. W., Proctor, M. C. F., Preston, C. D., Hodgetts, C. D. & Perry, A. R. (1997). Occurrence of epiphytic bryophytes in a 'tetrad' transect across southern Britain. 1. Geographical trends in abundance and evidence of recent change. *Journal of Bryology* **19:** 685-714.

Chew, M. K. & Laubichler, M. D. (2003). Metaphors, misuse and misconceptions. Response. *Science* **301:** 1481-1482.

Clement, E. J. & Foster, M. C. (1994). *Alien plants of the British Isles.* Botanical Society of the British Isles, London.

Crosby, J. L. (1986). *Ecological imperialism.* Cambridge University Press, Cambridge.

Davis, M. A. (2003). Biotic globalization: does competition from introduced species threaten biodiversity? *BioScience* **53:** 481-489.

Dickson, J. H. (1998). Plant introductions in Scotland. In *Species history in Scotland*, Ed. R. A. Lambert. Scottish Cultural Press, Edinburgh. pp. 38-44.

Dickson, J.H. (2001). Alien vascular plants in Scotland: concepts and consequences – Scotland no Hawai'i. *Glasgow Naturalist* **23**, suppl: 2-12.

Gilbert, O. (1994). Japanese knotweed - what problem? *Urban Wildlife News* **11(3):** 1-2.

Gilbert, O. (2001). Figs, Japanese knotweed and Himalayan balsam enhance the urban ecology of Sheffield. *Glasgow Naturalist* **23**, suppl: 52-56.

Goodwin, B. J., McAllister, A. J. & Fahrig, L. (1999). Predicting invasiveness of plant species based on biological information. *Conservation Biology* **13:** 422-426.

Green, T. (2005). Is there a case for the Celtic Maple or the Scots Plane? *British Wildlife* **16:** 184-188.

Hart, M. L., Bailey, J. P., Hollingsworth, P. M. & Watson, K. J. (1997). Sterile species and fertile hybrids of Japanese Knotweeds along the River Kelvin. *Glasgow Naturalist* **23:** 18-22.

Hayward, I. M. & Druce, G. C. (1919). *The adventive Flora of Tweedside.* T. Buncle & Co., Arbroath.

Hill, M., Baker, R., Broad, G., Chandler, P. J., Copp, G. H., Ellis, J., Jones, D., Hoyland, C., Laing, I., Longshaw, M., Moore, N., Parrott, D., Pearman, D., Preston, C., Smith, R. M. & Waters, R. (2005). *Audit of non-native species in England.* English Nature Research Report Number 662. English Nature, Peterborough.

Hodgetts, N. G. (1997). Atlantic bryophytes in Scotland. *Botanical Journal of Scotland* **49:** 375-385.

Kent, D. H. (1955). The Scottish records of *Senecio squalidus* L. *Proceedings of the Botanical Society of the British Isles* **1:** 312-313.

Lambdon, P. W. & Hulme, P. E. (2006). Predicting the invasion success of Mediterranean alien plants from their introduction characteristics. *Ecography* **29:** 853-865.

Loope, L. (1997). The Hawaiian islands as a laboratory for addressing alien species problems. In *Principles of conservation biology*, edn 2, Eds G. K. Meffe & C. R. Carroll. Sinauer Associates, Sunderland, Massachusetts. pp. 259-260.

Manchester, S. J. & Bullock, J. M. (2000). The impacts of non-native species on UK biodiversity and the effectiveness of control. *Journal of Applied Ecology* **37:** 845-864.

Maskell, L. C., Firbank, L. G., Thompson, K., Bullock, J. M. & Smart, S. M. (2006). Interactions between non-native plant species and the floristic composition of common habitats. *Journal of Ecology* **94:** 1052-1060.

Milne, R. I. & Abbott, R. J. (2000). Origin and evolution of invasive naturalized material of *Rhododendron ponticum* L. in the British Isles. *Molecular Ecology* **9:** 541-556.

Mooney, H. A. & Drake, J. A. (1986). *Ecology of Biological Invasions of North America and Hawaii.* Ecological Studies 58. Springer-Verlag, New York.

Pearman, D. A. & Preston, C. D. (2000). *A Flora of Tiree, Gunna and Coll.* Privately published, Dorchester.

Pearman, D. A., Preston, C. D., Rothero, G. P. & Walker, K. J. (2008). *The flora of Rum: an Atlantic island reserve.* Privately published, Truro.

Peretti, J. H. (1998). Nativism and nature: rethinking biological invasion. *Environmental Values* **7:** 183-192.

Preston, C. D. (1989). The spread of *Epilobium ciliatum* Raf. in the British Isles. *Watsonia* **17:** 279-288.

Preston, C. D. (2000). Engulfed by suburbia or destroyed by the plough: the ecology of extinction in Middlesex and Cambridgeshire. *Watsonia* **23:** 59-81.

Preston, C. D., Pearman, D. A. & Dines, T. D. (2002). *New atlas of the British and Irish flora.* Oxford University Press, Oxford.

Preston, C. D., Pearman, D. A. & Hall, A. R. (2004). Archaeophytes in Britain. *Botanical Journal of the Linnean Society:* **145:** 257-294.

Ratcliffe, D. A. (1977). *A nature conservation review. Volume 1.* Cambridge University Press, Cambridge.

Robertson, A. & Sydes, C. (2006). *Sorbus pseudomeinichii*, a new endemic *Sorbus* (Rosaceae) from Arran, Scotland. *Watsonia* **26:** 9-14.

Ryves, T. B., Clement, E. J. & Foster, M. C. (1996). *Alien grasses of the British Isles.* Botanical Society of the British Isles, London.

Sala, O. E., Chapin, F. S., Armesto, J. J., Berlow, E., Bloomfield, J., Dirzo, R., Huber-Sanwald, E., Huenneke, L. F., Jackson, R. B., Kinzig, A., Leemans, R., Lodge, D. M., Mooney, H. A., Oesterheld, M., Poff, N. L., Sykes, M. T., Walker, B. H., Walker, M. & Wall, D. H. (2000). Biodiversity - Global biodiversity scenarios for the year 2100. *Science* **287:** 1770-1774.

Stace, C. A. (1997). *New Flora of the British Isles*, edn 2. Cambridge University Press, Cambridge.

Walker, K. J. & Preston, C. D. (2006). Ecological predictors of extinction risk in the flora of lowland England, U.K. *Biodiversity and Conservation* **15:** 1913-1942.

Warren, C. R. (2007). Perspectives on the 'alien' versus 'native' species debate: a critique of concepts, language and practice. *Progress in Human Geography* **31:** 427-446.

Welch, D., Carss, D. N., Gornall, J., Manchester, S. J., Marquiss, M., Preston, C. D., Telfer, M. G., Arnold, H. R. & Holbrook, J. (2001). *An audit of alien species in Scotland.* SNH review no. 139. Scottish Natural Heritage, Battleby.

Wichmann, M. C., Alexander, M. J., Soons, M. B., Galsworthy, S., Dunne, L., Gould, R., Fairfax, C., Niggemann, M., Hails, R. S. & Bullock, J. M. (2009). Human-mediated dispersal of seeds over long distances. *Proceedings of the Royal Society (B)* **276:** 523-532.

Wilcove, D. S., Rothstein, D., Dubow, J., Phillips, A. & Losos, E. (1998). Quantifying threats to imperiled species in the United States. *BioScience* **48:** 607-615.

Williamson, M. H. & Brown, K. C. (1986). The analysis and modelling of British invasions. *Philosophical Transactions of the Royal Society (B)* **314**: 505-522.

Wilson, E. O. (1992). *The diversity of life.* Belknap Press, Cambridge, Massachusetts.

Preston, C.D. (2010). Alien plants in Scotland – is there a problem? In: *Species Management: Challenges and Solutions for the 21st Century*, ed. by J.M. Baxter and C.A. Galbraith. TSO Scotland, Edinburgh. pp. 193-208

208

Chapter 12

Ecological risk analysis of alien species – the Norwegian experience

Ingrid Salvesen[1], Lisbeth Gederaas[1] and Åslaug Viken[1]

Summary

1. The World Conservation Union (IUCN) definition of alien species has formed the basis for the work.
2. A total of 2,485 alien species have been recorded in Norway, nearly 70% of which are vascular plants.
3. Risk analysis have been carried out on 215 of the recorded species in Norway.
4. The 2007 Norwegian Black List is the first official overview of ecological risk analyses of alien species in Norway.
5. No economic or health effects of alien species have been assessed.
6. The most important dispersal route is through land-based primary industries, primarily by import of plants and plant material.

[1] The Norwegian Biodiversity Information Centre, Erling Skakkesgt. 47, 7491 Trondheim, Norway

12.1 Introduction

Greylag (*Anser anser*) and Canada (*Branta canadensis*) Geese. © Morten Ekk

Alien species have been dispersing in Norway for a long time, following both intentional and unintentional introductions (Tømmerås, 1994; Weidema, 2000; Bevanger, 2005). The "Tromsø palm" (*Heracleum persicum*) and the giant hogweed (*H. mantegazzianum*) were intentionally introduced to Norway as ornamental plants, the former as long ago as the 1830s. Both plants are among the most problematical alien species in Norway today. Another example is the American mink (*Neovison vison*) which became established in Norway shortly after the first mink farm was built in 1927. In the course of 50 years, it has colonized most of the country apart from some island areas. Examples of more recent introductions are the red king crab (*Paralithodes camtschaticus*) which was first recorded in Norway in 1977 and the Asian (Harlequin) ladybird (*Harmonia axyridis*) which was first observed on imported plants from the Netherlands in 2006 (Staverløkk and Sæthre, 2007).

Plate 12.1 American mink (*Neovison vison*) became established in Norway shortly after the first mink farm was built in 1927. In the course of 50 years, it has colonized most of the country apart from some islands. © Morten Ekker

Due to expected changes in climate and international patterns of transport and trade, introduction and establishment of alien species are expected to become a growing threat to the conservation of biodiversity and ecosystem functions in Norway. As a result of a growing awareness of alien species, the authorities have drawn up a cross-sectorial national strategy which was published in 2007 (For further details see http://www.regjeringen.no/en/dep/md/documents-and-publications/Reports-and-plans/Plans/2007/Norwegian-Strategy-on-Invasive-Alien-Spe.html?id=469655).The strategy is based on the precautionary principle where the main focus is to prevent introductions.

The Norwegian Biodiversity Information Centre (NBIC) was formally established by the Government in 2004 and was set up with the intention of providing information on biological diversity in Norway. The NBIC performs inventories, and makes information on biodiversity more easily accessible in close cooperation with research institutions, consultancy firms and voluntary organizations. The NBIC has no authority to implement efforts related to alien species and the responsibility of management lies with state, regional or community level authorities.

Plate 12.2 Red king crab (*Paralithodes camtschatica*). The red king crab was released in several places in the former Soviet Union over a considerable period of time to form the basis for a commercial fishery. It was first recorded in Norway in 1977 and since then the population has grown rapidly. It may pose a threat to both the general bottom fauna and cod fry, the latter because it is host to a lethal blood parasite of cod. © Anette Karlsen

As a part of its independent role, in autumn 2005 the NBIC started an initiative to compile a directory of alien species that have been recorded in Norway and to undertake ecological risk analyses of a selection of them. The work on alien species was undertaken by a team of scientific experts from several research institutions and concluded in May 2007 with the publication of the 2007 Norwegian Black List (Gederaas *et al.*, 2007). The Black List has primarily been drawn up to promote management of biological diversity based on knowledge of the threat posed by alien species, but also to spread information on alien species in Norway to relevant target groups in society.

12.1.1 Definition of alien species

The World Conservation Union (IUCN) definition of alien species has formed the basis for the work: *'An alien species (non-native, non-indigenous, foreign, exotic) means a species, subspecies, or lower taxon occurring outside of its natural range (past or present) and dispersal potential (i.e. outside the range it occupies naturally or could not occupy without direct or indirect introduction or care by humans) and includes any part, gametes or propagule of such species that might survive and subsequently reproduce'* (IUCN, 2000).

12.1.2 Delimitations of the work

Based on the IUCN definition, the following alien species were included in this study:

a) Species intentionally released into the wild.
b) Species that have escaped from captivity and breeding, or that have escaped into the wild from cultivation and commercial activity.
c) Species that have arrived as stowaways during transportation and/or movement of animals, plants, goods and people.
d) Species dispersed from wild populations in neighbouring countries, whose origin is due to a), b) or c).
e) Species spread with the aid of people, where information on the means of dispersal is inadequate.
f) Norwegian species (indigenous) spread to new parts of Norway by human activity.
g) Improved, indigenous species spread in Norway.

It was decided not to place a specific delimitation back in time from when species are to be considered alien. Any such delimitation was undertaken by the scientist(s) responsible for the individual group of species. The work nevertheless mainly covers species that have entered Norway during the past 200 years. Alien species that are spreading in neighbouring countries and which it is assumed will be able to establish themselves in Norway ("door-knockers") are not included in the work. Species such as musk ox (*Ovibos moschatus*) and wild boar (*Sus scrofa*) which have been reintroduced, but could be considered indigenous, are both included in the national survey of alien species.

Species that are regularly introduced to Norway, but which also already have indigenous populations here, are not included. Individuals of indigenous species that have entered the country with human

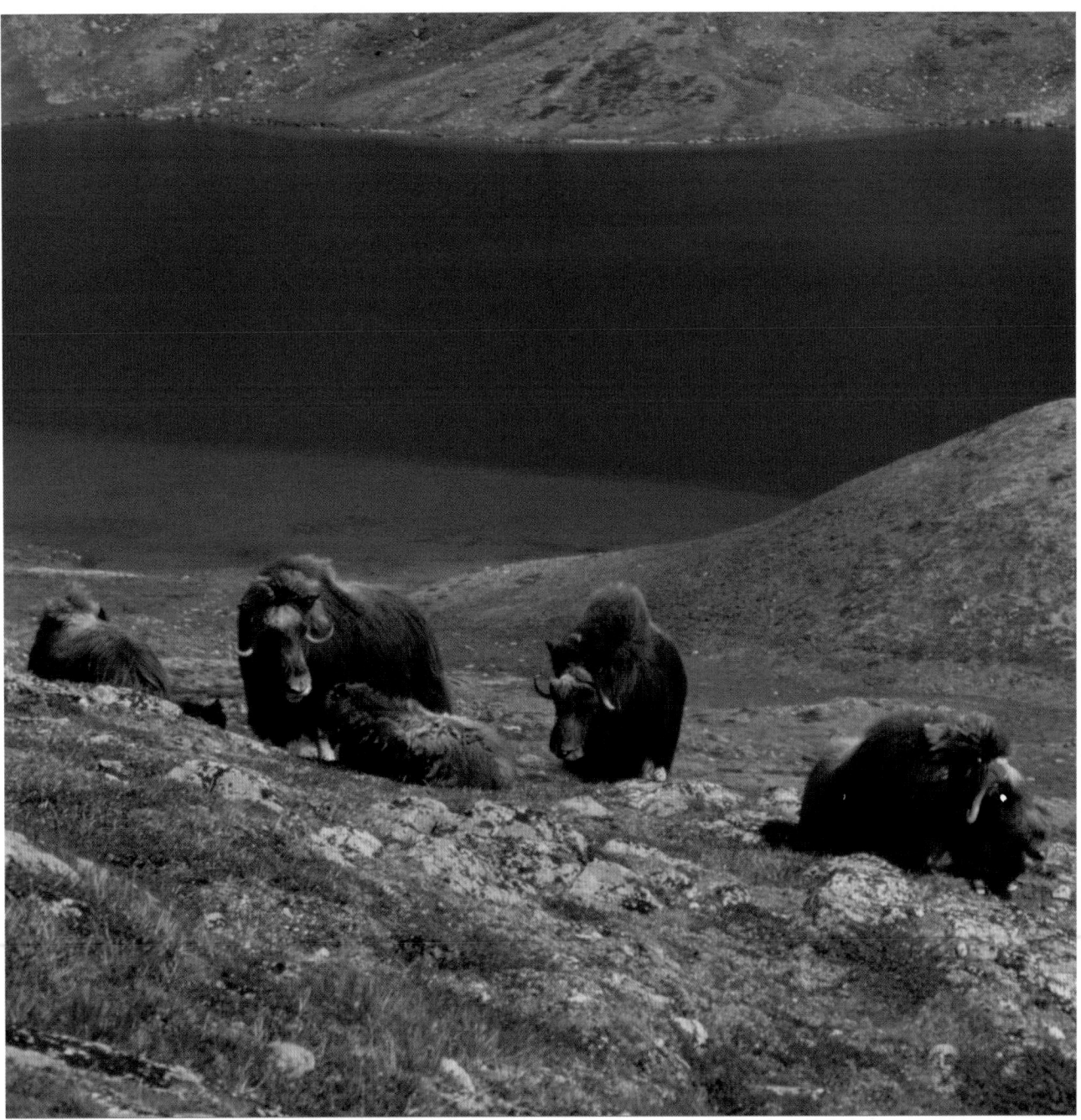

Plate 12.3 The musk ox (*Ovibos moschatus*) is an example of one of several alien species that have been intentionally released and spread in Norway. © Dag Karlsen

beings or through human activity as vectors may have genotypes that are adapted to other ecological conditions and, by cross-breeding with indigenous individuals, may transfer properties that are more poorly adapted to Norwegian environmental conditions. This problem is, nevertheless, not included in the work, and neither are genetically modified organisms (GMOs) which are regulated by a Gene Technology Act enacted in Norway in 1993 (http://www.lovdata.no/all/hl-19930402-038.html, in Norwegian).

Domesticated species from which humans have had direct benefit have achieved extensive global dispersal. Livestock and cultivated plants are not included in the present work, with the exception of cultivated plants that have been observed to have run wild outside the area of cultivation (e.g. the sweet cicely, *Myrrhis odorata*). Pets, experimental animals and indoor plants are not included either. With the exception of the sibling vole (*Microtus rossiaemeridionalis*), alien species in Svalbard (Bear Island) and Jan Mayen were excluded. The sibling vole was included since it is a host for the lethal human parasite *Echinococcus multilocularis*.

12.2 Survey of alien species recorded in Norway

On the basis of the IUCN definition of alien species, updated lists for various groups of species were prepared by a team of experts composed of scientists from six research institutions: the Norwegian Institute for Agricultural and Environmental Research, the Norwegian Institute of Public Health, the Norwegian Institute of Marine Research, the Norwegian Institute for Nature Research, the Norwegian Institute for Forest and Landscape, and the Museum of Natural History and Archaeology at the Norwegian University of Science and Technology. As required, the team has called upon the assistance of other scientists with appropriate expertise.

A directory of alien species recorded in Norway was first published in April 2006 on the Norwegian Biodiversity Information Centre's website. The directory has been updated on a regular basis since then. The last update of the survey in July 2008 showed that 2,485 alien species have been recorded in Norway, nearly 70 % of which are vascular plants. One reason for this predominance is that vascular plants have been documented in Norway for more than 150 years and the trend in the vascular plant flora is constantly monitored by professional and amateur botanists.

The survey is incomplete and does not cover every group of species. It should be looked upon as the start of a major, continuous task whose principal long-term objective is to close the existing

Plate 12.4 *Sargassum muticum* is a native of Japanese waters and was introduced to the Brittany coast in the early 1970s with imported oyster spat. It was first found on the coast of southernmost Norway in 1984. © Ingrid Salvesen

gaps in knowledge regarding which alien species are found in Norway. Our knowledge is particularly poor as regards fungi and invertebrate animals. The directory is divided into the following three lists:

a) Alien species in Norway (2,468 species).
b) Indigenous species spread by human activity in Norway (14 species).
c) Improved indigenous species spread in Norway (3 species).

Vascular plants have not yet been evaluated for inclusion in lists b) and c), and for other groups, too, there is incomplete coverage of the spread of indigenous species in Norway. However, they are included to give some notion of the diverse aspects surrounding the concept of alien species.

12.3 Ecological risk analysis

After the directory of alien species had been compiled, an ecological risk assessment was undertaken for a selection of species. On the basis of available knowledge and resources, the team of experts chose the species that were to be assessed based on whether a species was likely to have a negative impact on indigenous biological diversity. Certain indoor species that are pests on imported greenhouse and ornamental plants were also included. The ecological risk analysis is an evaluation of whether the alien species may have negative impacts on natural ecosystems, habitats, species or genotypes. In other words, it is a purely ecological risk analysis that does not include possible effects on the economy or health.

Risk analyses of ecological effects have been undertaken for a total of 215 alien species, i.e. only 9 % of the species in the national survey have been assessed. However, for some groups of species, almost all the known alien species in Norway have been assessed, e.g. marine and freshwater species (78-100 %), birds (88%) and mammals (100 %). Only 2 % of the vascular plants have been analysed. Approximately 66% of the analysed species are terrestrial and 33% aquatic (marine and limnic). Insects make up about 25% of the analysed species, and 33% of these are mainly found indoors.

The risk analyses have been carried out with the help of a common set of criteria for placing species in categories of risk. In cooperation with the team of experts, the NBIC has developed an Alien Species Database, which includes a facility to perform risk analyses of alien species. The premise for the risk analysis is that every alien species poses a potential threat to indigenous biological diversity until the opposite is proven. In addition to the actual risk analysis, the Alien Species Database can provide more information on the species, such as its habitat and substrate requirements, vector, country of origin, when it arrived in Norway, its population size and its distribution in Norway. Emphasis has been placed on providing good opportunities for recording all kinds of relevant information about the species in the database. At the same time, an attempt has been made to standardize the database so that it will be easy to retrieve information. In addition to the standardized check boxes in the database, there are boxes in which more detailed information can be written about each species. The NBIC web site (www.biodiversity.no) has a search tool where information about the species stored in the Alien Species Database is available, however, as most of this information is in Norwegian it is not accessible to a wider audience.

12.3.1 Criteria and categories

The criteria for the risk analysis are given in Box 12.1. The risk analysis process requires all the questions R (a) to (d) to be answered.

The following principles are applied to categorize the species into three categories:

- High risk: Species which have at least one negative impact on indigenous biological diversity or act as a vector for pathogenic organisms or parasites that have negative impacts on indigenous biological diversity. Thus, a species is classified as having high risk if one or more of the criteria R (a) i, ii, iii, iv, (b) i, ii, (c) i, ii and (d) i in Box 12.1 apply.

- Unknown risk: Species for which uncertainty exists as to whether they will have negative impacts and also species which could be pathogenic organisms or parasites with potential negative impacts on indigenous biological diversity but where this link is not proven. Thus, a species is classified as having unknown risk if at least one of the criteria R (a) vi, (b) iv, (c) iv and (d) iii in Box 12.1 applies and none of the criteria for high risk apply (see above).

- Low risk: Species which it is assumed do not have significant negative impacts on indigenous biological diversity, and which are not vectors for other species (pathogenic organisms or parasites) which may have negative impacts on indigenous biological diversity. Thus, a species is classified as having low risk if all the criteria R (a) v, (b) iii, (c) iii and (d) ii in Box 12.1 apply.

12.3.2 Results

The High risk category includes species from nearly all taxonomic groups (from bacteria to mammals) subjected to risk analysis in this study, (Figure 12.1, see Gederaas et al., 2007 for further details). The dominant groups in this category are vascular plants (18 %), freshwater fish (16 %) and fungi (11 %). Freshwater fish predominate in the group assessed to have negative impacts at the ecosystem level. Vascular plants that are classified in the High risk category are mainly considered to have a negative impact at the environment, habitat and species diversity levels.

In all, 78 of 92 species in the High risk category are considered to have a negative impact on indigenous species, and five of these have a negative impact on Red List species (Figure 12.2). An example of the latter is the alien vine *Vincetoxicum rossicum*, which preferentially grows in open habitats on calcareous soils where the species diversity is high and there are many rare or endangered species.

The majority of the vascular plants subject to risk analysis are already known to have negative impacts on ecosystems and indigenous species, and several have been the subject of attempted eradication at a

Box 12.1 Criteria for risk analysis.

R.   Assumed potential of the species to inflict damage

(a) Can the species negatively affect natural habitats or ecosystems?

i. Negative impact on ecosystems
ii. Negative impact on environments
iii. Negative impact on habitats
iv. Negative impact on species diversity
v. Assumed no significant negative impact
vi. Don't know

(b) Can the species negatively affect indigenous species?

i. Negative impact on Red List species
ii. Negative impact on indigenous species that are not Red List species
iii. Assumed no significant negative impact
iv. Don't know

(c) Can the species negatively affect the genetic diversity?

i. Genetic information can be transferred to natural populations
ii. Negative impact on locally adapted genotypes
iii. Assumed no significant negative impact
iv. Don't know

(d) Is the species a vector for other species (parasites and pathogenic organisms) which may be harmful for natural biological diversity?

i. Yes
ii. No
iii. Don't know

local level, such as giant hogweed (*Heracleum mantegazzianum*), "Tromsø palm" (*Heracleum persicum*), Japanese knotweed (*Fallopia japonica*) and Japanese rose (*Rosa rugosa*). Nearly 20 % of the species having a negative impact on indigenous species are plant pests (e.g. Aphanomyces root rot (*Aphanomyces euteiches*) and Dutch elm disease (*Ophiostoma novo-ulmi* and *O. ulmi*)).

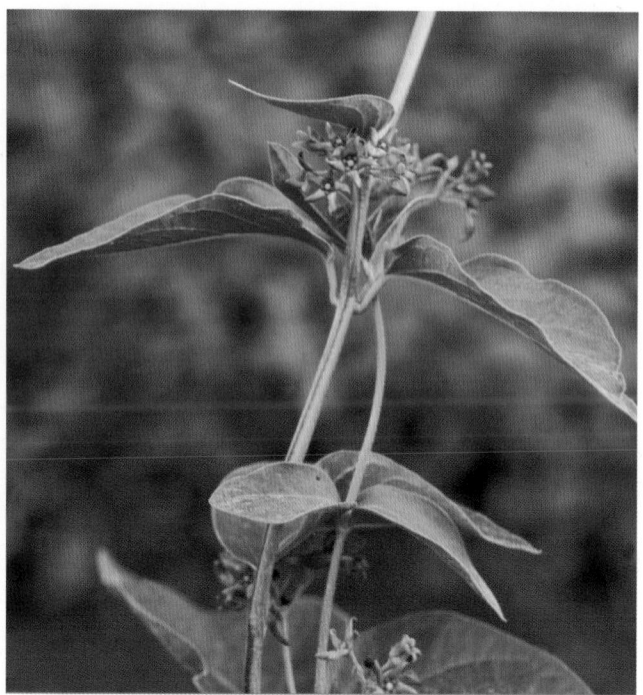

Plate 12.5 Buttonweed *(Cotula coronopifolia)* is a low risk species. It is only known to grow in Loerdalsøyri in west Norway. First found in 1875 it has never succeeded in establishing elswhere. © Eli Fremstad

Plate 12.6 *Vincetoxium rossicum* was first found on islands in inner Oslofjord in 1865. It can reach heights of 2m and climbs on other plants and is now a regional problem species threatening dry slopes and grassland and some endangered species. © Eli Fremstad

Plate 12.7 Japanese rose *(Rosa rugosa)* is a vigorous species easily spread from gardens and parks. It can form dense stands displacing most of what grew there previously. © Eli Fremstad

Plate 12.8 The Tromsø palm *(Heracleum mantegazzianum)* is one of the largest species of hogweed found in Norway. It was intentionally introduced as an ornamental plant in the 1830s. © Eli Fremstad

An example of a species in the High risk category that can oust local species in the marine environment is the red macroalga, *Heterosiphonia japonica*. It has spread rapidly following first being observed in Norway in 1996, and has, in a short time, become one of the most common seaweeds along the coast of west Norway. Another marine species in the High risk category is the Pacific oyster (*Crassostrea gigas*) which may have negative impacts on indigenous species, in particular the European flat oyster (*Ostrea edulis)*. Only a few individuals had been recorded up until August 2008 when a reproducing population of around 500 individuals was found on the southern coast of Norway. The High risk category also includes species that are considered as having potential to negatively affect genetic diversity (32 species) or may be a vector for parasites and diseases (18 species).

Knowledge of the biology and ecology of 82 of the species assessed is considered too poor to enable a full analysis of their ecological risk. These are placed in the Unknown risk category. Most of the groups assessed have species in this category, particularly the insects, which make up more than 40 % of the species in the Unknown risk category. One example of a species in the Unknown risk category is the South American pea leafminer (*Liriomyza huidobrensis*). This fly is a quarantine pest that is continually being recorded in Norway, but due to lack of knowledge its possible effect on the indigenous biological diversity is unknown.

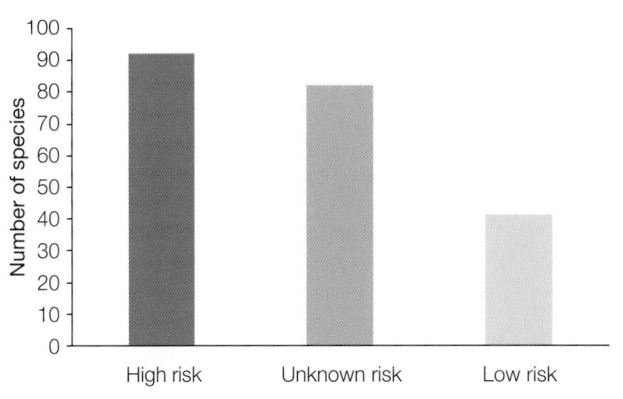

Figure 12.1 Number of species which are considered to constitute, respectively, **high**, **unknown** and **low** risk for indigenous biological diversity.

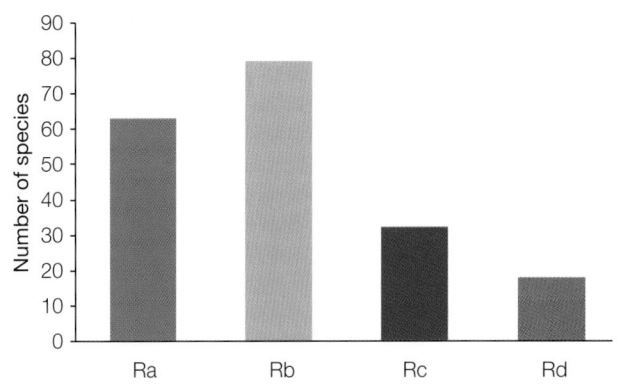

Figure 12.2 Distribution of species considered to constitute a high risk for indigenous biological diversity in the various criteria used in the risk analysis. **R(a)**: negative impact on natural habitats or ecosystems, **R(b)**: negative impact on indigenous species, **R(c)**: negative impact on genetic diversity, **R(d)**: the species is a vector for diseases/parasites. Species may be shown to have a negative impact on more than one level of biological diversity.

Species which, based on currently available information, are considered not to have a significant impact on biological diversity are placed in the Low risk category. In all, 41 species of pseudofungi, fungi, vascular plants, crustaceans, spiders and insects are placed there. The vascular plant, buttonweed (*Cotula coronopifolia*), is an example of a species considered to have Low risk. The buttonweed is an annual which, in Norway, is only known to grow in Lærdalsøyri in west Norway. It was found there as early as 1875, but has never succeeded in becoming established elsewhere. The only aquatic species considered to have Low risk is the European crayfish (*Astacus astacus*) which is an indigenous species but has been spread to new parts of Norway by human activity. More than 66 % of the species in the Low risk category are only found indoors, and these include species like the silverfish (*Lepisma saccharina*) and the webbing clothes moth (*Tineola bisselliella*). It is difficult to determine whether species of insects that live indoors in Norway can be considered as alien. Many of these species have been here since the recording of insects began in Norway, and many also have a cosmopolitan distribution. Some of them were probably introduced to Norway a long time ago, whereas others have been indigenous in natural habitats and have subsequently "moved" to a life in man-made habitats.

12.3.3 When did they come?

About 10 % of the species that have been analysed came to Norway more than 150 years ago, i.e. before 1850 (Figure 12.3) and we do not know when a similar proportion of the species, particularly insects, arrived. An example of an alien species that came before 1850 is sweet cicely (*Myrrhis odorata*), a perennial umbelliferal plant that has been grown as a medicinal and spice plant since the Middle Ages. Sweet cicely invades meadows and pastures that are no longer used, as well as road verges and

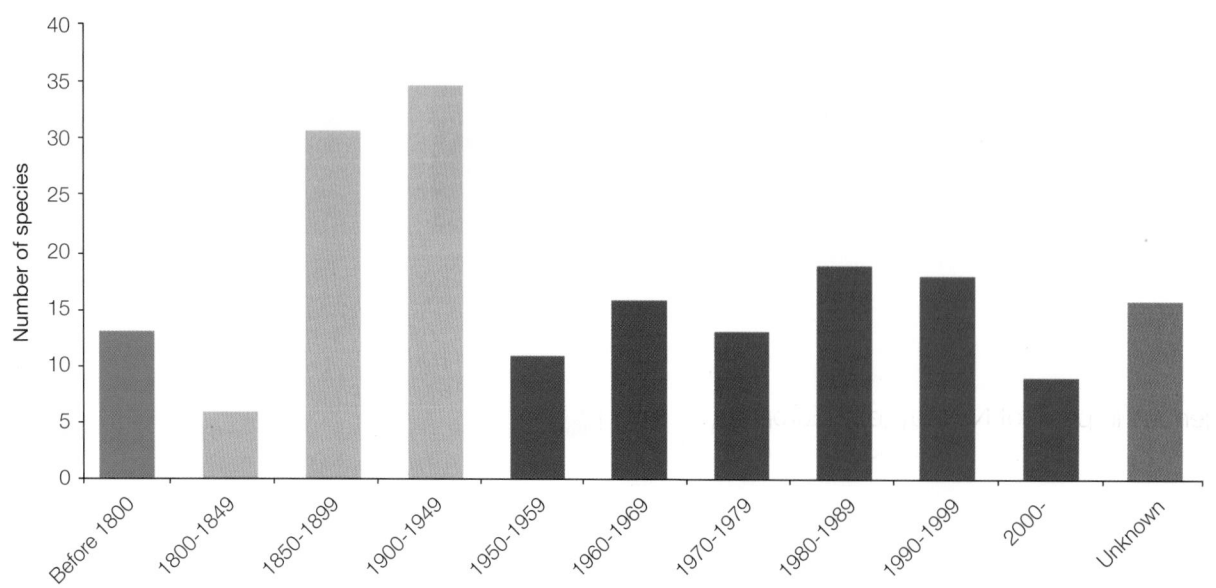

Figure 12.3 Distribution of when the risk-analysed species were first observed in Norway. Owing to the differing extent to which species were recorded previously, four groups of species are recognized: those which came before 1800; those first observed between 1800 and 1949 (divided into 50yr periods); those observed from 1950–1999 (divided into 10yr periods); and those first observed in Norway after 2000.

woodland borders. It can form extensive stands and out-compete other species. More recently it has experienced something of a renaissance as a spice plant and is increasingly being grown in some small gardens, which increases its chance of spreading further.

One-third of the species analysed were first observed in Norway between 1850 and 1949, including several fungi that damage plants and trees. The European red slug (*Arion rufus*), the great grey slug (*Limax maximus*) and the American mink (*Neovison vison*) were also introduced to Norway in this period. The American mink became established shortly after the first mink farm was built in 1927. In the course of 50 years, it colonized most of the country apart from island areas.

From 1950 up to the present day, between 10-20 of the 215 species analysed arrived in Norway each decade. The nine species that are thought to have reached Norway since 2000 include the winter tick (*Dermacentor albipictus*) and the comb jelly (*Mnemiopsis leidyi*). A large number of winter ticks were found in February 2002 on a horse imported from the USA to Ringsaker in Hedmark in December 2001. No finds of the tick have been recorded since then. The comb jelly, *M. leidyi*, was first observed along the Swedish west coast in autumn 2006 and was shortly afterwards found near Tjøme in south-east Norway and off Bergen. This comb jelly has had major impacts on the ecosystems in the Black Sea and the Caspian Sea. However, it is uncertain what impact it will have in Norwegian waters, where competitors and predators are present. The arrival of *M. leidyi* is, nevertheless, an example of how difficult it can be to prevent alien species in the marine environment from spreading once they have been introduced. Since the publication of the Norwegian Black List, a new marine species, the red alga *Antithamnion nipponicum*, has been observed along the Norwegian west coast (Rueness, 2007). This alga was first introduced to the Mediterranean Sea in 1988 from its native range in Japan and Korea, and has most likely been introduced to Norway via fouling on ship hulls or ballast water.

12.3.4 Where did they come from?

Just over 33 % of the analysed species are native to Europe and have reached Norway directly from areas within their natural ranges or by secondary dispersal from neighbouring countries (Figure 12.4). Some are also indigenous in parts of Norway (e.g. European hedgehog (*Erinaceus europaeus*)), but people have introduced them to new places in Norway.

A large proportion (57 %) of the analysed species have their natural origin in Europe. Examples of introduced vascular plants, insects and mammals of European origin are

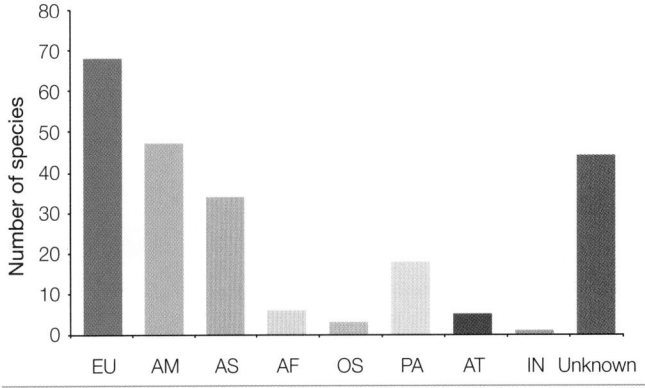

Figure 12.4 Distribution of the source of the risk-analysed species. Codes for the sources are: **EU**: Europe, **AM**: America, **AS**: Asia, **AF**: Africa, **OS**: Oceania, **PA**: Pacific Ocean, **AT**: Atlantic Ocean, **IN**: Indian Ocean. Species may be shown as having several sources.

giant hogweed (*Heracleum mantegazzianum*), Aphrastasia (Siberian silver fir louse) (*Aphrastasia pectinatae*) and European hare (*Lepus europaeus*). The analysed species also include many which have their origin in more distant continents with associated coastal areas such as America (47), Asia (34), Africa (6) and Oceania (3). A large majority of the marine species (40 %) which have been introduced to Norway have their natural origin in the Pacific Ocean. The origin is unknown for 20 % of the species that have been risk analysed.

12.3.5 How did they come?

By far the most important dispersal route for the alien species that have been analysed is land-based primary industries (Figure 12.5). In all, 77 of the 215 species analysed were introduced in this way, including species dispersed through nurseries and market gardens. Within this category are alien species of pseudofungi, fungi, vascular plants, insects and slugs.

One-fifth of the analysed species have spread by tourism, hunting, fishing and from private gardens. Around 20 % of the species have been spread by trading activities with insects making up 95 % of this dispersal route. Mammals and aquatic species form the majority of the analysed species that have reached Norway by secondary introduction from neighbouring countries. This dispersal route is particularly prominent in the marine environment, and accounts for more than 33 % of the analysed marine species.

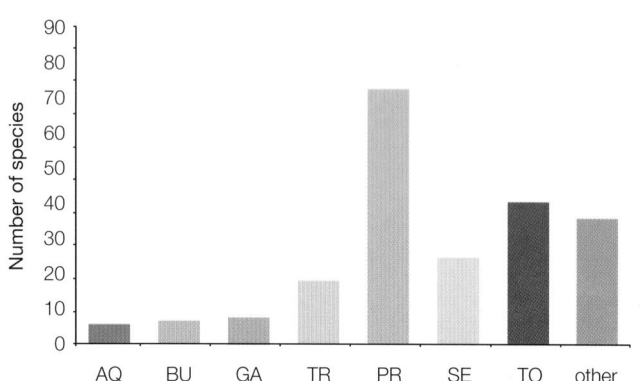

Figure 12.5 Distribution of dispersal routes for the risk-analysed alien species. Dispersal route codes are: **AQ**: from aquaculture and fisheries, **BU**: from building and construction sites, industry, military, **GA**: from botanical and zoological gardens, and research work, **TR**: from trade, **PR**: from primary industries on land, incl. nurseries and market gardens, **SE**: secondary dispersal from neighbouring countries, **TO**: from tourism, hunting, fishing, private gardens, etc., Other: other or unknown. Species may be shown as having more than one dispersal route.

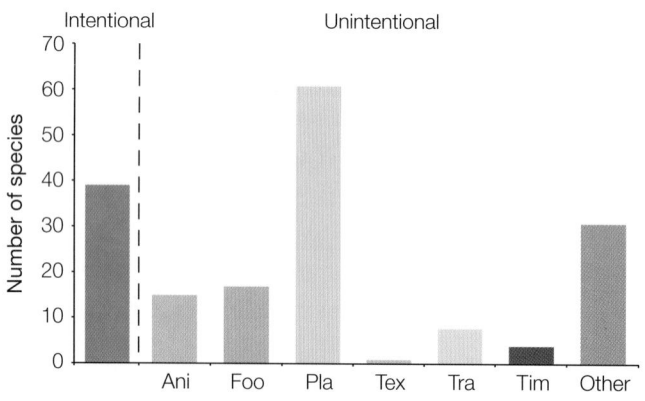

Figure 12.6 Distribution of how the risk-analysed alien species have come to Norway. Vector codes for Unintentional release are: **Ani**: animals/animal feed, **Foo**: foodstuffs, **Pla**: plants/plant parts, **Tex**: textiles/leather/shoes, **Tra**: means of transport, **Tim**: timber, **Other**: other or unknown. Species may be shown to have come with more than one vector.

Many alien species of crustaceans (5), mammals (7), freshwater fish (14) and birds (2) that have been analysed have been intentionally released and spread in Norway (Figure 12.6). Examples are the opossum shrimp (*Mysis relicta*), musk ox (*Ovibos moschatus*), brook trout (*Salvelinus fontinalis*) and Canada goose (*Branta canadensis*). This group also includes nine species of insects which were introduced to Norway for biological pest control. These include the Australian mealybug ladybird beetle (*Cryptolaemus montrouzieri*) used to control mealybugs in greenhouses.

The majority of insects are, however, dispersed by unintentional introduction through vectors (57 species) such as animals, animal feed, foodstuffs, timber, plants and plant parts, textiles, leather and shoes, and various means of transport. In general, the importation of plants and plant material is the vector that leads to the introduction of the majority of alien species to Norway. This vector leads not only to the introduction of alien plants, but also insects, pseudofungi, fungi and slugs.

12.3.6 What is their habitat association?

A large proportion of the analysed species are found within the agricultural landscape (96 of 215 species) through introductions of various species of vascular plants, pseudofungi, fungi, insects, birds and mammals (Figure 12.7). Many alien species are also introduced to habitats in forests and woodlands (43), fresh water (34) and the marine environment (42), as well as those established indoors, including 20 insect species.

12.4 Conclusions and the way ahead

The Norwegian Black List is the first official overview of ecological risk analyses of alien species in Norway, and the most comprehensive

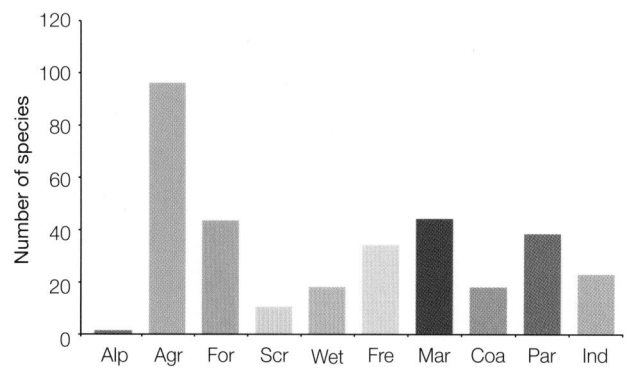

Figure 12.7 Distribution of in which habitats the risk-analysed alien species occur in Norway. Habitat codes are: **Alp** (alpine/tundra), **Agr** (agricultural landscape), **For** (forest and woodland), **Scr** (scree/rock/gully with stream), **Wet** (wetland/freshwater shore/mire), **Fre** (open fresh water), **Mar** (marine environment), **Coa** (coast/seashore), **Par** (parasite/pathogenic organism), **Ind** (indoors). Species may be shown to occur in more than one habitat.

overview of alien species in this country to date. To ensure a better knowledge base for the management authorities, it will be important to perform ecological risk analyses for a larger selection of alien species than those on the List. New alien species are continually entering Norway and it is important that risk analyses also include species that are standing on the threshold but are expected soon to be on their way into Norway ("door-knockers"). Ever-increasing globalization and the current climate change scenarios make it most likely that more alien species will reach Norway and have the chance to become established in the wild in Norway. Ecological changes due to a warmer, wetter climate may also create more optimal reproduction and dispersal conditions for many alien species that are already established, but currently experiencing sub-optimal conditions, in effect a 'climate release'.

Since the publication of the Black List and the cross-sectorial strategy in 2007, alien species have, in general, received more focus in Norway. Attention has, in particular, been paid to species such as the Spanish slug (*Arion lusitanicus*) and the newly introduced Asian (Harlequin) ladybird (*Harmonia axyridis*). For a large proportion of the species on the List existing knowledge of the biology and ecology is too poor to enable an assessment of their ecological risk, and this remains a challenge. Potential impacts of alien species on indigenous species and ecosystems are in general poorly documented through scientific studies. Since no systematic investigations and mapping of alien species have been carried out in Norway, knowledge of most alien species is inadequate. This lack of knowledge includes which species are truly alien, their ecology and distribution, how and when they have come to Norway and whether they have negative impacts on indigenous biological diversity. Implementation of the national cross-sectorial strategy will require an increased knowledge of Norwegian biodiversity especially with regard to biology and ecology of alien and indigenous species.

Plate 12.9 The Spanish slug (*Arion lusitanicus*) was first observed in Norway in 1988. When gardeners exchange plants, soil containing eggs may be included and this is how the slug is spread. This species is now found over large parts of southern Norway and is a significant pest not only in gardens but also in agriculture and horticulture. © Lisbeth Gederaas

Plate 12.10 The opossum shrimp (*Mysis relicta*) occurs naturally in some lakes in both south and north Norway but in the 1970s it was introduced to several regulated lakes to improve the nutritional conditions for char and trout. In reality this introduction disrupted the already well-adapted food chain resulting in less food for the fish. © Arild Hagen

Plate 12.11 Canada geese (*Branta canadensis*) were intentionally released in Norway from 1930 to the mid 1960s. Its population is increasing and in some places it has become one of the most common species of goose. © Per Jordhøy

Besides initiating mapping and surveillance of prioritized alien species to increase the knowledge base, it is very important that good routines are established to ensure that knowledge which is widely dispersed or which has limited accessibility is made more generally available. To facilitate this, the NBIC has established a web-based map service to import localized records of species. As part of this work, it should be ensured that discoveries are documented and recorded in a consistent manner in databases attached to Norwegian natural history collections.

Various methods of performing risk analyses for alien species have been employed in other countries, but there is still no standardized methodology for evaluating ecological impacts comparable to, for example, the IUCN criteria used for the red-listing of threatened species. Development of such internationally accepted criteria would be very important for the legitimacy and acceptance of risk analysis in society. The methodology used in the risk analyses for the 2007 Norwegian Black List does not allow a more detailed distinction of the degree of negative impact on indigenous biological diversity than a rough classification into the three categories High risk, Unknown risk and Low risk. As part of the continuing work, the NBIC has initiated a project together with the Centre for Conservation Biology, at the Norwegian University of Science and Technology that will consider the possibility of extending the set of criteria used in risk analysis to include species-specific qualities, such as potential for dispersal and population growth, habitat requirements and competitive ability. If these and other factors influencing the ability of species to become established and pose a threat to indigenous biological diversity are included, a more finely adjusted system of categories can be developed. This is a major task, however, and requires close cooperation with the foremost experts in the field and initiatives in other countries.

Acknowledgements

The contribution from the team of experts to the 2007 Norwegian Black List is highly acknowledged. Responsible experts for specific group of species are given below.

Pseudofungi, liver mosses, flatworms, annelids, crustaceans and ray-finned fishes
Odd Terje Sandlund, Norwegian Institute for Nature Research

Bacteria, algae, cnidarians, ctenophores, flatworms, nematods, crustaceans, gastropods, bivalves and tunicates
Anders Jelmert, Norwegian Institute of Marine Research

Vascular plants
Eli Fremstad, Museum of Natural History and Archaeology at the Norwegian University of Science and Technology

Bacteria, pseudofungi, fungi, nematodes, insects and mites
Trond Hofsvang and Leif Sundheim, Norwegian Institute for Agricultural and Environmental Research, Plant Health and Plant Protection

Reidar Mehl,
Norwegian Institute of Public Health

Karl H. Thunes,
Norwegian Institute for Forest and Landscape

Gastropods, birds and mammals
Kjetil Bevanger, Norwegian Institute for Nature Research

References

Bevanger, K. (2005). Nye dyrearter i norsk natur. Landbruksforlaget. ISBN 82-529-2840-4 (In Norwegian).

Gederaas, L., Salvesen, I. & Viken, Å. (2007). *2007 Norwegian Black List – Ecological Risk Analysis of Alien Species*. The Norwegian Biodiversity Information Centre, Norway. ISBN-13: 978-82-92838-01-3.

International Union for Conservation of Nature. (2000). Guidelines for the Prevention of Biodiversity Loss Caused by Alien

Invasive Species, 2000. Fifth Meeting of the Conference of the Parties to the Convention on Biological Diversity. Approved by the IUCN Council, Feb 2000, http://www.issg.org/infpaper_invasive.pdf

Rueness, J., Heggøy, E., Husa, V. & Sjøtun, K. (2007). First report of the Japanese red alga *Antithamnion nipponicum* (Ceramiales, Rhodophyta) in Norway, an invasive species to northern Europe. *Aquatic Invasions*, Vol 2 (4): 431-434.

Staverløkk, A. & Sæthre, M.G. (2007). Stowaways in imported horticultural plants: alien and invasive species – assessing their bioclimatic potential in Norway. Bioforsk Report. Pp. 70. Vol. 2 (66).

Tømmerås, B.Å. (1994). Introduksjoner av fremmede organismer til Norge. NINA Utredning 62, 1-141 (In Norwegian - abstract in English).

Weidema, I.R. (2000). Introduced species in the Nordic countries. Nord 2000:13, Nordic Council of Ministers, Copenhagen. ISBN 92-893-0489-8.

Salvesen, I., Gederaas, L. and Viken, Å. (2010). Ecological risk analysis of alien species – the Norwegian experience. In: *Species Management: Challenges and Solutions for the 21st Century*, ed. by J.M. Baxter and C.A. Galbraith. TSO Scotland, Edinburgh. pp. 209-227

Chapter 13

Freshwater non-native species – prevention, control or eradication?

Philip J. Boon[1] and Colin W. Bean[2]

Summary

1. Many non-native organisms, some featuring on lists of the 'world's worst', have invaded freshwater habitats of all types.
2. Action against invasive non-native species needs a broad consensus on how 'non-nativeness' should be defined. Statutory frameworks for controlling the movement and introduction of species, methods for recording and monitoring, comprehensive databases of species distributions, and procedures for risk assessment need to be produced.
3. Once established in any water body, non-native species are usually very hard to eradicate, emphasizing the importance of preventing new invasions from occurring.
4. Various techniques have been applied for controlling or eradicating freshwater non-native species, although few have been completely successful. Methods include the use of chemicals, trapping, and physical removal, and new techniques are constantly under investigation, including the use of biological control agents.
5. Insufficient funding, lack of collaboration, and inertia created by economic or political opinion are prodigious challenges that will need to be addressed if the present trends in freshwater invasions are to be halted.

[1] Scottish Natural Heritage, Silvan House, 231 Corstorphine Road, Edinburgh, EH12 7AT, UK
[2] Scottish Natural Heritage, Caspian House, Mariner Court, Clydebank Business Park, Clydebank, G81 2NR, UK

13.1 Introduction

Water hyacinth (*Eichhornia crassipes*). © David Fenw

On 22 May 2001 (International Day for Biological Diversity) the President of the UN General Assembly said: *"The fast spread of exotic species is one of the most serious threats to biological diversity, yet it might be the least acknowledged and most controversial one, because many alien species are economically important."* The seriousness of the threat has certainly not diminished, and whilst the threat may be acknowledged more now than then, it remains controversial and immensely difficult to tackle. Nevertheless, the Convention on Biological Diversity (http://www.cbd.int/) places obligations on all contracting parties (191 at the time of writing) to take action with respect to invasive non-native species:

> *'Each Contracting Party shall, as far as possible and as appropriate prevent the introduction of, control or eradicate those alien species which threaten ecosystems, habitats or species.'*

This chapter uses the terms 'alien species' and 'non-native species' inter-changeably, as in the definition by IUCN (McNeely *et al.*, 2001): *'A species, subspecies, or lower taxon introduced outside its normal past or present distribution; includes any part, gametes, seeds, eggs, or propagules of such species that might survive and subsequently reproduce.'*. The term 'invasive alien species' has a more restricted meaning: *'An alien species whose establishment and spread threaten ecosystems, habitats or species with environmental or socio-economic harm'* (McNeely *et al.*, 2001).

Fresh water supports one of the richest sources of biodiversity in any type of habitat, and provides a wide array of ecosystem services. It is not surprising, therefore, that the impact of invasive non-native species in fresh water can be extremely damaging. The European Commission project 'Delivering Alien Invasive Species In Europe (DAISIE)' has listed '100 of the worst' invasive aliens (http://www.europe-aliens.org/speciesTheWorst.do). These cover a wide range of species known to exert some of the greatest impacts on biodiversity, economy and human health, including 14 species associated with fresh water (Table 13.1). The Invasive Species Specialist Group of IUCN has conducted a similar exercise at a global scale: its own list of '100 of the world's worst' invasive alien species (Lowe *et al.*, 2004; Table 13.2) contains only five out of the 14 on the DAISIE list, but includes other species associated with fresh water such as common carp (*Cyprinus carpio*) (Figure 13.1), water hyacinth (*Eichhornia crassipes*) (Figure 13.2), and Japanese knotweed (*Fallopia japonica*) (Figure 13.3).

It is not easy to quantify the economic cost of non-native species invasions, and assessing the scale of the damage they cause to other aspects of native biodiversity is even harder. However, where estimates have been made they can be extremely high. Zebra mussel (*Dreissena polymorpha*) (Figures 13.4, 13.5), native to the Caspian and Black Sea regions of Central Europe, is now found widely throughout Europe and in other parts of the world. Its appearance in the Great Lakes (USA) in the late 1980s is thought to have occurred via the ballast water of European ships. Since then, it has caused immense damage: its

Table 13.1 Freshwater species listed by the DAISIE project in '100 of the worst' invasive alien species in Europe (http://www.europe-aliens.org/speciesTheWorst.do).

Species	Common name or Group	Habitat in fresh water
Anguillicola crassus	Eel swim-bladder nematode	Internal parasite of eels
Aphanomyces astaci	Oomycete pseudofungus	Parasite on crayfish
Cercopagis pengoi	Fish-hook waterflea	Lakes
Corbicula fluminea	Asian clam	Running waters; standing waters
Crassula helmsii	Australian swamp stonecrop	Standing waters; slow-flowing waters
Dikerogammarus villosus	Killer shrimp	Running waters; standing waters
Dreissena polymorpha	Zebra mussel	Running waters; standing waters
Elodea canadensis	Canadian pondweed	Standing waters; slow-flowing waters
Eriocheir sinensis	Chinese mitten crab	Running waters; standing waters
Gyrodactylus salaris	Salmon fluke	Parasite on salmon
Neogobius melanostomus	Round goby	Standing waters; slow-flowing waters
Procambarus clarkii	Red swamp crayfish	Running waters; standing waters
Pseudorasbora parva	Topmouth gudgeon	Running waters; standing waters
Salvelinus fontinalis	Brook trout	Running waters; standing waters

Table 13.2 Freshwater species (additional to those in Table 13.1) given in '100 of the world's worst invasive alien species' published by IUCN (Lowe et al., 2004).

Species	Common name or Group	Habitat
Batrachochytrium dendrobatidis	Fungus	Parasitic fungus in amphibians
Eichhornia crassipes	Water hyacinth	Running waters; standing waters
Fallopia japonica	Japanese knotweed	River banks
Pomacea canaliculata	Golden apple snail	Standing waters
Rana catesbeiana	American bullfrog	Running waters; standing waters; wetlands
Salmo trutta	Brown trout	Running waters; standing waters
Cyprinus carpio	Common carp	Running waters; standing waters
Micropterus salmoides	Largemouth bass	Running waters; standing waters
Oreochromis mossambicus	Mozambique tilapia	Running waters; standing waters
Lates niloticus	Nile perch	Running waters; standing waters
Oncorhynchus mykiss	Rainbow trout	Running waters; standing waters
Clarias batrachus	Walking catfish	Standing waters
Gambusia affinis	Western mosquito fish	Running waters; standing waters
Trachemys scripta	Red-eared slider.	Standing waters

Figure 13.1 Common carp (*Cyprinus carpio*). © Marc Ainsworth

Figure 13.2 Water hyacinth (*Eichhornia crassipes*). © David Fenwick

Figure 13.3 Japanese knotweed (*Fallopia japonica*) and Hymalayan balsam (*Impatiens glandulifera*). © Lorne Gill/SNH

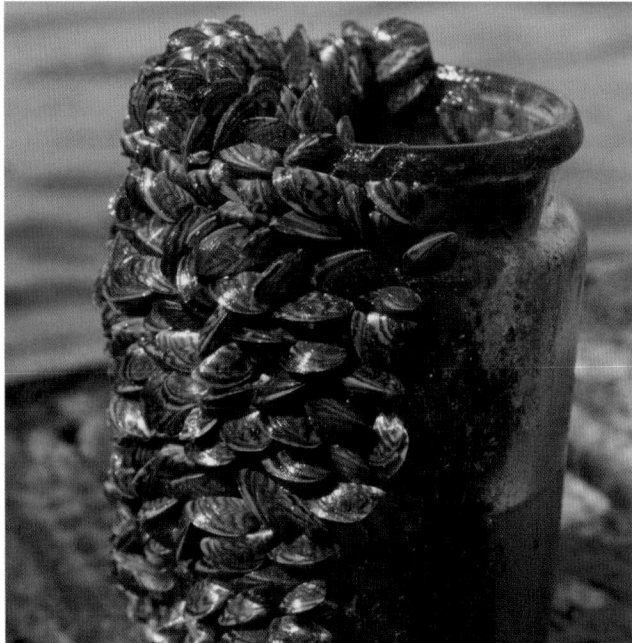

Figure 13.4 Zebra mussel (*Dreissena polymorpha*). © Robert Rosell

Figure 13.5 Aggregation of zebra mussels. © Robert Rosell

biofouling of cooling water pipes is estimated to have cost the power industry more than US$3 billion over the last 15 years (http://www.chesapeakebay.net/zebramussel.aspx?menuitem=16945).

A lack of historical data often hampers attempts at plotting trends in the rate at which individual species spread. Yet where patterns have been recorded there is much cause for concern. For example, in the UK, Australian swamp stonecrop (*Crassula helmsii*) (Figure 13.6) was first recorded in 1956, and by the turn of the century its distribution had expanded to more than 1,000 sites (European and Mediterranean Plant Protection Organization, 2007), assisted by its sale in garden centres and aquatic nurseries (CEH, 2004). A similar pattern of rapid spread has been observed for North American signal crayfish (*Pacifastacus leniusculus*) (Figure 13.7). Originally introduced into England in the 1970s for aquaculture it has escaped or been introduced into hundreds of rivers and lakes in England and Wales (Holdich, 2002). In the mid-1990s signal crayfish were recorded in the wild in south-west Scotland and the species is now spreading northwards to other waters. Studies by Bubb *et al.* (2005) have shown that this species can spread within a river system at more than 2 km yr^{-1}, making it extremely difficult to contain.

This chapter discusses ways in which the problems caused by non-native species in fresh water can be tackled, and focuses especially on three questions: "What are the imperatives for action?" What prospects are there for preventing non-native species from invading or spreading further?" and "Can non-native species be effectively controlled or eradicated?"

Figure 13.6 Australian swamp stonecrop (*Crassula helmsii*). © Stewart Clarke

Figure 13.7 North American signal crayfish (*Pacifastacus leniusculus*). © Colin Bean

13.2 Imperatives for action

Action against non-native species – whether prevention, control or eradication – needs certain prerequisites if it is to be effective. These include an agreed framework in which to work, statutory incentives to insure against institutional inertia, and various types of practical support. Seeking solutions to the problems caused by alien species is not new. For example, 30 years ago the Working Group on Introductions of the UK Committee for International Nature Conservation produced a set of policy guidelines for introducing or reintroducing species (Working Group on Introductions, 1979). The Committee concluded that from a conservation viewpoint deliberate introductions of alien species with the intent to naturalize them in native ecosystems are generally undesirable. They stressed the importance of legislation for controlling the import of species, and recommended that all species which are approved and introduced should be thoroughly monitored and recorded,

The following paragraphs are not intended as comprehensive but summarize some of the essential ingredients in any programme of action against non-native species.

13.2.1 Agreed definitions

Decisions on which species to target need a firm basis for defining what is 'native' and what is 'non-native'. The concept of a 'non-native species' requires some consideration of scale in order to make sense. At one extreme this is straightforward. For example, sea lamprey (*Petromyzon marinus*) (Figure 13.8) is native to much of the Atlantic coastal area of western and northern Europe, where it is considered threatened and listed on the EC Habitats Directive. In contrast, in the North American Great Lakes it is an invasive alien costing millions of dollars to control. However, the question "Is this species non-native?" is not always as simple as it sounds, as it depends not just on the scale at which such an assessment is made (e.g. country, region, catchment), but also on philosophical debates about what constitutes nativeness or non-nativeness. McNeely *et al.* (2001) define a native species as one '*living within its natural range (past or present), including the area which it can reach and occupy using its own legs, wind/water-borne or other dispersal systems, even if seldom found there*'. However, Holdich (2002) points out that purists, at least in Britain, consider that a species should have been present since prehistoric times, i.e. since at least the last glaciation, *c*.14 000 BP, or since the Neolithic, *c*.6 000 BP.

Figure 13.8 Sea lamprey (*Petromyzon marinus*). © Ted Lawrence

The IUCN definition of an 'introduction' (McNeely *et al.*, 2001) was discussed recently at a European workshop on the EC Water Framework Directive:

'The movement, due to human agency, of a species, sub-species, or lower taxon (including any part, gametes, seeds, eggs, or propagule that might survive and subsequently reproduce) outside its natural range (past or present). This movement can be either within a country or between countries and may also include (for example) the transport of alien species through canal systems.'

Several workshop participants stated that this definition has been modified in their countries by selecting a particular date (ranging from 3000 BC to 1943 AD) after which any species introductions will be considered as non-native. Yet because there are no agreed criteria for date selection it is difficult to achieve a consistent approach throughout Europe to tackling the problems of non-native species in fresh water.

13.2.2 Laws and conventions

Following the Rio Earth Summit in 1992, the Convention on Biological Diversity (CBD) identified non-native species as a major factor in the loss of biodiversity at the global, national and local scales. However, it was not the first international convention to recognize that non-native species could have a major impact on the status of terrestrial or aquatic ecosystems. For example, Resolution VII/14 of the 1978 Ramsar Convention on Wetlands of International Importance (http://www.ramsar.org/) required members to compile inventories of invasive species, to develop programmes to control or eradicate invasive species, and to review existing legislation to prevent their introduction and movement.

Taking its lead from the CBD, the European Commission developed its first European Biodiversity Strategy (European Commission, 1998). This identified the need to control non-native species, and, in 2006, Communication COM(2006)216 committed Member States to halt biodiversity losses by 2010, including those due to the action of non-native species (European Commission, 2006). Other European agreements, such as Article 11 of The Convention on the Conservation of European Wildlife and Natural Habitats (the Bern Convention), also oblige signatories to control the introduction of non-native species. This led to the Convention developing its own European Strategy on Invasive Alien Species (Genovesi and Shine, 2003).

European Directives play a major role in ensuring that Member States implement environmental management and conservation measures in a consistent and timely manner. Despite the fact that non-native species control is explicitly mentioned in nature conservation directives (e.g. Article 11 of the EC Habitats Directive 92/43/EEC and Article 22 of EC Birds Directive 79/409/EEC), such a reference is notably missing from the EC Water Framework Directive 2000/60/EC. Annex 2 of the WFD, however, does require Member States to identify and estimate the impact of human pressures on water bodies, and Annex 5 states that the taxonomic composition of a water body should correspond totally, or nearly totally, to undisturbed conditions.

In addition, guidance from the European Commission on selecting potential reference sites (REFCOND), explicitly includes alien species in its list of criteria (http://www-nrciws.slu.se/REFCOND).

The primary domestic legislation for controlling the introduction of non-native species into Great Britain is Section 14 and Schedule 9 of the Wildlife and Countryside Act 1981. Other controls, such as the recently developed restrictions on fish movement contained within the Aquaculture & Fisheries (Scotland) Act 2007, are available, although powers for limiting the spread of other organisms are fragmented and widely dispersed over a number of Acts and secondary legislation (Defra, 2008). The Review of Non-Native Species Policy (Defra, 2003) described the UK legislative framework concerning non-native species and assessed its ability to meet its international obligations. This review became the major driver for improving the way in which the UK meets the challenge posed by non-native species. Subsequent legislation, such as reviews of Schedule 9 of the Wildlife and Countryside Act, the development of the Nature Conservation (Scotland) Act 2004, and the Natural Environment and Rural Communities Act 2006, have been influenced by the Defra review and sought to strengthen non-native species controls. Nevertheless, continuing efforts are required to consolidate and strengthen existing legal controls and to develop a UK-wide framework for addressing non-native species issues.

13.2.3 Methods for recording and monitoring

Survey and monitoring provides the foundation for assessing the current status of species and habitats throughout the world. Issues such as sampling design and sampling frequency dictate the quality and usefulness of the data collected. Recording and monitoring non-native species which inhabit aquatic ecosystems is considered to be a difficult task when compared with the effort required to monitor terrestrial habitats. Routine monitoring programmes in rivers and lakes, such as those carried out by the UK environment agencies, do not always adequately sample non-native species. The detection of non-native species, even in small water bodies, can be difficult and success may depend on issues such as the time of sampling, the behaviour of particular species, their habitat use and their susceptibility to capture. In most cases, organisms will only be detected after they have become firmly established, often after being present for many years. Once such populations reach and exceed a minimum viable population density it may be impossible either to contain or to eradicate them.

In recent years some effort has gone into the development of standard sampling methods through the European Committee for Standardization (CEN), often in response to the need for agreed European-level guidance on the WFD. In future, these standards will form the basis of aquatic monitoring for all species, native and non-native.

13.2.4 Storing and sharing information

Effective action against freshwater invasive species requires a solid base of evidence. This may sometimes entail new research on the ecological requirements, population dynamics and the distribution of individual species. National databases already exist as repositories for species data, although few deal solely with non-native species. Given that species introductions may occur over large distances, there is a strong case for creating and maintaining broad-scale spatial databases. Sharing information internationally relating to the distribution, spread and monitoring of non-native species was the principal aim of the European Commission's DAISIE project (www.europe-aliens.org/). This was developed by a team from 15 European countries, and with contributions from a further 17 countries. Funded by the Sixth Framework Programme of the European Commission, the objectives of DAISIE and its website are to create a structured inventory of invasive species that threaten European terrestrial, freshwater and marine environments; to summarize the impacts of the most widespread or damaging species; and to use the data as indicators of early warning.

The DAISIE database now contains information on almost 9,000 species in Europe, lists 1,600 experts on biological invasions, and has a search facility covering 63 countries or regions.

13.2.5 Procedures for risk assessment

Article 8(h) (Decision VI/23) of the CBD states that action on non-native species should be based on risk assessment and a three-way approach: (1) to prevent invasive species from entering new areas; (2) to prevent them from becoming established; and (3) to develop priorities for controlling non-natives where they present a threat to a country's biodiversity. Risk assessment is a vital part of any comprehensive prevention strategy and is used to estimate the probability and magnitude of predicted impacts, to identify areas of uncertainty and to set priorities for responding to threats. In most cases, uncertainty over the impact of an introduced organism on native species or habitats drives the need for risk assessment.

There are many ways of apportioning a species to a specific risk category, although the uncertainty over ecological impacts suggests that these should not be overly complex. Simple models, using 'high', 'low' and 'unknown' impact categories have been used successfully to assist water body classification under the WFD (UKTAG, 2004). The recently launched *Invasive Non-Native Species Framework Strategy for Great Britain* (Defra, 2008; www.nonnativespecies.org) and the establishment of the GB Non-Native Species Secretariat will play an important role in undertaking risk assessments in future years. Freshwater species covered by this process so far include North American signal crayfish and red swamp crayfish (*Procambarus clarkii*). At a European level, guidance on aquatic risk assessment, developed under the EU-funded ALARM (Assessing LArge scale Risks for biodiversity with tested Methods) project, will focus on methods and protocols for assessing large-scale environmental risks to minimize negative impacts from non-native species (http://www.alarmproject.net/alarm/).

13.3 Prevention

The importance of continuing to search for new ways of eradicating non-native species, or at least of reducing their impact once they have invaded fresh water, cannot be overemphasized. However, experience has shown that in many cases this is impossible using techniques currently available. Thus, preventing invasive species from spreading still further should be an essential part of any alien species strategy. Legal controls are critical (as discussed above) but publicity campaigns and practical methods of containment are equally important. The few national awareness campaigns for non-native species which have been conducted in recent years have been concerned with individual species and are often aimed at a particular sector of the public. A recent example of this type of approach was the 'Home and Dry' campaign to raise awareness of the dangers of anglers, canoeists and other water users importing the monogenean fluke *Gyrodactylus salaris* into Scotland from infested areas in mainland Europe. This species, responsible for causing the loss of Atlantic salmon (*Salmo salar*) from more than 20 rivers in Norway alone (Peeler and Thrush, 2004), is considered to be a major threat both to salmon biodiversity in Scotland and to the £60 million industry that it supports. Preventing the introduction of this non-native species is therefore extremely important, and while steps have been taken throughout the UK to raise awareness of this parasite, prevention may only be achieved through greater control of sporting (e.g. angling) and commercial (e.g. aquaculture) activities.

Efforts at preventing the spread of alien species require public support. Some have gone further and suggested that involving people should be the main focus of invasive alien species (IAS) control. *"IAS prevention and control is the art and science of managing people. Once we stop focusing on IAS as the problem and focus on people's beliefs and resultant behaviour instead, new solutions become evident... If people see themselves as gardeners... with a flair for the exotic... you are unlikely get them to stop planting potentially IAS by suggesting they now plant only native species... If you can help gardeners see themselves as "someone who restores the environment" (for example), they will be able to adopt capabilities and behaviours that support the new definition of their identity"* (Reaser, 2001).

A recent survey in Scotland (Bremner and Park, 2007) found that the level of support for control and eradication programmes was generally high. It was even higher, however, where respondents had previous knowledge of such programmes, and for members of conservation organizations, indicating the importance of awareness and education in non-native species management. Support varied according to the species concerned, with two species often associated with river banks – Japanese knotweed and giant hogweed – attracting the most. A majority of respondents (73-84%) were in favour of controlling those species causing economic damage, but few people advocated the eradication of all invasive non-native species to protect native species.

An excellent example of the multiple approach to alien species prevention is the response in Ireland to the invasion of lakes by zebra mussel. This species was first recorded in 1997 in Lough Derg (McCarthy *et al.*, 1997) and since then has spread to the Shannon, Boyle and Erne catchments (Maguire and Sykes, 2004). Densities of zebra mussels can be extremely high ranging from 2,500m^{-2} in Lough Erne (Figure 13.9) to 36,990m^{-2} in Lough Key (Lucy and Sullivan, 1999; Maguire, 2002). Each mussel can filter as much as one litre of water per day and it is estimated that the population of zebra mussels in Lough Erne can filter the entire lake volume every two weeks.

A mussel education and awareness programme began in Northern Ireland in 1998 and is still continuing. This has comprised press releases, media coverage, exhibitions, fact sheets (Figure 13.10) and has mainly

Figure 13.9 Lough Erne, Northern Ireland. © Robert Rosell

targeted recreational water users such as anglers and boaters. Current activities include training for high-risk lake user groups, establishing a new website (www.invasivespeciesireland.com), and placing several hundred zebra mussel and aquatic weed awareness signs (Figure 13.11) around colonized lakes and the most vulnerable water bodies (John Early, NIEA, personal communication).

Finding ways of physically preventing alien species from spreading is far more of a challenge, requiring new ideas and approaches. Quagga mussels (*Dreissena bugensis*) have recently been recorded in the Colorado River system in California, while zebra mussels have so far invaded only one water body in the State – San Justo Reservoir. The California Department of Fish and Game (CDFG) considers that preventing the spread of these species is the best course of action because of the difficulty of eradication. As boats are the primary transporters of quagga and zebra mussels, the CDFG has put in place an innovative programme of action designed to prevent further spread. (http://www.dfg.ca.gov/invasives/quaggamussel/) This includes strategically placed checkpoints where specially trained sniffer dogs are used to detect mussels on boat hulls and trailers. The CDFG aims to train 22 dogs over the next three years at a cost of US$250,000 (http://www.sacbee.com/101/story/452592.html).

Figure 13.10 Zebra mussel fact sheet. © Northern Ireland Environment Agency

Figure 13.11 Zebra mussel poster. © Northern Ireland Environment Agency

13.4 Eradication or control

Once a species has been introduced and detected by a surveillance or monitoring programme, the options available for practical action are limited to eradication, control or mitigation. Regardless of the strategy chosen, intervention within the UK has generally been disjointed and uncoordinated. This has led to many eradication and control programmes being designed in ways which are neither economically nor biologically efficient (Bogich *et al.*, 2008).

When prevention has failed to stop the introduction of non-native species, eradication is the preferred course of action and must be the ultimate goal of any strategy. However, in most cases this is likely either to be impossible to achieve in practice or to be prohibitively expensive. The elimination of the entire population of a non-native species, including any intermediate or resting stages, is particularly difficult in aquatic ecosystems, and especially in large lakes and rivers. Eradication is often successful only if it is part of a rapid response to early detection, when species have a restricted distribution and have yet to become fully established.

Eradication programmes can use several methods which, either on their own or in combination, may provide the desired outcomes. In aquatic and riparian habitats these include:

- mechanical removal, e.g. hand-pulling of exotic weeds, catching fish in nets or trapping crayfish;
- chemical treatment, e.g. using biocides, chemical attractants (such as pheromones), using poisoned baits, use of herbicides and pesticides;
- releasing sterile males back into the affected area; and
- habitat management, e.g. creating physical barriers to restrict movement or access to critical areas required by a species to complete its life cycle.

Within the UK, large-scale eradication programmes have rarely been considered, although some positive action has taken place locally. Many species, however, are present at relatively few locations, making eradication at a national scale possible. Examples include the almost complete eradication of the water primrose (*Ludwigia grandiflora*) from the UK (Defra, 2007), and the extinction of localized populations of topmouth gudgeon (*Pseudorasbora parva*) (Allen *et al.*, 2006). For many other species, such as North American signal crayfish, eradication, even at a local scale, is likely to be impossible to achieve regardless of the method used (Peay, 2001; Keller *et al.*, 2008).

For many non-native species, such as North American signal crayfish, control by containment may be the only realistic option available. The aim of any containment strategy is to restrict the spread of the species to a defined geographical range, and thus it requires detailed information on species distribution. Containment may entail the use of the suite of measures described for eradication – with the aim of keeping populations down to manageable levels and to restrict the need for a resource-limited population to expand. It may also involve the use of structures or the physical modification of existing habitats, neither of which may be possible or acceptable. Once a population has been contained it is essential for monitoring to continue to ensure that containment measures remain effective.

Controlling established non-native species populations is usually costly and almost certainly long-term, and may demand new research in order to determine their impact on freshwater ecosystems. The primary aim of such strategies is to reduce impact, both on local biodiversity and (in the case of

G. salaris, for example) the economy. However, it is not always clear at what level these strategies should be set in order to achieve the management objective. Sadly, the failure of many eradication measures means the continued spread of non-native species leading to the loss of biodiversity and irreversible ecological damage.

Where eradication, containment, and control options fail, mitigation is an alternative measure that can be used to prevent the localized loss or extinction of species of conservation concern. Recent attempts to protect vendace (*Coregonus albula*), the rarest freshwater fish in the UK, provide a good example of how mitigation measures can be used to ensure that species of conservation value are not lost entirely when non-native species are introduced to host environments. Vendace populations were formerly present in two sites in south-west Scotland but a rapid deterioration in water quality in these water bodies meant these became extinct due to eutrophication in the 1960s. Until recently, it was believed to persist in only two lakes in the UK – Bassenthwaite and Derwent Water in north-west England (Maitland, 2004). In Bassenthwaite, water quality issues and the presence of locally non-native plants (e.g. Canadian pondweed (*Elodea canadensis*), Nuttall's pondweed (*E. nuttallii*), and Australian swamp stonecrop) and fish (e.g. roach (*Rutilus rutilus*), ruffe (*Gymnocephalus cernuus*) and dace (*Leuciscus leuciscus*)) (Winfield *et al.*, 2004), has meant that the Bassenthwaite population has been under risk of extinction for several years. In 1995 fish from Bassenthwaite were translocated to a new water body, Loch Skeen, in an attempt to provide a 'refuge' site for this population. Recent assessment work has shown that vendace have become fully established within Loch Skeen (Winfield *et al.*, 2008a) and that the Bassenthwaite population has now become extinct (Winfield *et al.*, 2008b).

This demonstrates that mitigation, through the establishment of 'refuge' sites, can be a valuable tool in preventing the loss of species of conservation value. It is probable that similar translocations, and the establishment of 'refuge' populations, will take place for a wider range of species in future years.

13.5 Future prospects

The rate at which non-native species are spreading and new species are invading suggests that these problems are likely to become increasingly difficult to manage. Globalization brings with it increased movements of goods and people, and an increased risk that species will be deliberately or inadvertently transported, sometimes over long distances. In many cases, introduced alien species will fail to become established as their environmental surroundings are not conducive to survival in the short term or to reproduction in the longer term. However, as conditions change alien species that have lain dormant may then become invasive.

The single most important factor likely to influence the success of future invasions is climate change. Already, the distribution of native plants and animals in fresh water is changing in response to increasing temperatures and adjustments in hydrological regimes. Reducing greenhouse gas emissions to levels where trends in climate change can be stabilized or reversed will take decades, even assuming there is the international will needed to tackle the problems effectively. Yet there are other obstacles to progress that must also be addressed in the short to medium term. Tighter controls are needed to prevent the import, movement and sale of non-native species. This may require new legislation backed up by suitable penalties for infringement, but full use should be made of opportunities provided by existing legislation. For example, discussions are under way in the European Commission to determine how non-native species should influence the assessment of freshwater quality through the provisions of the Water Framework Directive. This could provide a much-needed legislative impetus for including action against aquatic non-native species in WFD 'programmes of measures'.

The prevailing attitude towards alien species eradication or control often seems to be one of resignation, with many problems perceived as intractable. Although that may often be true, new lines of research are already yielding promising results. For example, a recent press release from New York State Museum (http://www.nysm.nysed.gov/press/releases/mdan.cfm) describes a new technique for eradicating zebra mussel using a highly specific strain of the bacterium *Pseudomonas fluorescens*. Research under way in the UK at the Centre for Agricultural Bioscience International (CABI) is showing the potential of new methods of biological control for invasive species that occur in and around water. These include tests on a leafspot pathogen *Mycosphaerella* sp. and a sap-sucking psyllid *Aphalara itadori* for attacking stands of Japanese knotweed (http://www.cabi.org/ProjectsDetail.asp?ProjectID=31).

New methods of combating non-native species cannot be effective, however, without well-developed protocols for collaboration. The many facets of the problem demand cooperation across a broad spectrum of society, including government bodies, local authorities, industry, horticultural suppliers, fishing clubs, boating interests and individual members of the public. Yet there are often real barriers to building the sort of practical partnerships needed to address these issues, thus hampering effective action, especially where significant amounts of money are needed for control measures or for new research. There is a strong case, too, for extending these partnerships internationally, especially where river corridors provide migration routes through which invasive species can pass freely within and between countries. Real progress will only be made when governments recognize that tackling species invasions requires significant long-term resources, coupled with determination, cooperation and imagination.

13.6 Acknowledgements

We wish to thank Professor Peter Maitland for his helpful comments on an earlier draft of this chapter.

References

Allen, Y., Kirby, S., Copp, G.H. & Brazier, M. (2006). Toxicity of rotenone to topmouth gudgeon *Pseudorasbora parva* for the species' eradication from a tarn in Cumbria. *Fisheries Management & Ecology* **13**: 337–340.

Bogich, T.L., Liebhold, A.M. & Shea, K. (2008). To sample or eradicate? A cost minimisation model for monitoring and managing invasive species. *Journal of Applied Ecology* **45**: 1134-1142.

Bremner, A. & Park, K. (2007). Public attitudes to the management of invasive non-native species in Scotland. *Biological Conservation* **139**: 306-314.

Bubb, D.H., Thom, T.J. & Lucas, M.C. (2005). The within-catchment invasion of the non-indigenous signal crayfish *Pacifastacus leniusculus* (Dana), in upland rivers. *Bulletin Français de la Pêche et de la Pisciculture* **376-377**: 665-673.

Centre for Ecology and Hydrology (CEH). (2004). Information Sheet 11: Australian Swamp Stonecrop. CEH, Wallingford.

Department for Environment, Food and Rural Affairs. (2003). Review of Non-Native Species Policy: Report of the Working Group. Department for Environment, Food and Rural Affairs, London.

Department for Environment, Food and Rural Affairs. (2007). Alien "nuisance" plant almost eradicated in the UK. http://www.defra.gov.uk/news/issues/2007/environ-0102.htm

Department for Environment, Food and Rural Affairs. (2008). The Invasive Non-Native Species Framework Strategy for Great Britain. Department for Environment, Food and Rural Affairs, London.

European and Mediterranian Plant Protection Organization. (2007). Data Sheets on Quarantine Pests. *Crassula helmsii*. *EPPO Bulletin* **37**: 225-229.

European Commission. (1998). *Communication Of The European Commission To The Council And To The Parliament On A European Community Biodiversity Strategy.* COM (98)42. Brussels.

European Commission. (2006). *Halting the Loss of Biodiversity by 2010 and Beyond: Sustaining Ecosystem Services for Human Well Being. Impact Assessment*. Council Communication. COM(2006)216. Brussels, 22.5.2006 SEC(2006) 607.

Genovesi, P. & Shine, C. (2003). *European Strategy on Invasive Alien Species*. Convention on the conservation of European wildlife and natural habitats. Council of Europe, Strasbourg.

Holdich, D.M. (2002). Distribution of crayfish in Europe and some adjoining countries. *Bulletin Français de la Pêche et de la Pisciculture* **367**: 611-650.

Keller, R.P., Frang, K. & Lodge, D.M. (2008). Preventing the spread of invasive species: economic benefits of intervention guided by ecological predictions. *Conservation Biology* **22**: 80-88.

Lowe, S., Browne, M., Boudjelas, S. & De Poorter, M. (2004). *100 of the World's Worst Invasive Alien Species: A Selection from the Global Invasive Species Database*. The Invasive Species Specialist Group, Species Survival (IUCN). http://www.issg.org/booklet.pdf

Lucy, F. & Sullivan, M. (1999). The investigation of an invasive species, the zebra mussel *Dreissena polymorpha* in Lough Key, Co. Roscommon. Environmental Research, Desk Study Report No. 13. Environmental Protection Agency, Ireland.

Maguire, C.M. (2002). The zebra mussel *Dreissena polymorpha* in the Erne system: invasion, population dynamics and early ecological impacts. PhD thesis. The Queens University of Belfast.

Maguire, C.M. & Sykes, L.M. (2004). Zebra mussel management strategy for Northern Ireland 2004-2010. http://www.ni-environment.gov.uk/zebramusselsreport_web.pdf

Maitland, P.S. (2004). *Keys to the Freshwater Fish of Britain and Ireland with Notes on their Distribution and Ecology* . Freshwater Biological Association, Scientific Publication No. 62.

McCarthy, T.K., Fitzgerald, J. & O'Connor, W. (1997). The occurrence of the zebra mussel *Dreissena polymorpha* (Pallas 1771), an introduced biofouling freshwater bivalve in Ireland. *Irish Naturalists' Journal* **25**: 413-416.

McNeely, J.A., Mooney, H.A., Neville, L.E., Schei, P. & Waage, J.K. (Eds). (2001). *A Global Strategy on Invasive Alien Species*, International Union for Conservation of Nature and Natural Resources, Gland.

Peay, S. (2001). Eradication of Alien Crayfish Populations. Environment Agency R&D Technical report W1-037/TRI. Environment Agency, Bristol.

Peeler, E.J. & Thrush, M.A. (2004). Qualitative analysis of the risk of introducing *Gyrodactylus salaris* into the United Kingdom. *Diseases Of Aquatic Organisms* **62**: 103–113.

Reaser, J.K. (2001). Invasive alien species prevention and control: the art and science of managing people. In McNeely, J.A. (Ed.) *The Great Reshuffling: Human Dimensions of Invasive Alien Species*. IUCN, Gland, Switzerland and Cambridge, UK, pp89-104.

UK Technical Advisory Group (UKTAG). (2004). Guidance on the assessment of alien species pressures (PR1-16-03-04). http://www.wfduk.org/tag_guidance/Article_05/Folder.2004-02-16.5332/TAG%202004%20%28PR1-16-03-04%29

Winfield, I.J., Fletcher, J.M. & James, B.J. (2004). Conservation ecology of the vendace (*Coregonus albula*) in Bassenthwaite Lake and Derwent Water, U.K. *Annales Zoologici Fennici* **41**: 155-164.

Winfield, I.J., Fletcher, J.M. & Lyle, A.A. (2008a). Assessment of the vendace refuge population of Loch Skeen. Scottish Natural Heritage Commissioned Report ROAME No. R06AC601A.

Winfield, I.J., Fletcher, J.M. & James, B.J. (2008b). Assessment of the Vendace Population of Bassenthwaite Lake Including Observations on Vendace Spawning Grounds. CEH Report to: Environment Agency (North West Region) and Scottish Natural Heritage, CEH Report Ref. LA/C03462/3.

Working Group on Introductions. (1979). Wildlife Introductions to Great Britain. Nature Conservancy Council, London.

Boon, P.J. and Bean, C.W. (2010). Freshwater non-native species – prevention, control or eradication? In: *Species Management: Challenges and Solutions for the 21st Century*, ed. by J.M. Baxter and C.A. Galbraith. TSO Scotland, Edinburgh. pp. 229-246

Chapter 14

Mink eradication – comparing Icelandic and Western Isles approaches

Arnór Þ. Sigfússon[1] and Iain Macleod[2]

Summary

1. The American mink (*Neovison vison*), has been introduced to many areas worldwide due to commercial fur farming, and their impact on indigenous wildlife can be devastating. The Western Isles of Scotland and Iceland are two such areas where the negative effects of these feral mink populations are currently being mitigated through active management measures.
2. In Scotland mink have been an unintended non-native introduction to our countryside since the early 1950s, due to their escape or intentional releases from fur farms. Feral populations exist throughout most of Scotland. In some areas the distribution and density of these populations is poorly understood.
3. In the Western Isles the feral population of mink has been shown to be particularly fecund. Due to the devastating effect they have had on the largely ground nesting bird populations the Hebridean Mink Project has been engaged in a trapping programme since 2001 with the aim of completely eradicating the mink population from the islands by the end of March 2011. Progress is encouraging with the southern half of the archipelago, North Uist, Benbecula and South Uist, effectively cleared of mink thanks to the trapping that took place during Phase I. The population in the northern section, Lewis and Harris, is dramatically reduced as part of the Phase II programme.
4. In Iceland the Ministry for the Environment and the Environment Agency are engaged in a three year experiment, started in 2007, to establish the feasibility of eradication from two topographically different areas – Eyjafjördur, a fjord with long valleys, in the north of Iceland and Snæfellsnes, a mountainous peninsula and small islands in the west of Iceland.
5. The methodologies used by the two projects will be compared and conclusions drawn as to the practicality of mink eradication, rather than control, from remote and rugged landscapes.

[1] VST Consulting Engineers, Armula 4, 108 Reykjavik, Iceland
[2] Project Manager, Hebridean Mink Project, Scottish Natural Heritage, 32 Francis Street, Stornoway, HS1 2ND, UK

14.1 Introduction

Mink trap in river bank. © Hebridean Mink Proj

The American mink (*Neovison vison*, formerly *Mustela vison*) were transported to Europe as fur animals and feral populations now exist in several areas of Europe including the United Kingdom, Iceland and Scandinavia (Dunstone, 1993). Due to the potential impact on wildlife in countries where escapes have occurred, mink control programmes have been initiated throughout the world, including Japan, Poland, Argentina and Scandinavia, and two such programmes, from the Outer Hebrides and Iceland, are compared in this chapter. The two eradication programmes use different approaches to reach the same goal and preliminary results can be compared to draw some important conclusions as to the likelihood of success and the costs involved.

The American mink was introduced to the Outer Hebrides in the 1950s as a fur animal and by the end of the decade it had escaped and spread throughout Lewis and Harris, causing considerable damage to breeding birds, poultry, aquaculture and fisheries (Angus, 1993). By the late 1990s they had spread from these islands further south to North Uist (Harrington *et al.*, 1999), Benbecula and most recently, South Uist (Figure 14.1) The fact that the archipelago is isolated means that it is therefore not susceptible to recurring

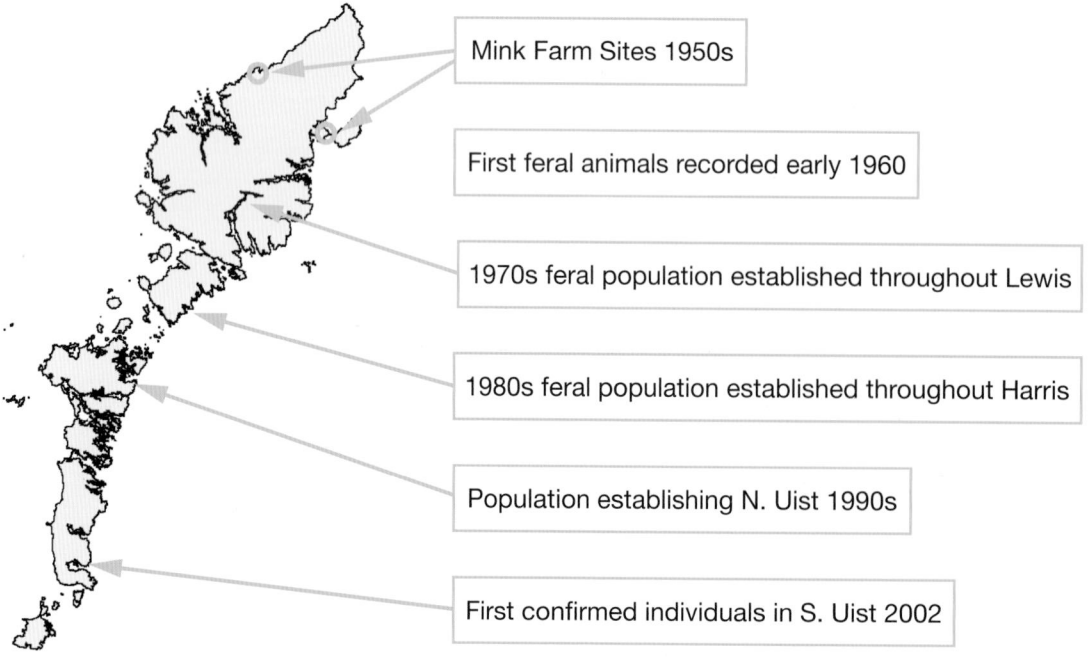

Mink Farm Sites 1950s

First feral animals recorded early 1960

1970s feral population established throughout Lewis

1980s feral population established throughout Harris

Population establishing N. Uist 1990s

First confirmed individuals in S. Uist 2002

Figure 14.1 Showing the distribution of mink through the Western Isles over time.

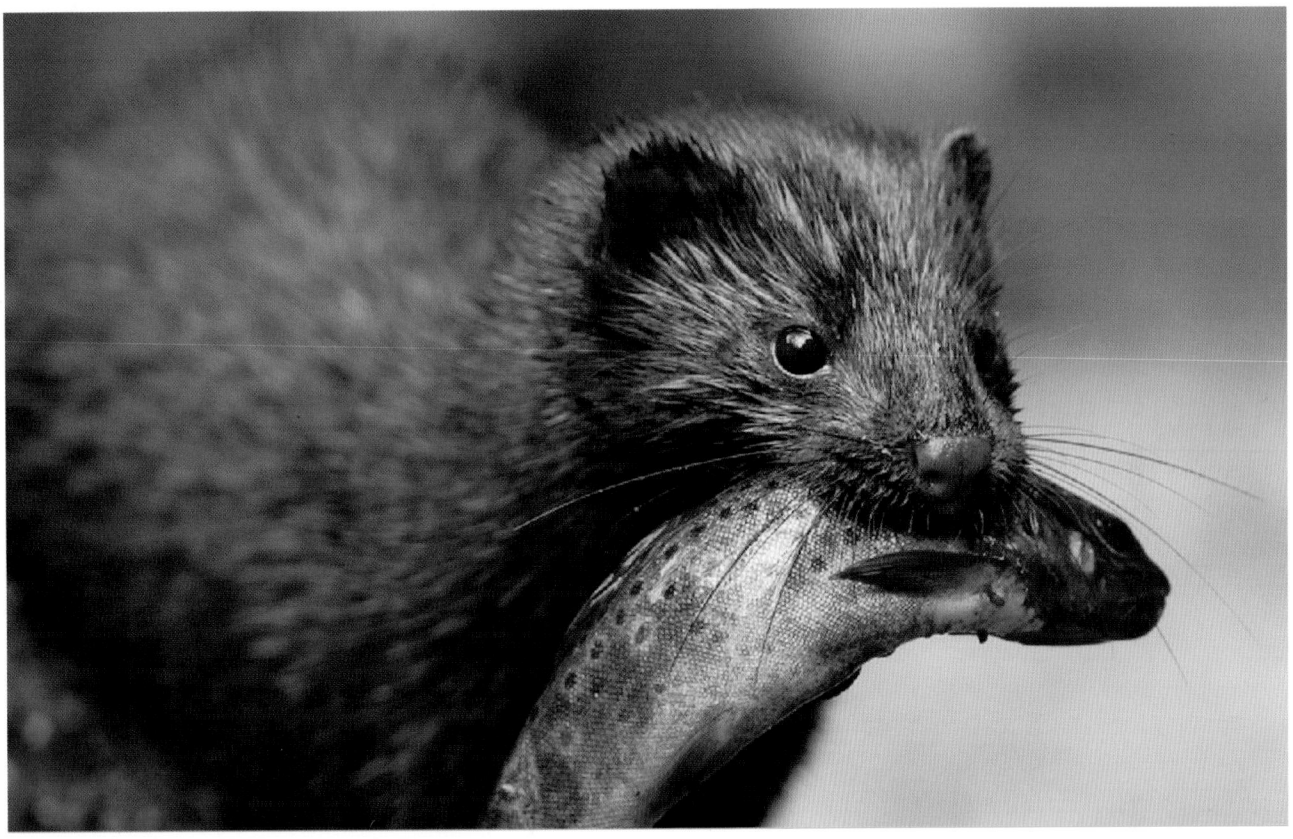

Plate 14.1 American mink with brown trout. © John MacAvoy

immigration pressure from mainland mink. In order to protect internationally important ground-nesting birds, in 2001 an EU Life project, the Hebridean Mink Project, was started with the objectives of eradicating mink from North Uist and Benbecula (South Uist was added subsequently) and reducing the population in South Harris. The first phase was viewed as a trial of eradication techniques but was ultimately successful and finished in 2006, a second phase started in 2007 with the objective of extending the eradication programme across the whole of the Western Isles, including Lewis and Harris.

The American mink was first introduced to Iceland in 1931 for fur farming. In 1937 the first mink den in the wild was confirmed and over the next four decades mink spread throughout Iceland colonizing all suitable habitats. This included the lowlands, islands close to the coast and into the highlands as well (Skírnisson *et al.*, 2004). Judging from hunting statistics collected by the Environment Agency of Iceland (EA), the mink population is still increasing. The Icelandic government started paying bounty for mink in 1939 and a bounty scheme is still in operation whereby the Government refunds half the cost to the municipalities who employ hunters to hunt mink. In addition, a bounty is paid to members of the public who hand in mink tails.

In 2006 the Icelandic Ministry for the Environment initiated a three year experimental mink eradication programme in two areas in Iceland. The aim was to increase hunting pressure on the mink populations in the experimental areas by changing the hunting practices and increasing the level of control. The programme started in 2007 and will run until the end of 2009. After the results of the programme are evaluated a decision can be made on whether eradication of mink in Iceland is feasible or if not, how management practices can be changed in order to better reduce mink numbers, increase efficiency and lower costs.

14.2 Study areas

14.2.1 Outer Hebrides

The Outer Hebrides are situated to the far north-west of Scotland, comprising an archipelago of several large islands many connected by causeways or bridges. There are numerous offshore islands creating a highly complex landscape which includes - dune, rocky shore, pebble and boulder bays, cliffs, beaches, estuaries and saltmarsh along the coast, with small to medium sized riparian habitats joining one of the most complex freshwater systems in the UK (Helyar, 2005).

Phase I of the Hebridean Mink Project started in 2001 and covered an area of 1,100 km^2; this included North Uist, Benbecula and South Uist where the mink population was eradicated and South Harris where the total number of mink was reduced to very low levels in order to create a buffer zone between cleared areas and untrapped areas of the archipelago, (Figure 14.2). By the end of this phase in 2006, 532 mink had been caught and many very important lessons learned.

The success of Phase I gave everyone involved, including the funders, the confidence that despite an even greater area of 1,600 km^2, and an estimated population of c.2,000 animals, the methodology and skills existed to achieve complete eradication of mink in the Outer

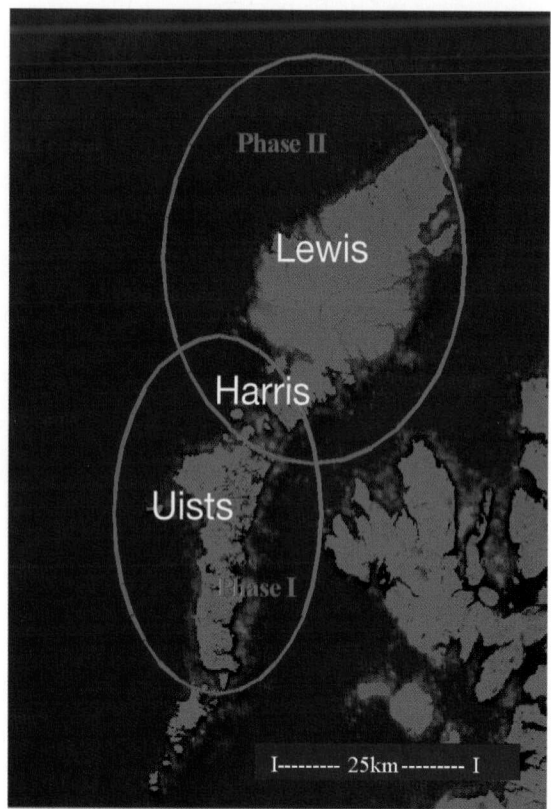

Figure 14.2 Satellite image of the Outer Hebrides showing control areas associated with each phase of the Hebridean Mink Project. ©2009 Google – Imager ©2009 TerraMetrics, Map data ©2009 Tele Atlas

Hebrides. Phase II started in February 2007 and by the end of October 2008, 759 mink have been killed. The project is funded until the end of March 2011 and needs to achieve its aim of eradication by this time.

14.2.2 Iceland

The long running bounty scheme in Iceland, of 60 years duration, had become increasingly expensive and it was recognized that it was having only limited effect on the mink population; therefore trial eradications were initiated in two topographically different areas. The two areas selected were Snæfellsnes peninsula in West Iceland and Eyjafjörður in North Iceland (Figure 14.3).

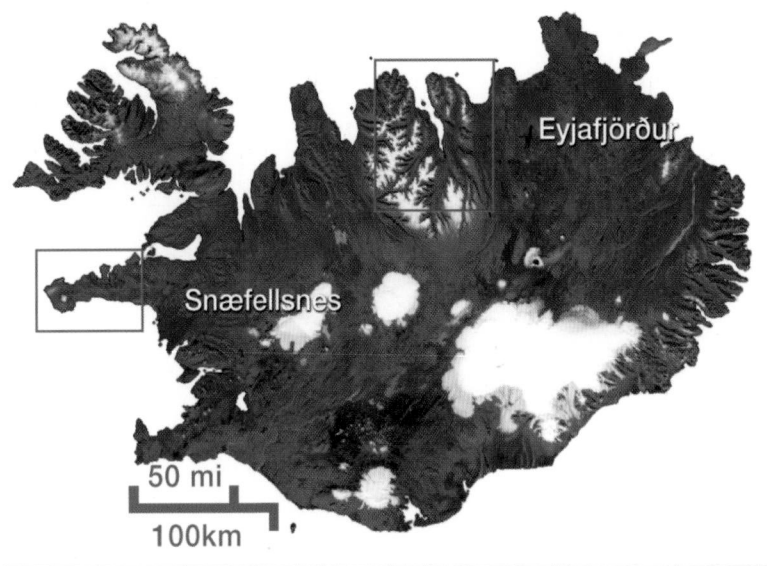

Figure 14.3 Satellite image of Iceland showing both study areas. ©2009 Google – Imager ©2009 TerraMetrics, Map data ©2009 Tele Atlas

- Snæfellsnes is a mountainous peninsula with a diversity of habitat types. The coastline includes sandy beaches and mudflats, sheltered and open rocky beaches and lagoons. Lakes, streams and wetlands are common as are lava fields where mink can easily hide. The area is around 1,300 km^2 and extends over five different municipalities. There are no mink farms in the area. The estimated size of the population in this area was 514 mink (95% confidence limits were 257-771) in November 2006, (Stefánsson *et al.*, 2008.)
- Eyjafjörður is a long fjord which extends into a long valley with numerous, sizeable tributaries. The habitat is less diverse than in Snæfellsnes, the coastline is more sheltered with mainly gravel and rocky beaches but also some sandy beaches and mudflats. Wetlands, rivers and streams are common but lava fields are less common and more overgrown than in Snæfellsnes. The total area is around 3,900 km^2 and extends over seven different municipalities. Two active mink farms are located in the area, one either side of the fjord. The population size of mink in Eyjafjörður is unknown.

14.3 Methods

14.3.1 Selection of hunters

14.3.1.1 Outer Hebrides

The recruitment of trappers in the Hebridean mink project was done nationally and was entirely skill driven. Twelve full time-equivalent trappers work on the project but in total 17 trappers are employed, some being seasonal or part time.

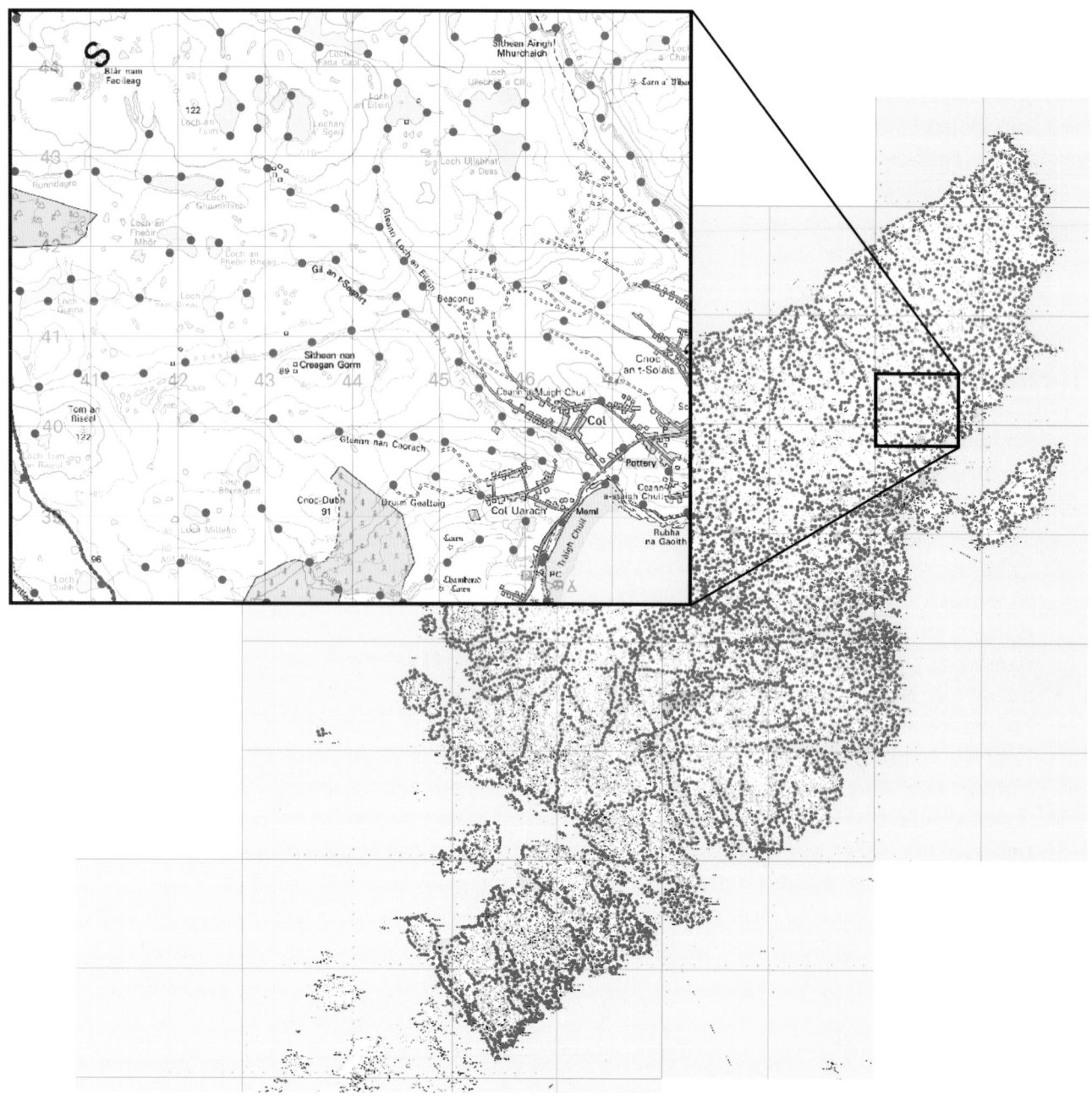

Figure 14.4 Map showing distribution of 7,535 traps over Lewis and Harris (red dots) with detail of distribution in magnified section.

14.3.1.2 Iceland

Municipalities in the experimental area were asked to nominate hunters with local knowledge for the programme. These nominated hunters were then given contracts by the EA to act as key-hunters, and as such were responsible for all data recording and submitting their data files to the EA on a regular basis. In Snæfellsnes three key-hunters are employed and six in Eyjafjörður. Some of the key hunters selected, hired assistants on a seasonal or a temporary basis.

14.3.2 Hunting methods

14.3.2.1 Trapping
14.3.2.1.1 Outer Hebrides

Trap positions were determined using GIS software and set out on a map between 300 and 500m apart; the emphasis was on placing them at intersections in the linear aquatic features (Figure 14.4). The trappers were then given 50m leeway to set the trap. In Phase I 4,100 trap positions were used for a total of 200,000 plus trapnights and in Phase II there are 7,535 trap positions which have so far had 37,000 trapnights (Figure 14.4). Only live catch cages are used due to the risk of non-target species capture and all mink caught were shot using air pistols. Traps were placed in trenches dug into the soil and covered with turf, providing shelter and camouflage for both the trap and any animals caught (Figure 14.5). Mink Gland Lure is used routinely in the traps along with, or instead of fish bait. This results in a four-fold increase in trapping efficiency especially during dispersal periods. (Roy *et al.*, 2006).

Figure 14.5 Trap dug into the bank next to a small stream.
© Hebridean Mink Project

14.3.2.1.2 Iceland

Based on information from the bounty scheme (Skírnisson *et al.*, 2004) an estimate was made on "effort" for each of the municipalities in the two areas. This formed the basis for the number of traps and man hours required for trapping, assuming that effort was increased eight times in Snæfellsnes and four times in Eyjafjörður. This resulted in around 2,000 hours and 260 trap sites in Snæfellsnes and 1,790 hours and 450 traps sites in Eyjafjörður. Trapping was started as early as conditions allowed in late winter, and in 2007 traps were permanently laid out in March. Trapping was planned to be concentrated on the period March to late June in every year of the project.

The key-hunters decided where to lay the traps, based on previous knowledge of the area and their experience. The most common trap was the Fenn trap (Figure 14.6), although other traps such as the

Ihjäel and two types of water trap were used, which are all death traps so trapping sites did not have to be visited daily. Live traps were only used in towns and near farms where pets could be expected. These traps were visited daily.

In order to obtain a figure for the number of nights that a trap had actually been open when only visited occasionally two protocols were used. For traps like the Fenn trap and other traps that only catch one mink and can also be triggered by other means, e.g. wood mice, the number of trap nights for a closed trap is half the number of days between visits. For the water traps that are always open and catching, and can catch several mink, the number is just the number of days they are operated.

Figure 14.6 Fenn Mark VI death trap. © Einar Guămann

14.3.2.2 Use of dogs

14.3.2.2.1 Outer Hebrides

Mink trappers make continuous use of their own trained dogs, including collies, spaniels, terriers etc., to track and locate mink and their den sites. Once located the den sites are then intensively trapped in order to catch the female and only when, in the opinion of the trapper, the kits are too young to leave the den site, are they then dug out and humanely destroyed. Dogs are used routinely by trappers in order to ascertain the success of each trapping week but specific dog searches are prioritized during the seasonal denning period, when no traps are opened, allowing the greatest possible area to be searched, and also towards the end of the project once the population had been reduced to below 10% of the original level. Assessing when this switch from trapping to dog searching should occur is based on the catch per thousand trap nights and information from the population model. During the seasonal denning period and the final stages of eradication, the selection of areas to search is heavily influenced by the habitat preference and population movement in response to reducing population density (Helyar, 2005), and also previous trapping success. The most useful feature of this work is the fact that it gives an indication as to the presence or absence of animals within a geographical area which can then be used to direct future trapping strategy.

14.3.2.2.2 Iceland

In Iceland the use of dogs is also an essential tool in tracking and locating mink and their dens, but the dogs are mainly specialist terrier breeds. Two dogs are usually used at a time followed by the hunters; once the mink or den are located the hunters will try to scare the mink into the open where it is shot but occasionally the dogs will catch and kill the mink. The use of dogs to kill mink is an accepted and legal method in Iceland, often smoke or exhaust fumes from a small engine will be used to force the mink out of the den once it is located. The measurement of the effort required to catch each mink is similar to that used in the Outer Hebrides, searches are saved as tracks and the number of mink caught per 100 km is calculated.

14.3.2.3 Shooting

In Iceland a few mink are shot by the hunters each year, either from a hiding place or by chance meeting. Shooting mink in the open/field is possible in Iceland due to the fact that suitable shotguns are carried by the hunters at all times. In the Outer Hebrides the trappers use air weapons to dispatch mink that have been caught in a cage trap, but these are not considered appropriate weapons for use in shooting free-ranging mink, therefore it is not appropriate to attempt to shoot a free-ranging mink with this type of weapon.

14.4 Results

14.4.1 Outer Hebrides

Phase I of the project had a significant scientific remit, which included a PhD study (Helyar, 2005), and other field work studies carried out in conjunction with the trapping staff. These findings were used to continually refine the trapping methodology and in some instances completely revolutionized the trapping effort, an example being the use of gland lure in the traps, (Roy *et al.*, 2006)

Table 14.1 shows the total mink caught in Phase I of the project. In a stable untrapped population sex ratios of mink remain close to equality (Dunstone,1993), but in a population being trapped the sex ratios can vary depending on factors such as trap distribution and the distribution of the actual trapping effort. When trap density is high each individual trap has an equal likelihood of encountering a male or a female mink, despite the differences in their home range, however, when at lower trap density the likelihood of encountering, and therefore trapping, a male in its larger home range increases. In the Uists, after initially being male biased in its captures, due to a lower overall density of traps and a dispersed trapping effort, ratios became female biased due to an improved trap density and the removal of immigration pressure from South Harris. In contrast, because of a very high density of traps in South Harris and a continued immigration of males, captures in South Harris moved from close to equality to being male biased (Figure 14.7).

Table 14.1 The total number of mink caught in the Phase I of the HMP.

	S. Harris	N. Uist Benbecula & S.Uist	Total
Male	162	93	**255**
Female	131	117	**248**
Unknown *	9	20	**29**
Total	**302**	**230**	**532**

* Mink caught by non-project trappers - no carcasses available for *post mortem*

The project caught a total of 532 mink, 203 in the Uists, from over 200,000 trapnights. On the Uists, only females were caught from November 2004 to March 2005. No mink were caught on the Uists in the last year of trapping from March 2005 to March 2006.

Original estimates at the start of Phase I for the population of mink on North Uist and its associated islands was 180-325 breeding females (Harrington *et al.*, 1999) with an estimated population of 5,000-9,500 breeding females for Lewis and Harris as a whole. The original estimates for the population as a whole where obviously overestimated based on subsequent captures and the population of Lewis and Harris was revised to *c*.2,000 animals, i.e. *c*.1,000 breeding females based on available suitable habitat and previous capture results from Phase I, but even this figure is likely to change as refinements are made to the current population model which Newcastle University have produced for Phase II.

Time series analyses of the long-term trends of catch/unit effort show that in the Uists, there was a marked rise in efficiency as trap lines and project infrastructure were established in the first stages of the project, followed by marked declines in catch/ unit effort as complete trapping coverage of the eradication area was achieved and trapping was having a real impact on mink populations (Scottish Natural Heritage, 2006).

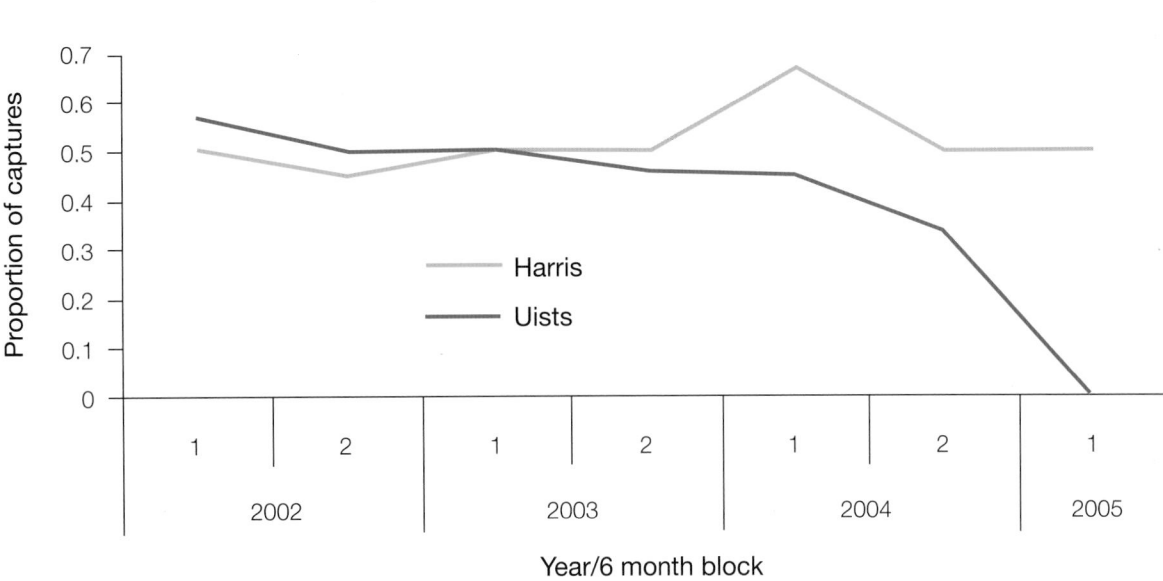

Proportion of males in the population

Figure 14.7 Changes in sex ratio of mink captured in Harris and the Uists during the first phase of the project.

Table 14.2 shows the total number of mink caught during Phase II up to the end of October 2008. The pre-positioning of the trap structure on a Geographical Information System (GIS) prior to actual deployment in the field, resulted in a very high trap density and subsequent trapping effort, given uniformity of coverage, resulted in an equal likelihood of each trap encountering a male or female, despite home ranges sizes being significantly different (Dunstone and Birks, 1985). The actual trapped ratio of males to females in Phase II averages 1:1.04 and indicates that the intensity of the trapping effort makes it unbiased, there being no significant difference in the captures of male and female. In addition, because we have moved to an almost exclusive use of mink gland lure, except during the dispersal period in August and September when food resources for the young are highly important, it provides confirmation that the use of commercially available gland lure to attract mink into the traps is not gender specific (Roy et al., 2006). (Lure purchased from: - www.kishelscents.com)

During Phase I only 10% of traps actually caught but it was not possible to identify why these traps were more effective. It is possible that the chance of being the first trap encountered was the most likely determining factor, although anecdotal evidence from marking behaviour of the dogs within the project would indicate that often an individual mink will visit a number of traps before finally entering one. Why this should be the case is unknown. Of those traps which did catch, approximately 70% of mink caught were

Table 14.2 The total number of mink caught in Phase II of HMP to end of October 2008.

Lewis and Harris Phase II	
Male	383
Female	368
Unknown*	8
Total	**759**
51% Male	49% Female

* Mink caught by non-project trappers - no carcasses available for post mortem

caught on the first night open (Figure 14.8), (Scottish Natural Heritage, 2006). Due to the fact that traps catch the majority of mink in any area relatively quickly, individual trap lines are worked for a week at a time when initially targeting the population, thereby increasing overall effectiveness and also covering the geographical area more quickly. The individual trapper's skills become increasingly important, however, as the population is reduced to less than 10% of its original size. At this stage following trap lines is less effective and the strategy is then to allow individual trappers to track down individual animals, by making use of their dogs, and extending the period of time traps are kept open in their chosen area.

During the seasonal dog searching period, which occurs when line trapping of mink, especially females, becomes very difficult in early summer (Dunstone, 1993) the rate of capture can be 0.11mink/trapnight initially, but can be much lower towards the end of the control period (Figure 14.9). It has been shown that dog searching combined with den trapping can produce rates of up to 0.94 mink/trapnight during the same period, (U = 411.0, P< 0.02, Moore *et al.,* 2003), though this figure is somewhat artificial in terms of the man hours required to find the den site in the first place.

Phase II of the project has shown some very significant improvements in trapping consistency and the results have been a huge rise in the mink caught per trap night with figures of as high as 0.25 mink/trapnight averaged over a month. During a single week the highest number of mink caught was 51 between 12 trappers and approximately 1,100 trapnights. This figure is unlikely to be repeated anywhere due to the very high density of mink in the area being trapped and the fact that it was during the autumn dispersal period. These figures will reduce rapidly over the lifespan of the project as impact on the mink population is realized.

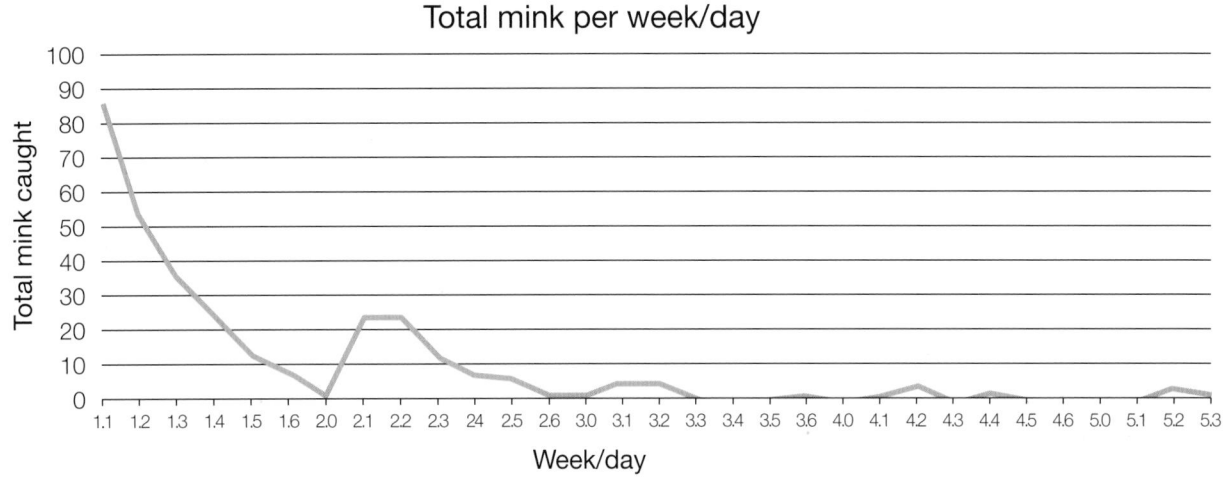

Figure 14.8 Showing that most mink captures occur in the first few days of setting a trap.

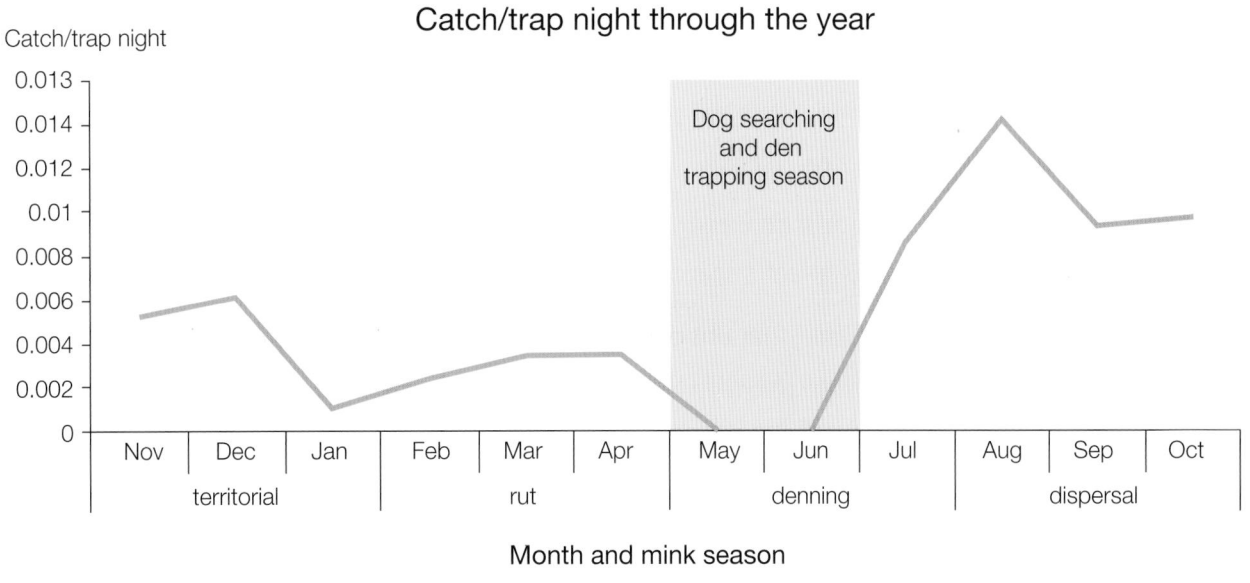

Figure 14.9 Showing the average catch/trapnight 2002-2004 throughout the project area, and the corresponding season of the mink breeding cycle. Males and females show similar seasonal patterns in capture.

14.4.2 Iceland

In 2007 most trap sites (76%) were laid out in March but new sites were added or traps moved throughout the trapping season until October. Some of the sites got snowed over in early winter 2007 and were opened up again in spring 2008. Due to more snow in spring 2008, opening up of traps and laying of new sites was delayed by approximately one month, to late March early April. In 2007 there were 736 trap sites, of which 543 were in Eyjafjörður and 193 in Snæfellsnes. The final number of traps laid in 2008 will be similar to 2007 as most of the sites are the same.

Dog searches started in March in Snæfellsnes and approximately a month later in Eyjafjörður in 2007, with the main effort from April to June (90%). In 2008, dog searches started later due to poor weather conditions and snow cover, but again the main effort was from April to June (78%) but less in April than the previous year.

In 2007 the total catch from both areas was 349 mink, of which 204 were caught in Eyjafjörður and 145 in Snæfellsnes (Figures 14.10 & 14.11). The preliminary number of mink caught until the end of September 2008 is 93 of which 29 were caught in Eyjafjörður and 64 in Snæfellsnes. Some mink will be caught in October – December but if the catch is compared up to October the catch in Eyjafjörður is around 15% of last year's catch and around 46% in Snæfellsnes.

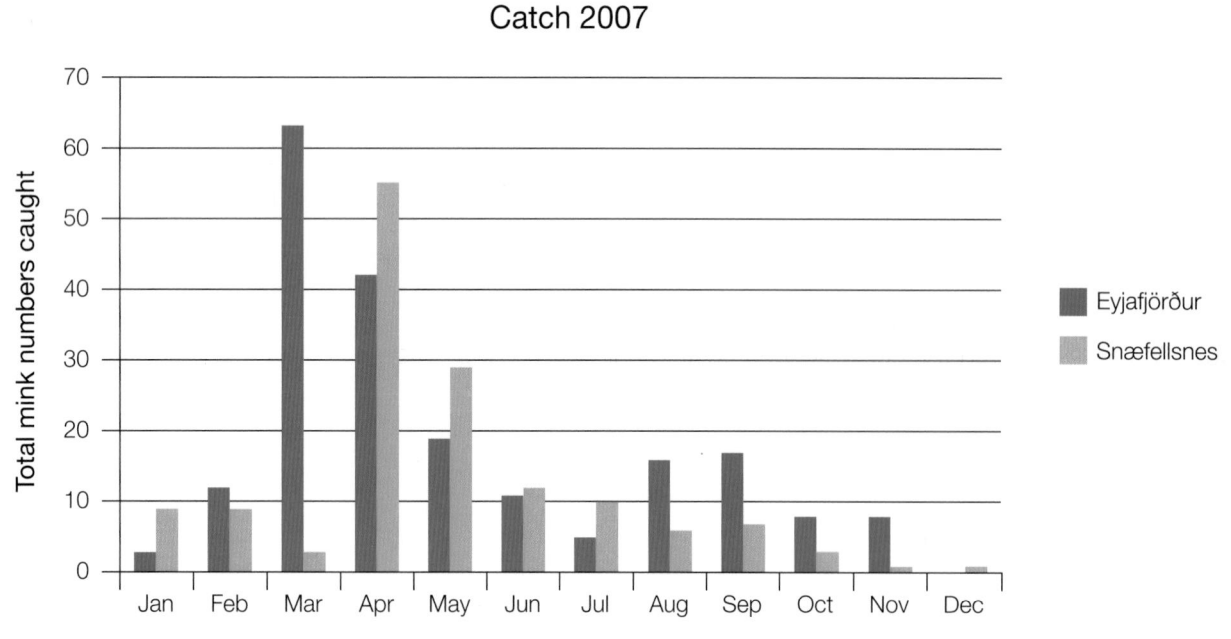

Figure 14.10 Comparison of the catch in 2007 of the Icelandic eradication project.

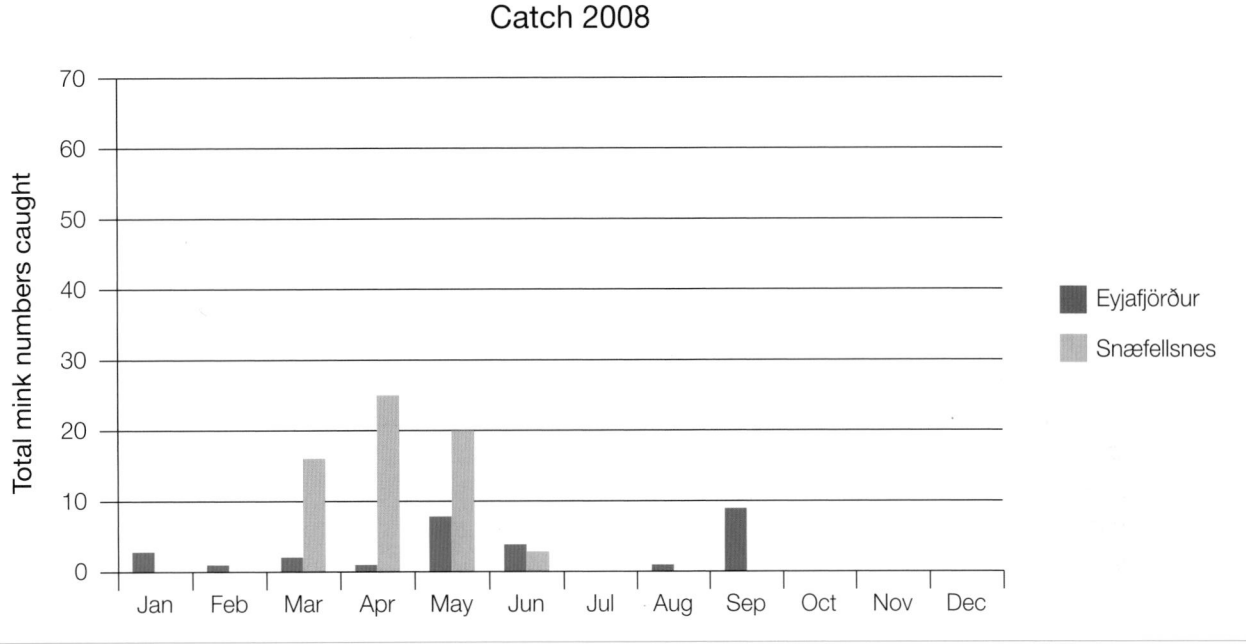

Figure 14.11 Comparison of the preliminary catch in 2008 of the Icelandic eradication project.

If the catch in 2007 is compared to the bounty scheme catch in the same areas in 2005 some adjustments have to be made to make them comparable. In the bounty scheme a female caught in spring was generally counted as five animals, the female and four pups. This was done to encourage hunters to catch early in the year. If the 2007 figures are subject to the same additional score, of a female and four kits, this would give us 780-900 mink which is higher than were caught in the two areas in 2005 which was 375 mink in Eyjafjörður and 269 in Snæfellsnes or 644 in total.

The sex ratio in the catch was 58% in favour of females in Eyjafjörður and 51% in Snæfellsnes in 2007. In the total catch the sex ratio was 55% females. The proportion of females in the dog search was 65% and 55% in the traps. This difference is not significant though (Chi-square =2.08, p=0149). Sex ratio in the 2008 catch is not known yet but indications are that it will be similar.

In the 2007 catch around 65% of the mink caught were trapped and around 28% caught in dog searches, the rest being shot. This is the opposite to what has been found in a previous study on hunting methods where 27% were trapped and 73% caught using dogs (Brynjólfsson, 2001).

In 2007 the total number of trapnights was 88,448 of which 67,341 were in Eyjafjörður and 21,107 in Snæfellsnes. Of these 88,448 trapnights around 73,000 were before October with the preliminary number of trapnights in 2008 being 68,290, of which 56,222 were in Eyjafjörður and 12,068 in Snæfellsnes. The catch in Eyjafjörður was around 2.6 mink/1,000 trapnights and in Snæfellsnes it was around 4.5 mink/1,000 trapnights. For 2008 the same numbers are 0.4 mink/1,000 trapnights in Eyjafjörður and 3.2 mink/1,000 trapnights.

Total distance searched with dogs in 2007 was 1,246 km of which 578 km were in Eyjafjörður and 668 km in Snæfellsnes. The catch in Eyjafjörður was 4.7 mink/100 km with dogs and in Snæfellsnes it 7.3 mink/100 km with dogs. Data for dog tracks in 2008 are not available yet for comparison.

14.5 Conclusions

These two mink eradication projects use very different approaches to environmental control of mink and Table 14.3 summarizes these differences.

In the Outer Hebrides the trap density and methodology are at the highest levels reasonably achievable to guarantee complete eradication in a timescale that is politically acceptable. The trap sites are determined on the basis of topography and with a predefined high density resulting in no areas being excluded where mink may be present, trap structure dictates the effort and captures are expected within a very short timescale. Only live traps are used which legally have to be visited daily resulting in a trapping effort that is very labour intensive and therefore costly. The control area is a group of isolated islands so there is a very limited risk of immigration, nor are there any mink farms in the area so if eradication is successful it should be permanent.   The project has been in operation for some time, Phase I finished in 2006 after five years of trapping with effective eradication of mink in North Uist, Benbecula and South Uist achieved and the same outcome is expected for the Phase II of Lewis and Harris by 2011.

In contrast Iceland has an extensive system of trapping based on trapping by key hunters that could potentially result in local extinction of mink for the limited time the project exists, though if successful an extension to the project area might be sought. The project relies on the local knowledge of the hunters and

Table 14.3 A summarized comparison of the two mink eradication projects.

	Iceland	Outer Hebrides
Control area	Extensive - continuous immigration	Isolated - no immigration
Hunters/Trappers	Local knowledge chosen by municipalities	National recruitment Skills driven
Traps	Kill traps Location chosen by trapper, low density high proportion catch	Live traps Determined during planning, high density only 10% ever catch
Mink farms	Present continuous escapees	None present
Use of dogs	Essential throughout trapping period	Mainly during denning period and at low population levels
Total Control Area (km²)	5,200km²	2,700km²
Costs (man hrs/km²/yr)	2 man hrs/km²/yr	11 man hrs/km²/yr

their experience resulting in prejudgments being made as to the distribution and trapability of mink, with difficult or low mink density areas being potentially avoided. Whilst this will lead to a higher proportion of traps catching mink, compared to only 10% ever catching in the Western Isles, the risk exists that mink in marginal low-density areas will be missed. The same applies for the dog searches, the trappers decide which areas to search and this means that the skills of the individual trappers can have a great effect on the outcome of the scheme. Any misconceptions the trappers have about where to expect mink can lead to areas being excluded from trapping and in these areas mink may survive and reproduce successfully. The differing skill levels between trappers is mitigated in the Western Isles due to the random allocation of traplines over time, resulting in trappers of differing skills alternating through areas of ground and reducing the risk of a single area being trapped poorly for a long period. This risk of individual trappers introducing bias does exist in Iceland as the key hunters are associated with a single municipality area. The control areas are also extensive and there will be continuous immigration pressure from adjacent areas which are uncontrolled other than by means of the bounty scheme that still runs concurrently. In Eyjafjörður two mink farms still exist so there are likely to be some escapes, this is documented on a regular basis, and will threaten the future of any large scale eradication programme. Use of kill traps means that trapping is less labour intensive but the legislation that applies in the UK would mean that traps would still require daily checking and therefore no advantage in terms of efficiency is gained by setting of kill traps. The legislative environment is a key aspect of any planned trapping campaign and can determine methods and manpower requirements and therefore costs.

Preliminary results from Iceland show a marked difference in the two areas. The drop in catch in Eyjafjörður is around 85% between years, whereas it is around 29% in Snæfellsnes. The explanation could be that in Snæfellsnes the initial mink density was much higher, as is indicated by higher catch per effort in traps and dog searches. The topography in the two areas is different and the Snæfellsnes area has more difficult habitat for dog searches, such as lava fields and more diverse coastline providing hiding places for mink. Trapper experience is also a factor that cannot be excluded and in general the hunters in Eyjafjörður are more experienced.

The success of Phase I in the Western Isles was due to the systematic trapping method which was developed giving everyone the confidence to make improvements to the trapping methodology and the trap distribution, in order to extend the project area and achieve the long term aim of mink eradication in the Western Isles.

Mink control is costly and staffing costs comprise approximately 70% of the budget. In order to compare costs between the two projects we calculated the number of man hours used to trap, divided by the total area, as comparing cost directly might be misleading due to the economic crisis and its effect on currency values. Using this method, the man hours required in the Hebridean Mink Project are 11 man hrs/km^2/yr compared to 2 man hrs/km^2/yr in the Icelandic project. These are trapping and dog search hours only and administrative cost are not included here The geographical scale of any project needs to be balanced against available funds and the likelihood of success if the aim is to achieve complete eradication.

The relationship between cost and the chance of success is interesting but should be viewed in context; eradication cannot be 95% successful! It remains to be seen how effective the two approaches will be but the comparison and shared experiences between the two projects are likely to enhance the results and allow informed decisions to be made about cost effective mink control in future programmes.

14.6 Acknowledgements

Western Isles: -

Phase I: EU "Life" Fund, Scottish Natural Heritage (SNH), Central Science Laboratory (CSL), Highlands and Islands Enterprise (HIE Innse Gall), Western Isles Council (CNES), and the Royal Society for the Protection of Birds (RSPB), All trapping staff, and in particular Dr S. Roy and Dr. A. Helyar for establishing the methodologies used .

Phase II: Scottish Natural Heritage (SNH), Esmée Fairbairn Foundation (EFF), Highlands and Islands Enterprise (HIE Innse Gall), Western Isles Council (CNES), Outer Hebrides Fisheries Trust (OHFT), Royal Society for the Protection of Birds (RSPB), Newcastle University (Modelling contract), Central Science Laboratory (Post mortem contract), Project foreman and all trapping staff who's efforts make this possible.

References

Angus, S. (1993). A mink control programme for Lewis and Harrris. *Hebridean Naturalist* **11**: 78-84.

Dunstone, N. (1993). *The Mink*. T. & A.D. Poyser, London.

Dunstone, N. & Birks, J.D.S. (1985). The comparative ecology of coastal, riverine and lacustrine mink *Mustela vison* in Britain. *Angewandte Zoologie* **72**: 52-70.

Harrington, L.A., Grogan, A.L., Bonesi, L. & Macdonald, D.W. (1999). Survey of American mink, *Mustela vison*, on North Uist. *Report to Scottish Natural Heritage.*

Helyar, A.F. (2005). The ecology of American mink (*Mustela vison*); Response to control. *PhD study York University,* 114-160.

Moore, N.P., Roy, S.S. & Helyar, A. (2003). Mink (*Mustela Vison*) eradication to protect ground-nesting birds in the Western Isles, Scotland,United Kingdom. *New Zealand Journal of Zoology* **30**: 443-452.

Roy, S.S., MacLeod, I. & Moore, N.P. (2006). The use of scent glands to improve the efficiency of mink (*Mustela vison*) captures in the Outer Hebrides. *New Zealand Journal of Zoology* **33**: 267–271.

Scottish Natural Heritage. (2006). Mink control to protect important birds in SPAs in the Western Isles - *Final Report to EU LIFE III – Nature, September 2006.*

Skírnisson, K., Stefánsson, R. A. og von Schmalensee, M. (2004). Minkur. Í: Íslensk spendýr (Páll Hersteinsson ritstjóri). Vaka-Helgafell. Bls. 88-97. (Mink. In: *Icelandic mammals* (P. Hersteinsson Ed.) Vaka-Helgafell. Pages 88-97).

Stefánsson, R. A., von Schmalensee, M., Skarphéöinsson, K.H., Hallbeck, B. og Hersteinsson, P. (2008). Stofnstærð og vanhöld minks á Snæfellsnesi 2006-2007. Niðurstöður fyrri rannsóknar vegan tilraunaverkefnis umhverfisráðuneytisins um svæðisbundna útrýmingu minks. Fjölrit Náttúrustofu Vesturlands nr. 14, maí 2008. 24 bls. (Population size and mortality of mink in Snæfellsnes 2006-2007. Results from first phase of research project for the Ministry for the Environment eradication programme. West-Iceland Institute of Natural History publications no. 14 May 2008, 24pp).

Sigfússon, A.Þ. and Macleod, I. (2010). Mink eradication – comparing Icelandic and Western Isles approaches. In: *Species Management: Challenges and Solutions for the 21st Century*, ed. by J.M. Baxter and C.A. Galbraith. TSO Scotland, Edinburgh. pp. 247-264

264

Chapter 15

Invasive non-native species in Scotland's seas: risk and reality

David W. Donnan[1] and Fiona J. Manson[1]

Summary

1. Invasive non-native species are acknowledged as one of the most important threats to the conservation of marine biodiversity.
2. A variety of human activities contribute to the spread of non-native species around the world. Scotland has a growing number of benthic non-native species and there are others with the potential to arrive in the near future.
3. To date, the impacts of non-native species in Scotland have been largely restricted to biodiversity impacts rather than economic ones; however, this may not remain the case in the future. Experience from elsewhere indicates that both biodiversity and economic impacts can be significant.
4. Targeted studies have been undertaken of the wireweed *Sargassum muticum*, a recently arrived invasive non-native species in Scotland. This work is being used as an opportunity to inform the development of the management response to invasive non-native species in Scotland and to raise awareness of the issues with stakeholders and the general public.

[1] Scottish Natural Heritage, Battleby, Redgorton, Perth, PH1 3EW, UK

15.1 Introduction

Sargassum muticum. © Lorne Gill/SNH

Despite the oceans of the world being inter-connected, the biodiversity they support is not globally homogenous. There are barriers to the free distribution of species at sea just as there are on land, including the continental land-masses, deep water, ocean currents, the Arctic ice-sheets, and temperature and salinity gradients. These factors provide ample opportunity for the evolution of distinct regional flora and fauna, particularly of benthic species, and accordingly Scotland has a rich and distinctive marine biodiversity of its own.

Over recent times there has been growing recognition that invasive non-native species pose one of the most significant threats to marine biodiversity. Invasive non-native species are those deliberately or unintentionally introduced by human action outside their natural distribution where they establish, proliferate and spread in ways that cause damage to biological diversity (CBD, 1992; Carlton and Ruiz, 2005; DEFRA, 2008).

15.2 The role of human activities in the translocation of marine species

There are a variety of activities with the potential to act as vectors of non-native species and contribute to their spread between geographic regions. Once a species has arrived in a new location, these same activities may also serve to facilitate its subsequent spread and colonization. These human-mediated vectors include shipping, the seafood industry, scientific research and public aquaria and can be either accidental or intentional (see review by Carlton and Ruiz, 2005). However, among the most relevant to Scotland are the potential pathways associated with vessel movements (both commercial and recreational) and mariculture.

Commercial shipping and recreational boating traffic have both experienced significant increases over the past few decades, with larger and faster vessels routinely moving between regions of the world. Vessels large and small have the capacity to transport a wide range of species in a number of ways. Ballast water and associated sediments within ballast tanks are commonly considered to be one of the dominant vectors in the introduction of non-native species. This is reflected in the extent of international action focused on ballast management, including the adoption of the International Maritime Organisation's (IMO) *'International Convention for the Control and Management of Ships' Ballast Water and Sediments'* due in 2009 (IMO, 2005).

However, ships and boats can transport 'passenger' species in other ways including in seawater pipework, in sea chests, attached or entangled on equipment such as anchors and anchor chains, and as fouling on hulls. Drake and Lodge (2007) surveyed the hull of a transoceanic ship arriving in the American Great Lakes and estimated that it was carrying a biofouling community of between 100 and 200 species. The solitary sea squirt *Styela clava* is likely to have been translocated into UK waters via hull fouling. This species is native to the north-western Pacific and was introduced to Plymouth Sound in the early 1950s, most likely by military vessels returning from the Korean war. It subsequently spread rapidly along the south coast of England. *S. clava* was not reported in Scotland until the late 1990s when it was recorded

Plate 15.1 Commercial shipping is an important vector of marine non-native species. © Lorne Gill/SNH

from Loch Ryan (Eno *et al*., 1997). It is likely that the species was transported on the hulls of military vessels which were towed from naval ports on the English Channel coast to Cairnryan on Loch Ryan to be broken up (Davis *et al*., 2007).

Globally, the cultivation of fish and shellfish at sea or on the shore has made a significant contribution to the movement of invasive species between regions (Carlton and Ruiz, 2005; Minchin, 2007). This can include the intentional cultivation of a non-native species that subsequently results in self-sustaining populations in the wild. However, the more frequent scenario is the unintentional movement of non-native species with fish or shellfish stock. Reise *et al.* (2002) listed 32 species thought to be associated with the movement of Pacific oysters (*Crassostrea gigas*) to the North Sea and English Channel. Fortunately, the extent to which mariculture has been a factor in the introduction of non-native species in Scotland is relatively small, although the arrival of the Japanese skeleton shrimp (*Caprella mutica*) in 2002 illustrates

Plate 15.2 Slipper limpets (*Crepidula fornicata*). © Keith Hiscock

the potential (Willis *et al.*, 2004). Elsewhere in the UK and in northern Europe, examples of invasive species introductions partly or wholly associated with mariculture activities are increasing and include the Pacific oyster (*C. gigas*) (Nehring, 2006), the slipper limpet (*Crepidula fornicata*), and the American oyster drill (*Urosalpinx cinerea*) (Eno *et al.*, 1997).

15.3 The impacts of invasive non-native species in the marine environment

As is increasingly evident on land, the potential impact of invasive non-native species at sea can be significant, having both biodiversity and economic implications. A graphic example of the capacity for invasive non-native species to affect local ecology is the case of two common species accidentally exported from the UK to the United States. The edible winkle (*Littorina littorea*) was first recorded in the Bay of Fundy in 1860 and has become one of the most common grazing animals on the north-east Atlantic coast. This species now regulates much of the intertidal biota and competes with native rocky shore snails. Meanwhile, the shore crab (*Carcinus maenus*), a voracious predator, has had similarly extensive impacts on prey populations including native clams and crabs (Carlton and Ruiz, 2005).

The environmental and economic damage arising from invasive non-native species, combined with the economic costs of prevention, control and/or eradication can be significant. For example, a species of comb-jelly – *Mnemiopsis leidyi* introduced to the Black Sea in the early 1980s has caused estimated losses of $17 million annually due to the part it has played in the collapse of the anchovy fishery there (Knowler and Barbier, 2000). Similarly, the introduction of the salmon parasite – *Gyrodactylus salaris* to rivers and fish farms in Norway has caused an 86% reduction in salmon abundance in affected rivers and the losses related to recreational angling alone amount to an estimated €20 million (Johnsen, 2006).

15.4 Management response to invasive non-native species in the marine environment

The threat of invasive non-native species is recognized at a global level in Article 8(h) of the Convention on Biological Diversity (United Nations, 1992). The obligation on parties to the CBD to 'prevent the introduction of, control or eradicate those alien species which threaten ecosystems, habitats or species' is a key driver of policy and action. Within Europe, the Communication on Biodiversity (COM(2006)216) sought the development of a comprehensive strategy to reduce the impact of non-native species on biodiversity, and in 2008 the Commission consulted on the development of an EU framework for invasive alien species (European Commission, 2008). This outlines a proposal for a European Strategy to substantially reduce the impact of invasive alien species on EU biodiversity, to contribute to halting the loss of biodiversity by 2010 and beyond, and to minimize economic and social costs caused by invasive alien species. Among the specific objectives of this strategy are:

- establishing measures to address eradication, containment and control;
- an early warning and information system supported by surveillance and monitoring;
- financial mechanisms to support control/eradication; and
- a requirement for member states to implement national strategies.

In the UK, a new invasive non-native species framework strategy was published recently (DEFRA, 2008). This strategy will be partly underpinned by existing biodiversity legislation. Section 14 of The Wildlife and Countryside Act (1981) is the principal UK legislation dealing with the release of non-native species, with amendments by the Nature Conservation (Scotland) Act 2004 in Scotland. Section 14 of the Act makes it illegal to allow any animal that is not ordinarily resident in Great Britain, or is listed on Schedule 9 to the Act, to escape into the wild, or to be released into the wild. It is also illegal to plant or otherwise cause to grow in the wild any plant listed on Schedule 9 of the Act.

Sector-specific mechanisms also have a key role to play. Perhaps the longest standing action on the invasive species issue in the marine environment has been in relation to ballast water. Ballast water exchange is widely seen as having the greatest potential for introducing new species but it is also a vector with significant opportunities for the application of mitigating measures.

The *International Convention for the Control and Management of Ships' Ballast Water and Sediments* (IMO, 2005) aims to prevent, minimize and ultimately eliminate the transfer of harmful aquatic organisms and pathogens through the control and management of ships' ballast water and sediments. This convention imposes legislative requirements, including the application of performance standards to regulate both the volume of water to be exchanged and the efficacy of ballast water treatment systems. The convention is due to come into force in 2009, although interim measures are already in place such as the Ballast Water Management Strategy for the North-east Atlantic, which provides guidance for shipping entering the OSPAR area on how to achieve the performance standards of the convention.

In addition to these legislative measures, new technologies are being developed to reduce the likelihood of transporting organisms in ballast water, including UV filtering technology, treatment with ozone and even vessels designed to be ballast-free.

Plate 15.3 The Chinese mitten crab (*Eriocheir sinensis*). © P. Lawson

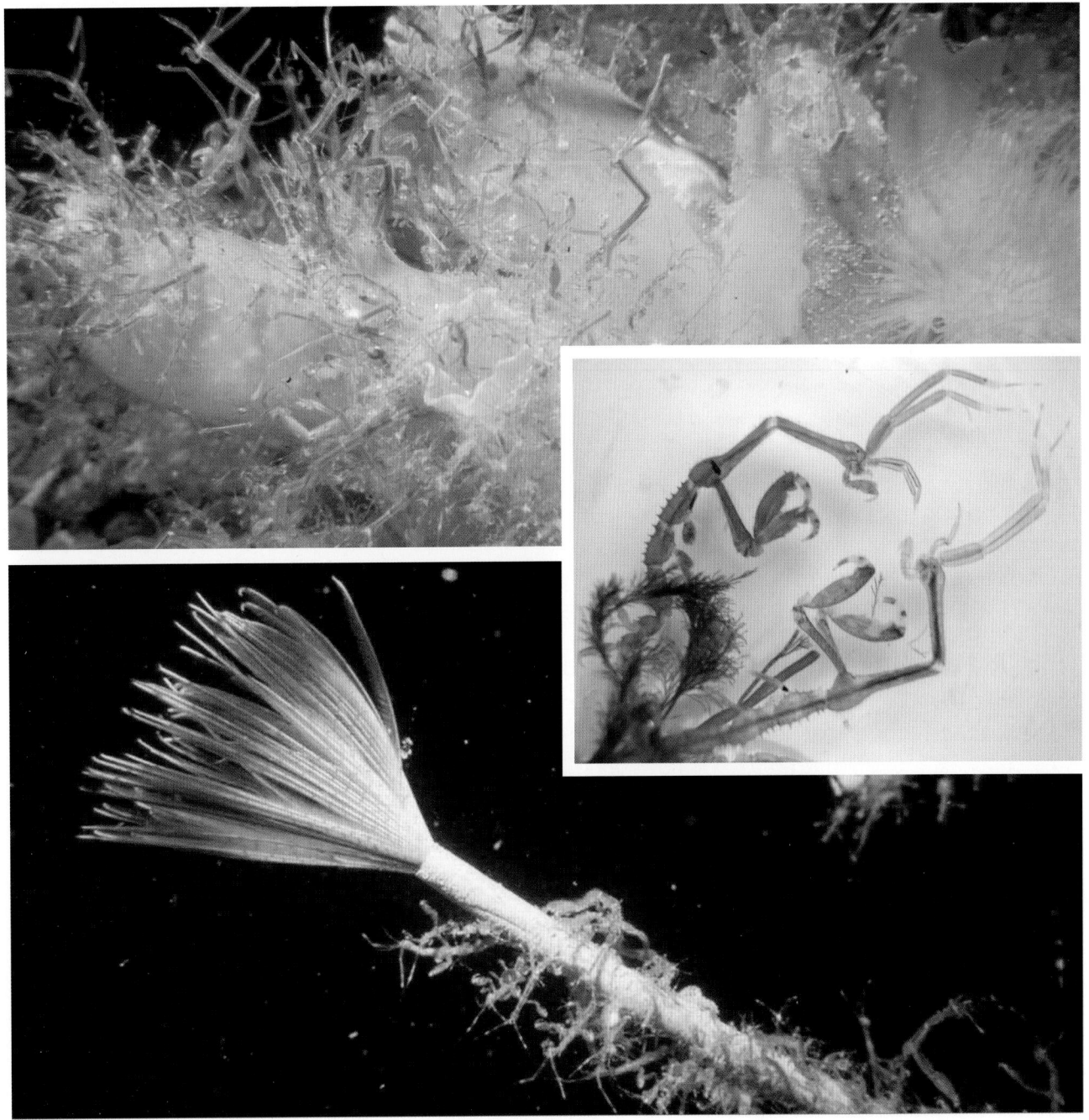

Plate 15.4 Japanese skeleton shrimp (*Caprella mutica*) (middle), on sea squirts (top), on a peacock worm (bottom). © E. Cook

In relation to aquaculture, a new regulation for use of alien and locally absent species (European Commission, 2007) will establish a system for the assessment and management of the risks associated with the introduction of new organisms for aquaculture. Already in existence is the ICES *Code of Practice on the Introductions and Transfers of Marine Organisms*; originally developed in 1973 it has been revised several times since, most recently in 2005 (ICES, 2005). The Code sets out recommended procedures and practices to diminish the risks of detrimental effects from the intentional introduction and transfer of marine organisms. These include: assessments of new species for aquaculture; transfers of species that are part of current commercial practices (e.g. *Crassostrea gigas*); protocols for inspection and quarantine; and release of GMOs and sterile polyploid organisms.

There are common themes within legislative mechanisms and tools which, in general, can be summarized into three stages for dealing with invasive species: prevention, detection and control. There are significant difficulties associated with detection and control in the marine environment, and consequently the highest priority must be given to preventative measures.

In addition, an essential component in the management of non-native species is international collaboration, as the issues of prevention, detection and control cannot be dealt with by any one country alone. Clearly, the chance of success of any attempted prevention or management strategy would be severely compromised by uncontrolled populations in neighbouring, or even distant, countries. For example, evidence of an increase in the occurrence of the Chinese mitten crab (*Eriocheir sinensis*) in the St Lawrence river and estuary appears to be related more to changes in the size of European populations (the source population in this case) than to changes in shipping activity (de Lafontaine *et al.*, 2008).

15.5 Marine invasive non-native species known to be in Scotland

There are a number of non-native species already present in Scottish waters. Few of these are invasive, but there are a number that have become widespread and well established. *Codium fragile* subsp. *tomentosoides* is a green alga which is now found throughout UK inshore waters (Eno *et al.*, 1997). Common cordgrass (*Spartina anglica*) originated from North America and, after hybridizing with the native UK species, is now the most common saltmarsh grass in the UK (Eno *et al.*, 1997). The Japanese red alga (*Heterosiphonia japonica*) was first sighted in the Moray Firth (B. Leyshon, pers. comm.), and as recently as summer 2008 was reported in Loch Sunart on the west coast (C. Moore pers. comm.). Another recent arrival, also originally from Japan, is wireweed (*Sargassum muticum*); more details of its introduction and spread can be found in section 15.7.

Several invertebrate non-natives are also present. Acorn barnacles (*Elminius modestus*) are already well established in Scottish waters, where they can outcompete the native barnacle species (Eno *et al.*, 1997). The Japanese skeleton shrimp (*Caprella mutica*) is a predator on several native species, and is now widespread in western Scotland (Ashton *et al.*, 2007). The leathery sea squirt (*Styela clava*) is a fouling organism that smothers native species and may affect aquaculture equipment if present in high density (Davis *et al.*, 2007). The focus of this chapter is benthic organisms but it should be noted that there are also a number of non-native planktonic species present in Scottish waters (see Eno *et al*., 1997).

The Marine Aliens project, led by the Scottish Association for Marine Science in collaboration with the Marine Life Information Network (MarLIN) and other UK research institutes, has undertaken monitoring of the distribution and spread of seven of the common marine non-natives in the UK (see http://www.marlin.ac.uk/marine_aliens/marine_aliens.htm).

15.6 The risk of further marine invasive non-native species in Scotland

Few, if any, of the invasive non-native species already present in Scotland have arrived in Scottish waters directly from their native location. The common pattern is for species to establish in a neighbouring country and then gradually spread into Scottish waters. The following examples are species that are in or close to the British Isles but have yet to reach Scotland.

The Pacific oyster (*Crassostrea gigas)* was originally introduced for cultivation in Britain in the early 20th century (Eno *et al*., 1997) and subsequently became widely used for cultivation on continental European shores from France to Germany. By the mid-1970s, self-sustaining settlements of *C. gigas* spat were becoming increasingly common in Holland and have subsequently occurred in Belgium, France and Germany. At a number of locations, *C. gigas* is now occurring in sufficiently high population densities to form distinct biogenic reefs, significantly altering the substrate and native faunal assemblages (Nehring, 2006; Kerckhof *et al.*, 2007). In the Wadden Sea, Pacific oyster beds are now rapidly developing into solid reefs at a number of locations and there are concerns that *C. gigas* will become dominant on the mudflats along the German and Danish North Sea coast, acting both as an ecosystem engineer and as a competitive suspension feeder (Nehring, 2006). Recently, similar reefs of *C. gigas* have been reported from estuaries in the south of England (Natural England, pers. comm.). Although there are no records of similar spatfalls of *C. gigas* in Scotland, increasing water temperatures and the prevalence of the species in oyster cultivation here mean that it is highly likely that this will occur.

The Chinese mitten crab (*Eriocheir sinensis*) is considered a major pest in both estuaries and rivers, partly due to its burrowing habit which has the potential to weaken or undermine the muddy banks of estuaries and rivers (Herborg *et al*., 2003). This crab was first recorded in the UK in the Thames estuary in 1935. It is now found in the Thames, Humber and Tyne estuaries and parts of the North Sea and English Channel coasts (Herborg *et al*., 2005). Recently, the Chinese mitten crab has been found in Ireland (Minchin, 2006) and it has the potential to establish in all the UK estuaries (and thence into major river systems). The translocation of *E. sinensis* is normally associated with ship movements (de Lafontaine *et al.*, 2008) but it is also another example of a species that has, on occasion, been introduced deliberately for use as seafood. In San Francisco Bay it is thought that deliberate introduction has been carried out illegally as consignments of live animals have been intercepted in the hand baggage of disembarking passengers at the airport (Cohen and Carlton, 1997).

Of significant concern has been the recent spread of the colonial sea squirts of the genus *Didemnum*. These fast-growing sea squirts have the potential to cause significant ecological and commercial impacts, as experienced on the east and west coasts of North America, New Zealand and several European countries (USGS, 2008). Didemnids are fouling organisms with a prodigious capacity to form dense and extensive growths on vessels' hulls, marina pontoons, ropes and aquaculture equipment. Their translocation is principally associated with vessel movements (Minchin and Sides, 2006).

Didemnids can be significant pests, particularly for shellfish farmers. Experience from Ireland and the United States has illustrated the capacity of non-native didemnids to readily overgrow other biota such as mussels grown in hanging culture (Minchin and Sides, 2006; USGS, 2008). Didemnid colonies can also overgrow the net bags used for oyster cultivation, reducing the free flow of water through the bags and decreasing the growth rates of the oysters (USGS, 2008).

The native range of didemnids is unclear, but they have been recorded as non-natives from the Pacific coast of Canada and the United States, the eastern United States, and New Zealand, and arrived in continental Europe in the 1990s (Minchin and Sides, 2006). However, more recent records documenting sightings in Wales (Kirsten Ramsay, CCW, pers. comm.) and Ireland (Minchin and Sides, 2006) mean that they are now very close to Scotland.

15.7 *Sargassum muticum* in Scotland: a case study

In recognition of the need to develop a better understanding and to raise awareness of invasive non-native species in Scotland, targeted work on a recently-arrived seaweed has been carried out as part of Scottish Natural Heritage's Species Action Framework (Scottish Natural Heritage, 2007).

Wireweed, (*Sargassum muticum*), is an invasive non-native brown alga (Figure 15.1) originally from Japan but now found extensively in Europe and North America (Eno *et al.*, 1997). It is a fast-growing species able to form dense stands where conditions suit and, by virtue of its life-history traits, is ideally suited to spread rapidly once established in a new region. Fronds of the alga readily become detached and can then disperse via natural drift. Crucially, these fronds can remain reproductively active for several weeks enabling dispersal over a wide area. *S. muticum* quickly exploits any open spaces that become available and it is considered to be an 'opportunistic gap-grabber' (Critchley, 1983).

S. muticum was first recorded in the UK in 1973 on the Isle of Wight and has since spread along the south coast of England, to Wales and around Ireland (Farnham *et al.*, 1973; Eno *et al.*, 1997). It is listed on Schedule 9 of the Wildlife & Countryside Act (1981). The first reports of *S. muticum* in Scotland were in Loch Ryan in 2004 and, by early 2007, populations had also been found at Great Cumbrae Island, the North Ayrshire coast, Arran and in Campbeltown Loch on the Mull of Kintyre. Drifting fragments of *S. muticum* had been recorded from Loch Fyne, Argyll and the Clyde Marina, Ayrshire, as well as on Arran and at Claonaig on the Mull of Kintyre. It had initially been thought that the Kintyre Peninsula would provide a temporary physical barrier to the continued spread of this species up the west coast of Scotland. However, during 2007, unattached drift *S. muticum* fragments were found in the Firth of Lorn at the Garvellachs and at Ganavan, near Oban (Harries *et al.*, 2007a,b). Thus, an opportunity was provided for tracking the spread, assessing the potential impacts and considering the management

Figure 15.1 *Sargassum muticum* growing in a low tidal rockpool, Great Cumbrae Island. © Lorne Gill/SNH

response to an invasive non-native species in Scotland, from what is likely to have been its first point of establishment.

A GIS model was developed to identify coastal areas where the establishment of *S. muticum* was most likely. The identification of predicted 'high risk' areas was achieved through a multi-staged approach:

- The area under investigation stretched from the Solway Firth to the Ardnamurchan Peninsula. Admiralty tidal data were used to determine the direction and maximum travel distance of floating material during an optimal spring tide regime. The influence of wind was then introduced, based on average wind speed and direction for the months of August, September and October (the time when detached fronds are most prevalent). This combined vector model was then applied to the locations where *S. muticum* was known to be established in order to determine the probable direction and range of spread from these points.
- The locations of shellfish farms (mussel and oyster) and marinas, as possible introduction or preferred settlement zones, were established using information from the Crown Estate's database.
- The presence of suitable or preferred *S. muticum* settlement substrate was mapped with data obtained from two sources: a selective interrogation of the Marine Recorder database and the DEFRA Coastal and Marine Resource Atlas (www.magic.gov.uk/camra.html).
- The data from Marine Recorder were further refined by selecting sites that satisfied *S. muticum*'s preference for sheltered or semi-sheltered shores.
- Locations of the native algae *Cystoseira* spp. and *Halidrys siliquosa* were also obtained from the Marine Recorder database, as these species are known to have similar habitat requirements to *S. muticum*.

The resulting model predicted the locations most vulnerable to colonization by *S. muticum*, (Figure 15.2) and allowed targeted field surveys to be carried out in these locations during July and August 2008. The field survey comprised two elements, a low tide survey (Figure 15.3) to identify sites where *S. muticum* had established, and strandline surveys (achievable at any state of tide) to find cast fronds. Full details of the survey sites can be found in Trendall *et al.* (2010).

The field surveys were complemented by a public relations campaign to raise awareness of *S. muticum,* and invasive non-native species issues more generally, and to encourage the reporting of new records. The combined public and field survey findings are illustrated in Figure 15.4 and these have extended knowledge of *S. muticum*'s distribution from Luce Bay in the Solway Firth, to as far north as Loch Sunart and Tarskavaig (Isle of Skye). These results also showed that *S. muticum* is widespread throughout the Firth of Clyde, with extensive, dense stands present at many locations. The campaign has demonstrated the value of involving the general public in greatly extending the search area far beyond what the surveyors alone could achieve.

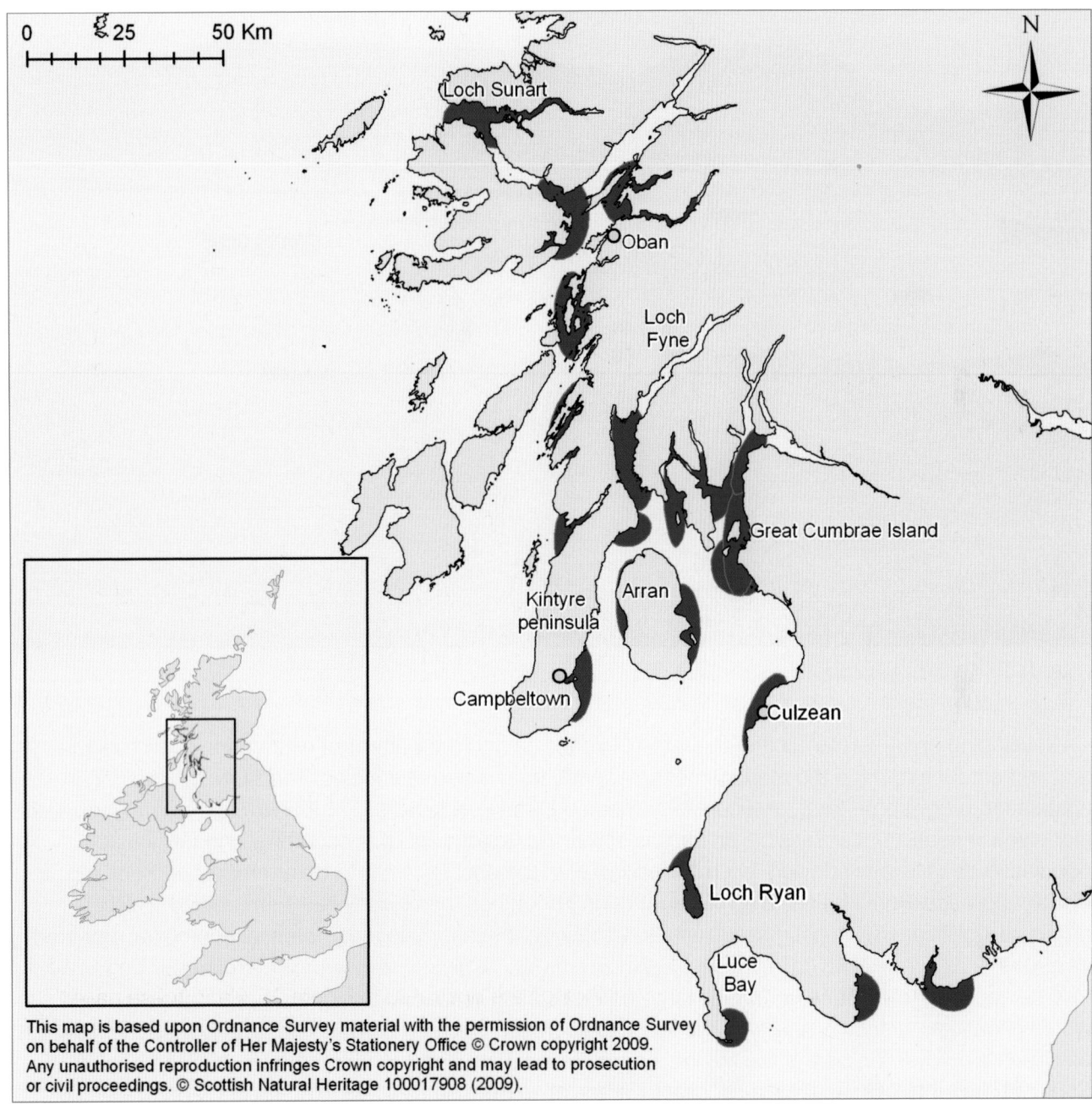

Figure 15.2 Locations predicted by GIS model as most vulnerable to colonization by *Sargassum muticum* (red areas).

Figure 15.3 Low tide surveys, Loch Craignish, Argyll. © SNH

Developing an understanding of the rate of expansion and the pattern of distribution is an essential requirement for informing the management response to an invasive species. The likely success of an eradication programme for *S. muticum* is hampered by several factors: *S. muticum* appears to be widely dispersed in relatively inaccessible areas; it is spreading rapidly; and it is occurring in highly variable population densities. In addition, even if eradication of the species were to be attempted in Scotland, a similar approach would be required in neighbouring countries, particularly Northern Ireland which harbours significant *S. muticum* populations. Otherwise these remain as a potential source for repeated invasions.

One approach may be to undertake targeted eradication in specific designated sites where *S. muticum* would negatively affect the quality of the features for which the site has been designated. Such a strategy has been employed on part of the Marine Nature Reserve at Lundy, where the manual clearance of *S. muticum* plants has resulted in successful eradication from small areas (Natural England, pers. comm.). The efficacy and cost-effectiveness of control and/or eradication techniques for *S. muticum* in designated sites requires further investigation.

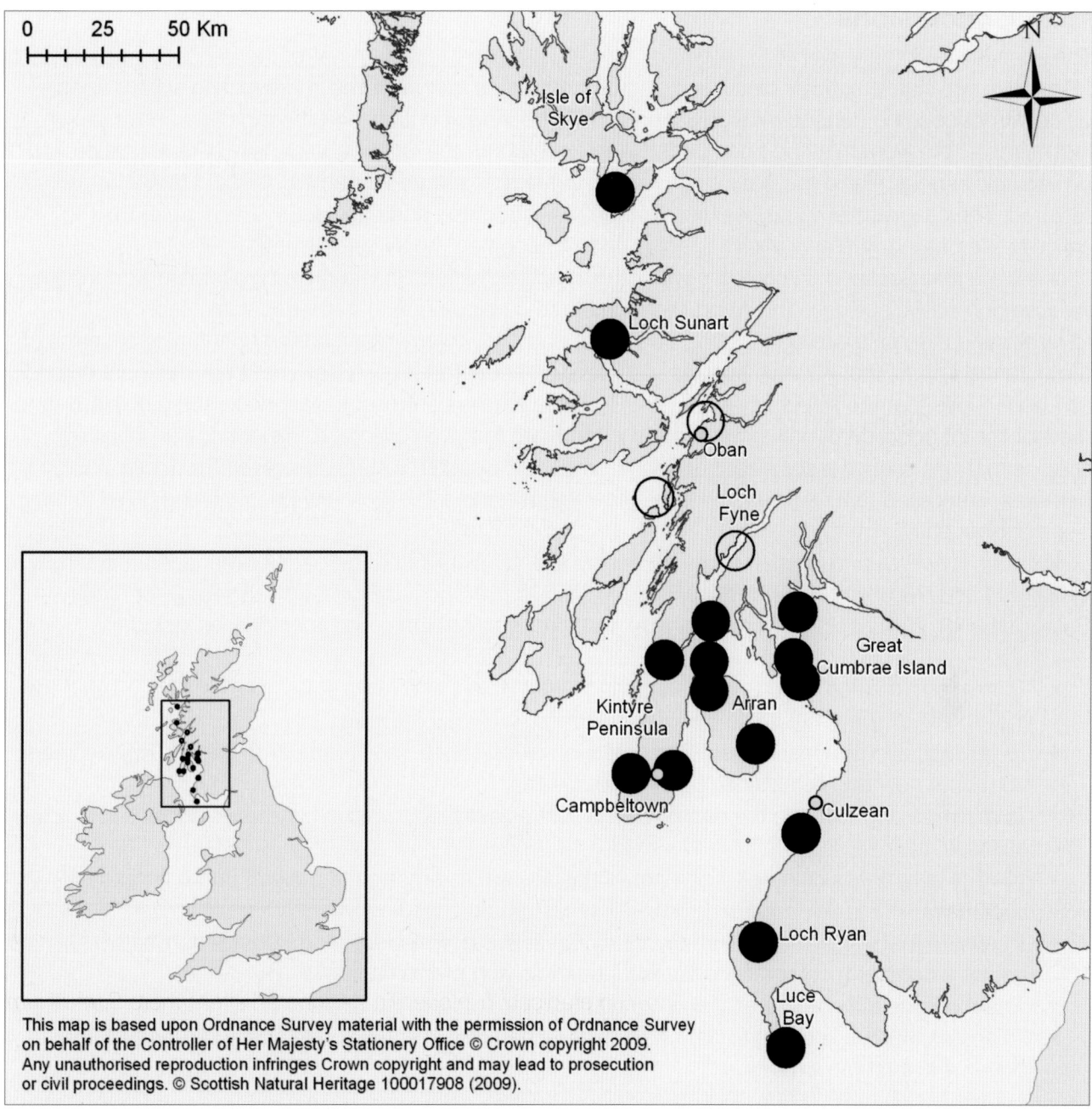

Figure 15.4 Known distribution of *Sargassum muticum* from results of survey and public sightings records in 2008. **Dark circles** = established plants. **Open circles** = drift fronds only.

15.8 Conclusions

The experience of the arrival of *S. muticum* in Scotland closely reflects most of the generic issues related to invasive non-native species discussed above. It illustrates the problems in preventing such a species being introduced, the dependence on action in neighbouring countries and the rapidity of colonization. Furthermore, the work that has been undertaken to establish the extent and density of colonization will be valuable in determining the likely costs related to future management actions should these be required. The case also emphasizes the value of taking targeted and early action because of the difficulties in dealing with an invasive species once it becomes widely established.

It is clear that Scotland, in common with other maritime nations, has a growing problem with marine invasive non-native species. This trend seems liable to continue due to further species, such as *C. fornicata* and didemnid ascidians, being very close and likely to arrive here in the near future. In terms of the potential impact that invasive species may have on economic activity, the most obvious cost thus far has been those that the shipping industry has incurred for the control of ballast waters and hull fouling to prevent the introduction of new organisms. It is fortunate that we have yet to experience an invasive species that has caused a significant economic impact in Scottish waters. However, this factor has perhaps contributed to a relatively low level of awareness and a relatively low priority being given to the issue until recently.

With the initiatives and legislative developments already highlighted the pace of management activity is picking up and the objectives within the *Invasive Non-Native Species Framework Strategy for Great Britain* (DEFRA, 2008) point towards the work that needs to be done. These objectives include:

- To minimize the risk of non-natives entering Great Britain and reduce the risks associated with the movement of species outside their natural range within Great Britain.
- To develop effective mechanisms for detection, surveillance, monitoring and responding to threats from both new and established non-native species.
- To minimize and manage the negative impact of established invasive non-native species in a cost-effective manner.
- To raise awareness of invasive non-native species issues among the general public and other key audiences.
- To ensure that the legislative framework for Great Britain for addressing invasive non-native species issues is coherent, comprehensive, fit for purpose and proportionate.
- To encourage a more strategic and coherent research stream to underpin policy and action.
- To ensure that we keep up to date with invasive non-native species developments within Great Britain and internationally.

All of these objectives apply in the marine environment and, amongst other things, point towards the need to continue and possibly expand the work started under the Species Action Framework (Scottish

Natural Heritage, 2007) and the Marine Aliens programme. Priorities will include continuing to raise awareness (particularly of preventative measures with relevant stakeholders), developing effective risk assessments for the potential vector activities and the development of best practice in the detection and management of marine non-native species.

The experience thus far points towards the need for some fundamental change in the way in which marine resources are managed. The current UK and Scottish Marine Bill processes offer the most significant opportunity to improve the management of marine resources. These Bills offer the potential to raise the priority attached to the threat of invasive non-native species and embed the necessary measures to ensure the objectives above are met. This is an opportunity that must not be missed.

References

Ashton, G.V., Willis, K.J., Cook, E.J. & Burrows, M. (2007). Distribution of the introduced amphipod, *Caprella mutica* Schurin, 1935 (Amphipoda: Caprellida: Caprellidae) on the west coast of Scotland and a review of its global distribution. *Hydrobiologia* **590**: 31-41.

Carlton, J.T. & Ruiz, G.M. (2005). The magnitude and consequences of bioinvasions in marine ecosystems: implications for conservation biology. In *Marine Conservation Biology: the science of maintaining the sea's biodiversity,* Eds Norse, E.A. & Crowder, L.B. Island Press, Washington DC. pp.123-148.

Cohen, A.N. & Carlton, J.T. (1997). Transoceanic transport mechanisms: the introduction of the Chinese mitten crab, *Eriocheir sinensis,* to California. *Pacific Science* **51**: 1 –11.

Critchley, A.T. (1983). The establishment and increase of *Sargassum muticum* (Yendo) Fensholt population within the Solent area of southern Britain. I. An investigation of the increase in number of population individuals. *Botanica Marina* **26**: 539-545.

Davis, M.H., Lutzen, J. & Davis, M.E. (2007). The spread of *Styela clava* Herdman, 1882 (Tunicata, Ascidiacea) in European waters. *Aquatic Invasions* **2**: 378-390.

Department of Food, Environement and Rural Affairs. (2008). The invasive non-native species framework strategy for Great Britain : protecting our natural heritage from invasive species. Department for Environment, Food and Rural Affairs, London.

de Lafontaine, Y., Sévigny, J.-M., Calvé, R., Verreault, G., Despatie, S.P. & Veilleux, E. (2008). Chinese mitten crabs (*Eriocheir sinensis*) in the St. Lawrence River and Estuary, Canada: new records and risk of invasion. *Aquatic Invasions* **3**: 153-163.

Drake, J.M. & Lodge, D.M. (2007). Hull fouling is a risk factor for intercontinental species exchange in aquatic ecosystems. *Aquatic Invasions* **2**: 121-131.

Eno, N.C., Clark, R.A. & Sanderson, W.G. (Eds). (1997). Non-native marine species in British waters: a review and directory. Joint Nature Conservation Commitee, Peterborough.

European Commission. (2007). Council Regulation (EC) No 708/2007 concerning use of alien and locally absent species in aquaculture.

European Commission. (2008). Developing an EU Framework for Invasive Alien Species: Discussion Paper. http://ec.europa.eu/environment/nature/invasivealien/docs/ias_discussion_paper.pdf

Farnham, D.E., Fletcher, R.L. & Irvine, L. (1973). Attached *Sargassum* found in Britain. *Nature* **243**: 231-232.

Harries, D.B., Harrow, S., Wilson, J.R., Mair, J.M. & Donnan, D.W. (2007a). The establishment of the invasive alga *Sargassum muticum* on the west coast of Scotland: A preliminary assessment of community effects. *Journal of the Marine Biological Association of the United Kingdom* **87**: 1057-1067.

Harries, D.B., Cook, E., Donnan, D.W., Mair, J.M., Harrow, S. & Wilson, J.R. (2007b). The establishment of the invasive alga *Sargassum muticum* on the west coast of Scotland: Rapid northwards spread and identification of potential new areas for colonization. *Aquatic Invasions* **2**: 367-377.

Herborg, L.-M., Rushton, S.P., Clare, A.S. & Bentley, M.G. (2003). Spread of the Chinese mitten crab (*Eriocheir sinensis* H. Milne Edwards) in Continental Europe: analysis of a historical data set. *Hydrobiologia* **503**: 21-28.

Herborg, L.-M., Rushton, S.P., Clare, A.S. & Bentley, M.G. (2005). The invasion of the Chinese mitten crab (*Eriocheir sinensis*) in the United Kingdom and its comparison to continental Europe. *Biological Invasions* **7**: 959-968.

ICES. (2005). ICES Code of Practice on the Introductions and Transfers of Marine Organisms. 30pp.

International Maritime Organization. (2005). *International Convention for the Control and Management of Ballast Water and Sediments*. Published by the International Maritime Organization. 138pp.

Johnsen, B.O. (2006). NOBANIS Invasive Alien Species Fact Sheet – *Gyrodactylus salaris*. Online Database of the North European and Baltic Network on IAS. www.nobanis.org

Kerckhof, F., Haelters, J. & Gollasch, S. (2007). Alien species in the marine and brackish ecosystem: the situation in Belgian Waters. *Aquatic Invasions* **2**: 243-257.

Knowler, D. & Barbier, E. (2000). The economics of an invading species: a theoretical model and case study application. In *The economics of an invading species,* Ed. By C.Perrings, M.Williamson, & S. Damazzone. Edward Elgar, UK.

Minchin, D. (2006). First Irish record of the Chinese mitten crab *Eriocheir sinensis* (Milne-Edwards, 1854) (Decapoda: Crustacea). *Irish Naturalist's Journal* **28**: 303-304.

Minchin, D. (2007). Aquaculture and transport in a changing environment: overlap and links in the spread of alien biota. *Marine Pollution Bulletin* **55**: 302-313.

Minchin, D. & Sides, E. (2006). Appearance of a cryptogenic tunicate, a *Didemnum* sp. fouling marine pontoons and leisure craft in Ireland. *Aquatic Invasions* **1**:143-147.

Nehring, S. (2006). NOBANIS – Invasive Alien Species Fact Sheet – *Crassostrea gigas*. From: Online Database of the North European and Baltic Network on Invasive Alien Species - NOBANIS www.nobanis.org

Reise, K., Gollasch, S. & Wolff, W.J. (2002). Introduced marine species of the North Sea coasts. In *Invasive Aquatic Species of Europe - Distribution, Impacts and Management,* Ed. by E. Leppäkoski, S. Gollasch, and S. Olenin. Kluwer, Dordrecht. pp 260-266.

Scottish Natural Heritage. (2007). A Five Year Species Action Framework: making a difference for Scotland's Species. SNH, Battleby, Redgorton. 80pp.

Trendall, J. R., Bedford, G., Lawton, P., Davison, D.M. & Saunders, G. (2010). Assessment of the spread of the non-native species *Sargassum muticum*: Solway Firth to the Ardnamurchan Peninsula. Scottish Natural Heritage Commissioned Report No.347

United Nations. (1992). Convention on Biological Diversity. *Treaty Series,* Vol. 1760 No. 30619.

USGS. (2008). Marine nuisance species: Genus *Didemnum*. http://woodshole.er.usgs.gov/project-pages/stellwagen/didemnum/

Willis, K.J., Cook, E.J. & Lozano-Fernandez, M. (2004). First record of the caprellid amphipod, *Caprella mutica*, for the U.K. *Journal of the Marine Biological Association of the UK* **84**: 1027-1028.

Donnan, D.W. and Manson, F.J. (2010). Invasive non-native species in Scotland's seas: risk and reality. In: *Species Management: Challenges and Solutions for the 21st Century*, ed. by J.M. Baxter and C.A. Galbraith. TSO Scotland, Edinburgh. pp. 265-282

282

Part 4

Conflicts of interest involving native species

The previous section of this book dealt with the issue of invasive non-native species, where much of the effort needed to concentrate on the identification of the species concerned, how to evaluate their likelihood of spread and consequently how to control or eradicate them. This section deals with a different set of circumstances, where the species are native and the problems arise when they have an impact on each other or in many cases where they interact with the human population or with crops or livestock. Many of the issues relate to our expectations in relation to these species. What do we consider to be a reasonable number of any particular species? What level of impact can we tolerate when native species damage crops or take livestock? All this is complicated stuff, with solutions requiring research and analysis that crosses traditional boundaries between ecological and social sciences. Finding solutions here is complicated also by the fact that people value wildlife in its own right, more now than ever before. There is a huge interest in wildlife in general, and in some of the most iconic species in particular. Species such as the golden eagle have become icons of the country, symbolizing Scotland's wild places and clean environment. In a related way, solutions to some of these "problems" that may have been publically acceptable some years ago, no longer are, as public awareness grows and concerns about animal welfare, and wildlife persecution gain greater prominence.

The following section reviews these issues and draws examples from across Europe on how solutions have been reached. It is clear that work in Scotland is in many cases leading the way, especially in terms of developing a scientific approach to clarify the exact nature of the problem, and in identifying practical ways to reach solutions.

The first chapter in this section by John Baxter and Colin Galbraith reviews the issues involved, noting that many have been long-running problems where finding sustainable solutions has proved to be elusive. Problems of crop damage or livestock predation can be found in virtually every country of the world and there is a multitude of ways to address the problem. Most problems relate to situations where human expectations of productivity from a crop or managed wildlife population are not met or where there is a direct impact on livestock. Managing expectations may be as important as managing the species concerned, and may in some cases lead to more cost-effective and durable solutions. This chapter stresses the importance of gaining a detailed knowledge of the ecology of the species involved before solutions can be derived. In short, you need to know what you are talking about from a technical viewpoint before solutions are likely. Whilst many of these problems are difficult, solutions are still possible and recent work from within Scotland has shown that with effective dialogue, compromise and determination, solutions can be found.

Des Thompson and his co-authors then explore some of these problems by examining case studies drawn from across Europe. They stress again the mix of science and cultural practices, attitudes and beliefs that are relevant in these situations and how important it is to understand why people believe what they do. They suggest that there is in essence, two types of conflict; firstly, those related to "facts", where people disagree over things such as how many individuals there are in a population, or on quantifying the impact predation may be having on domestic livestock; secondly, those related to "choices", where disagreement may occur over how to manage a population in terms of limiting numbers or in limiting impact. Particular difficulty occurs where a species that has a high conservation value in the opinion of the general public, comes into conflict with the interests of a small number of land-managers or other groups in society. How do we decide on the way ahead? What information is needed to inform decisions, and who is responsible for taking action to sort the problem? These are some of the key issues dealt with here.

Steve Redpath and his team review the issues involved in one of the most difficult species management problems at the present time. The challenge of how to resolve the hen harrier and red grouse dilemma, so that all sides involved can accept the way forward, has been one of the most complex ecological and socio-economic issues over recent decades. It is an area of science that the late Simon Thirgood (one of the co-authors of this chapter) in particular, committed much of his academic life, energy and enthusiasm to. Seeking a robust, objectively based solution was a key driving force for him and for many others involved here. The chapter notes that the hen harrier population is still fragile and persecuted in many areas of upland Scotland. Grouse shooting plays an important role in the economy of these same areas; so how can we find a solution that maintains the hen harrier population and grouse shooting in the same areas, and that does all this within the law? The chapter suggests two approaches that are not mutually exclusive; firstly, to enforce the existing law to ensure that the persecution of hen harriers is eliminated; and secondly to build consensus and cooperation between the parties involved. Issues such as the costs involved in any solution, the legality of management practices, the acceptability and feasibility of action, and the economic and social consequences all need to be considered.

Ian Boyd and John Harwood take us into the marine environment, focusing on some of the highest profile issues of species conflict at the present time. While public opinion is polarized in many instances where species conflict occurs, differences of opinion probably reach a peak in relation to the management of marine mammals. For example, public interest in the conservation of seals is considerable; set against the demands for some form of control of seal populations to limit the "take" by seals on fisheries. The chapter suggests that the conflict in many of these situations is, in fact, anthropogenic, based on human attitudes, perceptions and expectations. This echoes the views expressed in other chapters in this section and points the way to resolving problems based on the ecology of the species concerned, while taking full account of the socio-economic issues involved. Again, given the high conservation value attributed to many species of marine mammal and the pressures for management in a wide range of situations around the world, it is imperative that effective solutions are found. This chapter is a key contribution in seeking a resolution.

Like marine mammals, bats figure largely in our awareness of wildlife as part of our lives, though not always in a positive way. People either love them or hate them, yet most will probably have never seen them close up. Tony Mitchell-Jones discusses our relationship with bats and observes that most home-owners who have bats are probably unaware of their presence, and that many who do know that they are there are content with the situation. Some people are not so comfortable about their presence, however, and situations where this occurs need to be handled with sensitivity, so that bats are not perceived as an even bigger problem. The chapter notes that although bats are widespread across the country, they are dependent on a limited number of suitable roost sites, and can be badly affected by building renovations and other works, unless these are carried out sensitively. Many of their populations are fragile, and they are strictly protected in law in order to give their populations a better chance of recovery. The chapter highlights that the present country-wide initiative to enhance home insulation aiding domestic energy conservation, needs to be handled carefully, to achieve the desired results and to look after any bats present in the buildings.

The chapter by Bob Furness concludes this section of the book. Bob reviews the interactions between seabirds and fisheries, focusing on the situation around Scotland's coast. We have some of the largest seabird populations in Europe and still have an important fishing industry, despite considerable reduction over recent decades. The marine environment is of course not static, and recent changes have had an impact on the status of many seabird populations. Climate change has already had an effect and is likely to be increasingly noticeable in future. This factor, linked to human expectations of continued fishing at particular levels will be especially challenging, particularly if a sustainable approach is to be developed to fishery management and to the conservation of seabirds. Interestingly the chapter reveals some of the complexities involved in the "downstream" effects caused by changes to the diet of some of the larger seabird species. Where they have had to change their diet, due to some fish species becoming less available, they have switched to taking greater numbers of smaller seabirds. In some cases they are doing this to such an extent that the level of "take" may be unsustainable in terms of maintaining the smaller seabird species at present levels. The chapter considers also the practice of "discards", the unused catch from fishing boats, and the distorting effect this can have on seabird behaviour by my making large amounts of food available. The chapter suggests that this ecologically wasteful practice should be stopped.

As you read each chapter you will see there is a common thread running through each of the problems and situations discussed. Peoples' perceptions, values and expectations play a major part in defining the problem; and ecological knowledge, compromise and common sense, may lead to the solution!

Chapter 16

Species conflicts – real or perceived

John M. Baxter[1] and Colin A. Galbraith[1]

Summary

1. Species conflicts have arisen in numerous situations over recent years. Most relate to situations where human expectations for the productivity of a managed population are not met or where a farmed species is impacted by a wild one.
2. Seeking resolutions to these situations is often complex and difficult, yet recent examples from Scotland show that with dialogue, compromise and determination, solutions can be found.
3. A thorough and detailed understanding of the ecology of the species involved has been shown to be a prerequisite to developing enduring solutions.
4. This chapter discusses some of these situations and draws out the key approaches used.

[1] Scottish Natural Heritage, Silvan House, 231 Corstorphine Road, Edinburgh, EH12 7AT, UK

16.1 Introduction

OpenHydro tidal turbine test rig, Orkney. © John M. Baxt

Intra- and inter-species interactions in the natural world creates the inevitable winners and losers. In its purest sense interaction between species may be considered as a form of competition; the force that drives change and ultimately creates a transient balance between species' populations in the natural world.

Competition is a basic and fundamental ecological principle and in its simplest form is the interaction of two organisms striving for the same resource, which may be intensified by some limitation of that resource. For example there is competition for food, for space, for a mate, or for light. The establishment of a state of equilibrium in which a series of complex checks and balances operate usually results over time, influenced by a number of external factors acting on the relationship between the species or populations concerned.

Competition, therefore, in all its guises is the natural regulator of the natural world and only when we introduce the human dimension, placing our expectations of what the natural world should look like, and how it should operate, does conflict tend to arise. Whereas *competition* can be defined as 'a rivalry between individuals, groups, nations or animals for territory or resources', *conflict* is 'a state of discord caused by actual or perceived opposition of needs, values and interests'.

Conflicts can arise as a result of competing objectives resulting from various legislative commitments, and from sectoral economic pressures. In some instances the conflict may be more a perception by some parts of society depending on their expected or desired outcome, rather than a reality. In all cases, the solution and its consequences are likely to be more complex that it first appears and a detailed understanding of the intricacies of population ecology is usually required to fully understand the interactions observed in such situations.

16.2 Legislative pressures

A range of measures are in place at both the national and international levels that are designed to enhance the protection and conservation of a range of threatened or 'special' species. Much of this originates as over-arching law from the EU and is then translated into domestic law at the UK or Scottish levels as appropriate. There can be no doubt that this framework is important to the overall conservation of species in Scotland, and across the EU, but is becoming progressively more complex for practitioners "on the ground" to interpret.

The UK Biodiversity Action Plan, developed in response to the Rio Summit declaration in 1992 (United Nations, 1992), resulted in the development of a large number of individual Species or Habitat Action Plans. These plans have perhaps formed the key part of the UK's response to the need to conserve biodiversity over the past 15 years. In a recent review the number of species identified as in need of such a plan has increased. There are now over 1,000 species with such plans. A similar process has been undertaken at the Scottish level as part of the Scottish Biodiversity Strategy (Scottish Executive, 2004) which also sought to identify those species considered most important by the public.

The challenge in the face of these lists of species, and the expectations they create, is to deliver the required protection whilst taking into account the needs of other species, as well as meeting the expectations of those who would wish to exploit these species or others that are in competition with them. Furthermore, the commitment of world leaders signed in Sweden in 2001 to halt the loss of biodiversity by 2010 provided not only a further challenge but created another level of planning and an overarching objective, into which existing plans and strategies had to fit. It has been important, to be clear about how the measurement of the success of these various levels of planning will be judged. Indeed, the debate and discussion about this continues.

The Wildlife and Countryside Act 1981 and the Nature Conservation (Scotland) Act 2004 each identify a range of species in need of protection and conservation action on the ground that has over the years led to areas of conflict. The Conservation of Seals Act 1970 (soon to be replaced by measures in the new Marine (Scotland) Act) seeks to manage the manner and reason for any seal killing; a subject that has been contentious over many years.

16.3 Economic pressures

Expectations in relation to land use and to species management are, in many cases, driven by the aim of further economic development and expansion, albeit done in a sustainable way. Developments of a range of scales and types create inevitable conflicts with the conservation needs of a range of species. Recent examples of such difficulties are as a result of new developments, such as port expansion or road building. The apparent conflict is between progress and protection, yet in many cases there are solutions available if all parties want to find an agreed way forwards. The difficulty is in some cases that the solution may impact on the bottom line of the balance sheet. Early planning and dialogue between conservationists and developers is therefore an important part of any successful development and can help reduce the cost of mitigation enormously.

In the case of new road construction there can be issues around maintaining free and safe movement for wildlife such as badgers (*Meles meles*) and otters (*Lutra lutra*). One solution could of course be to not build the road, but often a 'better" and more realistic solution is to install badger/otter underpasses during

Plate 16.1 Otter underpass on road in Galloway. © Alan Wright/SNH

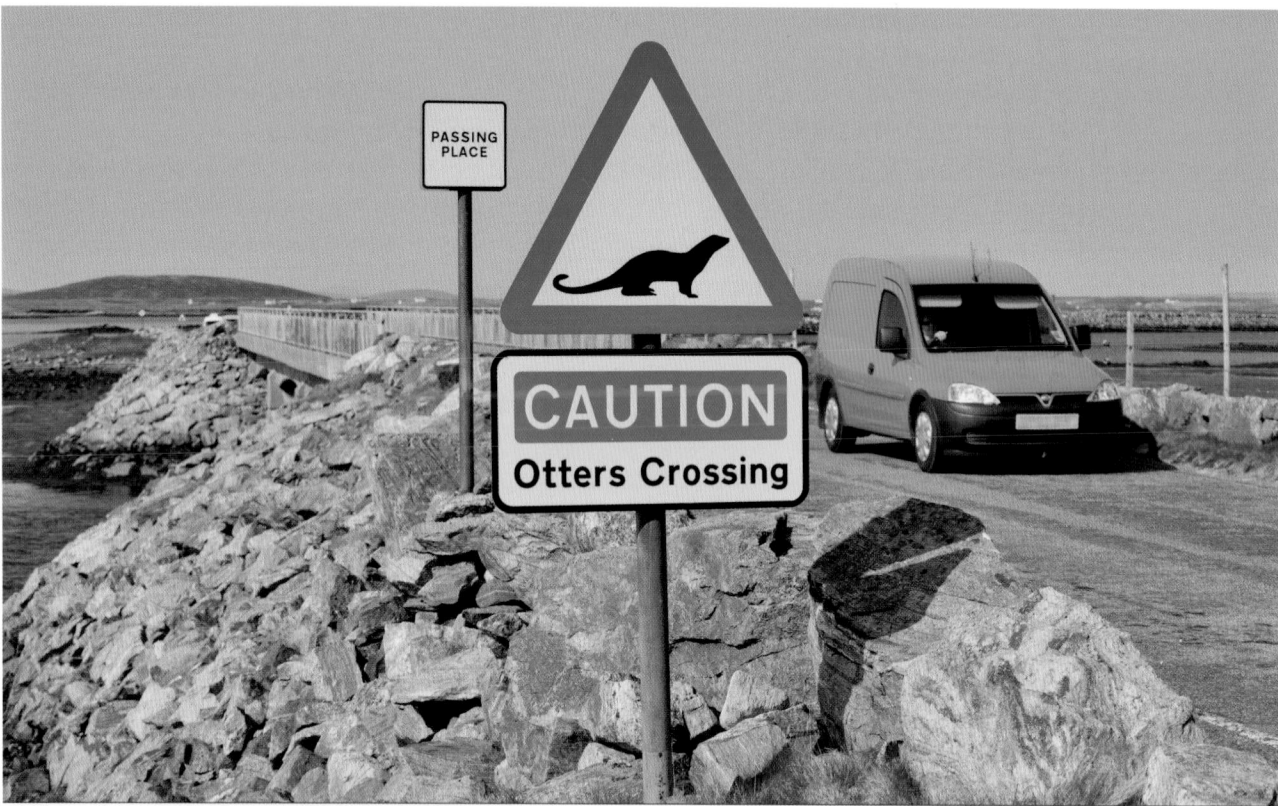

Plate 16.2 Warning signs alert motorists to otters on the Uists. © Lorne Gill/SNH

the construction phase. Whilst some would argue that the construction of the road should not have gone ahead, the underpass is a simple compromise that can go a long way to resolve such conflicts. In other cases where road kills are an issue then educating drivers of the risk of killing wildlife in particular areas can help reduce the problem.

New or novel developments present challenges and new conflicts to be overcome. In the past, many problems were either overlooked or in many cases probably not recognized early enough as a problem. Consequently, these situations developed into a conflict that might otherwise have been avoided. More recently developers and conservationists have become better at identifying potential conflicts at an earlier stage and thus seeking solutions to minimize or avoid difficulties before they arise.

The development of renewable energy generation capacity is probably one of the largest and fastest growing sectors in the UK at present where potential conflicts could arise. Whilst it is seen as the big new idea, renewable energy in the from of hydro power has of course been around for many years and solutions to the conflicts, in particular with fisheries but also with other wildlife dependent on natural river flow, have been found. Many of the rivers on which hydro dams have been built are also important for their Atlantic salmon (*Salmo salar*) runs and the development of fish passes in many cases has been the solution.

The conflicts between the development of wind farms on land and in particular the prevention of bird strikes continues to be a challenging and contentious issue. In some instances the risks to specific species have been considered so great, that developments have been denied, whilst in other cases developments have been able to proceed but with amendments to their design intended to minimize the risks. The secret of much of this conflict avoidance/resolution has been early and free communication between the different interested parties and an understanding by all of their respective goals. In such cases, however, the decisions have to be seen in the context of government targets to greatly increase the renewable energy generating capacity and consequently reducing carbon dioxide emissions. The pendulum of compromise may not always be able to swing true and achieving a balance in such situations will always be difficult.

Plate 16.3 Fish pass on the River Ericht. © Lorne Gill/SNH

Offshore renewable technology, in particular wave and tidal energy generation, present new questions and potential conflicts which may be even harder to quantify. Many of the technologies being deployed are still at the proving stage, to determine if they are viable options in terms of energy generation and financial return. The impacts that arrays of such installations may have on wildlife are unknown, but could include collision risks, habitat modification through the removal of energy from the natural system and the blocking/disruption of migration routes. Lessons have been learned from earlier developments on land and questions about impacts are being asked now, and a productive dialogue established between developer and conservationists, so that answers can be found that will hopefully avoid conflicts arising.

Within agriculture and aquaculture the nature of the conflicts that arise are different. In these cases it tends to be the direct exploitation of the 'farmed' resource by wildlife that is the issue.

A common issue in many parts of Scotland is the impact that over-wintering wildfowl, in particular geese, can have on autumn sown crops, particularly winter barley. In this instance, the loss of their traditional grazing lands due to changes in agricultural practices and other developments, combined with their increasing numbers, the result of successful conservation measures and greater protection, has driven them onto farmland to over-winter, where they can do significant damage. Over a period of years a dialogue between farmers and the government has led to the creation of a number of "goose management schemes" where public money is allocated to assist farmers in managing the geese on their ground (http://www.scotland.gov.uk/Topics/Environment/Wildlife-Habitats/Geese/Management-Schemes). Payments are made for damage to crops and a scaring regime is funded to scare the birds at times of maximum damage. The scheme has the backing of both farming and conservation organizations and helps maintain internationally important goose populations, which are of considerable public benefit by way of tourism in some of the remotest parts of the country.

In the marine environment the conflicts between predators and the aquaculture industry are equally significant. In most cases the fish farm (be it shellfish or finfish) presents itself as an often irresistible attraction to the natural predators of the farmed species. The blue mussel (*Mytilus edulis*) is the natural preferred prey of eider ducks (*Somateria mollissima*), and the long-lines of mussels at the farms are a highly nutritious source of food for the ducks to exploit. Similarly salmon farms represent an irresistible opportunity for an easy meal to seals. The damage that can be inflicted by seals is considerable, not only in terms of the take of stock and the stress caused to fish by a seal attack, but also to the fish farm infrastructure. If the cage net itself is damaged, then this can result in the loss of the entire stock. This can not only have significant financial consequences to the company concerned and to possible local employment but is likely to have serious environmental consequences if the escaped farm stock interact and hybridize with local wild salmon stocks.

Antipredator nets and other non-lethal control measures are available and in many cases, if deployed correctly, have been shown to work. As ever, the solutions to one problem, however, can in some circumstances lead to other conflicts. For example, the high frequency audio deterrent devices (ADDs) used at some fish farms to scare seals can have serious detrimental effects on cetaceans (Gordon and Northridge, 2002).

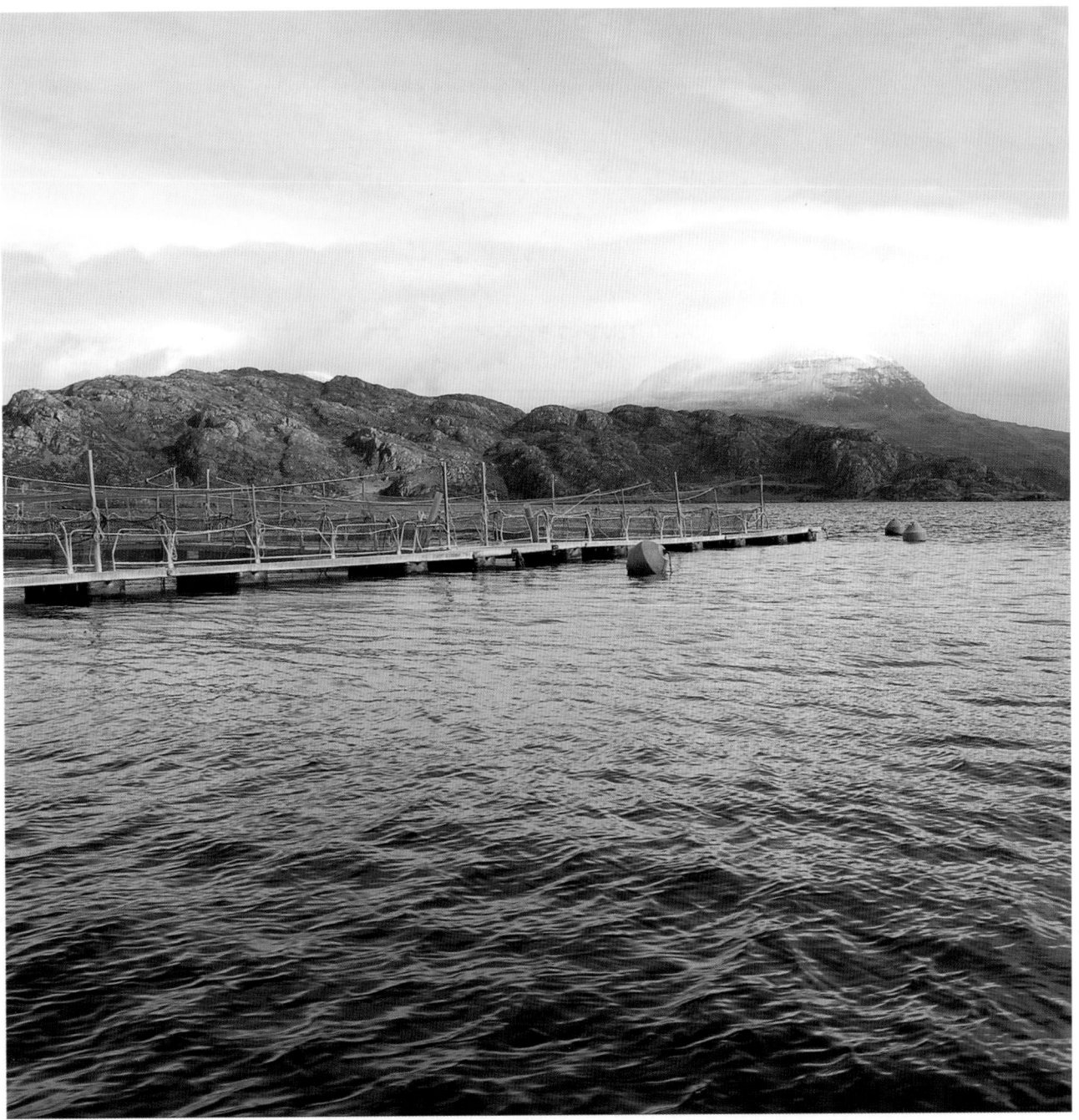

Plate 16.3 A salmon farm in Loch Torridon. © John M. Baxter

In all these cases progress is being made with better mutual understanding and respect between all sides being essential.

Whilst the conflicts described above are between a natural predator and 'introduced'/farmed prey, some of the greatest conflicts over recent years have arisen where both wildlife and humans seek to exploit the same wild prey.

Fisheries are perhaps the largest example of this type of conflict. For a long time there was enough fish in the sea to satisfy the demands of both the fishermen and the wild, natural predators. In recent years, with dramatic declines in many commercial fish stocks this is no longer the case, or so it is perceived. At the same time as fish stocks have been declining, the numbers of various predators, e.g. seabirds, seals, some cetaceans have been seen to increase around the UK. It is perhaps not surprising therefore, that these predators have been blamed by some, for the declining fish stocks, and indeed it is an inevitable fact that with greater numbers of predators they will eat more prey in total. This cannot, however, hide the fact that much of the decline of many commercial fish stocks is due to overfishing by humans, and is further exacerbated by the impacts of climate change which, is resulting in major changes to marine ecosystems (MCCIP, 2006, 2008, 2009). Nevertheless, there is a conflict between

Plate 16.5 Black-legged kittiwake (*Rissa tridactyla*). © Lorne Gill/SNH

fisheries and predators and in these circumstances it would seem reasonable to assume that the ire of fishermen would be directed at all wild predators equally, namely birds, cetaceans, other fish and seals. This is not the case, however, and most of their attentions focus largely on the seals. The reasons for this are complicated and unclear, and may well largely be down to human perceptions and bias. The issue to be resolved in the minds of many fishermen is why there is not so much fish in the sea for them to catch as there once was. A culprit must be found and a simple solution identified. The multifaceted explanation of a range of predators and overfishing is an uncomfortable one. Seabirds are not an easy target because of the very long-standing and wide-ranging support they receive from the general public and similarly cetaceans are sacrosanct which leaves seals as the main perceived culprit, whilst assuming humans are blameless. Seals are also the most visible of the large predators and whilst support for them is growing, they have historically not enjoyed the same level of love and attention that the other species groups have. As such, the targeting of seals may help alleviate the frustrations of fishermen but on its own will not resolve the problem of declining fish stocks.

The Moray Firth is an example of where such a scenario is found. Within the area there are a large number of important Atlantic salmon (*Salmo salar*) rivers supporting valuable fisheries. The area is also very important for a range of natural heritage interests and holds European designated sites at sea for various seabirds, waterfowl, harbour seals (*Phoca vitulina*), and bottlenose dolphins (*Tursiops truncatus*), and in the surrounding rivers for salmon and Eurasian otters (*Lutra lutra*). Such designations place requirements on all appropriate authorities to ensure the favourable conservation status of the features. Declining salmon returns have in the past led to high levels of essentially uncontrolled shooting of seals, sanctioned by the District Salmon Fisheries Boards (one of the above mentioned appropriate authorities) with a resultant significant decline in the number of harbour seals in the region, but little apparent improvement in salmon stocks as a result. Action was needed to halt the decline in harbour seal numbers but at the same time still trying to accommodate the aspirations of the salmon fisheries. As a result the Moray Firth Seal Management Plan was developed. Since its inception in 2005 it has undoubtedly resulted in a reduction in the number of harbour seals being shot, although as yet there is little sign of seal numbers recovering (Butler *et al.,* 2008). What is, as yet, even less clear is whether salmon numbers have recovered.

What the Moray Firth plan has done is address a perceived conflict between the salmon fisheries and seal predation, developing a clear agreement between those involved, and to that end it can be hailed a success. What it has not yet been able to achieve, however, is solve the overriding problem of declining salmon stocks, as this is a much more complicated and wide-reaching issue. In addition to the pressures placed on salmon from the full range of predators the species also has to overcome other major problems, most notably the impacts of climate change and increasingly, ocean acidification. The warming of the northern ocean is resulting in a shrinking area of sea in which salmon can thrive. The increasing acidity of the Arctic Ocean due to the absorption of increased amounts of atmospheric carbon dioxide is affecting the abundance of some key components of the salmon's diet such as pteropods (OARUG,

2009). In the scheme of things, this as perhaps a much larger problem that conservationists and salmon fisheries managers need to work together to address.

An important lesson therefore is that addressing a conflict may not solve the underlying problem in the short term, but is valuable none-the-less in developing a shared and common understanding of the issues involved. Indeed, even getting agreement on the numbers of predators and prey involved in some situations can be an achievement in itself and can lead to other more substantive agreement on the true nature of the problem and on possible solutions.

On land a similarly long running conflict exists between raptors and shooting estate managers where the historical persecution of raptors is seen as the solution to declining numbers of game birds. This issue is dealt with in detail in other chapters of this book, so will not be discussed further here.

Within all these situations where there is financial gain to be made from the exploitation of wildlife there lies a challenge to provide a comparable valuation of the natural resources that create the conflict. In some circumstances it is possible to ascribe some sort of counter valuation, but again often only in terms of the financial benefits of some other type of exploitation. For example, in the Moray Firth the seals have a 'value' to the wildlife watching industry if they remain alive. What is more difficult to do is to express the value of the ecosystem service they provide in terms that are transparent and readily understandable. Seeking solutions to conflicts will almost inevitably involve compromise between valuations; hence one challenge for the conservation community is to develop evaluations to demonstrate the true value of ecosystem services to the wider public.

16.4 Legislative pressures

The legislative instruments that have been created to provide protection to various wildlife can result in dilemmas which are almost self-imposed conflict situations. In such situations where two protected species come into conflict either through a simple predator – prey relationship or some other type of interaction, decisions must be taken on how to respond. Is the answer to step back and let natural competition take its course? This is of course possible, but would that provide the result we want!? Or alternatively do we intervene, and if so, how and to what end? In such cases there is a risk of being accused of undue arrogance in thinking that we can determine the outcome of what we perceive as a conflict by managing nature. If the purpose is noble then on occasion it may be justifiable.

One such example is the conflict on the Farne Islands between the grey seals and the nesting Atlantic puffins (*Fratercula arctica*). On some of the islands the puffins were being endangered by the grey seals (*Halichoerus grypus*) hauling out on the sandy cliffs causing the nest burrows of the puffins to collapse. At the time the number of puffins was declining and as a result it was decided that their needs took precedence so that measures were put in place to exclude the seals from sensitive areas on some of the islands. Such active management of a conflict was successful in the recovery of the puffin numbers and perhaps coincidentally resulted in the establishment of a new breeding colony of grey seals further along the coast on the Isle of May (Pomeroy *et al.,*2000).

Plate 16.6 Isle of May in the Firth of Forth where grey seals and Atlantic puffins exist together. © Patricia and Angus Macdonald/SNH

Similarly, the natural competition and predator prey relations between the protected capercaillie (*Tetrao urogallus*) and a range of predators, some of which are also protected such as the pine marten (*Martes martes*), the goshawk (*Accipiter gentilis*), and others such as the red fox (*Vulpes vulpes*) and carrion crow (*Corvus c. corone*) has become perceived as a conflict as the number of capercaillie has declined. This decline in capercaillie from around 20,000 birds in Scotland in the 1970s to a low of less than 1,000 is the result of a number of factors of which predation is just one. Collisions of both young and adults with fences, overgrazing in woodlands, lack of suitable habitat, loss of food plants have all contributed. The call therefore from some quarters for the control of predators including those that are protected species must be seen and taken in context. Whilst reducing the level of predation might be seen as conflict resolution, the solution to the problem of capercaillie decline is much more complex.

In a few cases the conflict is between a native and an introduced non-native species. Examples of such would be the predation by American mink (*Neovison vison*) on ground-nesting birds in the Western Isles or on water vole (*Arvicola terrestris*) on mainland Scotland; or the conflict between red (*Sciurus vulgaris*) and grey (*Sciurus carolinensis*) squirrels.

In both these cases the introduced non-native species is threatening the native species and the solution would seem simple, if not easy: the trapping and despatching of the non-native. As in all cases where the killing of individuals is required there are legitimate issues over animal welfare that need to be considered, but at the same time there can be little doubt about the need for the vigorous control of the alien species in an attempt to conserve the native biodiversity of the country. With respect to the grey squirrel, however, opinions are divided. It is a familiar sight in many public parks and gardens and there is considerable public support against it being killed, especially in areas where there are none or few red squirrels left. This may in part be due to the fact that the native red squirrel is much more elusive and not so much in the consciousness of the public. Clearly for the conservation of the red squirrel to be effective then the battle for the "hearts and minds" of the public has to be won in terms of accepting that widespread control of the grey will be necessary.

16.5 Communications and understanding

In all cases where conflict is perceived and there is a desire to intervene it is important to recognize that we are imposing a level of control on an otherwise natural process in order to either protect our interests or ensure a desired outcome. Almost inevitably this will require compromise between the various groups managing species.

In many cases such conflicts can be satisfactorily avoided or resolved. The underpass associated with a new road development, if well designed and positioned, will result in most animals being able to safely cross the road. The numbers killed in collisions will be greatly reduced. We understand the questions and we know the answers.

In the case of the developing renewable energy industries the ability to avoid conflict by providing reliable, well argued advice, backed up by sound science and good survey data is proven. Working with developers from a very early stage in the process means that not only are potential conflicts more likely to be avoided but also that any impacts can be minimized. In the case of marine renewables there is a steep knowledge gradient to be climbed by all involved, but crucially there is widespread recognition of this.

In all cases where there is conflict (real or perceived), early communication between parties is essential. With communication comes understanding and appreciation of another's position and ultimately there is trust and respect. In many cases this requires an individual to 'step forward' and take the moral high ground. There is no better example of this than in the development of the Moray Firth Seal Management Plan where an individual from one of the District Salmon Fishery Boards, who at the time were responsible for very heavy shooting of harbour seals, recognized that there had to be a better way.

Once channels of communication are opened then decisions and solutions can be found. The resolution of any conflict might at first seem 'simple' but it rarely is. In most cases it is likely to be a lengthy and expensive exercise and it is essential to have clear long-term commitment to the solution in place before embarking on a conflict resolution process. The return on such efforts can be great, not only to the species concerned but also to the erstwhile antagonists. The secret is in the development of trust and common goals and the acceptance of the other party's perspective on the issue. The progress that has been made towards the resolution of some long-running conflicts shows that it is possible and worth the effort.

References

Butler, J.R.A., Middlemas, S.J., McKelvey, S.A., McMyn, I., Leyshon, B., Walker, I., Thompson, P.M., Boyd, I.L., Duck, C., Armstrong, J.D., Graham, I.M. & Baxter, J.M. (2008). The Moray Firth Seal Management Plan : an adaptive framework for balancing the conservation of seals, salmon, fisheries and wildlife tourism in the UK. *Aquatic Conservation: Marine and Freshwater Ecosystems* **18**: 1025-1038.

Gordon, J. & Northridge, S. (2002). Potential impacts of Acoustic Deterrent Devices on Scottish Marine Wildlife. *Scottish Natural heritage Commissioned Report No. F01AA404,* Battleby, Perth.

Marine Climate Change Impacts Partnership. (2006). Marine Climate Change Impacts Annual Report Card 2006. Eds Buckley, P.J., Dye, S.R. & Baxter, J.M. Summary Report, MCCIP, Lowestoft, 8pp.

Marine Climate Change Impacts Partnership. (2008). Marine Climate Change Impacts Annual Report Card 2007-2008. Eds Baxter, J.M., Buckley, P.J. & Wallace, C.J. Summary Report, MCCIP, Lowestoft, 8pp.

Marine Climate Change Impacts Partnership. (2009). Marine Climate Change Ecosystem Linkages Report Card 2009. Eds Baxter, J.M., Buckley, P.J. & Frost, M.T. Summary Report, MCCIP, Lowestoft, 16pp.

Ocean Acidification Reference User Group. (2009). *Ocean Acidification: The Facts. A special introductory guide for policy advisers and decision makers*. Eds Laffoley, D. d'A. & Baxter, J.M. European Project on Ocean Acidification (EPOCA) 12pp.

Pomeroy, P.P., Twiss, S.D. & Duck, C.D. (2000). Expansion of a grey seal (*Halichoerus grypus*) breeding colony: changes in pupping site use at the Isle of May, Scotland. *Journal of Zoology* **250**: 1-12.

Scottish Executive. (2004). *Scotland's Biodiversity – It's In Your Hands.* Scottish Executive, Edinburgh.

United Nations. (1992). Convention on Biological Diveristy. *Treaty Series,* Vol 1760 No. 30619.

Baxter, J.M. and Galbraith, C.A. (2010). Species conflicts – real or perceived. In: *Species Management: Challenges and Solutions for the 21st Century*, ed. by J.M. Baxter and C.A. Galbraith. TSO Scotland, Edinburgh. pp. 289-301

301

Chapter 17

The nature of human-wildlife conflicts across Europe: a review

Des B.A. Thompson[1], Tim M. Reed[2], Judy Stroud[3], Mary F.B. Christie[4] and David A. Stroud[5]

Summary

1. This chapter presents an overview of human-wildlife conflicts sampled across Europe (notably in the UK, Sweden, Spain and Netherlands). Legal, scientific and cultural elements are reviewed, along with some of the conflict resolution and consensus-building techniques being developed to help resolve conflicts.

2. Conflicts between people and wildlife are numerous, diverse and, in many cases, complex and long-standing. They can be between different groups of people regarding wildlife, and/or between some of these groups and the wildlife itself.

3. There are two fundamental types of environmental conflicts: those which relate to facts (which are relatively easy to resolve through effective communication and exchange of sufficient information), and those which relate to choices (which are much more complicated because they are based on different value judgements, and where options for action can be mutually exclusive).

4. When the interests of species of high conservation status clash with people the conflicts can be acute, regardless of whether or not the root issues are actual or perceived. The social sciences have been instructive in helping understand some of the key issues. We propose that social science insights need to be better integrated into conflict resolution activities undertaken by conservationists.

5. We highlight three key needs in tackling these conflicts: a) leadership and transparency in decision making; b) inclusive stakeholder engagement and awareness of relevant social and cultural factors; and c) sufficient time for the parties to understand each other's positions.

[1] Scottish Natural Heritage, Silvan House, 231 Corstorphine Road, Edinburgh, EH12 7AT, UK
[2] EcoText Ltd., Hughfield House, Fenstanton Road, Hilton, Cambridgshire, PE28 9JA, UK
[3] Natural England, Northminster House, Northminster Road, Peterborough, PE1 1UA, UK
[4] Scottish Natural Heritage, Battleby, Redgorton, Perth, PH1 3EW, UK
[5] Joint Nature Conservation Committee, Monkstone House, City Road, Peterborough, PE1 1JY, UK

Greylag goose (*Anser anser*). © Lorne Gill/SN

17.1 Introduction

Humans have a diversity of relationships with their natural environment, varying from high dependence on some plants and animals for food, through to conflicts with other species on issues such as human welfare and safety. Within this broad spectrum of relationships there is a bewildering diversity of attitudes, impacts and alliances, often differing within different cultures. In response to these issues, different countries have developed a complex range of laws, policies and processes to address the status and management of human-wildlife conflicts.

17.1.1 History of conflicts

In Scotland, as in much of Europe, there is a long history of habitat change, wildlife adaptation and human-wildlife conflicts (e.g. Simmons, 2001; Smout, 2002; Galbraith *et al.*, 2003; Redpath and Thirgood, 2009). As people have caused many of these changes, so the natural environment and its animals and plants have had to adapt or decline. The losses of grey wolf (*Canis lupus*), brown bear (*Ursus arctos*) and Eurasian beaver (*Castor fiber*) amongst others, reflect the outcome of long-running human-species conflicts (see Box 17.1). For those species that have remained, the need for adaptation has continued, as the economic and social pressures on the landscape and species have continued to change (Smout, 2000; Sidaway, 2005).

The combination of economic, social and climatic drivers means that few areas within Europe are not undergoing some form of change. Over the last 50 years, a third driver – public recognition of the need for conservation and associated legislation – has appeared, acting as a potential brake or counterbalance to the other drivers. With this has come the need for governments to respond to human-species conflicts in a reasoned way (for review see Sidaway (2005)).

Countries which have signed the Convention on Biological Diversity (CBD), implemented through European Community conservation Directives, and acceded to other international conventions (such as the Bern Convention on the conservation of European habitats and species and the Ramsar Convention on wetlands) have had to place heavy emphasis on the sustainable care and management of habitats and species. One of the most challenging aspects of this work is the resolution of so called human-wildlife conflicts, and the development of clear, transparent and open frameworks for approaching and managing such conflicts.

Conflicts in Scotland are largely derived from species living within a managed landscape, rather than conflicts in or at the edge of wilderness areas such as in parts of the USA. This paper explores the range of conflicts which occur between people and nature.

The word 'conflict' is derived from the Latin *conflictus,* referring to a "struggle or clash between opposing forces…" (Oxford English Dictionary). Two broad types of conflicts occur: (i) those where different human interests rest with groups, and the groups conflict with one another over particular species, habitats, communities or ecosystems; and (ii) where one group of people conflicts directly with wildlife or other environmental interests. Both types of conflict can occur simultaneously, and some of these can involve the same elements interacting with each other. Most conflicts occur where a species whose protection is valued by one human interest impacts on another human interest (which may involve the protection or enjoyment of other species).

Box 17.1 Examples of key species in Europe which feature in human-wildlife conflicts. The species marked in bold-italic type are non-native species to Europe.

Icons	Grey wolf (*Canis lupus*), brown bear (*Ursus arctos*), Eurasian lynx (*Lynx lynx*), wolverine (*Gulo gulo*), European beaver (*Castor fiber*)
Large birds of prey	Eurasian black vulture (*Aegypius monachus*), lammergeier (*Gypaetus barbatus*), white-tailed eagle (*Haliaeetus albicilla*), golden eagle (*Aquila chrysaetos*)
Fish-eating birds	Cormorants (*Phalacrocorax* spp.)
Pinnipeds	Seals (Pinnipedia spp.)
Geese	Greylag (*Anser anser*), bean. (*A. fabalis*), **Canada (Branta canadensis)**, barnacle (*B. leucopsis*) geese
Meso-predators	Hen harrier (*Circus cyaneus*), red fox (*Vulpes vulpes*), ***American mink (Neovison vison), grey squirrel (Sciurus carolinensis), signal crayfish (Pacifastacus leniusculus)***

Plate 17.1 The re-establishment of white-tailed eagles in Scotland has raised concerns within the farming community as to their potential impact on sheep. A range of approaches have been used to successfully address these fears. © Lorne Gill

17.1.2 Broad responses to human-wildlife conflicts

Essentially, there have been three broad responses to human-species conflicts:

- **co-existence** with the impacting species, which may involve the payment of compensation/ subsidies for economic losses, or the acceptance of losses;
- **displacement** of the impacting species, by removal of the species (translocation) or provision of alternative habitat away from the principal location; and
- **controlling** numbers and/or impacts through culls (the 'take' referred to below) or application of non-lethal methods (such as immuno-contraception), or provision of diversionary food or other resources.

17.1.3 Pest species and non-protected species

Many countries refer to 'pest' species as 'nuisance' species which damage crops, injure or irritate livestock or people, or reduce the fertility of the land (the term comes from the Latin *pestis*, meaning plague). Often, though not always, these are ecological generalists, sometimes with large population sizes.

Legally, in the UK, domestic legislation defining the status of bird species follows the EC Birds Directive and Bern Convention. All species are protected, but some (mainly so-called 'pest' species – although this term is not used legally) may be controlled by authorized persons in order to prevent damage to human interests (where there are no other satisfactory solutions - Stroud *et al.,* 1999). Methods of killing must be quite specific, and indiscriminate or mass means of capture and killing is forbidden (e.g. bird-liming).

In the UK, control of certain species is permitted through Open General Licences (OGLs). A fundamental principle in the EC Birds Directive is the need for population scale monitoring of 'pest' species to allow policy change in the event of population decline ('adaptive management'). For example, the removal of house sparrow (*Passer domesticus*) from the OGL followed monitoring which revealed widespread declines and its consequent addition to the UK 'Red List' of bird species (Gregory *et al.,* 2002).

Non-avian European protected species are defined by the EC Habitats Directive. As for birds, control is only permitted under precisely defined circumstances and only under a specific licence. Some of these can impact on human interests (such as the red fox *Vulpes vulpes*), and the methods of control are regulated through multiple legislation frameworks within the UK, many of which are very long standing *e.g.* various extant 19th Century Ground Game Acts.

17.2 Conflicts across Europe: three countries

17.2.1 Country case studies

We have reviewed human-wildlife conflicts in Sweden, Netherlands and Spain and compared these with the UK. We have chosen countries with markedly varying human population densities, extent of wild country, differing intensities of land management, and contrasting historical-legal contexts. We have looked at policy and legislative contexts and formal frameworks (where existing) for managing conflicts.

We review a sample of cases across fish-eating birds, raptors, geese and seals, in order to compare approaches taken to reduce conflicts with those adopted in the UK.

17.2.2 Sources of information

Most of the information presented below was collated from material available on the internet and produced by statutory bodies concerned with conservation of the environment and natural resources in the countries reviewed. Some additional material was supplied by specialists in government, and their counterparts in the non-governmental organization (NGO) community. Considerable use was also made of NGO contacts and websites. In order to save space, we have not assiduously referred to each source reference in the text or tables. Full details of sources can be found in the more extensive report of EcoText (2004) on which parts of this chapter are based.

In the Netherlands, few natural areas remain untouched (Gorter, 1986). Human-wildlife conflicts are limited to those species that impact on agro-economic resources: grazing and fish. No large carnivores remain. Although bigger and with a much lower population density, the Swedish landscape has been managed relatively intensively since historical times (Groom and Reed, 2001), with the result that large species with direct impacts on agriculture (grey wolf, brown bear, wolverine) and birds of prey using other harvested resources (hunted bird and small mammal species) have been under pressure, with populations rendered locally or nationally extinct at various times. Conflicts occur with grazing and fish-eating species. Spain is intermediate between the former two European countries. Less intensively managed than the Netherlands, it retains blocks of low intensity uplands subject to extensive agriculture. Like Sweden, large carnivores have survived in these areas, but under continual pressure from hunting and herd protection.

In all three countries changes in extensive land-use practices are now rapid, and are leading to changes in habitats. However, in all, the development of conservation legislation over the past century has gradually imposed limits on the uncontrolled levels of 'take' of natural species populations, a process that is accelerating with the development and implementation of European legislation. However, conflicts between humans and native and non-native species remain, though these are increasingly mitigated by financial compensation, and reduced through changes in cultural attitudes towards wildlife.

17.2.3 Sweden

17.2.3.1 History

In common with other European countries, the flora and fauna of Sweden is a mix of predominantly native and some non-native species. The process of long-established human land use has produced long-term changes in biotas, and ecosystems are largely shaped by human intervention (Groom and Reed, 2001). Most current species conflicts involve fish-eating birds and seals in the coastal areas, whilst in the forest and mountain biomes conflicts also arise concerning residual populations of large carnivores and the Sami people - a culturally distinct reindeer (*Rangifer tarandus*) herding community.

17.2.3.2 Legislation

In Sweden the legislative background is complex, having grown autonomously, then adopting the EU *acquis communautaire* upon accession in 1985. Legislation regulates management of wildlife and natural resources at both national and local levels. Prior to 1998 the key piece of legislation was the Nature Conservation Act. Following the EC's 1997 Amsterdam Treaty, 15 laws were amalgamated into the 1999 Environmental Code absorbing previous laws under a single legislative biodiversity 'umbrella'. All species have some degree of protection under the Environmental Code, which provides the basis for national and regional action plans for specific species. The Action Plans allow species numbers to recover to a naturally sustainable level, and these may include the use of hunting as a social activity. The plans use Population Viability Analysis (PVA) calculations to help estimate sustainable levels of take.

At a national level the Swedish Environmental Protection Agency (SEPA) deals with broad legislation. County Administrative Boards (CABs) deal with hunting and practical issues of species conflict. Hunting is an important social activity, and includes a wide range of species. Culling policy is consistent with the EC Habitats Directive – making sure that there are viable populations of threatened species. The SEPA provides compensation for damage, which is disbursed by CABs. The social/cultural recognition of the Sami people of northern Sweden is reflected in their practices and compensation payments for large predators (brown bear, wolverine, grey wolf and Eurasian lynx) damage to reindeer stocks.

Domestic hunting legislation permits limited control of species listed in Annex II of the Habitats Directive. Overall, some £13 million is available for compensation payments, of which £5 million goes to compensate fishermen for seal damage. The Environmental Code (through the Nature Conservation Act) covers both native and alien species, and includes the action plan process for threatened species. These include brown bear, grey wolf, Eurasian lynx, wolverine, sand lizard (*Lacerta agilis*), European crayfish (*Astacus astacus*) and freshwater pearl mussel (*Margaritifera margaritifera*). Marine interests are covered by the Fisheries Act of 1993, and qualified by the 1994 Decree on Aquaculture, and the latter legislation controls fishing methods. Atlantic salmon (*Salmo salar*) fishing by net was restricted in 1995.

Table 17.1 Key human-wildlife conflicts in Sweden.

Impacting species	Affected interest/species
Brown bear	Stock and people
Wolverine	Stock and people
Eurasian lynx	Stock
Grey wolf	Stock

Plate 17.2 Causes of mortality of 245 adult, radio-marked Eurasian lynx (*Lynx lynx*) in Sweden were found to be very largely human related (Andrén *et al.*, 2006), and illegal killing remains a major cause of conservation concern. © Kari Eischer

The highest profile species on the protected list are carnivores, especially the larger species such as brown bear and grey wolf. The Environmental Code requires that sustainable populations of all species are maintained, consistent with other interests. This means that species can be shot to meet a prescribed quota, there is also dispensation for a take by the Sami factored into calculations. Each large carnivore species has its own action plan, and delivery of these plans is a key performance indicator of the Swedish biodiversity programme (SEPA, 2003).

The process of conflict management is based on trying to dissuade species from taking agricultural stock (sheep, cattle, and reindeer) by means of fencing, electric deterrence, and more interventionist methods. For predators there is acceptance of lethal take as a final resort. This is accepted for brown bear, wolverine, and Eurasian lynx. It is not yet accepted for grey wolf, until PVA analyses show a take compatible with a viable population. For wolves and stock losses to the Sami, there is relatively widespread availability of compensation[1]. There is a standard formula of value for reindeer or sheep, based on actual numbers of stock taken.

The system of compensation payable to those engaged in reindeer herding was changed in the mid-1990s in line with a proposal jointly drawn up by reindeer herding representatives and the Swedish Environment Protection Agency. Under the previous system, compensation was paid for all reindeer found dead or injured by predators. The Sami communities also received some compensation for inconvenience and disturbance caused by predators. However, compensation is no longer dependent on reindeer kills by predators. Sami communities now receive compensation for the presence of predators, particularly for breeding successes, with the Government setting compensation levels annually in its appropriation to the Sami Assembly.

For brown bears, the main problem is in the area of Sami herding. Compensation limits the degree of overall fiscal conflict impacts, supported by hunting as part of the management options.

Wolf numbers are low, with c.150 individuals in Sweden and Norway in winter 2006[2] and the population is being managed for an increase (target is 20 reproductions per annum equating to a population size of c. 200). As numbers increase, so ranges will extend. It is expected that agricultural stock will be "properly protected" through the use of strong/electrified fencing. Lethal take is very much a last resort, with a documented loss of 120 sheep deemed insufficient to cull in one area in 2002; instead, preventative measures and compensation totals increased. Furthermore, translocation as a means of removing single wolves to areas with existing populations is not supported other than as a last resort, and this has not yet occurred.

Wolverine, protected since 1969, are currently managed through a 1998 action plan. Co-occurring with the Sami reindeer herds, the first line of conflict reduction is through active herding. If this fails, compensation is the prime tool, not lethal take. Compensation is payable, related to the levels of wolverines and other predators verified in a particular area. These are counted by SEPA and the Sami, with numbers

[1] http://www.naturvardsverket.se/en/In-English/Menu/Nature-conservation_and_wildlife_management/The-large-predators/Grants-and-compensation-for-damage/

[2] http://www.naturvardsverket.se/en/In-English/Menu/Nature-conservation_and_wildlife_management/The-large-predators/Coherent-Predator-Policy/

checked against national trends. Eurasian lynx numbers have varied over time, making the use of culling and hunting more or less permissible according to monitored and modelled population levels. Currently Eurasian lynx can be taken under permit in Sami areas, and as part of a studied cull in southern Sweden. Where they do cause commercial damage it is assumed that preventative measures were insufficient. Compensation is available for losses of stock numbers directly attributable to Eurasian lynx.

The following management tools are used:

- *Promoting co-existence of predators with prey* – by retaining predator populations. In Sami areas this is also achieved locally by removing stock. Elsewhere this includes extensive use of fencing, or through compensation or harassment or other methods.
- *Promoting displacement.* In areas of Sami herding displacement is of limited potential as the grazing range of reindeer overlaps with all main predators. In sheep areas the need for displacement of predators is seen as bad protection, and is not used. Displacement is almost a last resort and translocation is not used.
- *Controlling numbers* is a last option. Reaching this point requires due process or a life-threatening situation where bears attack hunters or fishermen. It is rarely used, other than in scientific controlled cull studies for Eurasian lynx and brown bear. Numbers of bear are controlled through socio-cultural practices (hunting), as part of a modelled population to ensure long-term sustainability.

17.2.4 The Netherlands

17.2.4.1 History
The key to species survival here has been adaptation, and many of the top predators have gone extinct. Conflicts remain with those species that use the agricultural and marine environment (geese and fish-eating birds) and with those that compete with people for resources.

17.2.4.2 Legislation
The legislative background is complex, with laws having grown autonomously, and then adopting EU law. The 1990 Nature Conservation Plan set out a visionary policy for restoring biodiversity through a national network of protected areas, linked by managed areas, and underpinned by biodiversity-supportive agricultural mechanisms. The policy was revised in 2000, amended in 2003, and is due to deliver by 2018. The Policy is delivered through many laws including the Nature Conservation Act, the 1936 Bird Act, the Flora and Fauna Act, as well as implementation of the Biodiversity, Bern and Ramsar Conventions, the Wadden Sea Seals Agreement, EU Birds and Habitats Directives, and the Agreement on the conservation of African-Eurasian Migratory Waterbirds (AEWA). The Flora and Fauna Act (which came into force in 2002) brought together most of the existing legislation.

Conflict management is delivered through sectoral ministries, which make extensive use of financial support mechanisms (The Netherlands, 2008).

17.2.4.3 Species conflicts

The number of native species conflicts is small, though the extent of fish-eating bird and peri-urban goose damage is widespread. The absence of large predators limits conflicts of the sort noted in Sweden and Spain.

The approach to dealing with conflicts is founded on a strong legislative basis for species protection, and can be summarized as follows:

a) Reference to the species management plan for the species in question. For all species involved in any form of conflict there is an individual national species plan. The objective is retention of a viable species population, with minimized human–species conflicts.
b) The case for establishing that there is a problem of conflict needs to be made. The case will be made to a State agency, with full documentary evidence of immediate and past impacts. For most taxa this leads to the undertaking of a programme of research, and the identification of key factors involved.
c) Once established, and a full record kept, then a limited range of harassment options may potentially be available.
d) Any actions used are part of an integrated management approach: decisions are taken as part of an overall national plan.
e) Full compensation is available – either for direct damage, or in some taxa, such as geese, for per hectare use of the site.
f) There is no permitted take as a last resort.

The following management tools are used:

- *Promoting co-existence of the impacting species in close geographical proximity.* For geese this works by retaining populations under management agreements and offering alternative food sources.
- *Promoting displacement.* This works either by scaring, or active movement onto sacrificial areas, translocation is not used.
- *Controlling numbers.* This is no longer an option. Nearly all migratory birds (including geese) were removed from the national list of huntable species in 2002.

17.2.5 Spain

17.2.5.1 History

In common with other European countries, the Spanish flora and fauna is a mix of predominantly native with some non-native species. The use of EU funding in retaining old pastoral practices is potentially in conflict with obligations under EC Directives to support species such as brown bear and grey wolf, which remain in the most remote upland areas used for extensive pastoral grazing.

17.2.5.2 Legislation

In Spain conservation legislation is largely evolved law, which has adopted EU *acquis communitaire*. The 1989 Law 4/1989 on the Conservation of Natural Spaces and Wild Flora and Fauna adopted the EC Birds Directive into Spanish law, as well as widening protection of habitats and species. The Royal Decree 2488/1994 established the Wild Flora and Fauna Committee. Earlier sets of law were strengthened by Law 40/1997, which also limited hunting options for migratory species. The EC Habitats Directive and its update 97/62/EC were taken into Spanish Law by Royal Decree 1193/1998.

Whilst there are national-level laws, delivery is through the autonomous regions, and these have a degree of discretion in implementing the laws and deciding on exceptions (www.mma.es). As part of the implementation of the Habitats and Birds Directives, Spain is putting in place species action plans and safeguarding a national network of protected areas, partly linked by managed areas, and supported by biodiversity-supportive agricultural mechanisms, mainly under EU funding.

Reducing species conflicts is one of the keys to the nature conservation policy. The delivery is managed by the Directorate-General for Nature Conservation, in association with the Ministry of Agriculture partly through the National Nature Conservation Strategy, designed to balance potentially conflicting ministerial portfolios through a policy of sustainable use.

Table 17.2 Key human-wildlife conflicts in Spain.

Impacting species	Affected interest/species
Brown bear	Stock and people
Grey wolf	Stock
Eurasian lynx	Stock

Unlike the Netherlands, there are clear areas of conflict, both in the use of EU subvention funds and in the implementation of potentially conflicting Directives. For example, EU agricultural monies are used to retain rural land use practices, including traditional livestock management. These come into conflict with top predators (brown bears, grey wolves) and result in illegal culling of species protected under other EU legislation.

The Law 4/1989 required the autonomous regions (provinces) to develop regional management plans for the safeguard of endangered species, including bears and wolves. Since then, four provinces have passed decrees helping in the protection of brown bears. Delivery of the bear plan recognizes conflicts and includes direct compensation as part of the means of minimizing overall conflict. Actual conflicts causing direct damage to stock are low, averaging less than £25,000 annually. The recovery and management plan includes socio-economic, education and capacity building components. In spite of this there are cultural issues about bears, but the ready availability of compensation is helping break down some of these barriers.

Grey wolves, like brown bears, are subject to protection under domestic statute, but there are still direct conflicts. Retained on the hunting register a decade or more after the bear was subject to protection, the wolf is now subject to an integrated management plan, under which damage to stock is compensated.

The extent of damage is related both to stocking density, and more especially to the method of shepherding. Losses to grey wolves are highest in areas where stock is free-roaming. Where natural prey occurs at low densities, sheep and goats form 80% of prey. Overall compensation costs are c.£750,000 per annum. In Asturias, higher levels of natural ungulate prey were correlated with reductions in sheep and goat take. Like bears, significant problems remain with winning the support of rural communities, who see wolf predation as an economically competitive issue, as well as an historical socio-cultural problem.

The following management tools are used:

- **Co-existence:** this is achieved through the use of compensation payments and careful shepherding. Harassment is possible, but rarely used. The main alternative method for at-risk stock is strong fencing.
- **Displacement:** this is difficult given the range of individual wolf packs, or an individual bear's range. Translocation is not used.
- **Control numbers:** this is not an option under domestic law. However, there are annual deaths due to the illegal use of poison baits targeted at wolves or boar. Illegal shooting is also reported annually.

17.3 Comparisons across countries regarding human-wildlife conflicts

17.3.1 Fish-eating birds

Fish-eating birds are a source of considerable conflicts with people. From the perspective of the sport/commercial fishery/fishing fleets there is a clear issue of depredation (Tables 17.3 and 17.4). From the evidence gathered in the sample countries, it is clear that there is no hard and fast rule for the impacts of fish-eating birds. At critical stages in depleted fisheries there may be a significant potential take, but from our examination of the evidence, this take does not appear to be critical in most fisheries.

Table 17.3 Fish-eating bird conflicts in four European countries.

Conflict	Sweden	Netherlands	Spain	UK
Predation at fish farms	Yes	Yes	?	Yes
Predation of game fish	Yes	?	?	Yes
Raiding crayfish pots	Yes	Yes	?	?
Raiding fish in set nets	Yes	Yes	Yes	Yes
"Significant" take recorded in water bodies	Yes	Yes	?	Yes

Table 17.4 Fisheries and aquaculture conflicts with fish-eating birds in the UK.

Species	Predation of fish at fish-farms	Predation of salmonids in rivers	Predation at still-water fisheries
Cormorant *Phalacrocorax carbo*	Yes	Yes	Yes
Goosander *Mergus merganser*		Yes	
Red-breasted merganser *Mergus serrator*		Yes	
Common eider *Somateria mollissima*	Yes[3]		
Heron *Ardea cinerea*	Yes		Yes
Gulls *Larus* spp.	Yes		

In addressing these conflicts it is important to establish the case that there is significant depredation (Carss, 2003). This needs to go through a clearly documented procedure. A country may end up issuing of a permit to commence harassment techniques. Failure of these may in turn lead to the use of limited lethal take, with methods and terms of lethal take varying between countries (Table 17.5). There is much debate over whether the mechanisms used actually work; individually, there may be effects, but for any lasting effect there needs to be a coordinated and sustained approach (Galbraith, 1992; Carss, 2003).

There is a potentially wide range of options in use to deal with the effects of fish-eating birds (Table 17.5). In all countries there is a stated need to produce clear evidence of take and depredation, though there is no clear statement of what this will be, with a reliance on "case-by-case" assessments before a move from harassment to lethal take.

The pan-European REDCAFE (Reducing the conflict between cormorants and fisheries on a pan-European scale) which ran from 2000-2002 (Carss, 2003), and a successor project called INTERCAFE (Interdisciplinary initiative to reduce pan-European Cormorant-fisheries conflicts http://www.intercafeproject.net/) which has run from 2004-08, have both been innovative international

---

[3] At mussel farms only (*e.g.* Galbraith, 1992).

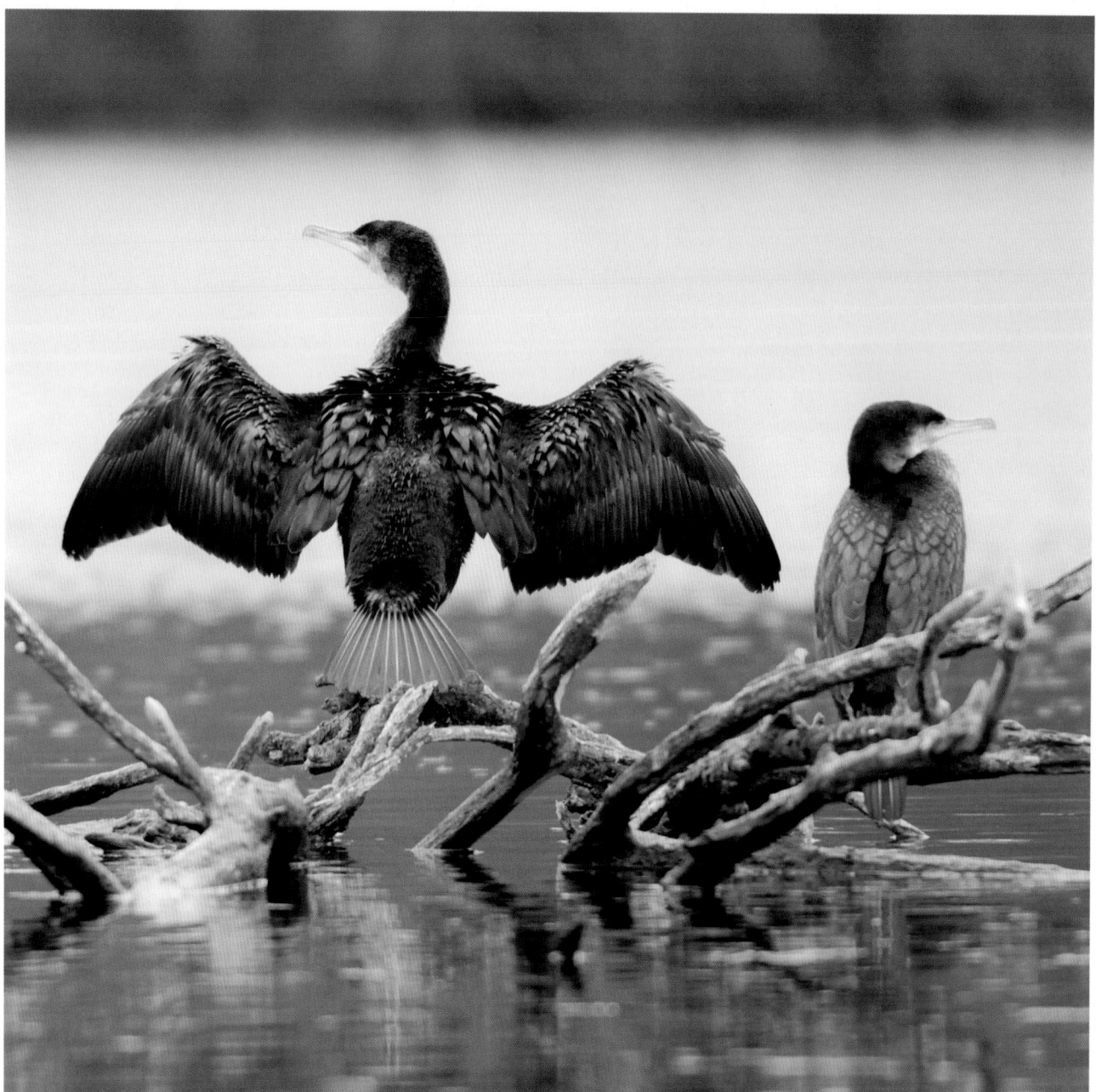

Plate 17.3 The EU-funded REDCAFE and INTERCAFE projects have highlighted the wide range of inter-linked issues involved in cormorant (*Phalacrocorax carbo*) and fisheries interactions, and thus have been valuable in informing potential policy development to try to reduce conflicts. © Lorne Gill/SNH

projects funded through EU-mechanisms. These have attempted to move the debate forward, particularly (in INTERCAFE) through the involvement of social scientists in better understanding the human elements of the fish-eating birds conflict.

Table 17.5 The range of deterrent methods and approaches recorded in four European countries for fish-eating birds.

Methods of conflict reduction	Sweden	Netherlands	Spain	UK
Actions dependent on making a documented case	Yes	Yes	Yes	Yes
Predation at fish farms and of game fish	Yes	Yes	?	Yes
netting	Yes	Yes	?	Yes
wires	Yes	Yes	?	Yes
fireworks/guns	Yes	Yes	?	Yes
acoustic measures	?	?	?	Yes
changes in fish stocking techniques	Yes	Yes	?	Yes
roost dispersal	?	?	?	?
nest removal	?	?	?	?
egg spraying	?	?	?	?
permits	Yes	No	?	Yes
shooting	?	No	?	
Raiding crayfish pots	Yes	Yes	?	?
change in pot design	?	?	?	?
Raiding fish in set nets	Yes	Yes	Yes	Yes
change in net gear	Yes	Yes	?	?

17.3.2 Goose conflicts

All four countries have recorded goose conflicts (Tables 17.6 and 17.7). As with fish-eating birds, each country tackles the issue on a progressive basis. The range of methods used to control goose damage is highly variable. The use of harassment to move birds between areas is of limited value unless associated with the provision of associated refuge areas into which birds can be moved (Owen, 1977, 1990). Like all other methods identified in individual case studies, there is relatively rapid habituation. Compensation works well as a mechanism to mitigate effects. In addition, cultural acceptance and linkage with developing tourism income should not be ignored (MacMillan *et al.*, 2001).

Table 17.6 Areas of goose conflict in four European countries.

Conflict	Sweden	Netherlands	Spain	UK
Grazing on livestock pasture	Yes	Yes	Yes	Yes
Fouling water troughs	No	No	No	No
Damage to fodder crops	Yes	Yes	Yes	Yes
Grazing winter/spring cereals	Yes	Yes	Yes	Yes
Marshland damage	Yes	Yes	?	Yes

In the majority of countries all native goose species are protected by law. Derogations from EU legislation are based on perceived impacts, and in terms of reporting to the EU locations of conflict are less important than type or extent of conflict.

The basic aim of goose management is to persuade geese to move to somewhere where they are more likely to be tolerated. Legislation has tended to limit the extent of goose shooting in many countries, and together with land-use changes there has inevitably been an increase in goose numbers and resulting conflicts. If the species are protected under law, then there is an immediate issue of balancing human and bird needs.

The use of licences for recreational shooting is predicated on carefully monitored populations, with clearly defined bags. There is clear concern in all four countries that degradation of habitats will affect survival and subsequent recruitment into goose populations. Shooting is used as part of the range of controls. Where numbers are higher than modelled targets, other methods, such as clutch destruction are used to reduce numbers. In all countries where shooting is used as part of control or recreational harvesting, sustainability is the goal, but different levels of carrying capacity are used.

Goose Management Schemes have been developed in some countries (especially Scotland: Cope *et al.,* 2006) to provide an integration of policy responses that help reduce local conflicts. Historically, conflicts involving geese have been multi-faceted and complex as outlined in Box 17.2, which gives a case-study from Scotland.

Plate 17.4 Locally very high densities of barnacle geese (*Branta leucopsis*) have the potential for agricultural conflicts, especially in spring. © Paul Marshall

Plate 17.5 Greenland white-fronted geese (*Anser albifrons flavirostris*) were at the centre of a number of land-use conflicts on Islay in the 1980s.
© Chris Wilson

Box 17.2 A case-study of a multi-faceted conflict in Scotland: geese: 1980-1985.

Conflicts concerning protected species of geese on the island of Islay in the early 1980s, followed the legislative protection in 1981-82 for Greenland white-fronted geese (*Anser albifrons flavirostris*) and barnacle geese (*Branta leucopsis*) (Bignal *et al.,* 1991).

Whilst the media simplistically reported 'the' conflict as one of farmers vs. geese (*e.g.* Abbott ,1987; Hardy, 1988; Dean, 1990), there actually were a large number of separate conflicts on the island variously involving landowners, tenant farmers, several government departments and agencies, and NGOs with differing responsibilities for land-use and species policy (Bignal *et al.,* 1991).

Making progress to resolve central conflicts was problematic with so many additional confounding issues in contention. An outline of 17 significant conflicts between and within the major stakeholders is presented largely drawn from Bignal *et al.* (1991); there were further conflicts related to some individual people which are not detailed here.

Box 17.2 A case-study of a multi-faceted conflict in Scotland: geese: 1980-1985 (continued).

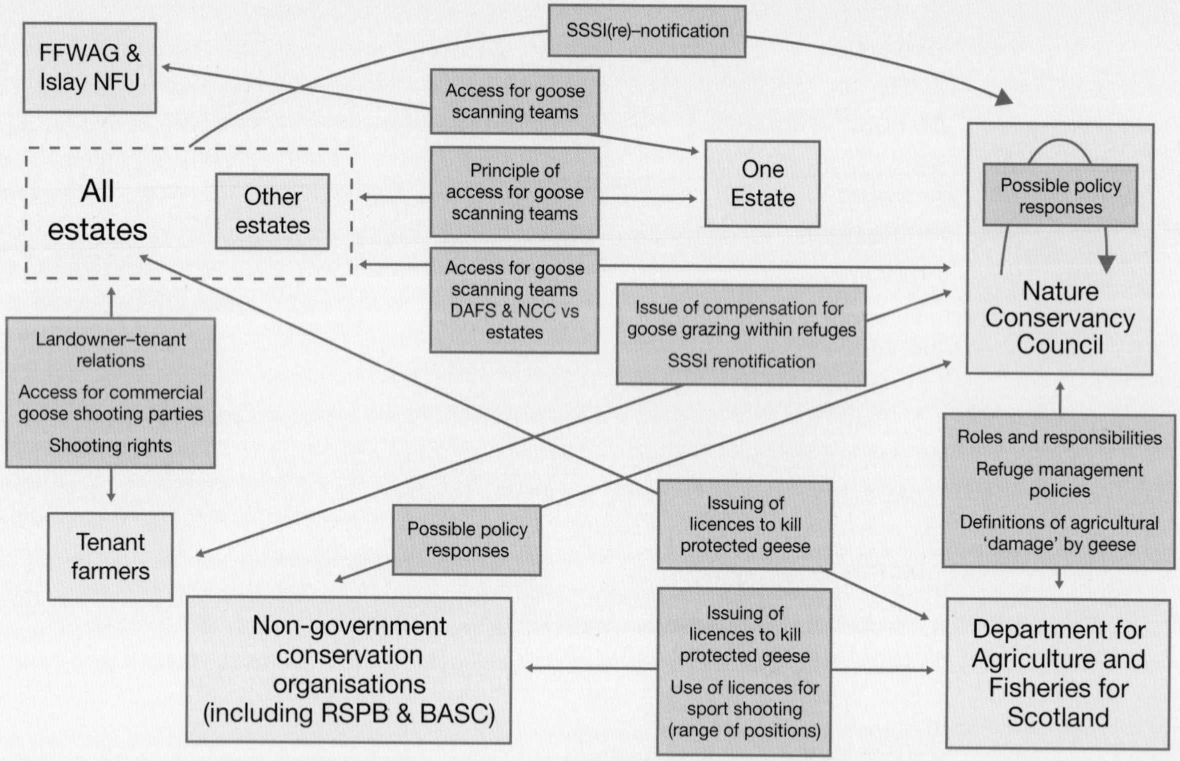

FFWAG & Islay NFU

SSSI(re)–notification

Access for goose scanning teams

All estates

Other estates

Principle of access for goose scanning teams

One Estate

Possible policy responses

Access for goose scanning teams DAFS & NCC vs estates

Issue of compensation for goose grazing within refuges

SSSI renotification

Nature Conservancy Council

Landowner–tenant relations

Access for commercial goose shooting parties

Shooting rights

Roles and responsibilities

Refuge management policies

Definitions of agricultural 'damage' by geese

Tenant farmers

Possible policy responses

Issuing of licences to kill protected geese

Non-government conservation organisations (including RSPB & BASC)

Issuing of licences to kill protected geese

Use of licences for sport shooting (range of positions)

Department for Agriculture and Fisheries for Scotland

Conflicts on Islay have largely been resolved following the establishment of a Goose Management Scheme in the early 1990s (Cope *et al.*, 2006). This has addressed both procedural and substantive issues which were in contention. Of major significance has been the establishment of consultation fora, and the involvement of representatives of the local farming community in the management structures through which financial management payments are made.

(Darker boxes summarize issues of contention.)

Plate 17.6 Greenland white-fronted geese. © Paul Marshall

17.3.3 Seals

Seals can be bracketed with the fish-eating birds: having potentially significant impacts locally under certain circumstances. For all countries reviewed, with the possible exception of Spain, for which data were not available, there was evidence of conflicts between seals and fisheries. Evidence of a biologically significant take was difficult to consistently establish, whilst commercial impacts were better documented. It should be noted that where commercial effects are noted these are in areas where other pressures have concurrently reduced fish stocks.

The range of methods used to control seals ranged from simple exclusion from potentially affected areas – fish farms or salmon runs — through to a suite of harassment methods. Most of the latter failed, or became habituated to rapidly. Translocation of errant seals is only effective in the short term. Programmes of lethal take were used, but were ruled out in several countries due to legislative reasons. Where it is used, lethal take has proven difficult to implement effectively. Use of scientific controls to demonstrate effectiveness of lethal take is scant. Take appears more reliant on political than scientific efforts, as demonstrated by the Swedish licences for seal take.

Seals are protected under national and/or international legislation, so that lethal take or control measures must be part of the standard case-proving approach noted for fish-eating birds. In many countries there is provision for reserves or exclusion areas to safeguard seal stocks. Exclusion areas have also been declared in a number of countries where by-catch of seals has been significant (Sweden).

Plate 17.7 Grey seal (*Halichoerus grypus*) mother and pup. © John M. Baxter

Table 17.7 Seal conflicts in four European countries.

Conflict	Sweden	Netherlands	Spain	UK
Predation of crayfish and bait from pots	Yes	?	?	Yes
Predation of squid	?	?	?	Yes
Damage to fishing equipment	Yes	Yes	Yes	Yes
Damage to fish stocks (perceived)	Yes	Yes	?	Yes
By-catch of pinnipeds	Yes	Yes	?	Yes

Table 17.8 Methods of seal control on fishery areas in European countries.

Methods for reducing impacts of seals	Sweden	Netherlands	Spain	UK
a) Predation at fish farms	Yes	Yes	Yes	Yes
Actions dependent on making documented case	Yes	Yes	Yes	No
Netting	Yes	Yes	?	Yes
Fireworks/guns	Yes	Yes	?	Yes
Acoustic measures	?	?	?	Yes
Changes in fish stocking techniques	Yes	Yes	?	Yes
Dispersal at haul-outs	Yes	No	?	No
Shooting	?	No	?	Yes
b) Predation of game fish	Yes	?	?	Yes
Actions dependent on making documented case	Yes	Yes	Yes	Yes
Fireworks/guns	?	?	?	Yes
c) Raiding crayfish/lobster pots	Yes	Yes	?	Yes
Change in pot design	?	?	?	Yes
d) Raiding fish in set nets	Yes	Yes	Yes	Yes
Change in net gear	Yes	Yes	?	?

17.3.4 Raptors

There are areas of conflict with large raptors in Sweden and Spain, but on nothing like the scale of that recorded in the UK (Redpath and Thirgood, 1997, 2009; Raptor Working Group, 2000; Summers *et al.*, 2003). The basic requirement in dealing with native species conflicts for raptors is the establishment of a clear case of impacts on the other interest involved. This has proved to be extremely difficult, with levels of take rarely being documented, or prolonged.

The UK presents a relatively unusual set of circumstances. We believe that the levels of conflict reported in the UK are not found elsewhere in Europe (in part a consequence of responses to conflicts with particular forms of long-established game management). As a result, alternative methods, such as substitute feeding or controlled disturbance, are not typically found. In Spain, feeding and protection methods are based on restoration of raptor populations, not minimizing conflicts as in UK.

In the UK, research over many years has led to the development of a range of actual or potential management interventions that aim to reduce or eliminate conflicts with raptors (Avian Predators Working Party, 1973; Moorland Working Group, 1999; Raptor Working Group, 2000; Galbraith *et al.*, 2003; Redpath *et al.*, 2004). Some techniques, for example to reduce depredation on young pheasants in lowland areas, have been widely adopted (*e.g.* guidance from British Association for Shooting and Conservation, 2002). In other

Plate 17.8 Grouse moor. © Lorne Gill/SNH

raptor conflicts, such as those related to the depredation of managed red grouse (*Lagopus lagopus scotica*) populations in heather moorlands, it has been more difficult to encourage the uptake of management techniques, even though research has shown these to have a high likelihood of success in reducing levels of predation (see Redpath and Thirgood, 2009; Redpath *et al.*, this volume).

Table 17.9 Areas of raptor conflict in four European countries.

Conflict	Sweden	Netherlands	Spain	UK
Livestock predation	?	No	Yes	Yes
Racing pigeon predation	?	?	?	Yes
Predating chicks of native species	Yes	Yes	Yes	Yes
Predating game bird chicks	Yes	?	Yes	Yes
Predating poultry	Yes	Yes	Yes	Yes

17.4 Understanding different values and choices

In their detailed and valuable account of conflict resolution with regard to peatland conservation, Joosten and Clarke (2002) highlight two fundamental types of conflicts in the natural environment.

1. **Conflicts dealing with facts** (true/not true)

    These are relatively easy to solve through effective communication and exchange of sufficient information so as to create a coherent and agreed knowledge base.

2. **Conflicts dealing with choices** (agree/not agree)

    Such conflicts are much more complicated as they are based on different value judgements and often the options for action can be mutually exclusive.

Many conflicts arise from differences in the values that different people, or groups in society, place upon species or issues, leading, in turn, to different positions, priorities and choices. Table 17.10 gives some examples of such differing conflicts.

Perhaps of particular note in the current context, are the different values that are often placed on animals by conservation and animal welfare lobbies. The principle concern of the conservationist is for the long-term survival of species and populations as viable entities – as repositories of unique gene-pools which reflect evolutionary history and which are adapted to particular environments. Those concerned with animal welfare place their principle emphasis on the short-term survival of the sentient individual animal (often over and above longer-term considerations).

Such differing values have given rise to a range of intense conflicts in recent years, notably related to the desirability of controlling invasive non-native species, and where animal welfare lobbies have contested lethal response measures needed to contain or eradicate non-native species so as to protect native species.

In the UK, two recent examples have surrounded the control of the North American ruddy duck (*Oxyura jamaicensis*), the spread of which threatens the white-headed duck (*Oxyura leucocephala*) with extinction

Table 17.10 Summary of the causes of environmental conflicts between humans with respect to choices (adapted from Joosten and Clarke, 2002).

	Conflict cause	Example
Conflicts dealing with facts	**Different understanding** of terms and concepts (because of miscommunication or insufficient information exchange)	Agreeing on the term 'sustainability' but attributing different meanings to it
	Different judgements as to the means most suited to achieving a particular end	Disagreement on best management options for a habitat so as to reduce greenhouse effect
Conflicts dealing with choices	**Different preferences** between different instrumental values	Preference for cultivated orchids in a vase c.f. wild orchids in a mire
	Different priorities with regard to instrumental values	Reducing malnutrition among contemporary humans vs. actions to reduce long-term environmental impacts on humans
	Different positions as to which entities have intrinsic moral value	Nature conservation (orientated on species) vs. animal protection (orientated on individual organisms)

through genetic introgression (Henderson, 2006; Hughes *et al.,* 2006). There has been conflict in Scotland regarding the control and eradication of introduced Eurasian hedgehogs (*Erinaceus europaeus*) on the Outer Hebrides so as to eliminate the major impacts these animals have been having on ground-nesting waders (Jackson and Green, 2000; Jackson *et al.,* 2004). A third example relates to attempts to control the spread of introduced American grey squirrels (*Sciurus carolinensis*) in northern Italy (Box 17.3). Here, control measures were suspended following legal action initiated by animal welfare groups. By the time these legal impediments were removed, the grey squirrel population had expanded beyond the possibility of eradication, with severe long-term consequences for the viability of red squirrels (*Sciurus vulgaris*) in their native Eurasian range (Bertolino and Genovesi, 2003; Bertolino, 2008; Bertolino *et al.,* 2008). In each of these cases, the basic conflicts related to different values and world-views of different sectors of society.

Box 17.3 Case study of grey squirrels *Sciurus carolinensis* in Italy.

1948: Grey squirrels (*Sciurus carolinensis*) were first introduced into Italy (two pairs escaped in Turin). There was a slow spread until 1970.

1970-1990: There was a 50% reduction of red squirrel (*Sciurus vulgaris*) range in northern Italy, with a further 55% decline in range from 1990-1996 due to grey squirrel expansion.

1997: An eradication programme was proposed before grey squirrels spread into the continuous woodlands of alpine foothills. However, this was constrained by legal rulings obtained by animal welfare groups.

2000-2006: Legal impediments to the eradication programme were finally removed, but in the meantime, the grey squirrel population had expanded and spread. Its range expanded into the wooded hills of the Alps and Piedmont. It is no longer considered feasible to eradicate grey squirrels from Italy (although a new initiative was proposed in 2006).

2008: There is a high risk of continued grey squirrel expansion throughout much of Europe as a result of a basic conflict of values; individual grey squirrels vs. value of survival of the red squirrel species. Delayed action has resulted in the major spread of grey squirrels and declines in red squirrels. Implications for the long-term conservation of red squirrels in Eurasia are severe.

Sources: Bertolino and Genovesi (2003); Bertolino (2008); Bertolino *et al.* (2008).

Plate 17.9 The potential spread of grey squirrels across mainland Europe is an issue of major conservation concern for the native red squirrel. © Lorne Gill

17.5 Some lessons from the European case studies

Several key issues have emerged in this review. In all countries there is a basic legislative presumption against the uncontrolled take of native species in human-animal conflicts, other than for certain 'pest' species, such as rodents and some carnivores. Typically national laws are reinforced by international legislative obligations.

All countries deal with conflicts through a staged approach, starting from the need to determine the basis of the conflict, through increasingly interventionist responses, such as disturbance or harassment through to consideration of translocation or lethal take.

Human-wildlife conflicts are best resolved within coordinated species management/action plans, with close involvement by key stakeholders. Compensation is an important tool in aiding the acceptance of species conflicts. Social/cultural practices are important in dealing with species conflicts and may, as in the Sami, lead to exceptions to laws. The international conservation importance of species is a key factor affecting perceptions of conflicts as well as the choice of outcomes. The IUCN Red List criteria inform countries' prioritization of species 'importance', and so help frame their decisions on suitability of different policies for resolving conflicts.

Three broad activities are needed to address human-wildlife conflicts in an open and accountable way:

- **Understanding the nature of conflict.** A robust and shared evidence base on impacts of 'conflict' species on other interests removes a lot of the uncertainties and ambiguities underlying discussions.
- **Recognising the multi-faceted nature of conflicts.** Most conflicts are complex (e.g. see Boxes 17.2, 17.3, 17.4), and involve a mixture of perceptions, traditions, economic and welfare issues.
- **Taking action collectively.** Where conflicts have been tackled well, the work has tended to be inclusive and undertaken rapidly.

Case studies point to the importance of taking action *early* and *quickly*. Many attitudes to conflict species develop over time, and of course are shaped and intensified through discussions with, or exposure to, other people's views. For example, in the USA, Tacha and Linder (1979) showed that the perception of goose grazing conflicts spread rapidly within communities, and that had a greater impact than the problem itself. Thus, it is important to resolve conflicts early before the perception of a conflict spreads within a community: in this context, a problem shared is a problem spread.

Sometimes innovative educational solutions can be very successful. Blanchard and Monroe (1990) reported the resolution of long-standing unsustainable taking of breeding seabirds in arctic Canada through engagement with local schools. Engaging with children role-playing seabirds and the threats they faced transformed parental awareness and resulted in the virtual elimination of the taking of seabirds and eggs which had been driving breeding colonies into decline.

Whilst solutions to conflicts always need to be tailored to local circumstances, the development of international perspectives and sharing of approaches and solutions between countries has been influential, and is important. The international reviews of waterbird grazing conflicts undertaken by IWRB in the 1990s (Fox *et al.*, 1991; van Roomen and Madsen, 1992; Madsen *et al.,* 1999), and more recent EU-funded programmes to assess fish-eating bird conflicts (Carss, 2003), have been very valuable in sharing best-practice solutions.

We highlight five lessons from the case studies we have reviewed:

- **Leadership.** This is needed to tackle the issues early, and should be at a 'senior level' and have access to professional expertise/experience. Many conflicts arise over time as a result of individuals with little authority in governments or their agencies dealing with problems, and it is only when the conflicts reach media or high profile outlets that senior officials become involved.
- **Transparency of decision-making is vital**. If government agencies can set out timelines indicating the process of considering the conflicts this can provide confidence and reassurance to the stakeholders. For example, the formal processes in the USA (*e.g.* Committee on Scientific Issues in the Endangered Species Act,1995; Batt *et al.,* 2006; Blohm *et al.,* 2006), with clear processes and timelines, provide a lot of reassurance to stakeholders.
- **Inclusiveness.** There should be explicit reference to management of conflicts within coordinated plans developed with stakeholders. This should lead to a greater degree of mutual respect and trust, honesty and integrity.
- **Social and cultural factors** are important in how conflicts are resolved. If the agencies and authorities involved in conflict resolution are not aware of these factors they will not be able to find a solution to the conflict. It is largely because of these factors that resolution processes are not necessarily transferable between different countries (even if affecting the same species).
- **Ensure adequate time is available.** Conflicts are generally complex and often involve multiple stakeholders. Adequate time is needed for parties to understand each others' positions and potential solutions. For example, the Raptor Working Group considered a number of controversial issues related to the impacts of raptors on game interests in the UK. Initial positions were polarised, but after five years and 25 meetings, a consensus report was agreed, supported by all parties (Raptor Working Group, 2000).

There is a major body of social sciences research and literature relating to the resolution of political and other conflicts within human society. Many of these findings provide insights and approaches that can assist in the specific issue of human-wildlife conservation. The conservation community needs to develop stronger engagement with social scientists to assist in resolution of some of the more problematic conflicts. Similarly, those concerned with the conservation of species can learn much from the resolution of conflicts related to land uses, rights or management (Claridge and O'Callaghan, 1997; Hamú *et al.,* 2004).

The joint International Peat Society and International Mire Conservation Group wise-use strategy for peatlands provides an outstanding example in this respect (Joosten and Clarke, 2002). Issues of conflict resolution related to management of indigenous (and other) peoples within protected areas (e.g. Lewis, 1993) also provide many valuable insights (Box 17.4).

Human-wildlife conflicts present governments and their agencies with some of their most challenging work areas, and present many stakeholder bodies with some of their most frustrating experiences in dealing with the agencies. If we can find ways of identifying and agreeing the issues, and develop a shared approach to tackling these, it should be possible to reduce the size of the challenge and the degree of frustration.

Box 17.4 Conflict management strategies.

Whilst many conservation conflicts have a large spatial element - often related to access or land-rights issues - many principles underlying resolution techniques (such as transparency of decision making, inclusiveness, involvement of neutral third parties as brokers, *etc*.) are just as relevant to species conflicts.

What follows is based on Lewis (1993) in the context of developing management strategies for conflicts between indigenous (and other) peoples and protected areas (or parks), but slightly modified to accentuate its application to species-related conflict resolution.

Assessment

Conflicts are uncomfortable for most people especially when it is their interests that are at stake. A constructive first step for embarking on a conflict management effort is to take a mental step away from the situation and to try and assess it as objectively as possible. The assessment may be as simple as writing down, in an organized fashion, what is already known about the conflict. The following may be useful questions to ask in the assessment:

- What are the issues in the conflict?
- What has been the history of the conflict so far?
- Who are the potentially affected stakeholders? What is their role in the conflict? What are their underlying interests, both procedural and substantive? What positions have they adopted?
- What other positions might serve their interests?
- What ideas do various stakeholders have about how to resolve the conflict?
- What are the relationships among the parties? How well do they communicate with one another?
- What is known and what is not known about the scientific, ecological, and technical aspects of the conflict?
- What is the institutional-legal context for the conflict, and what institutional and legal avenues exist for resolving it?
- What resources are available to deal with the conflict (financial, human, and institutional)?
- Is there any other pertinent information which might support an evidence base?

Developing a Conflict Management Strategy

After conducting an initial assessment, the next step is to use the information obtained to develop and implement a strategy. This should address both substantive and procedural issues at stake, and

> **Box 17.4** Conflict management strategies (continued).
>
> address education and research needs. It may be necessary to have both short- and long-term strategies. It will always be necessary to recognize the challenges and limitations of any conflict management effort.
>
> A few options that might be considered for addressing the procedural and substantive interests of stakeholders are as follows.
>
> *Addressing procedural interests*
>
> - Develop personal relationships with individual stakeholders.
> - Develop relationships with community leaders.
> - Hire local people to undertake relevant management.
> - Involve local people in technical research or social impact analysis.
> - Establish a management committee.
> - Set up a roundtable or dialogue.
> - Appoint a liaison officer to maintain relationships with local people.
> - Involve a neutral mediator or other respected third party to assist the process.
>
> *Addressing substantive interests*
>
> - Look for ways to give local people benefits from the presence of protected species.
> - Provide compensation for damage or losses.
> - Establish zones with varying types and intensities of protection and use.
> - Develop alternatives so that people do not have to be dependent on species that need to be protected.
> - Revive or adapt formerly used methods of stewardship (this can also be a way to address procedural and even cultural interests)."

17.6 Acknowledgements

We are grateful to the following for help in drawing material together: Jo Oldaker, Ian Carter, Steve Gibson, Peter Copley, Stuart Pimm, Carl McGuinness, Tony Fox, Suzanne Kolare, Henri Engström, Anthony P. Clevenger, Francisco J. Purroy, Javier Naves Cienfuegos, Carlos Nores Quesada, Robert Franzen, Torsten Larsson, Lars Berg, S.M. ten Houte, Joop Schaminee, Cosmo Morillo Fernandez, Doug Evans, Sander van Opstal, Borja Heredia, Juan Manuel de Benito, Helen Riley, Steve Redpath, Simon Thirgood, Sally Johnson, John Atle Kålås, Henk Revorte and Roger Sidaway. We thank John Baxter, Colin Galbraith and an anonymous referee for comments on the MS.

References

Abbott, B.G. (1987). Problems from over-zealous conservation. *The Scottish Farmer*, 20 June 1987: 37.

Andrén, H., Linnell, J.D.C., Liberg, O., Andersen, R., Danell, A., Karlsson, J., Odden, J., Moa, P.F., Ahlqvist, P., Kvam, T., Franzén, R. & Segerström, P. (2006). Survival rates and causes of mortality in Eurasian lynx (*Lynx lynx*) in multi-use landscapes. *Biological Conservation* **131** (1): 23-32.

Avian Predators Working Party. (1973). *Predatory Birds in Britain.* The British Field Sports Society and the Council for Nature. 64 pp.

Batt, B.D.J., Schmidt, P.R. & Wendt, S. (2006). Case study of conflict resolution in the management of overabundant light geese in North America. *Waterbirds around the world.* Eds G.C. Boere, C.A. Galbraith & D.A. Stroud. The Stationery Office, Edinburgh, UK. pp. 795-800.

Bertolino, S. (2008). Introduction of the American grey squirrel (*Sciurus carolinensis*) in Europe: a case study in biological invasion. *Current Science* **95**(7): 903-906.

Bertolino, S. & Genovesi, P. (2003). Spread and attempted eradication of the grey squirrel (*Sciurus carolinensis*) in Italy, and consequences for the red squirrel (*Sciurus vulgaris*) in Eurasia. *Biological Conservation* **109**(3): 351-358.

Bertolino, S., Lurz, P.W.W., Sanderson, R. & Rushton, S.P. (2008). Predicting the spread of the American grey squirrel (*Sciurus carolinensis*) in Europe: a call for a co-ordinated European approach. *Biological Conservation* **141**(10): 2564-2575.

Bignal, E.M., Stroud, D.A. & Easterbee, N. (1991). A case study in goose management: the island of Islay. In: Owen, M. & Pienkowski, M.W. (Eds) (1991): *Goose damage and management workshop. Proceedings of a meeting organised by the Wildfowl and Wetlands Trust at Martin Mere, Lancashire, on 27 April 1990. Research & survey in nature conservation* No. 33: 22-31. JNCC, Peterborough.

Blanchard, K.A. & Monroe, M.C. (1990). Effective educational strategies for reversing population declines in seabirds. *Proceedings of the Transactions of the 55th North American Wildlife and Natural Resources Conference:* 108-117.

Blohm, R.J., Sharp, D.E., Padding, P.I., Kokel, R.W. & Richkus, K.D. (2006). Integrated waterfowl management in North America. *Waterbirds around the world.* Eds G.C. Boere, C.A. Galbraith & D.A. Stroud. The Stationery Office, Edinburgh, UK. pp. 199-203.

British Association for Shooting and Conservation. (2002). *Birds of prey at pheasant release pens: a practical guide for game managers and gamekeepers.* BASC, Marford Mill. 14 pp.

Carss, D.N. (Ed.). (2003). *Reducing the conflict between Cormorants and fisheries on a pan-European scale.* Report to the European Commission. Centre for Ecology & Hydrology, Banchory, UK. 31 pp. [At: http://web.tiscali.it/cormorants/Redcafe/Redcafe_vol1_part1.pdf]

Claridge, G.F. & O'Callaghan, B. (Eds). (1997). *Community involvement in wetland management: lessons from the field. Incorporating the Proceedings of Workshop 3: Wetlands, Local People and Development, of the International Conference on Wetlands and development, Kuala Lumpur, Malaysia, 9-13 October 1995.* Wetlands International, Kuala Lumpur.

Committee on Scientific Issues in the Endangered Species Act. (1995). *Science and the Endangered Species Act.* National Academy, Washington DC, USA. 288 pp.

Cope, D.R., Vickery, J.A. & Rowcliffe, J.M. (2006). From conflict to coexistence: a case study of geese and agriculture in Scotland. *Waterbirds around the world.* Eds G.C. Boere, C.A. Galbraith & D.A. Stroud. The Stationery Office, Edinburgh, UK. pp. 791-794.

Dean, S. (1990). Conflicts, coming home to roost. *The Scotsman*, 21 April 1990.

EcoText . (2004). *Review of international policy and practice for the management of native species conflicts.* Scottish Natural Heritage Commissioned Report No. 33.

Fox, A.D., Madsen, J. & van Rhijn, J. (Eds). (1991). *Western Palearctic Geese. Proceedings of an IWRB International Symposium, Kleve, Germany, February 1989. Ardea* 79(2).

Fox, A.D., Madsen, J., Boyd, H., Kuijken, E., Norriss, D.W., Tombre, I.M. & Stroud, D.A. (2005). Effects of agricultural change on abundance, fitness components and distribution of two arctic-nesting goose populations. *Global Change Biology* **11**: 881-893.

Galbraith, C.A. (1992). *Mussel Farms. Their management alongside Eider Ducks.* Nature Conservancy Council for Scotland. 22 pp.

Galbraith, C.A., Stroud, D.A. & Thompson, D.B.A. (2003). Towards resolving raptor-human conflicts. pp. 527-535. In: Thompson, D.B.A., Redpath, S.M., Fielding, A.H., Marquiss, M. & Galbraith, C.A. (Eds) *Birds of prey in a changing environment.* The Stationery Office, Edinburgh.

Gorter, H. P. (1986). *Ruimte voor natuur.* Naturmonumenten, Amsterdam, The Netherlands.

Gregory, R.D., Wilkinson, N.I., Noble, D.G., Robinson, J.A., Brown, A.F., Hughes, J., Proctor, D., Gibbons, D.W. & Galbraith, C.A. (2002). The population status of birds in the United Kingdom, Channel Islands and Isle of Man: an analysis of conservation concern 2002–2007. *British Birds* **95**: 410–448.

Groom, G. & Reed, T.M. (Eds). (2001). Strategic landscape monitoring for the Nordic Countries. *TemaNord 2001*:523. 128 pp.

Hamú, D., Auchincloss, E. & Goldstein, E. (Eds). (2004). *Communicating Protected Areas.* Commission on Education and Communication, IUCN, Gland, Switzerland and Cambridge, UK. 312 pp.

Hardy, E. (1988). Islay geese upset farmers. *Shooting Times*, 26 May 1988.

Henderson, I.S. (2006). Recent measures to control Ruddy Ducks *Oxyura jamaicensis* in the United Kingdom. *Waterbirds around the world.* Eds G.C. Boere, C.A. Galbraith & D.A. Stroud. The Stationery Office, Edinburgh, UK. pp. 822-825.

Hughes, B., Robinson, J.A., Green, A.J., Li, Z.W.D. & Mundkur, T. (compilers). (2006). *International Single Species Action Plan for the Conservation of the White-headed Duck* Oxyura leucocephala. CMS Technical Series No. 13 & AEWA Technical Series No.8. 67 pp. Bonn, Germany.

Jackson, D.B. & Green, R.E. (2000). The importance of the introduced hedgehogs (*Erinaceus europaeus*) as a predator of the eggs of waders (Charadrii) on machair in South Uist, Scotland. *Biological Conservation* **93**: 333-348.

Jackson, D.B., Fuller, R.J. & Campbell, S.T. (2004). Long-term population changes among breeding shorebirds in the Outer Hebrides, Scotland, in relation to introduced hedgehogs (*Erinaceus europaeus*). *Biological Conservation* **117**(2):151-166.

Joosten, H. & Clarke, D. (2002). *Wise use of mires and peatlands: background and principles including a framework for decision-making.* International Mire Conservation Group and International Peat Society. 304 pp. [At: http://www.imcg.net/docum/WUMP_Wise_Use_of_Mires_and_Peatlands_book.pdf]

Lewis, C. (1993). Nature in the crossfire. In: *The Law of the Mother. Protecting indigenous peoples in protected areas.* Ed. E. Kemf. Sierra Books, San Francisco. pp. 123-130.

MacMillan, D., Daw, M., Daw, D., Phillip, L., Patterson, I., Hanley, N., Gustanski, J.-A. & Wright, R. (2001). *The costs and benefits of managing wild geese in Scotland.* Scottish Executive Central Research Unit, Edinburgh. 61 pp. [At: http://www.scotland.gov.uk/cru/kd01/purple/cbmwgs-00.asp].

Madsen, J., Cracknell, G. & Fox, A.D. (Eds). (1999). Goose populations of the Western Palaearctic. A review of status and distribution. *Wetlands International Publ. No.48*, Wetlands International, Wageningen, The Netherlands. National Environmental Research Institute, Rönde, Denmark. 344 pp.

Moorland Working Group. (1999). *Substitute feeding of hen harriers on grouse moors: a practical guide.* Scottish Natural Heritage, Battleby.

Owen, M. (1977). The role of wildfowl refuges on agricultural land in lessening the conflict between farmers and geese in Britain. *Biological Conservation* **11**: 209–222.

Owen, M. (1990). The damage – conservation interface illustrated by geese. *Ibis* **132**: 238–252.

Raptor Working Group. (2000). *Report of the UK Raptor Working Group.* Department of the Environment, Transport and the Regions and Joint Nature Conservation Committee, Peterborough. 123 pp. [At: http://www.jncc.gov.uk/pdf/raptors.pdf]

Redpath, S.M. & Thirgood, S.J. (Eds). (1997). *Birds of Prey and Red Grouse.* Centre for Ecology and Hydrology, NERC. 148 pp. The Stationery Office, London.

Redpath, S.M. & Thirgood, S.J. (2009). Hen harriers and red grouse: moving towards consensus? *Journal of Applied Ecology* **46**: DOI:10.1111/j. 1365-2664.01702X

Redpath, S.M., Arroyo, B.E., Leckie, F.M., Bacon, P., Bayfield, N., Gutierrez, R.J. & Thirgood, S.J. (2004). Using decision modelling with stakeholders to reduce human-wildlife conflict: a raptor – grouse case study. *Conservation Biology* **18**(2): 350-359.

Redpath, S.M., Amar, A., Smith, A., Thompson, D.B.A. & Thirgood, S.J. (2010). People and nature in conflict: can we reconcile hen harrier conservation and game management? In: Baxter J.M. & Galbraith C.A. (Eds) *Species Management: Challenges and Solutions for the 21st Century*. Edinburgh: TSO Scotland, pp. 335-350.

SEPA. (2003). http://www.snf.se/snf/english/threatened-species

Sidaway, R. (2005). *Resolving environmental disputes*. Earthscan, London.

Simmons, I.G. (2001). *An environmental history of Great Britain*. Edinburgh: Edinburgh University Press.

Smout, T.C. (2000). *Nature contested*. Edinburgh: Edinburgh University Press.

Smout, T.C. (2002). *People and woods*. Edinburgh: Edinburgh University Press.

Stroud, D.A., Gibson, S., Holmes, J.S. & Harry, C.M. (1999). The legislative basis for vertebrate pest management in Europe (with examples from the UK). pp. 85-108. *In*: Cowan, P.D. & Feare, C.J. (Eds) *Advances in Vertebrate Pest Management*. Fürth; Filander Verlag.

Summers, R.W., Green, R.E., Etheridge, B. & Sim, I.M.W. (2003). Changes in Hen Harrier (*Circus cyaneus*) numbers in relation to grouse moor management. pp. 487-497. In: Thompson, D.B.A., Redpath, S.M., Fielding, A.H., Marquiss, M. & Galbraith, C.A. (Eds) *Birds of prey in a changing environment.* The Stationery Office, Edinburgh.

Tacha, T.C. & Linder, R.L. (1979). Tolerance of farmers for a local Canada Goose flock. *Proceedings of the South Dakota Academy of Science* **58**: 52-58.

The Netherlands. (2008). *National report for The Netherlands for the period 2005-2008 to the African-Eurasian Waterbird Agreement.* 48 pp. [At: http://www.unep-aewa.org/meetings/en/mop/mop4_docs/national_reports/netherlands2008.doc].

van Roomen, M. & Madsen, J. (1992). Waterfowl and agriculture: review and future perspective of the crop damage conflict in Europe. *IWRB Special Publication* No. 21. 184 pp.

Thompson, D.B.A., Reed, T.M., Stroud, J., Christie, M.F.B. and Stroud, D.A. (2010). The nature of human-wildlife conflicts across Europe: a review. In: *Species Management: Challenges and Solutions for the 21st Century*, ed. by J.M. Baxter and C.A. Galbraith. TSO Scotland, Edinburgh, pp. 303-333

333

Chapter 18

People and nature in conflict: can we reconcile hen harrier conservation and game management?

Steve Redpath[1], Arjun Amar[2], Adam Smith[3], Des B.A. Thompson[4] and Simon Thirgood[1,5]

Summary

1. The hen harrier is one of the UK's most threatened birds of prey. The principal threat comes from illegal killing, allegedly by upland gamekeepers across moorland areas managed for 'driven' red grouse shooting. Some gamekeepers kill hen harriers because of the potential impact of their predation on red grouse populations and shooting bags. This chapter explores alternative approaches to help resolve the conflict which gives rise to illegal persecution.
2. There are two distinct, but not exclusive, types of approaches: those involving enforcement of existing laws, and those involving measures to achieve consensus and cooperation. Specific alternatives that are currently the focus of attention are: enforcement and support for a move to less intensive management; intra-guild predation by golden eagles; diversionary feeding; and a hen harrier brood management scheme.
3. We conclude that progress requires continued dialogue between the main stakeholders and a risk analysis based on improved understanding of the costs, acceptability, legality, feasibility and the environmental, economic and social consequences of following alternative approaches.

[1] Aberdeen Centre for Environmental Sustainability, Aberdeen University & The Macaulay Institute, Aberdeen, AB24 2TZ, UK
[2] RSPB-Scotland, Dunedin House, 25 Ravelston Terrace, Edinburgh, EH4 3TP, UK
[3] Game & Wildlife Conservation Trust, Couston, Newtyle, Angus, PH12 8UT, UK
[4] Scottish Natural Heritage, Silvan House, 231 Corstorphine Road, Edinburgh, EH12 7AT, UK
[5] Tragically, Professor Simon Thirgood was killed in an accident shortly after completing his input to this manuscript.

18.1 Introduction

The hen harrier (*Circus cyaneus*) is a species of high conservation concern, listed on the red-list of birds of conservation concern in the UK and on Annex 1 of the EU Birds Directive (79/409/EEC). Across Europe, the main threats to this species arise from habitat loss and illegal killing (Tucker and Heath, 1994). In the UK, the principal threat to the breeding population is thought to stem from illegal killing by those involved in the management of red grouse (*Lagopus lagopus scoticus*). This illegal activity limits breeding success, numbers and range of hen harriers on moorland managed for grouse shooting (Etheridge *et al.,* 1997; Stott, 1998; Anon., 2000; Holmes *et al.,* 2000, 2003; Summers *et al.,* 2003; Sim *et al.,* 2007; Natural England, 2008).

The conflict between those involved in hen harrier conservation and red grouse management continues to be contentious (Thirgood and Redpath, 2008). Solutions to the problem have proved elusive, despite the fact that many stakeholders on both 'sides' have expressed a desire and determination to work towards a resolution (Redpath and Thirgood, 2009; Sotherton *et al.,* 2009; Thompson *et al.,* 2009). As illegal killing on grouse moors continues to cause hen harrier numbers in large parts of their range to dwindle (Sim *et al.,* 2007), not least on Special Protection Areas where favourable conservation status is put at risk, and to restrict colonization of other areas (Anderson *et al.,* 2009), work is needed to improve the conservation status of hen harriers in the UK.

In this chapter we explore alternative approaches to resolving the conflict between hen harrier conservation and red grouse management, consider the pros and cons of each approach, and the current gaps in our knowledge required to reach a sustainable solution to the conflict. We start with a consideration of the background to the conflict and summarize the range of alternative management approaches that have been discussed so far.

18.2 The hen harrier – grouse moor conflict

The conflict between the conservation of legally protected hen harriers and the commercial hunting of red grouse is one of the most challenging conservation issues in the UK (Anon., 2000; Thirgood *et al.,* 2000a). Well practised grouse shooting is an important form of land-use in the uplands, providing economic benefits to rural communities (McGillivray, 1995; PACEC, 2006; Sotherton *et al.,* 2009) as well as conservation benefits, because it retains heather moorland (Robertson *et al.,* 2001) and associated biodiversity (Thompson *et al.,* 1995; Tharme *et al.,* 2001).

The aim of 'driven' red grouse moor management is to maximize the number of red grouse available for shooting in autumn. Hen harriers are perceived to reduce grouse harvests, and are killed or disturbed as a consequence. The killing of raptors was considered an essential component of traditional moorland management during the late 19th and early 20th centuries (Lovegrove, 2007). Legal protection of raptors in the UK was established in 1954 and subsequently reinforced in 1979 with the EU Birds Directive and the Wildlife and Countryside Act 1981 (as amended). Despite this legislation and the efforts of government

Plate 18.1 Hen harriers typically nest on the ground in heather-dominated vegetation. Red grouse are also reliant on this habitat and hence there is a high degree of overlap in their distributions within the UK. © Lorne Gill/SNH

agencies and non-governmental conservation organizations, the illegal killing of raptors continues on many moorland areas (Etheridge *et al.*, 1997; Scottish Raptor Study Groups, 1997; Anon., 2000; Natural England, 2008).

The perception by grouse moor managers that hen harriers can, in some circumstances, reduce the size of the red grouse harvest has been supported by research (Redpath and Thirgood, 1997, 1999; Thirgood *et al.*, 2000 b, 2000c). This work provided evidence that high densities of hen harriers can limit red grouse populations at low density and reduce shooting bags. That research highlighted the tendency for hen harrier breeding numbers, in the absence of illegal killing, to vary widely between areas and between years in relation to variation in the abundance of their main prey species – meadow pipits (*Anthus pratensis*) and field voles (*Microtus agrestis*) (Redpath and Thirgood, 1999). It is on grouse moors with high densities of hen harriers where significant rates of predation, and hence loss of income, may be incurred.

The concern amongst grouse moor managers is that hen harrier numbers may increase if not controlled and thereby reduce red grouse stocks, and this has evidently led to continued illegal killing and subsequent low densities of breeding hen harriers on grouse moors, especially those with driven shooting (Table 1). The absence of breeding hen harriers from many grouse moors suggests that some, possibly many, grouse moor managers will not tolerate even one pair of hen harriers on their land. We can infer from this that some land managers are either not prepared to put up with any predation on red grouse, even by a protected raptor, or because they fear that one pair of hen harriers will give rise to further hen harriers settling, with the associated problems of predation and even an interest by conservation bodies, possibly leading to more scrutiny and monitoring by enforcement agencies.

Table 1. Estimates of the expected and observed number of successful breeding hen harriers in 2008, on moors in the UK on which driven grouse had occurred between 2003 and 2007. Data on area of driven grouse moorland estimated by Game and Wildlife Conservation Trust and Moorland Association. Data on hen harrier density taken from Redpath & Thirgood (1997). Data on successful hen harrier nests taken from RSPB and Scottish Raptor Study Groups (pers. comm.). 2008 was the year of a national merlin (*Falco columbarius*) survey, so suitable heather habitat was searched intensively by surveyors and only 5 pairs of hen harriers were found successfully breeding – 1% of what was expected.*

Driven grouse moors (2003 - 2007)	
Estimated area of driven grouse moorland in UK (GWCT & Moorland Association data)	3,696 km^2
Predicted successful hen harrier density on two driven moors (Redpath & Thirgood, 1997)	0.135 km^{-2} (0.03 - 0.24)
Expected number of successful hen harrier nests	499
Successful hen harrier nests found in 2008 (RSPB & SRSG data)	5

* We are also aware of a grouse moor which shot driven grouse in 2008 and had four successful hen harrier nests in that year. However, this moor did not shoot driven grouse in 2003-07, so was omitted from the above table.

18.3 Approaches to resolving the conflict

A number of specific approaches to managing this conflict have been suggested, and these fall into two non-exclusive areas. One involves focusing on the illegal activity itself and the other involves working in partnership to find technical solutions that would reduce the impact of predation and thus end the motivation for illegal killing. The main difference between them is that focusing solely on increased enforcement might, given the relationships described above, involve the loss of some driven red grouse shooting, with potentially adverse consequences for rural economies and some upland biodiversity.

We group alternative approaches under five headings, according to whether they are aimed at enforcement, financial compensation, increasing red grouse numbers, reducing predation rates on red grouse, or reducing hen harrier breeding numbers; details are provided by Potts (1998), Anon. (2000), Thirgood *et al.* (2000a, 2002), Redpath *et al.* (2001, 2004), Smith *et al.* (2001), Watson and Thirgood (2001), Naylor *et al.* (2005), Thirgood and Redpath (2005), Woodroffe *et al.* (2005) and Tapper unpub.

18.3.1 Enforcement

As described above hen harriers are legally protected and hen harrier conservation efforts so far have primarily focused on attempting to catch gamekeepers involved in illegal activity. So far this has had little success (see Table 1), and there are increasing calls for more resources and police time to be directed towards catching those responsible (Anon., 2008, http://www.scotland.gov.uk/Publications/2008/04/03143616/0 http://www.rspb.org.uk/supporting/campaigns/birdsofprey/why.asp.).

Allied with increased enforcement, a recent proposal from some stakeholders has focused on encouraging landowners in certain circumstances to move away from driven red grouse shooting towards low intensive management (Thompson *et al.*, 2009). The argument put forward is that if driven shooting is only viable when birds of prey are killed then

Plate 18.2 The red grouse (*Lagopus lagopus scotica*) is a close relative of the circumpolar willow ptarmigan. It can occur at remarkably high densities on moorland managed through heather burning and predator control. © Lorne Gill/SNH

grouse managers need to consider moving to more sustainable forms of management. There currently appears to be little enthusiasm for this approach from grouse managers (Sotherton *et al.,* 2009).

18.3.2 Financial compensation

Under this approach, grouse managers would be compensated for the impacts of hen harriers on red grouse, or even for the mere presence of hen harriers on their land, much as reindeer owners are compensated for the presence of large carnivores in Sweden (Swenson and Andren, 2005). Noting the potential costs of this and the possibility of compensating for losses in support of a recreational activity which might be deemed to have a business risk of predation, there seems little appetite for this approach in the UK (Thirgood and Redpath, 2005). Evidently, grouse managers would prefer to have large numbers of red grouse to shoot, rather than compensation payments (Sotherton *et al.*, 2009). Conservation organizations and government agencies would have difficulty supporting potentially large payments for grouse managers to uphold the law. The public might also find this proposal difficult to accept, given that grouse moor owners comprise some of the wealthier members of society.

Plate 18.3 Very few hen harriers breed successfully on moorland managed for driven grouse. Most of the current population breed in the north and west of the country, away from managed grouse moors. © Sandy Sutherland/SNH

18.3.3 Increasing grouse numbers

Two techniques have been proposed. Red grouse could either be reared in captivity and released (Rear & Release), much as pheasants and partridges currently are. Alternatively, red grouse could be caught elsewhere and introduced onto places where hen harriers were having an impact on red grouse numbers (Trap & Transfer). These techniques were considered by Naylor *et al.* (2005) who concluded that whilst rear and release was feasible, although difficult to achieve, the practice was considered to be unacceptable to the majority of stakeholders. This was because red grouse shooting needed to maintain its image of 'wild' wildlife management and utilization, as well as concerns about genetics and behaviour of captive reared red grouse. Trap and transfer was also feasible, and more acceptable than rear and release, but it was not considered to be a practice that would be widely used.

18.3.4 Reducing predation rates

Three techniques have been proposed to reduce the rate at which hen harriers kill red grouse. First, conditioned taste aversion would involve the use of an emetic to discourage hen harriers from killing red grouse. Such techniques work for a variety of predators feeding on static prey (Nicolaus *et al.*, 1983, 1989; Gustavsen and Nicolaus, 1987). The techniques remain untested on raptors but would prove extremely difficult to apply to hen harriers feeding on wild red grouse chicks.

The second technique to reduce predation rate would be to manipulate the habitat, making it harder for hen harriers to catch red grouse. Whilst this approach is appealing, the scientific evidence suggests that although hen harriers were more likely to encounter red grouse chicks in certain habitats, they were just as successful at capturing them in any habitat (Thirgood *et al.*, 2002). Similarly there was no effect of habitat variability on adult red grouse survival (Thirgood *et al.*, 2002). Overall, the effects of habitat manipulation on red grouse susceptibility to predation appear limited.

The potentially most encouraging of the techniques aimed at reducing predation rates is diversionary feeding. This technique involves providing hen harriers with carrion during the breeding season, so that they reduce the rate at which they take red grouse chicks. An initial research trial showed considerable promise, as 'fed' hen harriers reduced the rate at which they took red grouse chicks to the nest by 86% (Redpath *et al.*, 2001). However, there are a number of concerns that have meant that the technique has not yet been widely used (Amar *et al.*, 2007). Perhaps the most important question is whether driven grouse shooting can be sustained in the presence of fed hen harriers. The Langholm Moor Demonstration Project aims to address this issue and will run from 2008-2018 (www.langholmproject.com). Amar *et al.* (2007) raise several other questions on the potential use of this technique: 1) Is predation on red grouse chicks consistently reduced by feeding? 2) What effect does feeding have on hen harrier population size? 3) What effect does feeding have on the abundance of other scavengers /predators (especially ravens (*Corvus corax*) which are also protected and cannot be controlled for the purposes of increasing red grouse bags)? 4) What effect does feeding have on other moorland bird species? 5) Is it a desirable or acceptable technique for large scale, long-term management?

Plate 18.4 The provision of carrion close to hen harrier nests can help reduce the extent of predation on grouse chicks. © Lorne Gill/SNH

18.3.5 Reducing hen harrier densities

A variety of techniques have been suggested to reduce the numbers of hen harriers settling on grouse moors, and thereby reduce the number of red grouse killed by hen harriers. Three techniques involve habitat manipulation. Hen harriers tend to nest in tall heather (Redpath *et al.*, 1995), and therefore the extent to which this habitat is available on grouse moors could be reduced through burning or cutting. It is not known how effective this approach would be, but the ability to remove suitable nesting habitat may only be achievable on small, highly managed estates; this technique would need to be deployed outwith the breeding season, because within the season it would be classed as 'reckless behaviour' if targeted at areas occupied by nesting hen harriers. An alternative approach would be to alter the habitat through grazing so as to reduce the abundance of the small prey associated with grassy mosaics (voles and meadow pipits) that attracts high hen harrier densities (Smith *et al.*, 2001). This would involve increasing heather cover and reducing grass cover. Concerns expressed here revolve around exact techniques required to give the desired habitats over large areas and the length of time required to achieve this. In the shorter term, reductions in sheep grazing could actually lead to higher small prey abundance, and therefore more hen harriers. However, there is considerable variation in red grouse predation rates between nesting areas and there is a positive relationship between predation rates and the proportion of heather around nests (Amar *et al.*, 2004). Modelling would therefore be needed to investigate the trade-off between the numerical and functional responses of hen harriers to changes in prey densities in relation to habitat management (Thirgood *et al.,* 2005). For both of these techniques, the potentially serious consequences for other moorland conservation objectives would also need to be considered, as management to increase heather cover is a widely held conservation objective (Thompson *et al.*, 1995). One further form of habitat manipulation has been suggested – that alternative patches of good hunting habitat be created away from the main red grouse areas (Arroyo *et al.*, 2009). Such an approach is possible, but may not succeed because hen harriers are attracted to breed in habitats favoured by red grouse (Redpath *et al.*, 1998). It is important to note, however, that there is a range of other measures that could reduce hen harrier densities, but such practices would be illegal.

An alternative approach to reduce breeding densities is to scare hen harriers in spring, using agricultural gas guns, falconry eagles or people. The use of falconry eagles is not considered to be feasible by falconers (Anon., 2007). Disturbance by people may be effective at preventing hen harriers from settling in specific areas. Indeed, keepers may currently be employing this technique on some estates (Tapper, unpub). However, these practices would be illegal if used within the breeding season.

Large predators can displace or kill small predators with impacts on population size, as has been shown in a variety of mammalian carnivore systems (Mulder, 1990; Sovada *et al.*, 1995; Gese *et al.*, 1996; Lindstrom *et al.*, 1996) and raptor assemblages (Sergio and Hiraldo, 2008). If measures were adopted to improve the conservation status of golden eagles (*Aquila chrysaetos*) (see Whitfield *et al.*, 2008 for constraints on golden eagle conservation status) ensuing intra-guild predation may reduce hen harrier settling densities over moorland. This approach merits further consideration; it has not been tested and would probably need to be tied in with increased enforcement and increased protection for golden eagles, given that the conservation status of golden eagles is also limited by illegal killing (Whitfield *et al.*, 2008).

The last potential method involves manipulating hen harrier densities directly through human intervention, rather than through a reliance on other predators or habitat management. This approach was originally suggested by Potts (1998) as a "quota" scheme, where grouse moors would support a given density (or quota)

Plate 18.5 The presence of golden eagles (*Aquila chrysaetos*) may potentially reduce densities of breeding hen harriers. © Lorne Gill/SNH

of hen harriers and breeding attempts above this density would be prevented. Clearly, direct manipulation is illegal under the Birds Directive, but if the law changed various approaches to preventing hen harrier breeding above a given limit are possible: birds could be killed or their eggs destroyed; they could be translocated; or there could be a brood management scheme. In this last case, there would be no limit on hen harrier settling densities, but should numbers of nests containing chicks on a given area exceed a certain threshold level, then young from additional nests would be removed, reared locally in aviaries and then released back into the wild (as proposed by Potts, 1998). Within the law, a similar technique is currently employed in France and Spain, where hen harriers have been successfully reared to protect them from being killed by agricultural harvesting (Amar *et al.*, 2000). As with diversionary feeding, a variety of questions remain over the practicalities of these techniques. We should also stress that any form of direct manipulation would require derogation from current legislation (see below) as well as broad acceptance from the main stakeholders.

Translocation would involve removing eggs or young chicks from grouse moors to a new site where they would be released back into the wild, based on techniques that have been employed for reintroductions for a range of species, most recently red kite (*Milvus milvus)* and sea eagle (*Haliaeetus albicilla)* in the UK (Watson and Thirgood, 2001). In this case, however, it is important to note that translocations motivated by the desire to remove hen harriers from areas where they are already persecuted would be illegal and would contravene the IUCN guidelines for species reintroductions.

18.4 Broader issues for conflict resolution

The development of suitable techniques to improve the conservation status of the hen harrier, whilst maintaining driven grouse shooting, is dependent on effective dialogue between the main stakeholder groups. To some extent, this has happened in Scotland through the Moorland Forum (see www.moorlandforum.org). In England, specific stakeholder dialogue on the hen harrier-red grouse issue has recently been established, mediated by The Environment Council, an independent NGO with experience in conflict resolution (http://www.the-environment-council.org.uk/hen-harrier-dialogue.html). The specific objective of this dialogue is to explore ways of moving the raptor-grouse conflict forward with the objective of securing driven grouse shooting together with an improvement in the conservation status of hen harriers. To date, this dialogue has not given rise to any improvement in the hen harrier's conservation status.

Arising out of discussions by these stakeholder dialogue groups, four of the above alternative solutions to the conflict are currently being considered: a) law enforcement with a move to low intensity shooting where necessary; b) measures which might result in intra-guild predation by golden eagles; c) diversionary feeding of hen harriers; and d) hen harrier brood management. It is worth emphasizing that these are not mutually exclusive and could be used in combination.

Each approach has associated advantages and disadvantages. All four approaches could, lead to improved hen harrier conservation status, although only two (diversionary feeding and brood

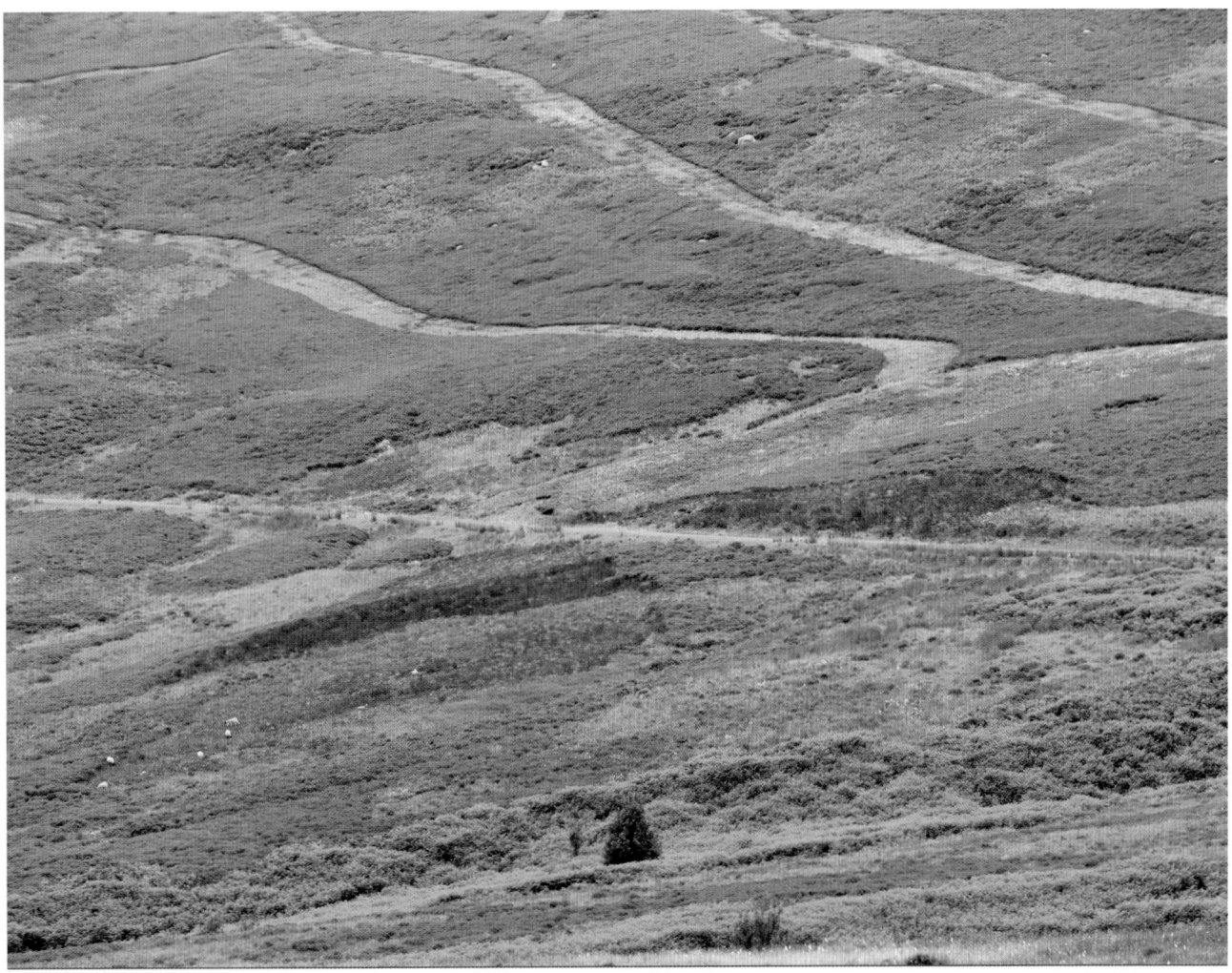

Plate 18.6 Well practised grouse management is an important form of land use, providing ecological, economic and social benefits to rural communities. © Lorne Gill/SNH

manipulation) are likely to be compatible with driven grouse shooting if they are effective at reducing hen harrier predation rates. Two of the techniques involve the movement and release of raptors and would require derogation from the Birds Directive (see Thompson and Galbraith, 1999; Anon., 2000), and at present there is no basis in law for such derogations to be granted.

In order to advise on how to move forward we need to address a number of outstanding issues. Whilst we already have a considerable amount of knowledge about this conflict, there are still many gaps in our understanding. We suggest four elements need to be considered further:

18.4.1 Feasibility

Consideration needs to be given as to whether the alternative approaches will work in practice. For example, increased prosecutions could lead to less illegal activity and therefore more hen harriers, but we have to ask if increased enforcement is achievable? We know that golden eagles kill hen harriers (Watson, 1997), but we do not know how easy it will be to recover, or indeed increase, golden eagle

Plate 18.7 Resolution to the conflict between grouse management and hen harrier conservation will require continued, open and inclusive dialogue between the main stakeholders. © Lorne Gill/SNH

populations on grouse moors, or the impact that golden eagles would have on hen harrier populations. We know that feeding individual hen harriers leads to reduced predation on red grouse at one study area (Redpath *et al.*, 2001), but we still do not know how feeding will affect local hen harrier populations and whether feeding hen harriers is compatible with driven shooting. We know that eggs or young hen harriers could be removed as part of a brood manipulation scheme, but significant questions remain over where to set the threshold for removal.

18.4.2 Consequences

In deciding how to manage the conflict, we clearly need to understand the consequences of each approach. Much of the research focus so far has been ecological; the legal, economic and social aspects of grouse management and this conflict require much more understanding. For example, we need to be able to estimate the consequences of moving away from intensive to more extensive forms of management. How will jobs, livelihoods and tourism be affected by changes in upland management? If driven grouse shooting stops in an area, what will replace it? If management measures are seen to benefit one interest over the other how that will affect numbers or perceptions of people living in or visiting upland areas?

18.4.3 Resources

Cost is clearly an important consideration. We can start to estimate the costs of feeding hen harriers (Redpath *et al.*, 2001), but the full cost of developing the other approaches is not fully understood. In addition, there is likely to be disagreement concerning where the funding would come from for any of the four approaches we have suggested above.

18.4.4 Acceptability

A central element tied in to the feasibility of the different approaches concerns how acceptable the alternative management options are to the stakeholders and the public. Unless grouse managers accept that diversionary feeding is a useful approach, they are unlikely to use it to manage hen harriers. Similarly, if a brood manipulation scheme is unacceptable to the main conservation stakeholders it will be harder to adopt it as a management option, and it would be less likely to receive a derogation (see Thompson and Galbraith, 1999). The precedence of adopting a hen harrier management scheme is in itself a concern to some stakeholders, because this may lead to applications for other species.

Clearly, there remain many gaps in our knowledge, and we need to start to understand some of these issues with a combination of ecological and social science if we are to move forward. In tandem with this, continued dialogue is critical in agreeing how to proceed and to find approaches that are supported by the main stakeholders which are likely to lead to sustainable solutions (Sidaway, 2005). Importantly, progress requires that all sides in this debate consider alternative viewpoints, are prepared to maintain an open and inclusive dialogue, and they will not retreat into pre-existing positions.

18.5 Acknowledgements

We thank the editors for improving the manuscript, and an anonymous referee for comments. We have drawn on field research and surveys undertaken by colleagues working for CEH, RSPB, GWCT, Scottish Raptor Study Groups and SNH.

References

Amar, A., Arroyo, B. & Bretagnolle, V. (2000). Post-fledging dependence and dispersal in hacked and wild Montagu's Harriers *Circus pygargus*. *Ibis* **142**: 21-28.

Amar, A., Arroyo, B., Redpath, S.M. & Thirgood, S.J. (2004). Habitat predicts losses of red grouse to individual hen harriers. *Journal of Applied Ecology* **41**: 305-314.

Amar, A., Redpath, S., Saunders, R. & Baines, T. (2007). Diversionary feeding experiments: What Langholm II can tell us and how we can fill the gaps. Report to the Environment Council Stakeholder Dialogue.

Anderson, B.J., Arroyo, B.E., Collingham, Y.C., Etheridge, B., Fernandez-De-Simon, J., Gillings, S., Gregory, R.D., Leckie, F.M., Sim, I., Thomas, C., Travis, J. & Redpath, S.M. (2009). Using distribution models to test alternative hypotheses about a species' environmental limits and recovery prospects. *Biological Conservation* **142**: 488-499.

Anon. (2000). *Report of the UK Raptor Working Group*. Depertment for Environment, Transport and the Regions/ JNCC, Peterborough.

Anon. (2007). A report by the British Falconers' Club on the practical considerations relating to the theoretical use of trained golden eagles as deterrents to nesting hen harriers in upland Britain. Report to the Environment Council Stakeholder Dialogue.

Anon. (2008). Natural Justice: A joint thematic inspection of the arrangements in Scotland for preventing, investigating and prosecuting wildlife crime. The Scottish Government, Edinburgh. http://www.scotland.gov.uk/Publications/2008/04/03143616/0

Arroyo, B., Amar, A., Leckie, F.M., Buchanan, G., Wilson, J. & Redpath, S.M. (2009). Hunting habitat selection by hen harriers on moorland: implications for conservation management. *Biological Conservation* **142**: 586-596.

Etheridge, B., Summers, R.W. & Green, R. E. (1997). The effects of illegal killing and destruction of nests by humans on the population dynamics of the hen harrier *Circus cyaneus* in Scotland. *Journal of Applied Ecology* **34**:1081-1105.

Gese, E.M., Stotts, T.E. & Grothe, S. (1996). Interactions between coyotes and red foxes in Yellowstone National Park, Wyoming. *Journal of Mammalogy* **77**: 377-382.

Gustavson, C.R. & Nicolaus, L.K. (1987). Taste aversion conditioning in wolves, coyotes, and other canids: Retrospect and prospect. In: *Man and wolf*. (Ed. Frank, H), Dr W. Junk Publishers, Dordtrecht, The Netherlands.

Lindstrom, E.R., Brainerd, S.M., Helldin, J.O. & Overskaug, K. (1995). Pine marten-red fox interactions: a case of intraguild predation? *Annales Zoologici Fennici* **32**: 111-116.

Lovegrove, R. (2007). *Silent fields: The long decline of a nation's wildlife*. Oxford University Press, Oxford.

Marshall, K., White, R. & Fischer, A. (2008). Conflicts between humans over wildlife management: on the diversity of stakeholder attitudes and implications for conflict management. *Biodiversity and Conservation* **16**: 3129-3146.

Mulder, J.L. (1990). The stoat (*Mustela erminea*) in the Dutch dune region, its local extinction, and a possible cause: the arrival of the fox (*Vulpes vulpes*). *Lutra* **33**: 1-21.

Natural England. (2008). A Future for the Hen Harrier in England? Report by Natural England. ISBN 978-1-84754-109-7.

Naylor, A.J., White, R.M. & Mougeot, F. (2005). Assessing the feasibility and acceptability of rear and release, trap and transfer and the use of dovecotes as management options for red grouse, *Lagopus lagopus scoticus*. Report to SNH and Scotland's Moorland Forum, Edinburgh.

Nicolaus, L.K., Herrera, J., Nicolaus, J.C. & Gustavson, C.R. (1989). Ethyniol estradiol and generalized aversions to eggs among free ranging predators. *Applied Animal Behavior Science* **24**: 313-324.

Nicolaus, L.K., Casel, J.F., Carlson, R.B. & Gustavson, C.R. (1983). Taste aversion conditioning of crows to control predation on eggs. *Science* **220**: 212-214.

PACEC. (2006). The Economic and Environmental Impact of Sporting Shooting. Public and Corporate Economic Consultants, Cambridge.

Potts, G.R. (1998). Global dispersion of hen harriers: implications for grouse moors in UK. *Ibis* **140**: 76-88.

Redpath, S.M., Amar, A., Madders, M., Leckie, F.M. & Thirgood, S.J. (2002). Hen harrier foraging success in relation to land use in Scotland. *Animal Conservation* **5**: 113-118.

Redpath, S.A., Arroyo, B.E., Leckie, E.M., Bacon, P., Bayfield, N., Gutierrez, R.J., & Thirgood, S.J. (2004). Using decision modeling with stakeholders to reduce human-wildlife conflict: a Raptor-Grouse case study. *Conservation Biology* **18**: 350-359.

Redpath, S.M. & Thirgood, S.J. (1997). Birds of Prey and Red Grouse. The Stationery Office, London.

Redpath, S.M. & Thirgood, S.J. (1999). Functional and numerical responses in generalist predators: hen harriers and peregrines on Scottish grouse moors. *Journal of Animal Ecology* **68**: 879-892.

Redpath, S.M., Thirgood S.J. & Leckie, F. (2001). Does supplementary feeding reduce predation of red grouse by hen harriers? *Journal of Applied Ecology* **38**: 1157-1168.

Redpath, S.M. & Thirgood, S.J. (2009). Hen harriers and red grouse – moving towards consensus? *Journal of Applied Ecology* **46**: 961-963.

Robertson, P.A., Park, K.J. & Barton, A.F. (2001). Loss of heather moorland in the Scottish uplands: the role of red grouse management. *Wildlife Biology* **7**: 11-16.

Scottish Raptor Study Groups. (1997). The illegal persecution of raptors in Scotland. *Scottish Birds* **19**: 65-85.

Sergio, F. & Hiraldo, F. (2008). Intraguild predation in raptor assemblages: a review. *Ibis* **150** (S1): 132-145.

Sidaway, R. (2005). *Resolving Environmental Disputes*, Earthscan, London.

Smith, A.A., Redpath S.M., Campbell, S. & Thirgood, S.J. (2001). Meadow pipits, red grouse and the habitat characteristics of managed grouse moors. *Journal of Applied Ecology* **38**: 390-401.

Sotherton, N., Tapper, S. & Smith A. (2009). Hen harriers and red grouse: economic aspects of red grouse shooting and the implications for moorland conservation. *Journal of Applied Ecology* **46**: 955-960.

Sovada, M.A., Sargeant, A.B. & Grier, J.W. (1995). Differential effects of coyotes and red foxes on duck nest success. *Journal of Wildlife Management* **59**: 1-9.

Swenson, J.E. & Andren, H. (2005). A tale of two countries: large carnivore depredation and compensation schemes in Sweden and Norway. In *People and Wildlife: Conflict or Coexistence?* Eds R. Woodroffe, S. Thirgood & A. Rabinowitz. Cambridge University Press.

Tapper, S. (2005). Nature's Gain: How gamebird management has influenced wildlife conservation. The Game Conservancy Trust, Fordingbridge, Hampshire.

Tapper, S. (unpub). Potential solutions to the grouse/hen harrier conflict. Report to the Environment Council Stakeholder Dialogue.

Tharme, A.P., Green, R.E., Baines, D., Bainbridge, I.P. & O'Brien, M. (2001). The effect of management for red grouse shooting on the population density of breeding birds on heather-dominated moorland. *Journal of Applied Ecology* **38**: 439-457.

Thirgood, S.J., Redpath, S.M., Newton, I., Hudson, P.J. (2000a). Raptors and grouse: conservation conflicts and management solutions. *Conservation Biology* **14**: 95-104.

Thirgood, S.J., Redpath, S.M., Rothery P. & Aebischer, N. (2000b). Raptor predation and population limitation in red grouse. *Journal of Animal Ecology* **69**: 504-516.

Thirgood, S.J., Redpath, S.M., Haydon, D.T., Rothery, P., Newton, I. & Hudson, P.J. (2000c). Habitat loss and raptor predation: disentangling long- and short-term causes of red grouse declines. *Proceedings of the Royal Society of London B* **267**: 651-656.

Thirgood, S.J., Redpath, S.M., Campbell, S. & Smith, A. (2002). Do habitat characteristics influence predation on red grouse? *Journal of Applied Ecology* **39**: 217-225.

Thirgood, S.J., Redpath, S.M. & Graham, I. (2003). What determines the foraging distribution of raptors on heather moorland? *Oikos* **100**: 15-20.

Thirgood, S. & Redpath, S. (2005). Hen harriers and Red grouse: the ecology of a conflict. In *People and Wildlife: Conflict or Coexistence?* Eds R. Woodroffe, S. Thirgood & A. Rabinowitz. Cambridge University Press.

Thirgood, S. & Redpath, S. (2008). Hen harriers and red grouse: science, politics and human-wildlife conflict. *Journal of Applied Ecology* **45**: 1450-1454.

Thompson, D.B.A., MacDonald, A.J., Marsden, J.H. & Galbraith, C.A. (1995). Upland heather moorland in the UK: a review of international importance, vegetation change and some objectives for conservation. *Biological Conservation* **71**: 163-178.

Thompson, D. & Galbraith, C.A. (1999). Report on Moorland Working Group visit to the European Commission, DGXI: 25 January 1999.

Thompson, P.S., Amar, A., Hoccom, D.G., Knott, J. & Wilson, J.D. (2009). Resolving the conflict between driven-grouse shooting and conservation of hen harriers. *Journal of Applied Ecology* **46**: 950-954.

Watson, J. (1997). *The Golden Eagle*. T & AD Poyser Ltd.

Watson, M. & Thirgood, S.J. (2001). Could translocation aid hen harrier conservation in the UK? *Animal Conservation* **4**: 37-43.

Whitfield, D.P., Fielding, A.H., McLeod, D.R.A. & Haworth, P.F. (2008). A conservation framework for golden eagles: implication for their conservation and management in Scotland. Scottish Natural Heritage Commissioned Report No. 193 (ROAME No. F05AC306).

Woodroffe, R., Thirgood, S. & Rabinowitz, A. (2005). *People and Wildlife: Conflict or Coexistence?* Cambridge University Press.

Redpath, S., Amar, A., Smith, A., Thompson, D.B.A. and Thirgood, S. (2010). People and nature in conflict: can we reconcile hen harrier conservation and game management? In: *Species Management: Challenges and Solutions for the 21st Century*, ed. by J.M. Baxter and C.A. Galbraith. TSO Scotland, Edinburgh, pp. 335-350.

Chapter 19

Conflicts between UK marine mammals and other native species

Ian L. Boyd[1] and John Harwood[2]

Summary

1. Conflicts between marine mammals and other native species may result from interactions that are direct, through predation, or indirect, through ecological linkages usually involving some form of competition.
2. We provide some examples of current conflicts, which demonstrate that conflict is an anthropic concept determined more by human attitudes, expectations and objectives than ecological theory.
3. In essence, conflicts are a consequence of the fact that different sectors of society value species in different ways. In general, marine mammals attract a high social valuation and this is reflected in the complex set of legal instruments that has been passed for their protection and management. However, this valuation also increases the probability of conflict.

[1] Sea Mammal Research Unit, Gatty Marine Lab, University of St Andrews, St Andrews, Fife, KY16 8LB, UK
[2] Centre for Research into Ecological and Environmental Modelling, University of St Andrews, St Andrews, Fife, KY16 8LB, UK

19.1 Introduction

Harbour porpoise (*Phocoena phocoena*) and killer whale (*Orcinus orca*). © Michael deRo[...]

"Conflicts" between species arise when an increase, or change in the behaviour, of one species has a negative impact on the other, but both species are deemed to be of high value by society. These conflicts become particularly difficult to resolve if different sectors of society place very different values on the two species. The best-documented conflicts involving marine mammals arise from their interactions with commercial fisheries (Harwood and Croxall, 1988). However, there are a number of other conflicts between marine mammals and native species that have implications for conservation. These are often less obvious, and even more challenging to document and study, than those involving fisheries.

The interactions which give rise to 'conflict situations' are, as we shall see, all examples of classic ecological processes. It is only when humans become involved in these interactions that they are perceived as conflicts. Marine mammals are far from being the only taxon that features in conflicts (see Thirgood and Redpath, 2008; Baxter and Galbraith, this volume; Thompson *et al.*, this volume) but the way in which different sectors of society value marine mammals does seem to encourage conflict. In addition, the fact that marine mammals are widespread, relatively abundant, migrate across international boundaries, and are accorded a high level of protection through legislation probably makes conflict inevitable.

A well documented example of conflict from outside the UK involves the way in which California sea lions (*Zalophus californinus*) interact with an endangered population of steelhead salmon (*Oncorhynchus mykiss*) at Ballard Locks in Seattle (NMFS, 1997). Here, there is a real danger that one protected species (steelhead salmon) could be driven close to extinction by another protected species (the sea lion), because human modifications to the environment (the construction of a weir) have made salmon more vulnerable to predation. Similar conflict involving depleted salmon stocks and harbour seals (*Phoca vitulina*) exist elsewhere in the Pacific North-west of the United States (Wright *et al.*, 2007) and may also occur in specific locations in the UK involving predation of Atlantic salmon (*Salmo salar*) by both harbour and grey seals (*Halichoerus grypus*). These conflicts are manifestations of natural predator-prey interactions but they often arise as a result of long-standing human intervention in the management of both populations. This usually involves exploitation but, as in the case of Ballard Locks, it can also involve modification of habitat in a way that makes one species more vulnerable to predation by another, or that changes resource availability. The extent to which sea lions could cause serious depression of the steelhead salmon will depend upon the way in which the diet of sea lions varies with the abundance of all its potential prey species (i.e. its multi-species functional response Smout and Lindstrom (2007), Matthiopoulos *et al.* (2008)). The Ballard Locks example illustrates the close linkage with past management actions that often exists within conflicts between marine mammals and native species. Where the linkage is less obvious there is a tendency to assume by default that a linkage exists and then take appropriate management action.

Conflicts involving marine mammals and their prey can be conveniently categorized into those that involve direct interactions between the marine mammal and human society and those in which the

Plate 19.1 Harbour seal (*Phoca vitulina*) are common around the coast of Scotland. © Lorne Gill/SNH

interaction with society is indirect, via changes in prey abundance (Harwood and Croxall, 1988). Direct interactions include the entanglement and death of marine mammals in fishing gear (Read *et al.*, 2006), and the removal of fish from fishing gear and associated damage to the gear. Fjalling (2005) provides a detailed description of the different ways in which grey seals can affect the number of Atlantic salmon caught in fixed nets in the Baltic Sea. In this chapter we will limit our examples to those involving indirect interactions. It is, of course, a moot point as to where direct human-marine mammal conflicts stop and conflicts between marine mammals and other native species start because, as we have argued, all are part of the same syndrome of anthropogenic intervention in natural processes. Setting this aside, conflicts can be classified broadly into (1) those involving direct interactions between a marine mammal and another native species, usually through predation, and (2) those in which the interaction is indirect, via an intermediate resource that may be prey, breeding habitat or a parasite. Most of the conflicts that arise from direct interactions involve marine mammals preying on protected species, but there are some well-publicized cases in which protected marine mammals are the prey.

19.2 Current conflicts arising from direct interactions between marine mammals and other native species in the UK

By the definitions already given, there can be no such thing as an unobserved conflict, because conflicts are the result of human perception of the underlying interactions. Interspecies conflicts involving direct interactions between marine mammals and other native species in the UK include:

19.2.1 Predation of harbour seals by killer whales (*Orcinus orca*)

There has been a marked decline in harbour seal populations in the North Sea over the last decade (Lonergan *et al.*, 2007). Although the causes of this decline are not known, killer whales have been observed predating on harbour seals around the Shetland Islands, and this may be a contributory factor.

19.2.2 Predation of cod (*Gadus morhua*) by a range of marine mammmals

Cod stocks in the North-east Atlantic and North Sea have been severely depressed by over-fishing and there are recovery plans in place to help restore these cod stocks . Diet analysis has shown that grey seals could have a detrimental effect on the recovery of some local cod stocks. However, considerably more information is required (Matthiopoulos *et al.*, 2008) before the actual implications of this interaction for cod recovery can be assessed.

19.2.3 Predation of Atlantic salmon and sea trout (*Salmo trutta*) by seals and bottlenose dolphins (*Tursiops truncatus*)

Salmon are particularly vulnerable to predation by seals and dolphins when they congregate at the entrance to rivers in which they spawn, or when they return to the sea after breeding.

19.2.4 Predation of harbour porpoises (*Phocoena phocoena*) by bottlenose dolphins

This appears to be an example of intra-guild predation, in which one member of a guild of predator species that exploit a common resource kills other members of the same guild, but does not necessarily consume them.

19.3 Current conflicts arising from indirect interactions between marine mammals and other native species in the UK

There are fewer specific examples of conflicts that arise as a result of indirect interactions, but a classic example involves competition for breeding space between grey seals and Atlantic puffins (*Fratercula arctica*). During the 1970s and 1980s wardens at the Farne Islands National Nature Reserve became concerned about the erosion of the delicate topsoil on these islands, caused by the activities of breeding grey seals. A good topsoil layer is essential to enable puffins to construct their breeding burrows and it was anticipated that the loss of this layer would have a serious impact on the puffin population. Although there was no temporal overlap between the species, grey seals were seen as a threat to puffins.

Plate 19.2 Atlantic puffins (*Fratercula arctica*) on the Farne Islands. © John M. Baxter

Consequently, since the 1980s they have been intentionally excluded from breeding on the islands most used by puffins by having a human presence on these islands during the grey seal breeding season.

Future conflicts are most likely to occur in cases where marine mammals and other predators share a resource that has been depressed by fishing or ecosystem change (possibly linked with climate change). One such resource is the lesser sandeel (*Ammodytes marinus*) in the North Sea, which is shared by many marine mammal and seabird species, and which has shown dramatic declines over the last decade. However, it is also possible that there may be facilitation, rather that competition, between the members of the guild that exploits this resource, so that a decline in one member species might induce inverse density-dependent changes in other members through a process akin to the Allee effect (Stephens and Sutherland, 1999). New conflicts may, therefore, become apparent as our understanding of how guilds of marine predators function improves, and some of these are likely to highlight the need for clear objectives for the restoration, maintenance and management of entire guilds.

Conflicts involving marine mammals are in evidence even at the ecosystem level. For example, some whaling nations have proposed that large-scale manipulation of the number of predators in the upper trophic levels of marine ecosystems may be required to optimize ecosystem yields (Yodzis, 2001). It is clear that manipulation of predator populations has been a feature of past human exploitation of marine resources (Worm *et al.*, 2006) and it is conceivable that such top-down forcing could be a practical tool for resource management. However, the extent to which any such approach might be pursued will depend upon the relative value that society places upon marine mammals and other ecosystem resources.

Finally, interactions between marine mammals and other native species may be mediated by their shared parasites. There is increasing evidence from pathology studies that human colonic bacteria may have a significant effect upon the health of some marine mammal populations (Gulland and Hall, 2007). In addition, grey seals are hosts to a number of micro- and macroparasites that may have contributed to the recent decline of harbour seals in the North Sea (Lonergan *et al.*, 2007). Seals are also the definitive host for a number of macroparasites, such as nematodes (*Pseudoterranova* sp., known as 'seal worms') that have gadoid fish as an intermediate host, and these parasites could affect the population dynamics of these fish species.

19.4 The role of large-scale ecosystem dynamics

Although the basis for any conflict between a marine mammal and another native species will usually be one of the classic ecological interactions (predation, resource competition, or parasite-mediated competition), larger-scale processes may have created the context in which these interactions occur. Such processes are difficult to study directly and their existence is often inferred from circumstantial evidence. For example, there has been much speculation about the potential effect of killer whales on other marine mammal populations in the North Pacific (Springer *et al.*, 2003), which might be a consequence of a trophic cascade initiated by large-scale industrial whaling. However, the basic hypothesis is largely untestable, and the circumstantial evidence in support of it can be interpreted in many other ways (Wade *et al.*, 2006).

Plate 19.3 Grey seal (*Halichoerus grypus*) eating an adult Atlantic salmon (*Salmo salar*) in a Scottish river. © Rob Harris

The decline of penguins in the Scotia Sea, South Atlantic has been attributed to competitive interactions with marine mammals (Barlow *et al.*, 2002), and there is a long-standing hypothesis that marine mammal populations can drive the dynamics of many other krill predators in this part of the Southern Ocean. There are many other examples of such "wasp-waisted" marine communities (Rice, 1995) in temperate and polar regions, in which a number of marine mammal species share a single prey resource. Examples include: harp seals (*Phoca groenlandica*), humpback whales (*Megaptera novaeangliae*) and minke whales (*Balaenoptera acutorostrata*) preying on capelin (*Mallotus villosus*); grey seals, harbour seals and minke whales preying on sandeels; South African or South American fur seals (*Arctocephalus pusillus* and *A. australis*) preying on anchovies (*Engraulis* spp.); California sea lions, blue whales (*Balaenoptera musculus*) and fin whales (*Balaenoptera physalus*) preying on anchovies and sardines (*Sardinops sagax*); and many species of Antarctic seals and whales preying on krill (*Euphausia superba*). Many seabirds and larger predatory fish and squid also share these common food resources. There is still no consensus within competition theory about how such guilds persist, but the most likely explanation is that each predator is adapted to forage at a different spatial and temporal scale, and that the fluctuating distribution of the resource prevents any one species from dominating all others. This implies that such systems may never settle to a single equilibrium, and that conflicts within them must be evaluated over long time scales. Although changes in these systems may simply be part of a natural process of re-adjustment to normal fluctuations in resource availability, they may also be induced by human intervention. In the latter case, the common view is that they need to be managed as a conflict.

19.5 The sociological link to marine mammal ecology: learning to live with conflicts

In general, it is difficult to determine from first principles an appropriate population size for any species, although it clearly needs to be sufficiently large for the species to maintain itself over many generations. Subject to this constraint, the desired size of a population is a matter of societal choice, and this can lead to conflicts between conservation objectives.

For example, both killer whales and harbour seals are protected species, but killer whales feed on harbour seals and other protected marine mammals. Provided society's valuation of harbour seals is less than for killer whales, then there is no obvious conflict. A similar situation exists with predation of Atlantic salmon by bottlenose dolphins or commercial fish species by harbour porpoises. However, predation of Atlantic salmon by grey and harbour seals is generally perceived as a conflict. This implies that dolphins are more highly valued than salmon, so that the effects they may have are tolerated, whereas the relative valuation of seals and salmon is much less clear cut. Of course, there is little or no ecological justification for this difference in attitudes but it has a strong bearing upon how conflicts are perceived and managed. Moreover, the relative valuations of species often differs between different sections of society and this can add to conflict because people cannot agree on a consistent approach to management of perceived inter-species conflicts.

There are many other examples of how differing societal values drive the perception of conflict. Even though there is considerable uncertainty about the role of killer whales in the decline in some marine mammal populations in the North-east Pacific (Wade *et al.*, 2006), it is quite likely that removing killer whales from this region would reduce mortality rates in these populations and promote their recovery. However, this is not normally considered as a viable management option, even if it were feasible, because of the high valuation society places upon killer whales. By the same measure, there is much current focus upon ecosystem approaches to management but these approaches rarely integrate explicitly the relative societal valuation of ecosystem components. Approaches that do not do this are very likely to fail.

19.6 Social valuation

These examples illustrate that many of the conflicts that involve marine mammals and other native species are the result of the way in which different sectors of society value these species. Obtaining an absolute valuation in a common and useful currency is certainly difficult (Wilson and Tisdel, 2006), although this is a particularly active area for econometric research (Haab and McConnell, 2003). However, what is clear from domestic and international legislation is that some form of valuation process does exist, even if it is unwritten and undefined. Understanding the basis of this *ad hoc* valuation is vital if we are to manage conflicts. Social valuation of the species involved in these conflicts appears to be the result of combining a number of different currencies, which may be given different weights depending upon circumstances. These currencies include straight-forward financial valuations of direct, indirect and amenity benefits, but may also include less easily quantified aspects such as the existence, bequest and transformative benefits (Kellert, 1995) associated with each species.

19.7 Conflict resolution: a case study from the UK

If the conflicts we have described are to be resolved, there must be some agreement among stakeholders on the relative valuations of the species that are involved. A framework for the relative valuation of wildlife resources was proposed by Helliwell (1969). The mechanisms used to obtain such a valuation involve the open exchange of information and face-to-face meetings in which those who have specific interests in the subject can discuss, and hopefully resolve, conflicting interests. Science has an important role to play in this process because it can provide grounding in the state of knowledge for the species concerned, and it may also be able to predict the broad outcomes of different management approaches.

This approach has been applied successfully to the conflicts that existed between the management of seals and salmon in the Moray Firth region in north-east Scotland (Thompson *et al.*, 2007; Butler *et al.*, 2008). This region has 16 major catchments draining through rivers that are important habitat for spawning and juvenile Atlantic salmon, some of which are recognized as Special Areas of Conservation (SAC) under Council Directive 92/43/EEC of the on the Conservation of Natural Habitats and of Wild Fauna and Flora (usually known as the Habitats Directive). Anadromous salmonid fish have been a focus for conservation efforts because of their commercial importance and their value as an indicator of the health of river catchments. Similar arguments support the conservation objectives for harbour seals in the region. This species is used implicitly by society as an indicator of the health of marine habitats, and this is reflected in its protection under the Habitats Directive.

The way in which salmon and seals can be used as indicators of the broader ecological health of their respective habitats is an interesting research question in its own right. However, the predation of salmon by seals, and the economic implications of this for salmon fisheries, results in a complex set of conflicting objectives for salmon and seal management in the Moray Firth. Although harbour seals probably have little effect on salmon populations in this region (Butler *et al.*, 2006), salmon has such a high economic value as a sport fish that the managers of rivers and the owners of salmon netting stations have

Plate 19.4 Harbour porpoise (*Phocoena phocoena*) predation by a killer whale (*Orcinus orca*). © Michael deRoos

sanctioned considerable levels of shooting of seals. At the other extreme, some stakeholder groups saw a need for complete protection for seals, even if this placed local salmon stocks at risk.

A relative valuation for seals and salmon in this situation was obtained by the establishment of a pilot management plan for the region and a process of consultation and debate amongst stakeholders. This was underpinned by research to reduce uncertainty about the possible outcome of different management approaches, and to inform all stakeholder groups of the current state of knowledge and to improve current knowledge. The ultimate valuation required both extremes in the debate to make compromises. In this case, those advocating total protection for seals agreed to a highly constrained form of management, which focused upon individual seals that were likely to have learned to feed on salmon, together with a promise to investigate the development of non-lethal methods for controlling seals in salmon rivers. Those advocating extermination of seals accepted that there was little evidence to support the view that all seals in the region were predating salmon, and they agreed that a policy of complete removal was both expensive and unnecessary. An upper limit on the number of seals that could be killed each year was calculated using a methodology developed by Wade (1998) and, as a result, the total number of seals being shot was reduced by almost an order of magnitude in a period of five years.

Time will tell if the management scheme for the Moray Firth will endure, but it has defined a new relative societal valuation for seals and salmon in the region by persuading stakeholders to agree a compromise between extreme positions that is based upon current knowledge. While this valuation is dimensionless, the ratio of the number of salmon caught to the number of seals shot provides an implicit indication of their relative values. It may be possible to use this relationship to answer the question, "How many seals is society willing to sacrifice in the interests of conserving salmon stocks and salmon fisheries?". The answer may act as a guide in other, more difficult, cases where the underpinning scientific evidence is poor or where stakeholders cannot agree a compromise.

An important message from this example is that it is possible to derive a valuation, and to make progress in management, without compromising the positions of individual stakeholders. While it is possible that some stakeholders may have changed their views as a result of the process, this is unlikely. Instead, a process of social facilitation has led to a societal valuation that could be viewed as some form of averaging process across the stakeholder views. This type of behaviour can be modelled within a game theoretical framework and probably involves a cost-benefit trade-off by each of the stakeholders. Theory shows that in most cases the group does better as a whole by cooperating, especially where there are reputational costs involved (Ohtsuki et al., 2009). In the case of the Moray Firth issue, the equilibrium in this game reflects the valuation of the resources.

Plate 19.5 Dall's porpoise (*Phocoenoides dalli*) predation by a killer whale (*Orcinus orca*). © Michael deRoos

19.8 Conclusions

Like other authors in this volume, we believe that conflicts between marine mammals and other native species are largely a consequence of public attitudes or perceptions. Socio-economic drivers are all-pervasive in these conflicts. However, they are moderated by public attitudes towards different species groups; as a result, all sectors of society may be willing to accept high socio-economic costs if the conflict involves species that receive a high level of social valuation. Marine mammals generally attract these valuation levels, but some seal species appear to be a special case because the public view of these animals is ambivalent. We provide a detailed description of the attempts that have been made to arrive at an agreed relative social valuation of seals and wild salmon in the Moray Firth region. This was probably only possible because the socio-economic drivers of conflicts were not explicitly included in the valuation process.

References

Barlow, K., Boyd, I., Croxall, J., Staniland, I., Reid, K. & Brierley, A. (2002). Are penguins and seals in competition for Antarctic krill at South Georgia? *Marine Biology* **140**: 205-213.

Baxter, J.M. & Galbraith, C.A. (2010). Species management – real or perceived. In: Baxter J.M. & Galbraith C.A. (Eds) *Species Management: Challenges and Solutions for the 21st Century*. Edinburgh: TSO Scotland, pp. 289-301.

Butler, J., Middlemas, S., Graham, I., Thompson, P. & Armstrong, J. (2006). Modelling the impacts of removing seal predation from Atlantic salmon, *Salmo salar* L., rivers in Scotland: a tool for targeting conflict resolution. *Fisheries Management and Ecology* **13**: 285-291.

Butler, J., Middlemas, S., McKelvey, S., McMyn, I., Leyshon, B., Walker, I., Thompson, P., Boyd, I., Duck, C., Armstrong, J., Graham, I. & Baxter, J. (2008). The Moray Firth Seal Management Plan: an adaptive framework for balancing the conservation of seals, salmon, fisheries and wildlife tourism in the UK. *Aquatic Conservation: Marine and Freshwater Ecosystems* **18**: 1025-1038.

Fjalling, A. (2005). The estimation of hidden seal-inflicted losses in the Baltic Sea set-trap salmon fisheries. *ICES Journal of Marine Science* **62**: 1630-1635.

Gulland, F. & Hall, A. (2007). Is marine mammal health deteriorating? Trends in the global reporting of marine mammal disease. *EcoHealth* **4**: 135-150.

Haab, T. & McConnell, K. (2003). *Valuing Environmental and Natural Resources: The Econometrics of Non-market Valuation*. Edward Elgar Publishing Ltd Cheltenham Glos.

Harwood, J. & Croxall, J. (1988). The assessment of competition between seals and commercial fisheries in the North Sea and the Antarctic. *Marine Mammal Science* **4**: 13-33.

Helliwell, D. (1969). Valuation of wildlife resources. *Regional Studies* **3**: 41-47.

Kellert, S.R. (1995). *The Value of Life*. Island Press, Washington DC.

Lonergan, M., Duck, C., Thompson, D., Mackey, B.L., Cunningham, L. & Boyd, I.L. (2007). Using sparse survey data to investigate the declining abundance of British harbour seals. *Journal of Zoology* **271**: 261-269.

Matthiopoulos, J., Smout, S., Winship, A.J., Thompson, D., Boyd, I.L. & Harwood, J. (2008). Getting beneath the surface of marine mammal – fisheries competition. *Mammal Review* **38**: 167-188.

NMFS. (1997). Investigation of Scientific Information on the Impacts of California Sea Lions and Pacific Harbor Seals on Salmonids and on the Coastal Ecosystems of Washington, Oregon, and California. NOAA Tech. Memo. NMFS-NWFSC-28, U.S. Dep. Commer., Seattle, WA.

Ohtsuki, H., Iwasa, Y. & Nowak, M.A. (2009). Indirect reciprocity provides only a narrow margin of efficiency for costly punishment. *Nature* **457**: 79-82.

Read, A., Drinker, P. & Northridge, S. (2006). Bycatch of marine mammals in US and global fisheries. *Conservation Biology* **20**: 163-169.

Rice, J.C. (1995). Food web theory, marine food webs, and what climate changes may do to northern marine fish populations. *Canadian Special Publications in Fisheries and Aquatic Sciences* **121**: 561-568.

Smout, S. & Lindstrom, U. (2007). Multispecies functional response of the minke whale *Balaenoptera acutorostrata* based on small-scale foraging studies. *Marine Ecology Progress Series* **341**: 277–291.

Springer, A., Estes, J., van Vliet, G., Williams, T., Doak, D., Danner, E., Forney, K. & Pfister, B. (2003). Sequential megafaunal collapse in the North Pacific Ocean: An ongoing legacy of industrial whaling? *Proceedings of the National Academy of Sciences of the United States of America* **100**: 12223-12228.

Stephens, P.A. & Sutherland, W.J. (1999). Consequences of the Allee effect for behaviour, ecology and conservation. *Trends in Ecology and Evolution* **14**: 401-405.

Thirgood, S. & Redpath, S. (2008). Hen harriers and red grouse: science, politics and human-wildlife conflict. *Journal of Applied Ecology* **45**: 1488-1492.

Thompson, D.B.A., Reed, T.M., Stroud, J., Christie, M.F.B. & Stroud, D.A. (2010). The nature of human-wildlife conflicts across Europe: a review. In Baxter, J.M. & Galbraith, C.A. (Eds). *Species Management: Challenges and Solutions for the 21st Century*. Edinburgh TSO Scotland, pp. 303-333.

Thompson, P.M., Mackey, B., Barton, T.M., Duck, C. & Butler, J.R.A. (2007). Assessing the potential impact of salmon fisheries management on the conservation status of harbour seals in NE Scotland. *Animal Conservation* **10**: 48-56.

Wade, P. (1998). Calculating limits to the allowable human-caused mortality of cetaceans and pinnipeds. *Marine Mammal Science* **14**: 1-37.

Wade, P., Burkanov, V., Dahlheim, M., Friday, N., Fritz, L., Loughlin, T., Mizroch, S., Muto, M., Rice, D., Barrett-Lennard, L., Black, N., Burdin, A., Calambokidis, J., Cerchio, S., Ford, J., Jacobsen, J., Matkin, C., Matkin, D., Mehta, A., Small, R., Straley, J., McCluskey, S., VanBlaricom, G. & Clapham, P. (2006). Killer whales and marine mammal trends in the North Pacific – a re-examination of evidence for sequential maegfauna collapse and the prey-switching hypothesis. *Marine Mammal Science* **23**: 766-802.

Wilson, C. & Tisdel, C. (2006). Information and wildlife valuation: Experiments and policy. *Contemporary Economic Policy* **24**: 144-159.

Worm, B., Barbier, E.B., Beaumont, N., Duffy, J.E., Folke, C., Halpern, B.S., Jackson, J.B.C., Lotze, H.K., Micheli, F., Palumbi, S.R., Sala, E., Selkoe, K.A., Stachowicz, J.J. & Watson, R. (2006). Impacts of biodiversity loss on ocean ecosystem services. *Science* **314**: 787-790.

Wright, B., Riemer, S., Brown, R., Ougzin, A. & Bucklin, K. (2007). Assessment of harbor seal predation on adult salmonids in a Pacific Northwest estuary. *Ecological Applications* **17**: 338-351.

Yodzis, P. (2001). Must top predators be culled for the sake of fisheries? *Trends in Ecology & Evolution* **16**: 78-84.

Boyd, I.L. and John Harwood, J. (2010). Conflicts between UK marine mammals and other native species. In: *Species Management: Challenges and Solutions for the 21st Century*, ed. by J.M. Baxter and C.A. Galbraith. TSO Scotland, Edinburgh. pp. 351-363

Chapter 20

Bats in houses – the conservation challenge

Tony J. Mitchell-Jones[1]

Summary

1. Many species of bats in the UK have a close association with houses, which provide a variety of opportunities for roosting at various times of the year. Although most householders coexist happily with 'their' bats, often because they are unaware of their presence, conflicts do arise from time to time, either because of problems caused by the presence of a bat roost or because the presence of the bats constrains the use or maintenance of the building.
2. The way in which such conflicts are resolved has far-reaching effects on how bats are perceived by society and the tolerance of householders to their presence.
3. The high dependence of bats on buildings also means that they are vulnerable to changes in building practices and construction methods that may, over time, affect the availability of roosting opportunities.
4. Current efforts to improve the energy-efficiency of houses, which can make a significant contribution to tackling climate change, could have an unplanned adverse impact on bat conservation unless appropriate measures are taken.

Combined swift and bat box. © John M. Baxter

20.1 Introduction

There are 16 species of bats breeding in Britain, each with their own distinct ecological requirements for roosting and feeding. Species richness is greatest in southern England, where all 16 species may be found, reducing to probably only five species in northern Scotland. Although the details vary between species, all bats form maternity colonies during the summer (May-August), when adult females gather together to give birth and rear their young. These colonies vary considerably in size. In Britain, the mean colony size for pipistrelles (*Pipistrellus* spp.), the most common species is about 50 (Mitchell-Jones *et al.*, 1986), but more than 3,000 bats have been recorded in one exceptional case. Once the young are independent, these colonies tend to disperse to use different roosts during the autumn, when mating takes place. Between October and March, depending on the weather, bats hibernate, though they can be active in all months of the year and will wake up and emerge to hunt if the temperature is high enough for insects to fly.

The seasonal phases of a bat's life demand different conditions for roosting. During the summer, maternity colonies seek out warm places or gather in confined spaces that they can warm with their own body heat. This reduces their energy requirements at a time when the demands of pregnancy and lactation are high. Although individuals can become torpid to save energy at any time of year, this option is not available to pregnant or lactating females, which endeavour to maintain a high body temperature during this period (Racey and Entwistle, 2000). At the same time, males and non-breeding females, which do not form colonies, often seek out cooler roosts, where they can become torpid and so minimize their energy expenditure.

During the hibernation period, bats seek cool and undisturbed places, providing buffering against external temperature changes and protection against very low temperatures. For many species, underground sites, such as caves and abandoned mines, provide ideal conditions, but other species may remain in less buffered environments, moving to more protected places only if the weather turns really cold.

20.2 Why bats roost in houses

Bat species in Britain can be divided into those that originally depended on caves or rock crevices for roosting and those that depended primarily on trees. This dichotomy is not complete, however, as many species may exploit both primary types of roost at different times. For example, the brown long-eared bat (*Plecotus auritus*), a common and widespread species, is found hibernating in underground sites in small numbers, though it is clearly primarily a tree-roosting species. In Britain, the most cave-dependent species are the two horseshoe bats, the greater (*Rhinolophus ferrumequinum*) and the lesser (*R. hipposideros*), which are found only in areas of south-western Britain with suitable underground sites for hibernation. In many parts of their range, these species also breed in underground sites, seeking domes in the roofs of caves, where they can create a warm cluster.

Plate 20.1 A mixed colony of Daubenton's bats (*Myotis daubentonii*) and soprano pipistrelles (*Pipistrellus pygmaeus*) in a house roof. © John Haddow

Despite these differences in primary roost types, virtually all species of bats in Britain have adopted buildings as roosts for at least part of the year. The two cave-dependent horseshoe bats, for example, typically form maternity sites in the roofs of buildings, including houses, to the extent that underground breeding sites for these species are now considered unusual in Britain, though less so in warmer climates. The serotine (*Eptesicus serotinus*), which in southern Europe roosts in rock crevices, is rarely found roosting anywhere except buildings in Britain (Stebbings and Robinson, 1991). The most common species in Britain, pipistrelles (the common pipistrelle (*P. pipistrellus*) and the soprano pipistrelle (*P. pygmaeus*)) and brown long-eared bats are also commonly found in house roofs. Although the difficulty of finding roosts in trees makes it difficult to estimate what proportion of the population is associated with house roofs, the small number of maternity colonies of these species that have been recorded in bats boxes, which are artificial tree roosts, suggests that their dependence on houses, at least for the summer, is very high.

A commonly used response to the question often posed by householders as to why bats roost in houses is that human activity has removed the majority of natural tree roosts. There is certainly some justification for this as the UK is one of the least forested countries in Europe, well below the European average (Table 20.1). Whilst this lack of forest cover must have an impact on roosting opportunities for bats, the problem is further compounded by the state of the trees themselves. Virtually all woodland in the UK is deficient in old, dead or damaged trees, that contain the cavities, splits and crevices used by bats. Whilst counting the number of cavities available to bats is difficult (Ruczyński and Bogdanowicz, 2005), some surrogate measures of roost availability illustrate the problem. Table 20.2 shows the volume of dead wood and the number of standing dead trees (snags) in different types of woodland. Most woodland in the UK has probably received some management within the last 50 years and thus falls into the category most likely to be deficient in natural cavities for bats. Studies on many species, including bats (Boyd and Stebbings, 1989), dormice (Juškaitis, 2008) and birds (Lundberg and Alatalo, 1992), have shown that natural roosting or nesting sites can be a limiting factor, so that the provision of artificial sites can raise the density of the species significantly.

Table 20.1 Forest as percentage of land area in some European countries. Data taken from Forestry Commission (2007).

Country	Forest as % land area (2005)
UK	11.8
France	28.3
Germany	31.7
Finland	73.9
European average	44.3

Table 20.2 Surrogate measures of bat roost availability in different forest types. Adapted from Kirby et al. (1998).

Forest type	Dead wood (m³/ha)	Snags per ha	Snag diameter
Managed	< 20	0-10	All < 10 cm
Unmanaged for 50 yr	20-40	11-50	Some > 10 m
Unmanaged for > 70 yr	> 50	>50	Some > 40 cm
Białowieża, Poland	60-94		

A lack of natural roosts does not entirely explain the enthusiasm with which many species of bats have adopted houses for roosting. For example, studies on roost selection by brown long-eared bats (Entwistle et al., 1997) and pipistrelles (Jenkins et al., 1998) showed that both species tended to select buildings to roost in that were closer to woodland than randomly selected buildings. Whilst the authors interpreted this as positive selection for buildings close to suitable foraging areas, it also suggests that even where natural roosts in trees were likely to be more available than average the bats still chose to roost in buildings. It is also notable that even in more heavily forested European countries, bats are still closely associated with the built environment.

The need for maternity colonies of bats to maintain consistently high body temperatures during pregnancy and lactation provides another clue to the selection of buildings over natural roosts. Many studies have shown that bats seek warm places during this period, so as to minimize the energetic cost of thermoregulation. In a study of temperature selection in pipistrelles (*P. pygmaeus*), Lourenço and Palmeirim (2004) found that maternity colonies of bats selected the hottest roosts available up to a temperature of about 40°C. Beyond this temperature, bats moved to seek lower temperatures. In this respect, roofs had an advantage over bat-boxes as they provided a wider range of environmental conditions and thus more opportunities for temperature selection. Similarly, Entwistle *et al.* (1997)

Plate 20.2 Brown long-eared bats (*Plecotus auritus*) in a typical roosting position at the apex of a roof. © John Haddow

showed that brown long-eared bats selected houses for roosting that had roofs significantly warmer than adjacent or random buildings. Few data are available on the thermal regime in natural tree roosts, but it seems certain that natural roosts within woodland (and so not in direct sunlight) are unlikely to reach the high temperatures preferred by the bats. In eastern England, noctule (*Nyctalus noctula*) maternity colonies selected dead trees out in the open that received full sunlight for much of the day whereas males selected living and shaded trees (author's data).

The preference of maternity colonies for warm locations has also been used to advantage in the management of rare species. Ransome (pers. comm.) showed that maternity colonies of greater horseshoe bats preferentially selected roosting areas with electric heaters compared with nearby areas in the same roof void that were not heated. Similarly, heaters have been used to improve roosting conditions for maternity colonies of lesser horseshoe bats or to manage the way the bats use roost areas (J. Matthews, pers. comm.).

It may thus be concluded that the thermal conditions found in house roofs provide a strong attraction for maternity colonies of bats, which take advantage of the high temperatures to minimize the energetic cost of thermoregulation during a critical period, allowing them to divert more energy to reproduction.

This combination of a lack of natural tree roosts and the attractive roosting conditions provided by buildings has had a significant impact on the selection of roosts by bats, with all species of bats in Britain having been found in the roofs of houses. Whilst the serotine represents the most extreme example of this synanthropic lifestyle, the most common and widespread species are strongly associated with buildings, so their successful conservation depends on the maintenance of an adequate roosting resource. This has, rightly, been a focus of attention for bat conservationists over the past few decades, though attention is now turning to the other resources, such as foraging areas and their associated commuting routes, needed by these species.

20.3 Conflict resolution

The high dependence of bats on houses, particularly during the maternity period, inevitably brings them into conflict with householders from time to time. Such conflicts arise in two main ways. In many cases, the presence of the bats themselves causes problems, either because they are not liked or because of associated noise, smell or the presence of bat droppings. In other cases, the presence of the bats constrains the freedom of the householder to do as they wish with their property. This may include repairs or maintenance works or, in more extreme cases, loft conversions or the construction of extensions. As the latter are likely to involve the planning system they are not considered further in this review.

When confronted with a problem involving bats, householders seek a source of help and advice. This can take them on a variety of routes, but most eventually end up with either one of the statutory nature conservation agencies (SNCOs) or the Bat Conservation Trust, which runs a national bat helpline and may also operate under contract to one or more of the SNCOs. Whichever route is followed, the enquirer should end up speaking to someone with expertise and experience in dealing with such problems. Many problems can be resolved satisfactorily at this stage, either by the provision of information, reassurance or advice, but many are offered a personal visit to provide on-site advice and problem resolution. Experience suggests that a personal visit is more likely to resolve problems satisfactorily than a phone conversation and that better outcomes for the bats are achieved.

When resolving problems, the conservation community has a hierarchy of objectives. For problems attributable to the presence of the bats, the optimum

Plate 20.3 Bat droppings on a window sill below the roost entrance. © John Haddow

outcome is to secure the existence of the roost for the foreseeable future. If this cannot be achieved, the next best outcome is to secure the roost for the current breeding season, accepting that it will be destroyed (excluded) once the maternity colony has dispersed. In exceptional cases, where even this outcome cannot be achieved, the most fundamental objective is to ensure that no bats are directly killed or injured. This outcome can almost always be achieved. A similar, though simpler, hierarchy applies to enquiries involving maintenance or repairs, where the preferred objective is to leave the roost available after works are complete and the fallback objective is to ensure that no bats are killed or injured if the works unavoidably destroy their roost.

Advisory visits are delivered in slightly different ways in the four countries of the UK. In England, Natural England works with more than 800 registered and trained volunteers to deliver advisory visits, with the management of the process being contracted out. In Scotland, Scottish Natural Heritage employs 34 batworkers on call-off contracts, but also uses staff for some visits. Similarly, in Wales, the Countryside Council for Wales retains batworkers on call-off contracts, but also uses some staff. In Northern Ireland, the Northern Ireland Environment Agency (NIEA) employs a coordinator at the Ulster Museum, with visits being delivered by NIEA staff and a few volunteers.

20.3.1 Householder concerns

When seeking advice about the presence of bats, householders express their concerns in a wide variety of ways. A number of callers are seeking only extra information and express no concerns about the presence of the bats, with some even welcoming their presence. However, the majority of callers express concerns in ways ranging from the mild to the hysterical. Analysis of the reasons for such concerns suggests that the presence of bat droppings is a major concern (Mitchell-Jones *et al.*, 1986; Moore *et al.*, 2003) (Figure 20.1). This concern, which tends to be expressed either in terms of the mess or a potential health hazard, is likely to be related particularly to the presence of pipistrelles (*Pipistrellus* spp.), which are the most common species in houses and tend to mark the outside of their roosts with droppings. Other major concerns include a general fear of bats (and often any other flying things), the presence of bats in the living area of the building, smell and noise. In Scotland, data collected between 2001-8 indicated that bats in the living area was the most frequent problem, followed by 'other' and then droppings. However, the data were categorized slightly differently to those in Moore *et al.* (2003) (J. McKinnell, pers. comm.).

Whilst some concerns are well-founded, particularly those relating to smell, noise and bats in the living area, others may arise because of a lack of understanding of bats and their lifestyles. In such cases, roost visitors are often able to persuade householders to tolerate the presence of the bats. Although comparisons between studies are not straightforward, because of the way the data were collected and

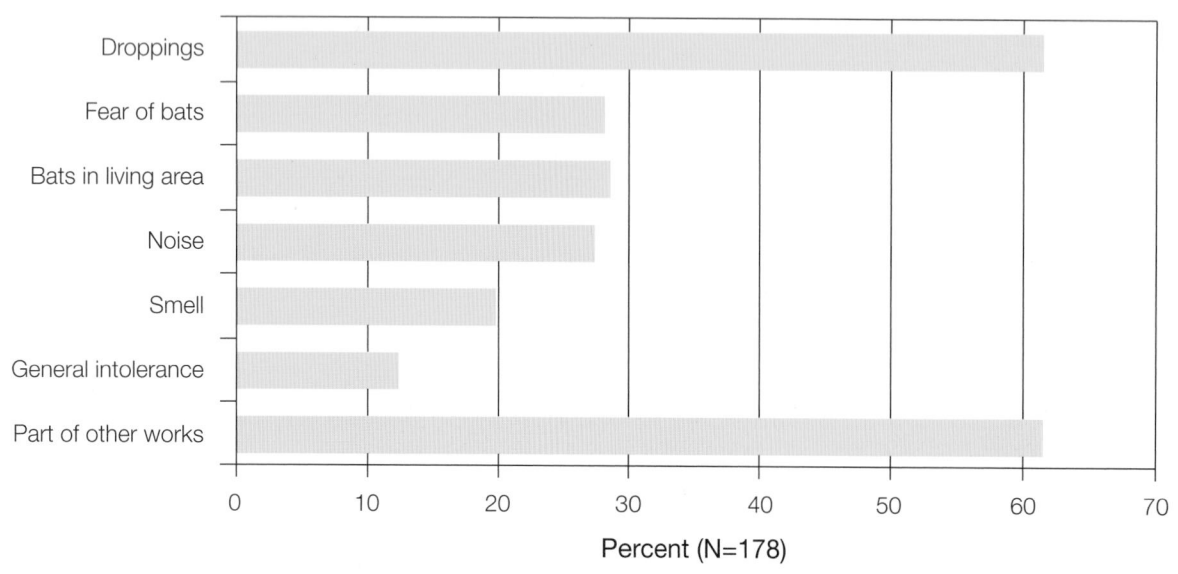

Figure 20.1 The reasons given by a sample of householders for wishing to exclude bats from their house. Adapted from Moore *et al.* (2003).

because it is often a matter of judgement as to whether a householder wished to exclude their bats, Watson (1985), Mitchell-Jones *et al.* (1986) and Moore *et al.* (2003) all showed that roost visitors have a high success rate in persuading householders who were initially determined to exclude their bat colony to leave it undisturbed for the foreseeable future.

When discussing concerns and possible outcomes with householders, roost visitors must consider both the outcome for that particular situation as well as the wider implications for bat conservation. The high dependence of bats on houses means that public tolerance is crucial to their conservation, so pressing householders to retain bat colonies they are deeply unhappy about is likely to have a negative influence on this tolerance, as the roost owners relate their personal experience to others. It has long been recognized that in such cases it is better to accept the loss of the individual roost, at the correct time of year, and gain the approval of the householder for the provision of good and helpful advice. The success of individual roost visitors in gaining the best outcome for bat conservation thus depends on their appreciation of the fine balance between the conservation of individual roosts and the wider objectives of bat conservation.

20.3.2 Maintenance, repairs and renovation

Requests for advice about maintenance, repairs or renovation, including remedial timber treatment, where bats are present have become increasingly frequent over the past two decades. Whilst the overall level of enquiries has risen slightly, demands for this type of advice in England have risen from 18% in 1982 (Mitchell-Jones,1989) to more than 50% in 2003 (Moore *et al.*, 2003), with a similar increase being recorded in Scotland (J. McKinnell, pers. comm.). Over the same period, the threat to bats from remedial timber treatment had declined significantly, thanks to the introduction and universal adoption of treatments that are much less toxic to mammals (Mitchell-Jones *et al.*, 1989). As with other types of enquiry, roost visitors are generally asked to provide on-site advice to householders.

20.3.3 Exclusions

Where roost visitors are unable to persuade householders to retain bat colonies, licences can be issued, permitting the householder to exclude the bats and seal the roost once the maternity colony has dispersed. During the 1980s and 1990s, such exclusions were generally carried out by stopping up the holes once signs of bat occupation had ceased. However, a growing realization that, in some cases at least, bats may remain in occupation well into the autumn, perhaps living in the wall cavity, has led to the widespread adoption of the one-way exclusion systems first described by Constantine (1982). These devices allow bats to leave the roost but not return and thus provide a safe and effective way of excluding a colony. Such devices are not the most appropriate solution in every case, but where they appear to be suitable, their use is often specified in the licence. Householders are also advised to block any other potential roosts, as experience shows that excluded colonies may try to reoccupy alternative roosts in the same building.

20.3.4 Public appreciation

The advisory service provided by the conservation agencies, their contractors and volunteers is highly valued. Moore *et al.* (2003) carried out a questionnaire survey in England and found that 93.9% (N = 1,273) of a sample of householders were either satisfied or very satisfied with the advice they received (Figure 20.2). Very few respondents (1.9%) were very unsatisfied. Similar results were obtained in Scotland by Wray *et al.* (2002), who reported that 85% (N = 180) of respondents were either satisfied or very satisfied with the advice they received.

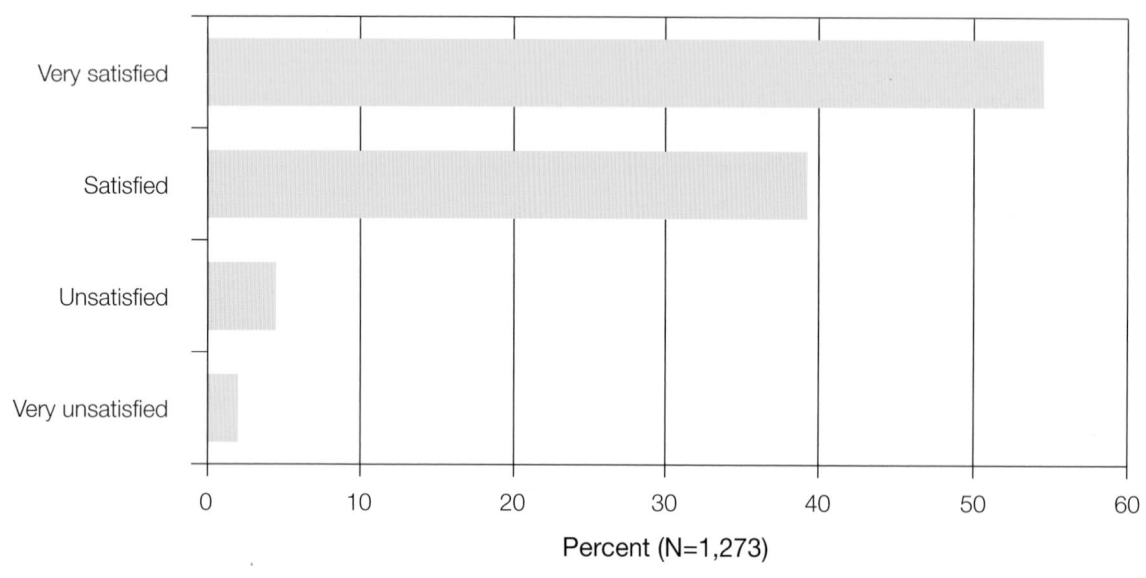

Figure 20.2 The response given by a sample of householders about their degree of satisfaction with the advice about house bat management they received from the conservation agency. Adapted from Moore *et al.* (2003).

20.4 The future

The demand for advice about bats in houses continues unabated, although the nature of the demand has changed somewhat, as illustrated by the increasing demand for advice about building maintenance where bats are present. The ability of the SNCOs, in partnership with the voluntary sector, to service this requirement, remains central to the conservation of house-dwelling bats. The use of personal visits has been a particularly important feature of this service delivery and has considerably increased the number of roosts left undisturbed. Over the past two decades, awareness of the need to conserve bats has risen considerably, with the majority of those seeking advice now aware they are protected species. The appearance of 'the bat' in the top ten favourite animals in a recent wildlife magazine poll (Stratton, 2008), illustrates the extent to which public opinion has changed since all bats were first protected in 1981. However, misconception about the nature of bats remains widespread, as evidenced by some of the enquiries received, and efforts must continue to improve yet further public appreciation of this group of mammals.

The high dependence of bats on houses, the product of a combination of lack of natural roosts and the attractive roosting conditions provided by houses, leaves them vulnerable to changes in the nature of this resource. Some species are particularly associated with larger houses with high open roof voids unobstructed by construction timbers, allowing space for the bats to fly within the roof void. Roosts of this type are particularly favoured by lesser horseshoe bats and brown long-eared bats. Data from past enquiries shows that these species are particularly associated with older buildings with this traditional type of roof construction. However, this method, requiring large timbers and skilled carpenters on site, has been largely superseded by the use of trussed rafters, which are constructed off-site and tend to use light timber bracing. This results in a roof void that has a very obstructed flight area, rendering it much less suitable for these bat species. In time, therefore, the resource of buildings with large open roof voids will decline as any that are lost are likely to be replaced with buildings with trussed-rafter construction. Although replacement may take hundreds of years, it is nevertheless a significant threat to the resource available to some species of bats.

Other changes in the way houses are constructed may have even more far-reaching effects. Efforts to improve the energy-efficiency of houses, which must be welcomed, have led to ever-tighter regulations about ventilation and insulation. This means that modern houses are less and less likely to have suitable access points for bats and other building-dependent species such as swifts, and fewer opportunities for wildlife in general. At present, the method used to assess the environmental performance of new houses in England, the Code for Sustainable Homes, focuses entirely on the use of energy and other resources and does not take into account situations to enhance the ecological opportunities of the built structures. In this respect, it is a retrograde step from the BREEAM Ecohomes standard (Building Research Establishment, 2006) it replaced, which gave credit for ecological enhancement and which is still available in Wales and Scotland.

If opportunities for bats are to remain a feature of new houses that meet emerging environmental standards, it is essential that these are built-in at the design stage, rather than relying on faulty construction to allow bats access. For crevice-dwelling species, such as pipistrelles, the provision of specific roosting areas in the eaves, which will allow the bats to take advantage of solar warming, is not difficult, and such features can even be retrofitted to existing buildings (Simpson and Brown, 1996). In addition, careful design can ensure that the bats do not cause problems for the human occupants, such as droppings, smell, noise and bats in the living area, that sometimes arise when bats occupy buildings opportunistically. Such an approach needs to be incorporated into environmental standards.

Where modern house-building methods are unlikely to provide appropriate opportunities, such as for species needing flight space within the roost, others must be sought. Where bats are already present on a site due for redevelopment, the conservation agencies may be in a position to require mitigation for any roosts lost as part of their licensing process. In such cases, possible mitigation might include the use of purpose-built bat houses, sometimes quite elaborate, or the allocation of space within a non-domestic building, such as public buildings or detached garages. If this is considered at the design stage, it is certainly possible to provide the environmental conditions that bats require. Such a scheme could also be incorporated into environmental standards for new houses, so that developers are encouraged to provide opportunities for a range of bat species within new build.

Plate 20.4 Bat box on the conference centre wall at Battelby, SNH. © Lorne Gill/SNH

20.5 Conclusions

The relatively treeless landscapes of Britain, compared with most European countries, together with a lack of natural tree holes in managed woodland, may limit natural roosting opportunities for bats. However, this alone does not explain the widespread dependence of bats on the built environment. A number of studies have emphasized the attractiveness of warm roost sites to bat maternity colonies and it appears likely this has been the main driver in the widespread adoption of buildings for roosting. We are now left with a situation where the conservation of bats depends on maintaining the roosting resource in buildings. This, in turn, depends on public tolerance for these heavily protected species.

Interactions between bats and householders inevitably arise and result in a high demand for species management advice. This is met by a partnership between the country conservation agencies and the non-government sector, with a particular strength being the ability to put a trained and knowledgeable person on the enquirer's doorstep. Most problems are resolved in a way that both maintains the bat roost and satisfies the householder, but in a minority of cases householder cannot be persuaded to tolerate bat roosts and the bats are safely excluded. This approach strikes an acceptable balance between maintaining individual roosts and maintaining wider public sympathy for bats.

Although the public image of bats has improved hugely over the past two decades, as evidenced by the recent appearance of 'the bat' in a magazine poll of favourite mammals (Stratton, 2008), the conservation agencies continue to receive many enquiries indicating that further improvements to public acceptability are needed. The Bat Conservation Trust and local Bat Groups continue to be very active in this area and it seems likely that their efforts will be needed for the foreseeable future.

Changes to the architecture and construction methods of domestic buildings have a significant impact on their value to bats, affecting both accessibility and roosting conditions. Changes to roof construction methods during the 20th century mean that large open roof voids, suitable for bats to fly around, are now rare in new houses, so the roosting resource for species that need such conditions will slowly decline. More recently, efforts to improve the energy efficiency of houses, which is part of the move to a low carbon economy, are likely to make house roofs less accessible even to crevice-dwelling species. Unless steps are taken to build-in space for wildlife, which is neither difficult nor expensive at the design stage, this may place yet more pressure on the roosting resource. This is the 21st century challenge for bat conservation.

References

Boyd, I.L. & Stebbings, R.E. (1989). Population changes of brown long-eared bats (*Plecotus auritus*) in bat boxes at Thetford Forest. *Journal of Applied Ecology* **26**(1): 101-112.

Building Research Establishment. (2006). *Ecohomes 2006 –The environmental rating for homes. The guidance – 2006/ Issue1.2.* Building Research Establishment, Watford.

Constantine, D.G. (1982). Batproofing buildings by installation of valve-like devices in entryways. *Journal of Wildlife Management* **46**(2): 507-513.

Entwistle, A.C., Racey, P.A. & Speakman, J.R. (1997). Roost selection by the brown long-eared bat *Plecotus auritus*. *Journal of Applied Ecology* **34**: 399-408.

Forestry Commission. (2007). *Forestry facts & figures 2007*. Forestry Commission, Edinburgh.

Jenkins, E.V., Laine, T., Morgan, S.E., Cole, K.R. & Speakman, J.R. (1998). Roost selection in the pipistrelle bat, *Pipistrellus pipistrellus* (Chiroptera: Vespertilionidae), in northeast Scotland. *Animal Behaviour* **56**(4): 909-917.

Juškaitis, R. (2008). *The common dormouse* Muscardinus avellanarius: *ecology, population structure and dynamics.* Institute of Ecology of Vilnius University Publishers, Vilnius. 163pp.

Kirby, K.J., Reid, C.M., Thomas, R.C. & Goldsmith, F.B. (1998). Preliminary estimates of fallen dead wood and standing dead trees in managed and unmanaged forests in Britain. *Journal of Applied Ecology* **45**: 148-155.

Lourenço, S.I. & Palmeirim, J. M. (2004). Influence of temperature in roost selection by *Pipistrellus pygmaeus* (Chiroptera): relevance for the design of bat boxes. *Biological Conservation* **119**: 237-243.

Lundberg, A. & Alatalo, R. V. (1992). *The pied flycatcher.* T & A D Poyser, London.

Mitchell-Jones, A.J. (1989). The effect of legal protection on bat conservation in Britain. In: *European Bat Research 1987,* Eds V. Hanák, I. Horáček, & J. Gaisler. Charles University Press, Prague. pp. 671-676.

Mitchell-Jones, A.J., Jefferies, D.J., Stebbings, R.E. & Arnold, H.R. (1986). Public concern about bats (Chiroptera) in Britain: an analysis of enquiries in 1982-83. *Biological Conservation* **36**: 315-328.

Mitchell-Jones, A.J., Cooke, A.S., Boyd, I.L. & Stebbings, R.E. (1989). Bats and remedial timber treatment chemicals: a review. *Mammal Review* **19**(3): 93-110.

Moore, N.P., Jones, S., Hutson, A.M. & Garthwaite, D. (2003). Assessing the outcome of English Nature advice on bat colony management and mitigation works. *English Nature Research Reports* 517. English Nature, Peterborough.

Racey, P.A. & Entwistle A. C. (2000). Life-history & reproductive strategies of bats. In *Reproductive Biology of Bats*. Eds E. G. Crichton & P. H. Krutzsch. Academic Press, New York. pp. 364-414.

Ruczyński, I. & Bogdanowicz, W. (2005). Roost cavity selection by *Nyctalus noctula* and *N. leisleri* in Białowież a primeval forest, eastern Poland. *Journal of Mammalogy* **86**(5): 921-930.

Simpson & Brown (Architects). (1996). The design and construction of bat boxes in houses. Scottish Natural Heritage, Perth. 32 pp.

Stebbings, R.E. & Robinson, M.F. (1991). The enigmatic serotine bat: a case of human dependency. *British Wildlife* **2**(5): 261-265.

Stratton, M. (2008). The rise of the otter. *BBC Wildlife* **26**(10): 58-59.

Watson, A.P. (1985). Follow-up survey of 1983 bat enquiries. Unpublished report to the Nature Conservancy Council, Peterborough. 51pp.

Wray, S., Reason, P., Haddow, J. & Sargent, G. (2002). *Assessing the outcome of SNH advice on bat colony management.* Unpublished report to Scottish Natural Heritage.

Mitchell-Jones, T.J. (2010). Bats in houses – the conservation challenge. In: *Species Management: Challenges and Solutions for the 21st Century*, ed. by J.M. Baxter and C.A. Galbraith. TSO Scotland, Edinburgh. pp. 365-378

Chapter 21

Scottish seabird predator-prey relationships

Robert W. Furness[1]

Summary

1. Scotland holds some of the largest populations of seabirds in Europe. Climate change and cumulative impacts of human activities represent major threats to the sustainability of Scottish seabird communities.
2. Climate change may be having major effects on Scottish seabirds through its influence on sandeel stocks, since sandeels are the most important food resource for most Scottish seabirds, but causes of the recent collapse of North Sea sandeels are not clear.
3. Collapse of sandeel stocks in the North Sea has undoubtedly been a major factor causing rapid declines in breeding success, and numbers, of most of our seabirds after many decades of population increases. There is evidence that part of this impact can be attributed to local depletion of sandeels by the industrial fishery.
4. Fisheries also affect seabird communities by provision of large quantities of offal and discards, especially from trawl fisheries. Recent reductions in amounts discarded at a time when sandeel availability is also low, have caused prey switching by seabirds such as great skuas and great black-backed gulls. These birds are now killing large and possibly unsustainable numbers of smaller seabirds as diverse as black-legged kittiwakes, auks and storm-petrels.
5. Great skuas show considerable individual specialization in diet and feeding behaviour. Selective culling of a few specialist individuals could greatly reduce specific impacts without need for extensive removal of skuas.
6. Management objectives may require setting of targets for seabird numbers, an issue that has not yet been addressed by conservationists. However, a broad aim of marine management should be to end all discarding at sea, to reduce the disruptive effect that this supplementary feeding has on seabird community composition.

[1] Faculty of Biomedical and Life Sciences, Graham Kerr Building, University of Glasgow, Glasgow, G12 8QQ, UK

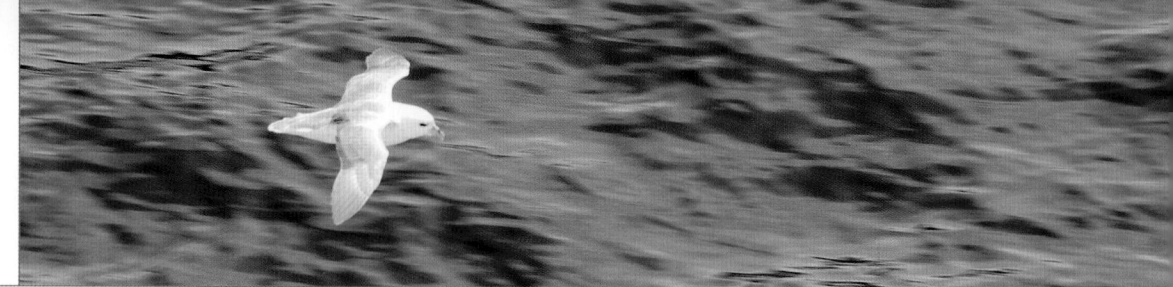

21.1 Introduction

Northern fulmar (*Fulmarus glacialis*). © John M. Baxt

It can easily be argued that from an international perspective, seabirds represent the most important bird populations in Scotland, both in terms of conservation and commercial value for tourism. A country with a very large sea area, numerous islands, and a range of coastal habitats, not surprisingly Scotland holds some of the largest and most visited populations of seabirds in Europe. Many of Scotland's seabird colonies are extremely spectacular. Visitors to Orkney and Shetland list seeing colonies of Atlantic puffins (*Fratercula arctica*) as a major motivation for their trip. Thousands of day visitors see (and smell) northern gannets at close quarters from boat trips around the Bass Rock in the Firth of Forth and Noss in Shetland. There are over 1 million seabirds on St Kilda, where day visitor numbers are rapidly increasing with improved boat access despite a high fare and potentially rough sea crossing. Scotland holds approximately 60% of the world's breeding population of great skuas (*Stercorarius skua*), 48% of the northern gannets (*Morus bassanus*), 34% of the Manx shearwaters (*Puffinus puffinus*); the world's largest colony of great skuas is on Foula, the world's largest colony of northern gannets is on St Kilda, and the world's largest colony of Manx shearwaters is probably the one on Rum (Mitchell *et al.*, 2004).

Climate change and changing human activities may alter the availability of different food supplies to seabirds, and may cause changes in the ecological relationships between species that may drastically affect seabird community composition. Mitchell *et al.* (2004) concluded "Perhaps the single most important factor in sustaining an internationally important assemblage of seabirds over the course of the last century or so, certainly of those species that scavenge at sea, has been the fishing industry". This chapter reviews our somewhat limited understanding of these relationships and their implications for conservation of our internationally important seabird populations.

21.2 Diets and feeding ecology of Scottish seabirds

Seabird diets can be studied by a variety of methods, including direct observation, collection of voluntary regurgitates, sampling by water offloading, collecting pellets of indigestible remains (Barrett *et al.*, 2007), and various more forensic methods such as analysis of stable isotopes and fatty acids (Käkelä *et al.*, 2006, 2007, 2009). Our knowledge of seabird diets is mostly based on studies of seabirds at breeding colonies in summer. We have much information on diets fed to seabird chicks at colonies, but rather little on diets of seabirds in winter (Barrett *et al.*, 2007). Even diets of adult seabirds during breeding are sometimes not well known, as they may differ from the foods brought to chicks. Seabirds often feed their young on more energy-rich foods than they take themselves (Wanless *et al.*, 2005; Barrett *et al.*, 2007).

Most seabirds that breed in Scotland feed predominantly on small pelagic fish during the summer breeding season, and such fish are very important as energy-rich food for seabird chicks (Wanless *et al.*, 2005; Österblom *et al.*, 2008). In the North Sea the key food of most seabirds while breeding is the lesser sandeel (*Ammodytes marinus*) (Furness and Tasker, 2000; Furness, 2002, 2007; Frederiksen *et al.*, 2005).

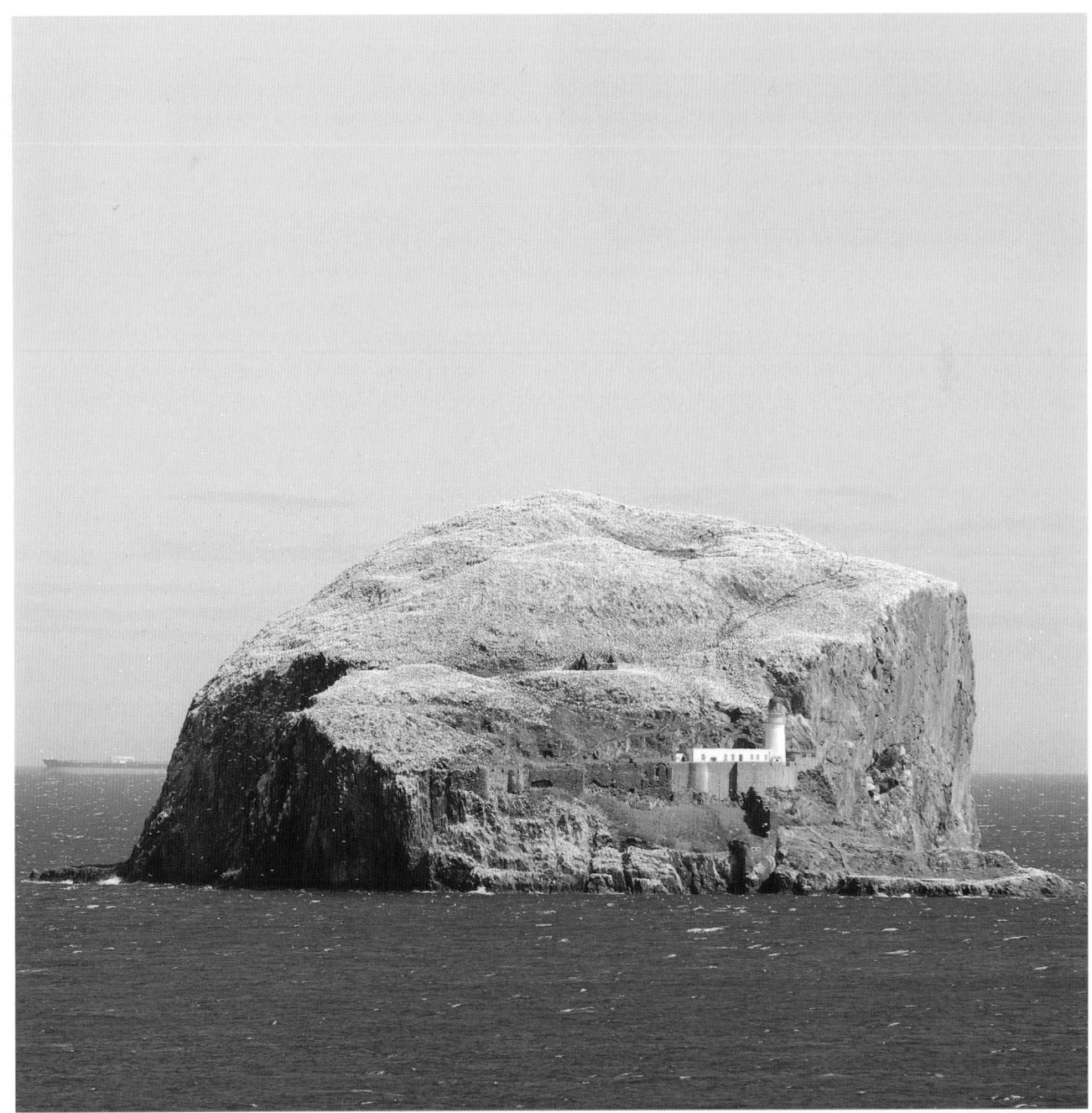

Plate 21.1 The Bass Rock, an easy daytrip from Edinburgh, is an important colony of the northern gannet from which the bird takes its scientific species name *Morus bassanus*. © John M. Baxter

Sandeels become unavailable to surface-feeding seabirds from late summer to spring, as they bury in the sand of the seabed during this period. In consequence, many seabirds leave the area in autumn, or switch to feeding on other foods. However, small pelagic fish such as sandeels are not the only food even in summer. Different species of seabirds can take a range of natural foods and may also take foods made available only through human activities. Some, such as black-legged kittiwakes (*Rissa tridactyla*) and northern fulmars (*Fulmarus glacialis*), may feed extensively on zooplankton (Mitchell *et al.*, 2004), while northern fulmars take a high proportion of offal discharged by fishing vessels (Garthe *et al.*, 1996). Some, such as northern gannets, large *Larus* gulls and great skuas, may feed on moribund haddock (*Melanogrammus aeglefinus*), whiting (*Merlangius merlangus*) and other bottom-living fish discarded by fishermen, predominantly from benthic trawl catches (Garthe *et al.*, 1996; Furness *et al.*, 2007). Some, such as great skuas and great black-backed gulls (*Larus marinus*) may kill smaller seabirds as food (Bearhop *et al.*, 2001; Mitchell *et al.*, 2004; Votier *et al.*, 2004a,c, 2006, 2007). These large predatory seabirds tend to breed in small numbers in association with big colonies of the species on which they prey. For example, isolated pairs of great black-backed gulls often nest around Atlantic puffin colonies. However, in places where these large predatory seabirds are able to scavenge on fishery discards, or feed on abundant pelagic fish, their numbers can increase to form sizeable colonies. Individuals breeding in large colonies of great skuas and great black-backed gulls rarely feed by killing smaller seabirds, whereas individuals nesting in small colonies may often do so (Hudson, 1982; Votier *et al.*, 2004b, 2008). In large colonies, the numbers of these potentially predatory seabirds can greatly exceed numbers that could be sustained by a predatory lifestyle. Their ecological relationships are then dependent on the sustained availability of the food supply that has allowed their population to increase.

21.3 Effects of fish stock fluctuations and fisheries on Scottish seabirds

Fisheries can affect seabirds in a variety of ways. Fisheries can reduce the abundance of target food-fish stocks, such as sandeels (Frederiksen *et al.*, 2004; Furness 2007). They can increase food supplies to scavenging seabirds through provision of offal and discards (Garthe *et al.*, 1996; Furness *et al.*, 2007). They can cause direct mortality of adult seabirds through collision, drowning in nets or on longline hooks (Mitchell *et al.*, 2004). They can alter abundance of top predator fish, and thereby change abundances of food-fish through reduction in top-down control by predatory fish (Heithaus *et al.*, 2008).

Long time-series on breeding success show that many seabird species have low breeding success when food-fish stocks are depleted (Furness, 2007; Österblom *et al.*, 2008). For example, 77% of the considerable variation in Arctic skua (*Stercorarius parasiticus*) breeding success at Foula, Shetland, can be explained by variation in the biomass of sandeels at Shetland (Figure 21.1). However, the relationship varies according to the ecology of each species (Furness and Tasker, 2000). Davis *et al.* (2005) used a supplementary feeding experiment to show that increasing availability of food did increase breeding success of Arctic skuas, but that it also allowed breeding adults to work less hard to provision the brood, and led to a higher survival rate of the adults. Many other studies of seabirds show the key role of fish

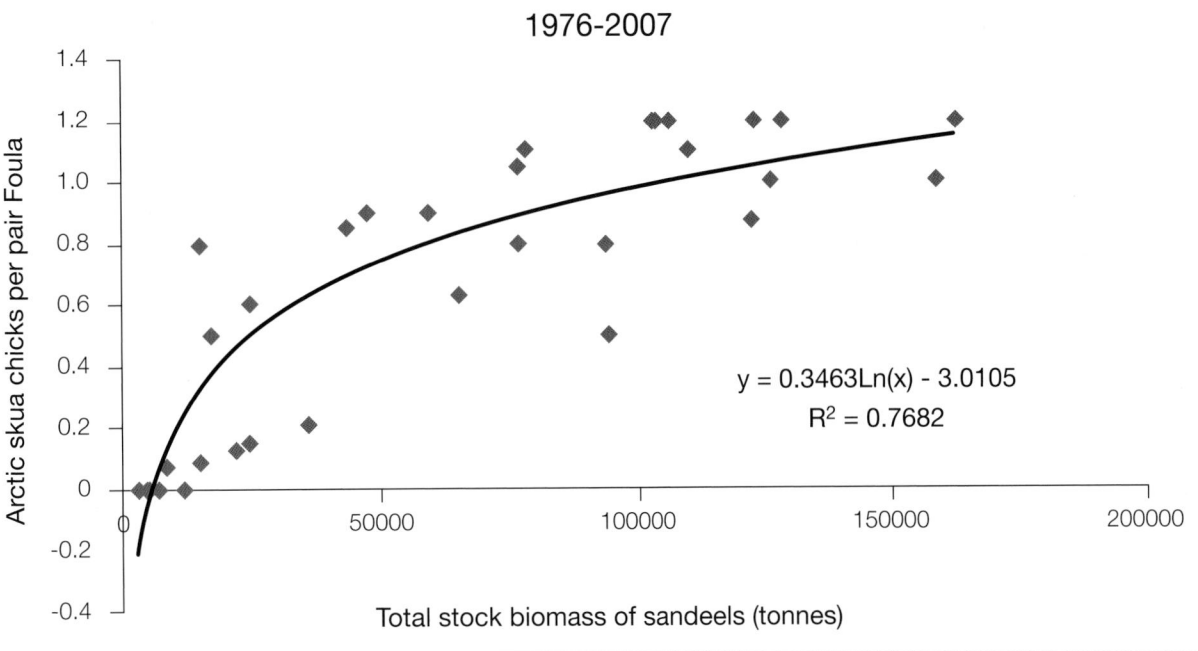

Figure 21.1 Breeding success of Arctic skuas at Foula, Shetland, in relation to the estimated biomass of the Shetland sandeel stock from 1976 to 2007. Sandeel data from Fisheries Research Service, Aberdeen.

abundance in determining breeding success (Österblom *et al.*, 2008), although in a few cases the quality of fish (lipid content) may also be critical (Wanless *et al.*, 2005; Österblom *et al.*, 2008).

Fisheries directed at food-fish stocks will inevitably reduce stock biomass, but there are few opportunities to test the hypothesis that seabird breeding failure is caused by such fisheries rather than by natural fluctuations in the environment. One clear example is the analysis by Frederiksen *et al.* (2004) which showed that black-legged kittiwake breeding success at the Isle of May was significantly reduced in years when sandeel fishing occurred nearby, a signal additional to that of sea temperature effects.

Some fisheries, especially trawl fisheries for demersal fish, generate large quantities of offal (gutted intestines and livers) and discards (unwanted whole fish that are below legal limits, in excess of quota, or species of no commercial value) that are discharged at sea and provide an important food resource for scavenging seabirds (Garthe *et al.*, 1996; Furness *et al.*, 2007). In the North Sea, many scavenging seabirds prefer to consume lipid-rich pelagic fish during the summer, but switch to discards in winter when pelagic fish are less available (Garthe *et al.*, 1996). However, great skuas take large quantities of discards even in summer (Votier *et al.*, 2004a, 2008). Species composition of the great skua diet at different colonies reflects local fish stock distributions and fishery catches, and thus local variation in numbers of each fish species being discarded (Votier *et al.*, 2008).

Plate 21.2 The Arctic skua (*Stercorarius parasiticus*) is particularly vulnerable to reductions in the abundance of small pelagic fish. © Lorne Gill/SNH

21.4 Effects of climate change on Scottish seabirds

The El Nino/Southern Oscillation has profound impacts on the breeding success and survival rates of seabirds in the Southern and Pacific Oceans, but climate oscillations are much less pronounced in the North Atlantic (Sandvik *et al.*, 2005). The North Atlantic Oscillation (NAO), which is a fluctuation in the atmospheric pressure patterns in the North Atlantic influencing wind direction and strength, has obvious effects on birds and other biota in terrestrial and freshwater ecosystems in Europe, particularly through its influence on winter and spring temperatures. However, its influences on seabirds in the North Atlantic are not very clear (Durant *et al.*, 2004). Since wind speed and temperature vary with the sign (positive or negative) and amplitude of the NAO, we can expect seabirds to be influenced by this oceanographic variation; for example the energy costs of flight increase in northern fulmars when the wind strength is low (Furness and Bryant, 1996). Although there is clear evidence of changes in plankton in the North Sea relating to climate change (Beaugrand, 2004; Richardson and Schoeman, 2004), the relative importance of climate change and fisheries in altering North Sea lower trophic level fish stocks is uncertain (Frederiksen *et al.*, 2007).

Irons *et al.* (2008) showed that numbers of common guillemot (*Uria aalge*) and Brunnich's guillemot (*U. lomvia*) attending breeding colonies fluctuated throughout the Arctic and sub-Arctic regions in response to climate. Decreases occurred when changes in sea surface temperature (SST) were rapid, while

Plate 21.3 Common guillemots (*Uria aalge*). © Lorne Gill/SNH

increases occurred when changes in SST were more modest. Presumably the changes in numbers are driven by bottom-up shifts in the ecosystem rather than direct effects on the birds. However, direct impacts of climate change are also possible. Oswald *et al.* (2008) argued that great skuas in Scotland may be nesting at the upper thermal limits of tolerance for successful breeding, as they apparently have to spend increasing amounts of time cooling off in warm weather. But long term study of adult survival rates of great skuas shows no correlation with local SST or with the NAO, although survival rates have declined considerably with reductions in sandeel abundance and rates of discarding (Kalmbach and Furness, unpublished data). Grosbois and Thompson (2005) did find effects of the NAO on survival rates of northern fulmars. Sandvik *et al.* (2005) found correlations between adult survival rates of several seabirds and the NAO, but reported stronger links between survival rates and SST than with the NAO. Furthermore, they inferred that these relationships were probably indirect, through the food chain, rather than direct impacts on seabird survival. Frederiksen *et al.* (2006) reported breeding success of several seabirds to correlate with sandeel larval biomass, which in turn related to abundance of plankton.

Frederiksen *et al*. (2004) showed that breeding success and adult survival of black-legged kittiwakes were negatively correlated with winter sea temperature as well as with the presence or absence of a local fishery for sandeels. In this context, previous work by Arnott and Ruxton (2002) had already shown that sandeel recruitment tends to be better following colder winters. Wanless *et al*. (2004, 2005, 2008) reported several important changes in the conditions for seabirds that may be driven by climate change, including a trend to later breeding in the northern gannet in recent years, but in these cases too it is rather unclear whether the changes being seen are due to fisheries impacts or to climate change.

21.5 Great skua predation

In the 1970s great skuas in Shetland fed mainly on sandeels if these were available, and on fishery discards as an alternative if sandeels were scarce (Furness and Hislop, 1981; Ratcliffe *et al*., 1998). Kleptoparasitism was a relatively minor activity, while great skuas scavenged opportunistically, and only occasionally killed birds. Not only have Shetland sandeels declined to very low levels (Davis *et al*., 2005; Furness, 2007), but amounts of fish discarded by fisheries in the NW North Sea have been greatly reduced in the last few years (Figure 21.2) partly because fishing effort has been constrained to reduce mortality of cod, partly because of technical measures to reduce catches of undersized fish, and partly

Plate 21.4 A Manx shearwater (*Puffinus puffinus*) fledging (note the little traces of down on the throat and abdomen). © Laurie Campbell/SNH

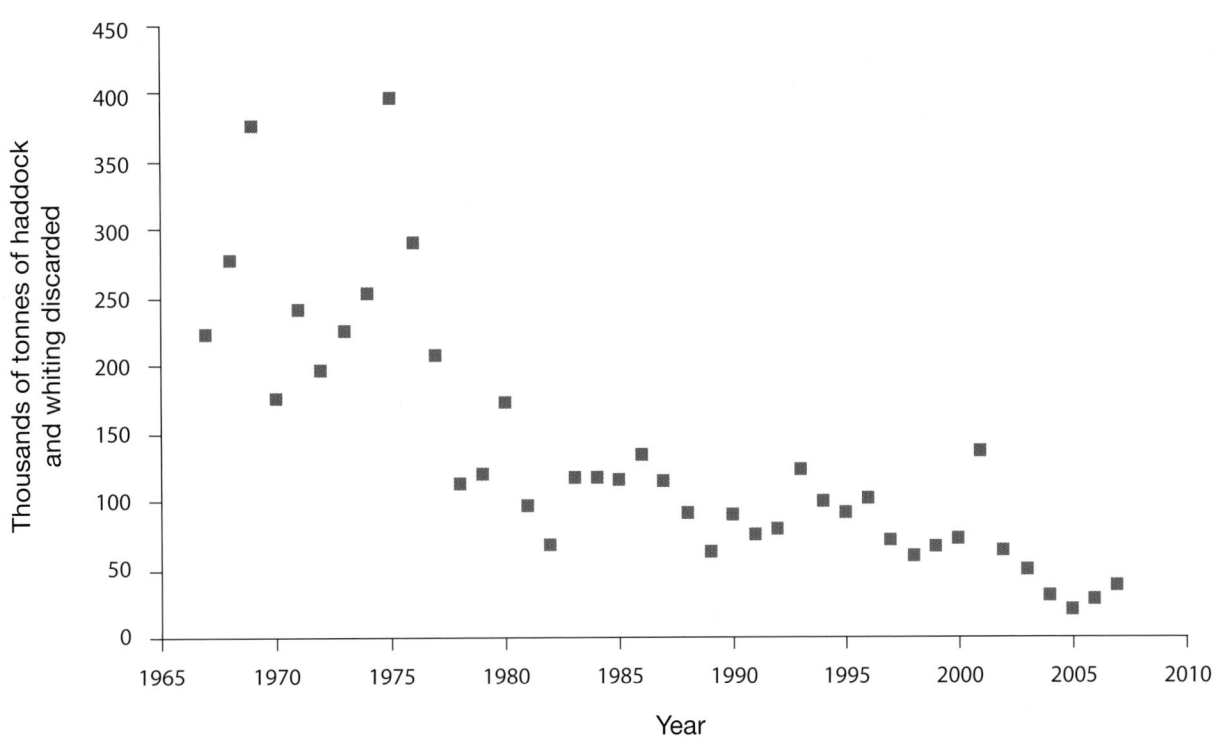

Figure 21.2 Quantities of haddock and whiting discarded each year in the north-western North Sea (these two species represent a high proportion of all discards in this region). Data for 1967 to 2007 from International Council for the Exploration of the Sea www.ices.dk Working Group report WGNSSK 2008.

because of increased quotas for haddock and whiting leading to less high grading of these species by fishermen. This decrease has led to diet switching by great skuas, increasing the numbers of seabirds killed (Votier *et al.*, 2004a), although only the fittest great skuas can feed exclusively by killing seabirds, and killing birds tends to be more frequent in smaller colonies but is only seen in a small proportion of pairs at large colonies suggesting density-dependent constraints on this feeding strategy (Votier *et al.*, 2004b,c, 2007). Great skuas spend more time foraging when food availability is low so have some capacity to buffer reduced food supplies (Caldow and Furness, 2000), but in recent years large numbers have refrained from breeding due to low food availability, and breeding success of those that do lay has been low (Mavor *et al.*, 2007). One of the birds killed in largest numbers by great skuas has been black-legged kittiwakes (Votier *et al.*, 2004c). Oro and Furness (2002) showed that black-legged kittiwake survival rates in Shetland were reduced in years when sandeel abundance was low and additionally in years when great skua breeding success was high when presumably they kill more black-legged kittiwakes to sustain breeding.

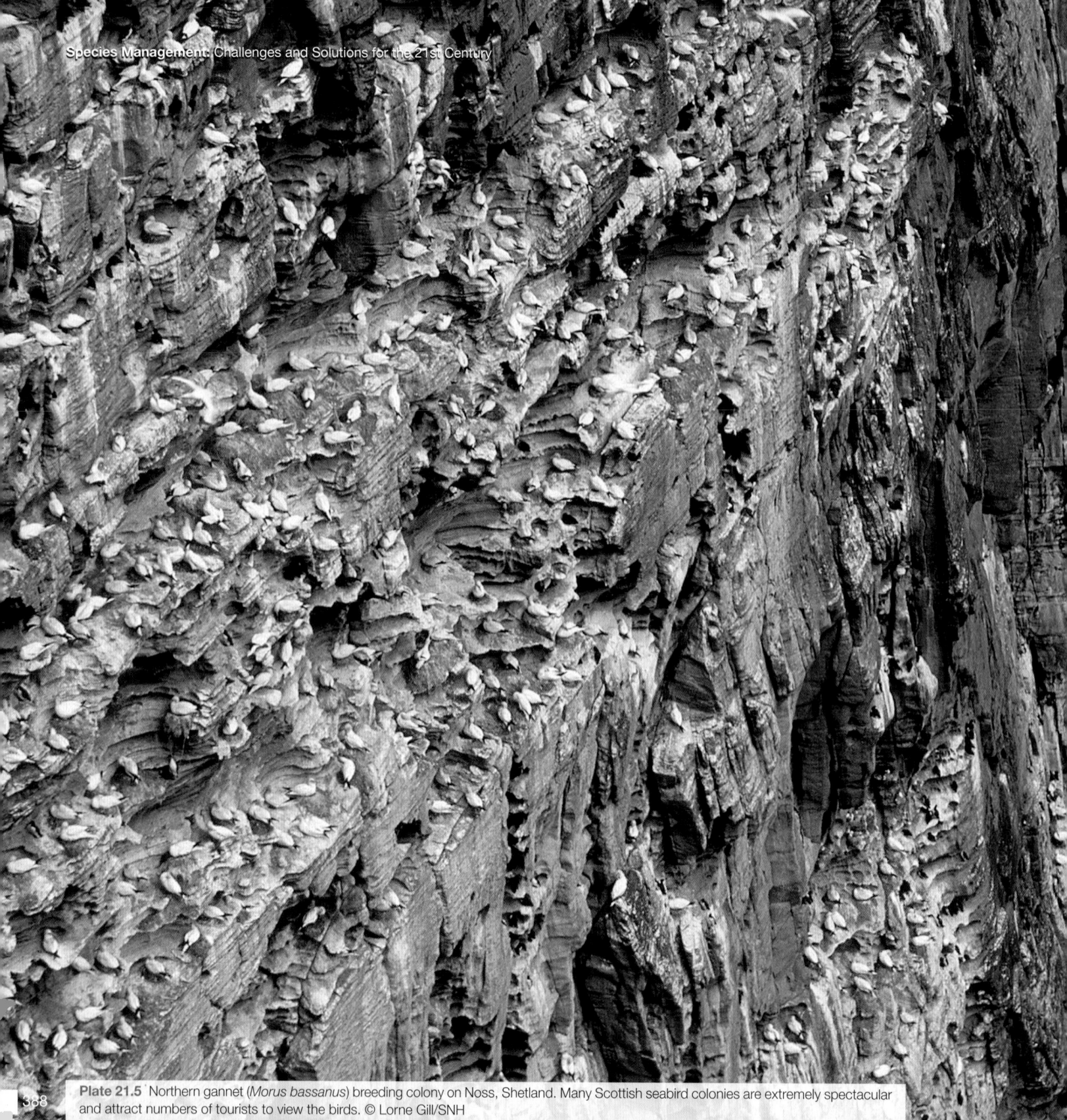

Plate 21.5 Northern gannet (*Morus bassanus*) breeding colony on Noss, Shetland. Many Scottish seabird colonies are extremely spectacular and attract numbers of tourists to view the birds. © Lorne Gill/SNH

Problems of great skua predation on other seabirds have not been confined to Shetland colonies. On St Kilda, breeding numbers of great skuas increased extremely fast in the 1990s, due to immigration of birds that were probably mostly hatched in Shetland but abandoned that region due to food shortage there. It was discovered in 1996 that great skuas on St Kilda were then killing very large, and almost certainly unsustainable, numbers of Leach's storm-petrels (*Oceanodroma leucorhoa*), and this has continued in subsequent years although apparently at a declining rate (Votier *et al.*, 2006). This is the only large colony of Leach's storm-petrels in the European Union, and according to the limited data available, breeding numbers appear to have fallen by about 44,000 birds between 1999 and 2003 (Mitchell *et al.*, 2004). It is still unclear how much of this apparent decline can be attributed to great skuas. However, in addition to the direct predation impacts of great skuas on other seabirds, it is likely that the behaviour and distribution of some seabirds will be adversely affected by the presence of large numbers of bird-killing great skuas, and such changes in behaviour to reduce risk of predation could further reduce their populations (Creel and Christianson, 2008). These effects have not been explored in vicitims of great skua predation, except in the case of the Arctic skua (Phillips *et al.*, 1998) where it was found that Arctic skuas abandoned many breeding areas and moved into increasingly smaller breeding territories in residual colony areas in response to great skuas.

21.6 Management objectives

"Ecosystem management" of fisheries implies that the needs of top predators will be taken into account. An obvious need is to maintain adequate stocks of "food-fish" such as sandeels that sustain higher trophic levels. Sandeels are very difficult to count by fisheries techniques, but their abundance can be indicated by breeding success of sensitive seabirds (Furness and Tasker, 2000). Low breeding success of black-legged kittiwakes on the east coast of Scotland led to the closure of sandeel fishing in a box off the east of Scotland because it indicated poor status of the local sandeel population (Frederiksen *et al.*, 2004). Subsequent collapse of the sandeel stock in most of the North Sea has now led to a closure of the entire North Sea fishery (Anon., 2005), but it is unclear how much this collapse is due to the fishery, to bottom-up effects caused by climate change, and to top-down effects of changes in stocks of predatory fish (Frederiksen *et al.*, 2007; Heithaus *et al.*, 2008). Better understanding of the dynamics of the ecosystem is required, and that needs, as a start, the pooling of time series of data on all trophic levels of the ecosystem and a collaborative approach between seabird and marine mammal ecologists with fisheries biologists, plankton ecologists and oceanographers. Such work needs cross-disciplinary collaboration.

Discards and offal represent a subsidy to scavenging animals, especially large seabirds such as great skuas and great black-backed gulls that can switch to killing smaller seabirds in times of food shortage. To reduce the disruption to seabird communities it would be desirable to move as quickly as possible to a zero discard policy. Although in the short term such a move will exacerbate the problem of predation by skuas and gulls (Votier *et al.*, 2004a; Oro *et al.*, 2005), only a zero discard policy can eventually bring seabird communities to a more natural balance between species. One further approach to reduce the impact of great skuas on vulnerable populations of seabirds could be culling. However, widespread culling of large numbers of great skuas is certainly undesirable, as well as impractical since most great skuas breed on Special Protection Areas (SPAs) where they are protected by European law. Great skuas are one of the least numerous of the world's seabirds, even though numbers in Scotland have been artificially increased by provision of discards. However, in the local context, impacts on vulnerable seabirds are often due to a very small number of specialist skuas. For example, on Foula an entire colony of about 60 pairs of black guillemots (*Cepphus grylle*) was extirpated in a period of just five years by a single pair of skuas that specialized in killing adult black guillemots as they entered or left their nests in the boulderfield (R W Furness, unpublished data). Although the legality is dubious, crofters in Shetland have long understood that removal of the occasional "rogue" great skua that has developed the habit of killing lambs solves that problem without the need to cull indiscriminately. This practice has been more successful in reducing local predation problems caused by great skuas than has the irregular unselective culling practiced at colonies such as Fair Isle from time to time (Mitchell *et al.*, 2004).

21.7 Acknowledgements

My thanks to Scottish Natural Heritage for the invitation to contribute to the "Species Management" Conference and this publication. I am grateful to FRS for provision of Shetland sandeel stock biomass estimates, to the Secretary General of ICES for permission to use ICES data on discards, and to the numerous postgraduates who have helped to collect data on seabirds, especially skuas, in Shetland over the past 30 years.

References

Anon. (2005). Commission regulation (EC), 1147/2005 of 15 July 2005 prohibiting fishing for sandeel with certain fishing gears in the North Sea and the Skagerrak. *Official Journal of the European Union*, 185/19.

Arnott, S.A. & Ruxton, G.D. (2002). Sandeel recruitment in the North Sea: demographic, climatic and trophic effects. *Marine Ecology Progress Series* **238**: 199–210.

Barrett, R.T., Camphuysen, C.J., Anker-Nilssen, T., Chardine, J.W., Furness, R.W., Garthe, S., Hüppop, O., Leopold, M.F., Montevecchi, W.A. & Veit, R.R. (2007). Diet studies of seabirds: a review and recommendations. *ICES Journal of Marine Science* **64**: 1675-1691.

Bearhop, S., Thompson, D.R., Phillips, R.A., Waldron, S., Hamer, K.C., Gray, C.M., Votier, S.C., Ross, B.P. & Furness, R.W. (2001). Annual variation in great skua diets: the importance of commercial fisheries and predation on seabirds revealed by combining dietary analyses. *Condor* **103**: 802-809.

Beaugrand, G. (2004). The North Sea regime shift: evidence, causes, mechanisms and consequences. *Progress in Oceanography* **60**: 245–262.

Caldow, R.W.G. & Furness, R.W. (2000). The effect of food availability on the foraging behaviour of breeding great skuas *Catharacta skua* and Arctic skuas *Stercorarius parasiticus*. *Journal of Avian Biology* **31**: 367-375.

Creel, S. & Christianson, D. (2008). Relationships between direct predation and risk effects. *Trends in Ecology and Evolution* **23**: 194-201.

Davis, S.E., Nager, R.G. & Furness, R.W. (2005). Food availability affects adult survival as well as breeding success of parasitic jaegers. *Ecology* **86**: 1047-1056.

Durant, J.M., Stenseth, N.C., Anker-Nilssen, T., Harris, M.P., Thompson, P.M. & Wanless, S. (2004). Marine birds and climate fluctuation in the North Atlantic. In: *Marine Ecosystems and Climate Variation: the North Atlantic – a Comparative Perspective* Eds N.C. Stenseth, G. Ottersen, J.W. Hurrell & A. Belgrano, pp. 95-105. Oxford University Press, Oxford.

Frederiksen, M., Wanless, S., Harris, M.P., Rothery, P. & Wilson, L.J. (2004). The role of industrial fisheries and oceanographic change in the decline of North Sea black-legged kittiwakes. *Journal of Applied Ecology* **41**: 1129-1139.

Frederiksen, M., Wright, P.J., Heubeck, M., Harris, M.P., Mavor, R.A. & Wanless, S. (2005). Regional patterns of kittiwake *Rissa tridactyla* breeding success are related to variability in sandeel recruitment. *Marine Ecology Progress Series* **300**: 201–211.

Frederiksen, M., Edwards, M., Richardson, A.J., Halliday, N.C. & Wanless, S. (2006). From plankton to top predators: bottom-up control of a marine food web across four trophic levels. *Journal of Animal Ecology* **75**: 1259-1268.

Frederiksen, M., Furness, R.W. & Wanless, S. (2007). Regional variation in the role of bottom-up and top-down processes in controlling sandeel abundance in the North Sea. *Marine Ecology Progress Series* **337**: 279-286.

Furness, R.W. (2002). Management implications of interactions between fisheries and sandeel-dependent seabirds and seals in the North Sea. *ICES Journal of Marine Science* **59**: 261-269.

Furness, R.W. (2007). Responses of seabirds to depletion of food fish stocks. *Journal of Ornithology* **148**: S247-S252.

Furness, R.W. & Bryant, D.M. (1996). Effect of wind on field metabolic rates of breeding northern fulmars. *Ecology* **77**: 1181-1188.

Furness, R.W. & Hislop, J.R.G. (1981). Diets and feeding ecology of great skuas *Catharacta skua* during the breeding season in Shetland. *Journal of Zoology, London* **195**: 1-23.

Furness, R.W. & Tasker, M.L. (2000). Seabird-fishery interactions: quantifying the sensitivity of seabirds to reductions in sandeel abundance and identification of key areas for sensitive seabirds in the North Sea. *Marine Ecology Progress Series* **202**: 253-264.

Furness, R.W., Edwards, A.E. & Oro, D. (2007). Influences of management practices and of scavenging seabirds on the availability of fisheries discards to benthic scavengers. *Marine Ecology Progress Series* **350**: 235-244.

Garthe, S., Camphuysen, C.J. & Furness, R.W. (1996). Amounts discarded by commercial fisheries and their significance as food for seabirds in the North Sea. *Marine Ecology Progress Series* **136**: 1-11.

Grosbois, V. & Thompson, P.M. (2005). North Atlantic climate variation influences survival in adult fulmars. *Oikos* **109**: 273–290.

Heithaus, M.R., Frid, A., Wirsing, A.J. & Worm, B. (2008). Predicting ecological consequences of marine top predator declines. *Trends in Ecology and Evolution* **23**: 202-210.

Hudson, A.V. (1982). Great black-backed gulls on Great Saltee Island, 1981. *Irish Birds* **2**: 167-175.

Irons, D.B., Anker-Nilssen, T., Gaston, A.J., Byrd, G.V., Falk, K., Gilchrist, G., Hario, M., Hjernquist, M., Krasnov, Y.V., Mosbech, A., Olsen, B., Petersen, A., Reid, J.B., Robertson, G.J., Strøm, H. & Wohl, K.D. (2008). Fluctuations in circumpolar seabird populations linked to climate oscillations. *Global Change Biology* **14**: 1455-1463.

Käkelä, A., Crane, J., Votier, S.C., Furness, R.W. & Käkelä, R. (2006). Fatty acid signatures as indicators of diet in great skuas *Stercorarius skua*, Shetland. *Marine Ecology Progress Series* **319**: 297-310.

Käkelä, A., Furness, R.W., Kelly, A., Strandberg, U., Waldron, S. & Käkelä, R. (2007). Fatty acid signatures and stable isotopes as dietary indicators in North Sea seabirds. *Marine Ecology Progress Series* **342**: 291-301.

Käkelä R, Furness, R.W., Kahle, S., Becker, P.H. & Käkelä, A. (2009). Fatty acid signatures in seabird plasma are a complex function of diet composition – a captive feeding trial with herring gulls. *Functional Ecology* **23(1)**: 141-149.

Mavor, R.A., Parsons, M., Heubeck, M. & Schmitt, S. (2007). *Seabird Numbers and Breeding Success in Britain and Ireland, 2006*. UK Nature Conservation Report no. 31. Joint Nature Conservation Committee, Peterborough.

Mitchell, P.I., Newton, S.F., Ratcliffe, N. & Dunn, T.E. (2004). *Seabird Populations of Britain and Ireland*. T. & A.D. Poyser, London.

Oro, D. & Furness, R.W. (2002). Influences of food availability and predation on survival of kittiwakes. *Ecology* **83**: 2516-2528.

Oro, D., de Leon, A., Minguez, E. & Furness, R.W. (2005). Estimating predation on breeding European storm-petrels (*Hydrobates pelagicus*) by yellow-legged gulls (*Larus michahellis*). *Journal of Zoology, London* **265**: 421-429.

Österblom, H., Olsson, O., Blenckner, T. & Furness, R.W. (2008). Junk food in marine ecosystems. *Oikos* **117**: 1075-1085.

Oswald, S., Bearhop, S., Furness, R.W., Huntley, B. & Hamer, K.C. (2008). Heat stress in a high-latitude seabird: effects of temperature and food supply on bathing and nest attendance of great skuas *Catharacta skua*. *Journal of Avian Biology* **39**: 163-169.

Phillips, R.A., Furness, R.W. & Stewart, F.M. (1998). The influence of territory density on the vulnerability of Arctic skuas *Stercorarius parasiticus* to predation. *Biological Conservation* **86**: 21-31.

Ratcliffe, N., Furness, R.W. & Hamer, K.C. (1998). The interactive effects of age and food supply on the breeding ecology of great skuas. *Journal of Animal Ecology* **67**: 853-862.

Richardson, A.J. & Schoeman, D.S. (2004). Climate impacts on plankton ecosystems in the Northeast Atlantic. *Science* **305**: 1609–1612.

Sandvik, H., Erikstad, K.E., Barrett, R.T. & Yoccoz, N.G. (2005). The effect of climate on adult survival in five species of North Atlantic seabirds. *Journal of Animal Ecology* **74**: 817–831.

Votier, S.C., Furness, R.W., Bearhop, S., Crane, J.E., Caldow, R.W.G., Catry, P., Ensor, K., Hamer, K.C., Hudson, A.V., Kalmbach, E., Klomp, N.I., Pfeiffer, S., Phillips, R.A., Prieto, I. & Thompson, D.R. (2004a). Changes in fisheries discard rates and seabird communities. *Nature* **427**: 727-730.

Votier, S.C., Bearhop, S., Ratcliffe, N. & Furness, R.W. (2004b). Reproductive consequences for great skuas specializing as seabird predators. *Condor* **106**: 275-287.

Votier, S.C., Bearhop, S., Ratcliffe, N., Phillips, R.A. & Furness, R.W. (2004c). Predation by great skuas at a large Shetland seabird colony. *Journal of Applied Ecology* **41**: 1117-1128.

Votier, S.C., Crane, J.E., Bearhop, S., de Leon, A., McSorley, C., Minguez, E., Mitchell, I.P., Parsons, M., Phillips, R.A. & Furness, R.W. (2006). Nocturnal foraging by great skuas *Stercorarius skua*: implications for conservation of storm-petrel populations. *Journal of Ornithology* **147**: 405-413.

Votier, S.C., Bearhop, S., Crane, J.E., Arcos, J.M. & Furness, R.W. (2007). Seabird predation by great skuas *Stercorarius skua* – intra-specific competition for food? *Journal of Avian Biology* **38**: 234-246.

Votier, S.C., Bearhop, S., Fyfe, R. & Furness, R.W. (2008). Temporal and spatial variation in the diet of a marine top predator – links with commercial fisheries. *Marine Ecology Progress Series* **367**: 223-232.

Wanless, S., Wright, P.J., Harris, M.P. & Elston, D.A. (2004). Evidence for decrease in size of lesser sandeels *Ammodytes marinus* in a North Sea aggregation over a 30-yr period. *Marine Ecology Progress Series* **279**: 237–246.

Wanless, S., Harris, M.P., Redman, P. & Speakman, J. (2005). Low energy values of fish as a probable cause of a major seabird breeding failure in the North Sea. *Marine Ecology Progress Series* **294**: 1–8.

Wanless, S., Harris, M.P., Lewis, S., Frederiksen, M. & Murray, S. (2008). Later breeding in northern gannets in the eastern Atlantic. *Marine Ecology Progress Series* **370**:263-269.

Furness, R.W. (2010). Scottish seabird predator-prey relationships. In: *Species Management: Challenges and Solutions for the 21st Century*, ed. by J.M. Baxter and C.A. Galbraith. TSO Scotland, Edinburgh. pp. 379-394

Part 5

Sustainable use of species

Many of the chapters in this book explore our relationship with species in terms of conservation practice, management of the interaction between populations, either native or aliens, and how we view them as part of our history and culture. This section takes this exploration one step further and examines the key issues involved in how we use the species around us as a resource. We use a wide range of species for a variety of purposes, and exploit them in a number of ways. Our history of exploitation has, in fact, been a history of over-exploitation in many cases, and the challenge now is to learn how to manage species sustainably, so that the overall resource remains available for future generations.

Our collective view of which species should be exploited is evolving as our wider views of what is acceptable in society changes. In particular, our views of what techniques are acceptable for killing animals is certainly a key issue for future discussions. So for example, it was quite acceptable not so long ago for the basking shark (*Cetorhinus maximus*), to be hunted in Scottish waters. This is, however, no longer the case and laws have been introduced to make the killing of the species illegal. Whilst this legal change is valuable, perhaps even more significant is the fact that the vast majority of the human population now regard the basking shark as something to be treasured, studied and conserved. The contribution the species makes to the Scottish tourist industry is important also, as the country is now seen as one of the prime basking shark viewing areas in Europe. So a combination of economic, conservation and cultural changes have come together to alter the way we view the species.

Many species are, of course still directly exploited in a carefully managed way. Deer management, for example, makes a major contribution to the Scottish economy and our fishing industry is of key cultural and economic value. Each of these and other industries have their own history, culture and accepted best practice techniques, which have become the norm over the decades. One of the key issues for discussion now is how applicable these techniques are to the present world where societal expectations are changing rapidly, where there is an expectation of multiple objectives being realized from the same piece of land or sea, and where climate change is exerting an increasingly noticeable influence on the species being exploited.

Opposite – Chanterelles (*Cantharellus cibarius*). © David Genney

This section explores these issues, focusing on some of the most high profile and contentious case studies.

The chapter by John Milne, Nick Halfhide and Robbie Kernahan examines the issues involved in managing red deer (*Cervus elaphus*) and other mammals for multiple objectives. They note that the objectives for management can be ecological, economic or social depending on the priorities in play at any one time. There is an expectation of being able to deliver multiple objectives at times, demanding trade-offs between various interest groups and requiring a more complex approach to management than was the case previously. This in turn demands a much better understanding of the ecology of the species concerned, in order to facilitate clearer and more focused management over time. Historically species managers worked to determine the ecological carrying capacity of any area; however, this has now to be increasingly considered alongside the economic carrying capacity; what any area can support in financial terms, and alongside consideration of the impact, direct or indirect, that any management might have on other non-target species. These new levels for consideration do lead to increasing complexity and the need for workable, technical solutions has never been greater. The authors suggest that a new paradigm is needed for the sustainable management of deer populations and that a combination of greater accountability and empowerment is needed for stakeholder groups to deliver sustainable management. They propose that this should be explored further in relation to the management of deer in the uplands in particular.

Chris Quine and Duncan Ray then address one of the key questions facing modern forestry; which species for which site for which world"? Again they highlight the complexities involved in decision making for foresters and note how the views of the public have changed over the years. There is a need to balance the demands of the wider public, for forests that are accessible, nice to look at and to be in, with the commercial realities for the production of timber in an economically viable way. The choice of what species to plant in a new forest is perhaps the most important decision for a land-manager to make and will have a profound influence on the composition and appearance of the forest over many decades in the future. The selection of particular species will influence greatly the biodiversity found in woodland and, as most tree species are long lived, it will take a long time to alter the composition of woods across the country. Again echoing the first chapter in this section, the authors suggest that we may be entering a new and more complex phase of woodland design and species choice for planting as climate change impacts more seriously and multiple objectives are required from woodland areas. The concept of "ecosystem services", what we get from the world around us, is a developing area of thinking and is beginning to change the way we view the value of woodlands as they become a more holistic supplier of a variety of "goods" such as biodiversity, carbon storage, and water retention, for example. Ensuring that these woodland areas are climate change "proofed", becomes ever more important.

A theme running through many of the chapters in the book has been the importance of the marine environment in the conservation of biodiversity and in our overall economic wellbeing. The same is true of course in terms of the direct harvesting of species. Our history here has not been good with many species overfished and fragile habitats destroyed in the process. Kevin Stokesbury and his co-authors review the ecological issues involved in one classic study of the sea scallop fishery off the east coast of the USA. The population of scallops fluctuated from the 1960s and went in to a steep decline in the 1990s. In the mid 1990s three large areas of seabed were closed to the fishery and after four years the biomass of scallops in these areas had been seen to increase dramatically. New techniques using video technology were introduced to monitor the populations of scallops *in situ*, allowing much more accurate measures of population levels that had previously been possible. As a consequence of this it is now possible to manage the scallop fishery in a precise manner and the stock is now no longer considered to be overfished. There is estimated to be around $2 billion worth of scallop stock on the seabed of the areas concerned; a truly astounding value, making a powerful statement about the economic benefits that can accrue if species' exploitation is managed effectively.

Continuing with the marine theme, Mike Hammill and Garry Stenson examine the harvesting of the harp seal (*Pagophilus groenlandicus*), the largest marine mammal harvest in the world. This harvest is highly controversial, polarizing views and leading to direct action by protesters in attempts to limit the harvest of seals each year. The harvest has been taking place since the 18th century, peaking in the 19th century. Since the mid 1990s around 264,000 animals have been taken each year, a level that appears to be more or less sustainable. The harvest reveals the interplay between the ecological sustainable limits of the population, and the economic and political considerations in determining the harvest levels allowed. A precautionary approach allows the identification of clear management objectives and actions that are triggered when the population approaches a pre-determined reference level. The Precautionary Management framework used in the management of the harvest levels has proved to be one of the key developments in searching for a sustainable level of harvest and in achieving at least a degree of recognition that the population will survive in the long-term. The flexibility introduced, so that the annual total allowable catch retains the overall population above the precautionary level has been important in achieving this result. Climate change is of course now impacting on the population and may change some of the parameters for the future.

Moving back on land, the exploitation of mosses, lichens and fungi is reviewed by Dave Genny and Alison Dyke. These species have been used by humans for a variety of purposes over the millennia. They form an important part of Scotland's biodiversity and in the case of mosses are the building blocks of our internationally important peat bogs. This is surely one of the best examples of where one type of plant can come to form a unique habitat, supporting many other rare and endangered species. Given the importance of this habitat in Scotland for biodiversity and as significant store of carbon, it is essential that any exploitation is undertaken sparingly, respecting its wider significance. That is not to say that no exploitation is possible and many communities in rural parts of the Highlands in particular have a long history of relatively modest use of the resource; indeed the use of peat is part of the history and culture of these communities. Looking ahead, the adoption of clear codes of conduct is likely to be key in the long-term sustainable use of all these species. The direct harvesting of some species of wild fungi is, once again becoming a popular activity, and some measure of good practice guidance is likely to be needed by all and welcomed by most who harvest in this way. The potential for sustainable harvesting of these species is important in its own right and would have the clear benefit of allowing people to continue to interact with nature by harvesting, and to do this in a way that minimizes any long-term impact.

Finally in this section, Dave Goulson reviews the conservation priorities of bumblebees, highlighting the decline in the populations of various species over the past 60 years or so. These declines are not limited to Scotland or the UK but have been recorded across Europe. The cause has been shown to be habitat loss, and the decline in floral abundance and diversity in particular. These changes have been driven by agricultural intensification in the most part, as farmers strive to remain viable by responding to policy incentives from Governments and the European Union. The problems caused by rapid agricultural change are compounded due to the ecology of the bumblebee species themselves, where many species are social yet monogamous, with only one queen bee breeding in each colony. Some species are now so rare in the UK that the whole breeding population possibly holds as few as 30 breeding females. This makes these populations extremely vulnerable to chance events that could lead to their extinction, and vulnerable to progressive inbreeding reducing their fitness overall. In addition to habitat changes, it is sobering to note that bumblebee populations in North America have undergone catastrophic declines, probably as a result of the accidental introduction of non-native species of parasites via the global trade in domestic bees to be used as pollinators of a range of crops. Given our dependence on bees as pollinators of our crops, and the particular value of bumblebees as part of our native wildlife, we really do need to ensure that their survival is safeguarded more effectively than at present. Simple actions to regulate the international trade in non-native bees as crop pollinators, and changes to EU agricultural funding mechanisms to support "bee friendly" farming seem obvious changes, but are difficult to implement. To repeat an analogy used in an earlier linking section of this book—if bees are effectively like "canaries in the coal mine", acting as indicators of the state of the environment, then the present laws and policies across Europe are actually stopping us saving the canary! This is doubly ironic, since within reason, we know what needs to be done to rectify the situation.

Chapter 22

Management of red deer and other mammals for multiple objectives

John A. Milne[1], Nick R. Halfhide[1] and Robbie P. Kernahan[1]

Summary

1. Objectives for the management of populations of mammals can be ecological, economic and social, and management is often expected to deliver several of these at the same time. Moreover objectives are set not only by private individuals but also by the state to meet public objectives. This has increased the complexity of the technical solutions for the management of such populations once issues such as conflicts between objectives and their prioritization have been resolved.

2. Greater understanding of the biology of these populations is required in order that these multiple objectives can be met. For example, in the past, an understanding of the ecological carrying capacity of a population and the factors influencing it was sufficient to manage a population. It is likely now that an understanding of the economic-carrying capacity for the management of game, forestry or agriculture, of the interaction with other species and of the relationship with tourism or other cultural objectives is also required.

3. In the context of deer species, an understanding of the biology and the feasibility of delivering technical solutions to meet objectives is likely to reside, to a considerable extent, with those who manage the population locally supported by external experts as appropriate.

4. It is argued that a new paradigm for the sustainable management of deer species is needed whereby stakeholder groups are provided with the necessary accountability and empowerment to identify potentially complex solutions and deliver them. How this new paradigm might work is explored in the context of the management of red deer in the uplands of Scotland.

[1] Deer Commission for Scotland, Great Glen House, Leachkin Road, Inverness, IV3 8NW, UK

22.1 Introduction

Red deer (*Cervus elaphus*). © By kind permission of the Deer Commission for Scotlan

22.1.1 Concepts of sustainable management

Sustainable use of a species is defined in this paper as the achievement of a balance between the population of the species, existing in a productive state in a functioning ecosystem, and the current and future socio-economic objectives. For many species there are no socio-economic objectives within an ecosystem although there are often trade-offs to be considered between the priorities that need to be set between species that exist in the same ecosystem. These instances, however, are not considered in this chapter but the more specific case of the sustainable use of one species within an ecosystem is explored.

There are many cases around the world where the sustainable use of wild mammalian species is important, but in Europe there are few current examples because of the intensively managed nature of land resources under forestry or agriculture. Most of the examples in Europe relate either to mammalian species that can cause damage to agricultural or woodland activities, for example deer species, or that are a source of food, for example game birds and wild boar. In some cases the process whereby species are managed to avoid causing damage or as a source of food has created a culture where the control of these species has now developed into a sporting occasion. Particularly where the mammalian species was a source of food, the easy access to other foods has resulted in the sporting occasion becoming the paramount socio-economic interest.

As will be described below, a body of research has led to methods of estimating an appropriate off-take or sustainable yield from a wildlife population, depending on whether the population is required to increase, be stable or whether there are environmental fluctuations from year to year. On the basis of such an off-take or yield, the carrying capacity of a resource for a wildlife population can be described. Carrying capacity has been defined in a number of different ways which has led to much confusion (Caughley, 1976). The simplest definition is that of ecological carrying capacity. This can be defined as the natural limit set by resources in a particular environment (Caughley and Sinclair, 1994). The special case of ecological carrying capacity has been widened to cases where there is a need to control or manage the numbers of a species to meet a specific management objective which has a socio-economic interest. There are other cases where carrying capacity is also important such as where there are biodiversity objectives to be met or ecosystem services to be delivered. Ecosystem services can include water, air and soil quality, water quantity and mitigation of climate change. Carrying capacity of a resource can be different for each of these management objectives whether they be socio-economic or in relation to biodiversity or ecosystem services. In addition there are supporting services that are necessary to make ecosystems function and other services, such as possible future uses, and cultural services. These latter services are not considered in this paper because few or no attempts have been made to quantify their carrying capacity.

Plate 22.1 Red deer (*Cervus elaphus*) stag roaring during the breeding season. The red deer is an example of a keystone or foundation species in many woodland and moorland ecosystems in Scotland. © Lorne Gill/SNH

22.1.2 Ecosystems and their management

In many situations in Europe, there are a number of objectives to be met from a single resource, i.e. an area of land and its plant and animal life, and, hence, in terms of the appropriate populations of keystone species to determine the ecosystems within that resource. A keystone species is one that has a disproportionate effect on its environment relative to its abundance. Such species affect other organisms in an ecosystem and help to determine the types and numbers of other species in an ecosystem (Paine, 1995). The term, foundation species, which is a dominant primary producer in an ecosystem, both in terms of abundance and influence, could also be used but the more widely-used term, keystone species, is used in this chapter. An example of a keystone or foundation species in this context relates to species of deer. A first stage is to describe the carrying capacity of a resource for the species of interest. This is not necessarily an easy task and there are surprisingly few examples where this has been achieved for all objectives for a resource. The lack of such information is one of the reasons for the conflicts described in other chapters in this volume. A next stage is the prioritization of objectives. The resources over which a mammalian species may range are often not owned by one individual and the impacts of the species may influence a range of stakeholders. For this reason it is generally considered that stakeholders, informed by information on the carrying capacity of a resource for a species to allow the different objectives to be achieved, are the most appropriate group to agree the prioritization of objectives and hence the carrying capacity of the resource. How these stakeholder groups are formed and operate is likely to depend on the legal and cultural framework that exists in relation to the resource. These are different in different countries in Europe and it is likely that their operation may need to change to meet the needs of the 21st century.

The purpose of this chapter is firstly to describe the current understanding of carrying capacity of a land resource for mammalian species to meet a range of economic, conservation and cultural objectives. The second purpose is to explore the different approaches to decision-making in relation to sustainable management of a species and how they can be delivered within the legal and cultural framework that exists in Scotland with specific reference to deer species. The conclusions that are reached suggest that a different paradigm to the current one is needed if sustainable management of the most iconic mammalian species in Scotland is to be achieved.

22.2 Carrying capacity

Population density can be changed by emigration and immigration and by births and deaths. If the proportion of a population dying increases, or if the proportion entering as births decreases then these changes are defined as being density-dependent and the causes of these changes are density-dependent factors. These factors are usually associated with availability of resources such as food and cover. There are also density–independent factors, such as weather and intervention by man, which can regulate the size of a population. The combination of density-dependent and density-independent factors affects the size of equilibrium populations, but the return to an equilibrium population density is entirely due to density-dependent factors which hence regulate the size of populations. Caughley and Sinclair (1994) provide an extended discussion of these concepts.

22.2.1 Ecological carrying capacity

Ecological carrying capacity is the natural limit set by resources in a particular environment and is a point of equilibrium which a population tends towards through density-dependent effects on deaths and births associated with food, territory or other resources. Predation and the incidence of disease are special cases in that predation and disease may not influence births and deaths to the same extent but may lead to different equilibria. Obviously, factors, such as weather, can also influence the absolute population density. Measuring ecological carrying capacity requires knowledge of the initial population and also the measurement of birth rates and mortality which are not easy to estimate in all cases.

22.2.2 Economic carrying capacity

Economic carrying capacity is the population density that produces the maximum off-take (or maximum sustainable yield) for control or cropping purposes. In an agricultural context for grazing livestock, for example sheep and cattle in extensive systems, economic carrying capacity is often referred to as livestock carrying capacity. The demands of the market for a particular product, for example in the context of cropping meat of a particular age or maturity, or, in a hunting context, males with particular trophy antlers, increase the complexity of the concept of economic carrying capacity. Population densities at economic carrying capacity are usually much less than those at ecological carrying capacity. Measuring economic carrying capacity requires not only measurements of initial populations, birth rates and mortality but also harvesting rate in cropping situations and control rates. In control situations it may be possible to use methods other than culling such as exclusion, habitat manipulation and by manipulating fertility. The economic costs and benefits must also be assessed.

22.2.3 Other senses of carrying capacity

There are an increasing number of land uses which have been outlined above that merit consideration in relation to carrying capacity. The most important of these is in the delivery of biodiversity objectives. There are several examples of how ecosystems are managed to achieve such nature conservation objectives in this volume. The biodiversity objectives for habitats and species under the Habitats Directive of the European Union (European Union, 1992) are a good example of where objectives for species and habitats in favourable condition interact with the carrying capacity of large herbivores. A set of criteria are used to assess condition for the plant species in the habitat and compared to achievable targets. This can then be translated into a population density for the land resource containing the large herbivore to meet the biodiversity objective. It is possible to obtain some reasonable estimates of the population density required because information on the distribution of plant communities within a resource is often available, a reasonable understanding of the diet selection by large herbivores exists along with knowledge of the impact of grazing, browsing and trampling on the productivity of a plant species. What has to date proved impossible is to predict accurately the time course of any change in the plant community associated with changes in grazing pressure of large herbivores to reach an equilibrium carrying capacity. An iterative approach of monitoring and adjusting herbivore densities has had to be adopted. It is difficult to undertake an economic cost-benefit analysis because the value of the biodiversity is difficult to assess.

The impact that mammalian species can have on other land uses or outcomes of land uses is often indirect, spatially and temporally discreet and hence difficult to quantify. For example in relation to birds and the Habitats Directive (European Union, 1992), impacts on plant habitats by large herbivores are often used as surrogates of food supply and nesting cover. In relation to water quality, burrowing in river banks or trampling in riparian zones may lead to sedimentation and a reduction in water quality. To translate such impacts into a carrying capacity is a complex and difficult task.

Plate 22.2 A digital camera mounted on a helicopter is used to count populations of red deer on open ground in winter, in Scotland.
© By kind permission of the Deer Commission for Scotland

The requirements of tourism have also been converted into carrying capacity for large herbivores. To take an example quoted by Caughley and Sinclair (1994), large umbrella-shaped *Acacia tortilis* trees make a picturesque back-drop to the tourist accommodation in the Serengeti National Park, Tanzania. They were being knocked down by elephants and consequently the carrying capacity of the land resource for tourism was reduced, but by controlling the number of elephants, so that such damage did not occur in those areas the landscape benefits for tourists would be improved.

Thus, it can be concluded that (i) although there is a good theoretical understanding of the concepts of carrying capacity, the information needed to estimate carrying capacity may be difficult to obtain, (ii) the carrying capacity may differ considerably from one objective to another, and (iii) carrying capacity can be difficult to determine for some objectives.

22.2.4 Carrying capacity of resources with red deer as a keystone species

Before using red deer in Scotland as an example, some background information on their management is required. Red deer are a keystone species in several important upland and woodland ecosystems. There are approximately 450,000 red deer (Clutton-Brock *et al.*, 2004) and in Scots law they are not owned by anyone although landowners have rights to take deer at certain times of the year. There are a number of objectives for the resource that they inhabit including sport and tourism, forestry, agriculture and biodiversity, including native woodlands, and their aesthetic appeal in relation to tourism. In the case of red deer in Scotland, Figure 22.1 shows schematically the sustainable yield required to maintain population densities for ecological carrying capacity, economic carrying capacity in relation to a sporting objective and to meet a biodiversity objective of native woodland regeneration (Milne, 2001). It can be seen that the estimates of carrying capacity are different. The population density to achieve woodland

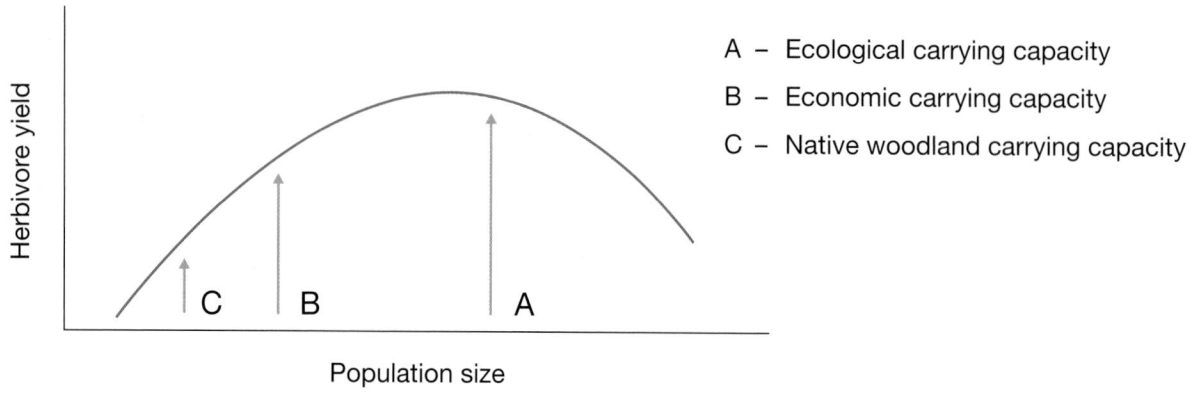

Figure 22.1 Relationship between herbivore yield and population size with ecological carrying capacity, economic carrying capacity and native woodland carrying capacity indicated by arrows.

regeneration of red deer is usually considered to be around five deer peer square kilometre whilst those for economic carrying capacity can be two or three times that density (Staines, 1994; Clutton-Brock et al., 2002). Estimates of carrying capacity require knowledge of population numbers, which can be obtained with confidence limits of 10-20% from counts obtained by the use of helicopters, birth rates, which can be obtained from visual estimates of samples of the population and mortality rates, which are difficult to obtain accurate values for because of their low rates in most circumstances. Harvesting rates and the monetary value of carcasses can be measured accurately but the costs of management are less easy to estimate. In relation to the impact of red deer on woodland regeneration, the foraging behaviour of red deer in the winter and spring in relation to weather, for example, is difficult to predict and population densities to meet woodland regeneration objectives are difficult to describe with any accuracy. No carrying capacities have yet been identified in relation to wildlife tourism for red deer in Scotland. These would be desirable but estimating them could prove exceedingly difficult.

For an evidence-based approach to work, more is required than the measurements described in the previous paragraph because of the cost and lack of accuracy in the estimates obtained. Expert knowledge through the use of a consultant or alternatively local expert knowledge from land managers needs to be used to provide estimates for carrying capacity where direct measurements cannot be made.

22.3 Approaches to decision-making by land users

If carrying capacity relates to one objective for a land resource then it is possible to immediately move to designing a plan to achieve that carrying capacity through management actions. There are principles in relation to sustainable yield about how to achieve the desired population density depending upon the starting population, the choice of age and sex of the species and the method of control used.

Assuming that there are different carrying capacities for a species or, in an even more complex case, a number of species in relation to a number of desired objectives for a land resource, then decisions need to be made about prioritizing the objectives for that resource before a population density can be arrived at, a plan developed and management actions taken. Decision-making theory in combined socio-economic and ecological systems where there are likely to be several stakeholders is in its infancy but simulation approaches have been explored. Farnsworth et al. (1999) developed a multi-objective optimization model based on ideal free distribution game theory which identified two distinct types of equilibrium, one relating to the decision-making process and the other to ecosystem processes when applied to an ecosystem in the mid-Zambezi valley in Africa where there were three objectives for the use of the resource. Estimation of the distance between these equilibria, relating to decision-making and to ecosystem processes, provided an indication of overall sustainability of the system. The closer the equilibria, the more sustainable the system is likely to be. Whilst such approaches merit further development, simpler approaches have to be used.

Wildlife tends to be owned by nobody, and hence is considered a common resource. For example, in Scotland landowners have the right to kill deer under certain circumstance but the person killing the deer only owns it once it is dead. If species and resources are unmanaged through a lack of decision-making, the Tragedy of the Commons, as described by Hardin (1968), can unfold. Ostrom (1990) described the rules for managing a Commons to avoid such a circumstance. These are:

1. What a stakeholder takes out of the resource has to be proportional to the input by the stakeholder.
2. Usage should not damage the health of the resource.
3. All stakeholders should have a say in the rules governing the management of the resource.
4. Monitoring abuses and conflict resolution are more important than sanctions or punishment.

Plate 22.3 Scottish blackface sheep grazing moorland often managed in association with red deer. © Lorne Gill/SNH

The management of land and water resources and their species by groups has a long history and has become an accepted means whereby the management of resources can occur. For example, the setting up of Salmon Fishery Boards of riparian owners by an Act of Parliament in the UK occurred in 1823 to manage salmon populations. They are still in existence although their structures have evolved somewhat to meet changing circumstances. In Scotland rabbit and fox control groups were numerically significant in the middle of the 20th century although there are only a few that exist today. For deer species in Scotland approximately 50 voluntary deer management groups were set up in the 1980s and 1990s with encouragement from the Red Deer Commission for Scotland to manage mainly red deer to meet the sporting objectives of landowners who were the principal stakeholders. It was recognized by the end of the 1990s that such groups should prepare, and use, deer management plans as a means of describing the state of the land resource, prioritizing objectives (since landowners now had a range of objectives as well as the sporting objective), for the resource utilized by deer species, and setting targets for populations and monitoring their achievement. Guidelines for developing such plans were published in 1999 (Deer Commission for Scotland, 1999). Since 1999 various reports (e.g. Nolan et al., 2001; Hunt, 2003) have concluded that only a proportion of groups have developed plans and once developed they have not been used systematically.

The evidence cited above suggests that for some species for which there are multiple objectives in Scotland, the approach of using groups of resource managers to manage species has been adopted. All such groups have found it difficult to deal with the increasing role that the public interest has in the management of resources with implications for species under discussion. The impact of public interest, for example, for deer species in Scotland has increased due to the Land Reform (Scotland) Act 2003 influencing access and ownership patterns, biodiversity regulations (European Union, 1992) and food hygiene and welfare regulations. There has been little or no role for groups of resource managers in planning the implementation of these regulations which have a major impact on the prioritizing of objectives at a resource level. This lack of a role is one reason for their disengagement in addressing issues of public interest. The current approach where public agencies seek to deliver solutions for issues of public interest is not effective because of this lack of engagement.

It is argued that a new approach to the role that these groups of resource managers can have in managing terrestrial mammals to meet multiple public and private objectives is required. This is not only because of the need to address the issues raised above but because there is a new rural governance agenda being proposed which involves partnership between the state and private and voluntary sectors, with the state as an enabler rather than a provider, operating at a distance, governing through the private and voluntary sectors by empowering them to deliver and implement solutions (Shucksmith, 2008). This poses issues of how to achieve participation and empowerment of all those with a stake in the land resource to deal with issues of complexity, accountability, inclusion and scale when considering the use of such an approach for the management of terrestrial mammals to deliver multiple objectives. Healey (2006) has made suggestions as to how the concept of spatial planning can be adapted to deal with such a governance agenda and the important role that there is for capacity building.

22.4 A new paradigm

The development of a new paradigm for the sustainable management of terrestrial mammalian species with specific reference to the deer species found in Scotland to meet multiple objectives is now considered. Because deer are a common resource, since in Scotland they are not owned by anyone although landowners have the right to take deer on their land under certain circumstances, it is argued that the rules for managing a Commons apply (Ostrom, 1990) which implies that, for the sustainable management of the resource, a stakeholder group approach is required. As has been argued above, the current voluntary system of deer management groups is not designed to meet the achievement of multiple objectives, particularly where there is a combination of public and privately driven objectives.

This is partly because of the difficulty in obtaining information to describe the carrying capacity of the resource to meet these multiple objectives and in collecting this information on an annual basis to keep it up-to-date. The costs of obtaining such information and the large confidence limits attached to the information present major obstacles. Currently much of the collection of habitat information is funded by government agencies and obtained by experts, and more and more information on numbers of deer are obtained by government agencies because of the lack of resources available to deer management groups. There is thus a lack of capacity in deer management groups and a lack of involvement because the data are not collected by the group in a form appropriate to address the objectives that they identify with. Capacity in terms of human resources to collect biological, economic and other data is thus a key constraint of the current system.

The prioritization of objectives has proved difficult because groups do not have a mechanism whereby a set of priorities can be easily agreed. With the increase in the number of objectives, there is now a range of stakeholders who are not deer managers that feel that they have a right to influence the objective-setting process. Examples are those with an economic interest through wildlife tourism, or those whose livelihoods or lifestyle is influenced by the impacts of deer, such as farmers and local residents. Government agencies, representing the public interest, are also not members of groups, except where they are landowners. Consequently, effective decision-making rarely takes into account the public interest. This means that there is a need to develop an approach that involves a larger number of local stakeholders than at present and which allows public objectives to be considered by the stakeholder group in a manner that facilitates their acceptance by the group. An exploration of the costs and benefits associated with delivering public and private interests by local stakeholder groups is also overdue.

Moreover, even if a set of priorities are agreed where the public interest is not involved, there is little that the group can do to ensure that the agreed priorities are implemented in a management plan as the groups are currently constituted. In consequence, conflict resolution is not easy because the group has no sanctions that can be used. Furthermore, some of the tools that a group might wish to use, are not directly available to them and are currently in the hands of the state. For example, the dates of the Closed Seasons for males are set by Scottish Government Ministers.

Plate 22.4 Roe deer (*Capreolus capreolus*) are widespread throughout Scotland. © Lorne Gill/SNH

The current geographical scale of stakeholder groups is an issue as groups do not all relate to populations of deer as these have changed over time and will probably continue to do so with changes in land use, associated with the removal of hill sheep from the Highlands (RSE, 2008) or the proposed increase in the proportion of Scotland with a tree cover (Forestry Commission Scotland, 2006).

The new rural governance agenda (see Schucksmith, 2008) also does not fit in with the way that the current system operates. The agenda involves partnership between the state and private and voluntary sectors but with the state as an enabler rather than a provider, operating at a distance. This suggests a contract between the state and the stakeholder interests, whereby the state contracts them to deliver its objectives and leaves them to decide how to deliver these objectives in the context of other priorities. To provide the necessary accountability and empowerment to identify potentially complex solutions and deliver them the group may need to have a statutory basis.

The geographical scale of groups also needs re-evaluation in terms of how best to deliver the capacity required to collect relevant data, facilitate the prioritization of solutions and deliver some of the technical aspects of management which groups currently cannot provide themselves.

This new paradigm for the sustainable management of deer, which involves empowerment of local stakeholders to manage a common resource, could be applied to other species. It also has the potential to fit into the jigsaw of how land management will occur in the next two decades of the 21st century.

22.5 Conclusions

The above analysis has identified that a new paradigm is needed for the sustainable management of mammalian species to meet multiple objectives of resources used by such species. New approaches to the empowerment of local stakeholder groups have been identified which fit into the rural development framework for Scotland now and in the future.

References

Caughley, G. (1976). Wildlife management and the dynamics of ungulate populations.In *Applied Biology, Volume 1*, Ed. T.H. Coaker. Academic Press, New York, pp. 183-246.

Caughley, G. & Sinclair, A.E.R. (1994). *Wildlife ecology and management.* Blackwell Scientific Publications, Oxford.

Clutton-Brock, T.H., Crawley M.J. & Milner J.M. (2002). Deer in the highlands. In *A highland deer herd and its habitat,* Eds J.M. Milner, J. Alexander and C. Griffin. Red Lion House, London, pp.237-250.

Clutton-Brock, T.H., Coulson, T. & Milner, J.M. (2004). Red deer stocks in the Highlands of Scotland. *Nature* **429**: 261-262.

Deer Commission for Scotland. (1999). *Collaborative deer management – guidelines for a Deer Management Plan.* Deer Commission for Scotland, Inverness.

European Union. (1992). *Council Directive 92/43/EEC of 21 May 1992 on the conservation of natural habitats and of wild fauna and flora. OJ L 2006. 7-50.* European Commission, Brussels.

Farnsworth, K.D., Beecham, J. & Roberts, D. (1999). A behavioural ecology approach to modelling decision-making in combined economic and ecological systems. In *Ecosystems and sustainable development II*, Eds J.L. Uso and C.A. Brebbia. WIT Press, Southampton, pp. 133-146.

Forestry Commission Scotland. (2006). *Scottish Forestry Strategy.* Forestry Commission Scotland, Edinburgh.

Hardin, G. (1968). The tragedy of the commons. *Science* **162**: 1243-1248.

Healey, P. (2006). *Transforming governance: shaping places in fragmented societies.* Palgrave Macmillan, London.

Hunt, J.F. (2003). *Impacts of wild deer in Scotland: how fares the public interest?* RSPB, Edinburgh.

Milne, J.A. (2001). Principles of range management. In *Integrated upland management for wildlife, field sports, agriculture and public enjoyment*, Eds J.D.P. Phillips, D.B.A. Thompson and W.H. Gruellich. Scottish Natural Heritage, Battleby, pp. 1-7.

Nolan, A.J., Hewison, R.L. & Maxwell T.J. (2001). *Deer management groups: operation and good practice.* Deer Commission for Scotland, Inverness.

Ostrom, E. (1990). *Governing the Commons: the evolution of institutions for collective action.* Cambridge University Press, Cambridge.

Paine, R.T. (1995). A conversation on refining the concept of a keystone species. *Conservation Biology* **9**: 962-964.

Royal Society of Edinburgh. (2008). *Committee of inquiry into the future of Scotland's hills and uplands*. Royal Society of Edinburgh, Edinburgh.

Schucksmith, M. (2008). Does the idea of Integrated Rural Development still have a place in Scotland? 32nd T.B. Macaulay Lecture. Macaulay Institute, Aberdeen.

Staines, B. W. (1994). The management of red deer (*Cervus elaphus*) in the context of other land uses in Scotland. In *Recent developments in deer biology* Ed. J.A. Milne. Macaulay Institute, Aberdeen, pp.385-400.

Milne, J.A., Halfhide, N.R. and Kernahan, R.P. (2010). Management of red deer and other mammals for multiple objectives. In: *Species Management: Challenges and Solutions for the 21st Century*, ed. by J.M. Baxter and C.A. Galbraith. TSO Scotland, Edinburgh. pp. 401-415

Chapter 23

Sustainable forestry – which species for which site for which world?

Chris Quine[1] and Duncan Ray[1]

Summary

1. Sustainable forest management, the prevailing paradigm for UK forestry, seeks to balance both present and future needs and cater for a range of societal and individual demands.
2. Choice of tree species to plant or encourage may be the first, and is the most direct, of a set of management actions that influence the presence (or absence) of woodland-dependent species and is governed by a set of factors that reflect the limitations of a particular site, and the intentions of management.
3. Changes in societal expectations, owner objectives, and the prospect of climate change add to the complexity of decisions relating to selection of long-lived organisms that will form the basis for an enterprise spanning generations.
4. A forest site classification system has been developed to help guide the choice of tree species or woodland community towards those with a good ecological fit. The Ecological Site Classification has been modified to incorporate climate projections to 2080 as well as summary data for recent past climate.
5. Other methods are being developed to provide support to managers in analysing the multiple criteria necessary in matching the species to site, social and economic objectives.
6. Recent research has shown that, notwithstanding the importance of tree species choice, biodiversity and other ecosystem services can be enhanced by careful attention to the landscape placement of forests, and to the subsequent management of the growing stands. Ensuring the resilience of such forests in future climates may require a reassessment of the current emphasis placed on nativeness and localness in species choice rather than adaptedness.

[1] Centre for Human and Ecological Sciences, Forest Research, Northern Research Station, Roslin, EH25 9SY, UK

23.1 Introduction

Conifer plantation. © Lorne Gill/SN

Forestry covers approximately 12% of the land area of the UK, and 17% of Scotland (Forestry Commission, 2007). There are aspirations to increase this – for example in Scotland, to about 25% by the middle of the 21st century (Anon., 2006). Forestry has developed to make use of particular life forms and species of plants and, at its most basic, involves the protection, manipulation, and harvesting of the tree cover. Forest managers choose the species of tree, their placement in the landscape, the density of planting, and the timing of subsequent interventions. The lifespan of trees, or the imposed rotation length when treated as a crop, are such that choices made at time of establishment have consequences that last decades or centuries.

Before focusing on tree species management, it should be noted that there are other forms of species management contained within 21st century forestry in Britain. In particular:

- Conservation measures to conserve and enhance populations of rare, priority and protected species and associated habitats – e.g. Forestry Commission Scotland 'Woods for Nature' and associated species action notes (www.forestry.gov.uk/woodsfornature); the decision tool for Habitats and Rare Priority and Protected Species (HaRPPS) (Ray and Broome, 2007) (see www.forestresearch.gov.uk/harpps); and the priority species research carried out by Forest Research for the Forestry Commission (Broome et al., 2005) (see www.forestresearch.gov.uk/saps).
- Population control – removal or reduction of populations of animals that are injurious to trees e.g. deer (Gill, 2000); control of pathogens and diseases e.g. red band needle blight (Brown et al., 2003; Brown and Webber, 2008); control of populations of alien and invasive species (e.g. grey squirrel (Sciurus carolinensis) (Mayle et al., 2007), Rhododendron ponticum (Edwards, 2006) and vegetation management (Willoughby et al., 2004).
- Tree-breeding – conventional breeding to obtain genetic gains in traits that are valued (Lee, 2004); there is currently little work on genetically modified (GM) forest trees in the UK.

In addition, forestry exerts an indirect effect on many species in that choice of forestry as a land use and the subsequent management of wooded habitats, for example through thinning, has an impact upon a range of forest and open ground species. Such land use changes were previously the source of much conflict, notably over some upland afforestation and the loss of associated upland flora and fauna, and particularly birds (Stroud et al., 1988). However, improved processes have now been developed to guide land allocation. There is also a growing body of evidence of the woodland biodiversity that develops in these forests (Humphrey et al., 2003; Brockerhoff et al., 2008), and the opportunities to encourage it through a range of stand management choices (Humphrey, 2005; Quine et al., 2007).

Plate 23.1 Scottish crossbill (*Loxia scotica*) feeding two day old chicks. © David Whitaker FC Picture Library/1009802

23.1.1 Historical context

Any discussion of the choice of tree species in Scotland needs to take into account the consequences of, and context provided by four major legacies:

- *Glaciation.* Past glaciation and the vagaries of recolonization of species since the last glacial maxima have resulted in a limited number of tree species being native to this country. Most of Scotland's tree flora is thought to have survived in refugia in southern Europe and recolonized relatively rapidly. However, the early separation of Britain from the rest of Europe (approx. 7,500 B.P.) prevented other tree species from dispersing into Britain and becoming established in Scotland – for example, Norway spruce (*Picea abies* (L). Karsten) and sycamore (*Acer pseudoplatanus* L.). In fact there is a general paucity of tree flora in western Europe compared to other continents such as North America due to colder glacial periods in Europe (Davis, 1983), smaller refugia sites in Europe and unfavourable geography of mountain chains (Huntley, 1993). A consequence was a very limited choice of native tree species for productive forestry.
- *Neglect and loss of woodland.* A large proportion of the land area of Scotland may once have been wooded, but the impact of man and of climate led to long-term loss of woodland cover. This was exacerbated by excessive exploitation and an absence of care and management of Scotland's surviving forests; the effects of two world wars accelerated the long decline. A consequence was a depleted natural resource in terms of extent, and arguably quality of the genetic resource (Forrest and Fletcher, 1995).
- *Plant collecting.* A long tradition of plant collecting, and the pre-eminence of the Scottish tree collectors and their sponsors, led to the establishment of collections of tree species from around the world. This resulted in many potential options for using new species, much curiosity and some unique and culturally valued landscapes such as the 'Big tree country' in Perthshire. A consequence was clear evidence for the suitability of Scotland's environment for a number of temperate tree species from elsewhere, most particularly conifers.
- *Afforestation.* The loss of woodland triggered a number of initiatives to restore woodland cover and control of woodland felling. There were early efforts to replant and afforest by individual estate owners in 1700s – who used European species such as European larch (*Larix decidua* Miller) and Norway spruce; it has been suggested that the Scottish crossbill (*Loxia scotica*) may have evolved to exploit food resources in these plantations (Marquiss and Rae, 2002). However, the main afforestation phase occurred in the 20th century using only a very small subset of vigorous, mainly introduced pioneer species which were well suited to Scotland's climate. The main driver for afforestation was timber production, and species choice reflected the desire to rapidly recreate a strategic reserve of timber. A small selection of North American species were used extensively, the most frequent being Sitka spruce (*Picea sitchensis* (Bong.) Carrière).

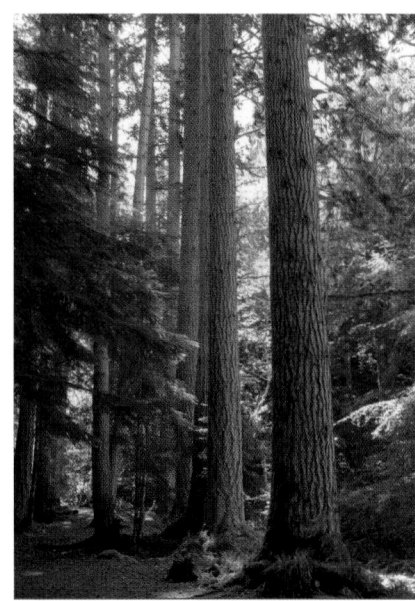

Plate 23.3 Large Douglas fir (*Pseudotsuga menziesii*) in Reelig Glen Inverness. © FC picture Library/Isobel Cameron No. 20005454

Plate 23.4 Native Scots pine (*Pinus sylvestris*). © Lorne Gill/SNH

Plate 23.2 David Douglas (1799-1834) – Scottish plant collector. © FC Picture Library/1009802

23.1.2 Sustainable forest management

The objectives for forestry, and for public support for forestry through permission and incentive, broadened in the latter decades of 20th century (Rollinson, 2003). Shifts in domestic policy towards rural employment, balance of land use, and multi-purpose forestry, merged with international action (e.g. on biodiversity) to prompt the concept of sustainable forest management (SFM), defined as:

> 'The stewardship and use of forests and forest lands in a way, and at a rate, that maintains their biodiversity, productivity, regeneration capacity, vitality, and their potential to fulfil, now and in the future, relevant ecological, economic and social functions, at local, national and global levels, and that does not cause damage to other ecosystems' Helsinki Ministerial Conference 1993 (MCPFE, 1993).

The UK is widely acknowledged to have made substantial efforts to develop and implement the SFM paradigm. Indeed, the UK was the first country in the world to certify all of the publicly managed forest. A number of supporting mechanisms and guidance include the UK Forestry Standard (Anon., 2004; currently undergoing revision), and the UK Woodland Assurance Scheme (UKWAS) under which 45% of forests are certified as being sustainably managed (Forestry Commission, 2007).

23.2 The challenge of choosing tree species for the 21st century

Choice of tree species is one of the most important decisions made by forest managers, and is affected by a variety of ecological, financial, and practical considerations (Pyatt et al., 2001). The means of choosing which tree species to plant has been developed from experience of field trials (starting in the 1700s), and experimentation during the 20th century. The choice of species in early afforestation projects evolved through trial and error; later theories of matching tree species to vegetation communities and soil types (Anderson, 1950) were influential, and then soil mapping was adopted as a guide. However, for a period (1970-1990), little use was made of the extensive range of potential species. Instead, species-related choice focused on the type of intervention required to render a site suitable for the preferred species (largely Sitka spruce) through site preparation (including drainage), nutrient addition (typically nitrogen, potassium and phosphate fertilizers), and herbicide treatment. Choice of provenance was coupled with the site modification, harnessing the clinal phenotypic variation present in species that have ranges spanning 20 degrees of latitude. However, this forest management paradigm is now considered unsustainable; it requires high energy inputs, may introduce potential pollutants into the environment, and reduces the contribution that forests provide to ecosystem services. Instead, choice of tree species has increasingly been informed by the development of the Ecological Site Classification (Pyatt et al., 2001) [further details below]. In addition, species choice has been influenced by incentives, for example in supporting a shift to broad-leaved and native tree species (Rodwell and Patterson, 1994) in new planting since 1988. The continuing market demand for softwoods has also meant that restocking of many first rotation forests has been with a similar range of productive conifer species, albeit more carefully chosen to match site limitations.

The Scottish Forestry Strategy (Anon., 2006) suggests further expansion of woodland area in response to climate change amongst other reasons; this was recently supported by the Royal Society of Edinburgh inquiry into the future of Scotland's hills and islands (RSE, 2008) as a 'tough' but worthwhile target. There remains plenty of scope for further tree planting, although land availability may be problematic, but is it more of the same? Are there other factors to be taking into account when deciding the appropriate species and site?

Compared even to a decade or so ago, there are a number of new drivers:

- *Climate change* – the physical reality and the magnitude of the predictions. It is unclear how the future climate will unfold and which of the number of climate change scenarios may be realized. However, from examining the range of scenarios it is possible to identify risks and challenges that are common to all, but differ in terms of intensity or timing (Ray, 2008). This allows preliminary advice on impacts and an appropriate adaptation response to projected scenarios, and can inform species and/or provenance choice (Broadmeadow and Ray, 2005; Hubert and Cottrell, 2007). The forthcoming UK Climate Program 2009 (UKCP09) will provide probabilistic data on climate change outcomes and will substantially strengthen the basis for decision making.
- *Adaptation to climate change* – the strategies and decisions that can be taken to assist in coping with future changes. Choices extend beyond the species/provenance to encompass the appropriate forest management system, including consideration of risk management. Species and provenance choices do provide options for management, but forest managers must assess the risk of not meeting their objectives due to future climate impacts. Impacts can be divided into abiotic and biotic components, although often the damage to woodlands is from a combination of both (Green and Ray, 2009). Early recommendations on adaptation are based broadly on spreading risk by, for example, establishment and management of mixed species woodlands and mixed age structures. This is not possible in all situations. For example, the thinning of mixed stands on some sites may not be feasible because of the risk of wind damage in future climates (Quine and Gardiner, 2002). However, there can be growth benefits of mixing conifers and broadleaves (Frivold and Frank, 2002), the approach may be cost neutral (Nichols *et al.*, 2006), and there can be improvements in biodiversity and reduction in pest damage (Barbaro *et al*., 2007; Jactel and Brockerhoff, 2007).
- *Mitigation of climate change through policies and practice* - a range of measures is being developed that seek to mitigate future effects, including some specific to forestry. There are considerable differences in the productivity of species that may be suited to a particular site. More research is needed to help foresters choose the appropriate species to match site constraints but

Plate 23.5 Mixed land uses and a range of woodland types in Dumfries and Galloway. © Lorne Gill/SNH

that would still meet the objectives for end products. This research will need to assess the carbon lifecycle of products (Newell and Stavins, 2000; Broadmeadow and Matthews, 2003).

- *New markets* - such as biofuels and carbon offsetting. Should faster or slower growing species be selected for biofuel production and carbon sequestration? More research is needed to clarify how soil carbon and nitrogen pools, nitrogen uptake and root turnover rate are affected by site conditions (Xenakis *et al.*, 2008).
- *Woodland expansion* - including the development of woodland habitat networks. There are challenges in assessing the benefit of developing woodland networks – not least in predicting the land that may become available, and how expansion can occur without compromising open ground networks. Current approaches assess the functional connectivity of habitat for focal species (Watts *et al.*, 2007; Humphrey *et al.*, 2009).
- *Biodiversity legislation and policy* – influencing the woodland species targeted for management. The list of woodland species that foresters proactively manage are set by statute (implementation of the EC Habitats Directive through the Nature Conservation (Scotland) Act 2004), and policy (UKBAP). Research provides guidance (www.forestresearch.gov.uk/saps) and best practice support (Ray and Broome, 2007).
- *Integrated decisions* – including environmental linkages and ecosystem approaches. A growing interest in ecosystem services such as flood control (Anon., 2003), erosion control (Anon., 1998), landscape character (Anon., 1994), the attraction of 'naturalness' provided by forests, and the possible health benefits of exercise in these environments; and the continued pressure to reduce chemical inputs (not least as a requirement under certification) (Anon., 2004).

And some drivers remain influential:

- *Sustainable economic growth and security of supply for the domestic timber industry* – which has now developed to utilize the harvest from the forests established in the past century.
- *Tradition, values and beliefs* – including the perceived benefits of use of local, native, and even site-native tree species; past experiences of use of particular tree species and the extent to which seed and plant availability reflects past demands.

These drivers suggest a number of challenges – which species will be most suited to the climates of today and tomorrow? Which species will provide for the range of services (and markets) in the future? Are different species needed for the different contexts of new planting, replanting (restocking), transformation and conversion? Will the choice of tree species continue to be at the restocking stage? With a move towards continuous cover forestry and increased reliance upon natural regeneration will there then be an acceptance of the species that are already present and providing the seed rain – or continued attempts to amend the composition, e.g. through enrichment planting or selective thinning?

23.3 Solutions to some of the challenges of species choice and management

Research is underway to provide the evidence to support decision making in this new context. Current knowledge is being condensed into a number of decision aids to provide guidance to foresters. Two are briefly described here, and comments introduced on two areas for further development and reappraisal of existing practice.

23.3.1 Ecological Site Classification (ESC)

The Ecological Site Classification (ESC) (Pyatt *et al*., 2001) has been based upon principles developed in Canada (Pojar *et al*., 1987) and Europe (Wagenknecht *et al*., 1956; Kuusipalo, 1985; Ellenberg, 1988) that identified linkages between site characteristics and tree species suitability. This tool has been developed for use by foresters in choosing how best to match species to the character of a site as determined from soil and climate constraints (Figure 23.1). The underlying principle is that a good ecological match will reduce the need for chemical interventions to redress site nutrition, and improve plant vigour (and thus pest/disease resistance).

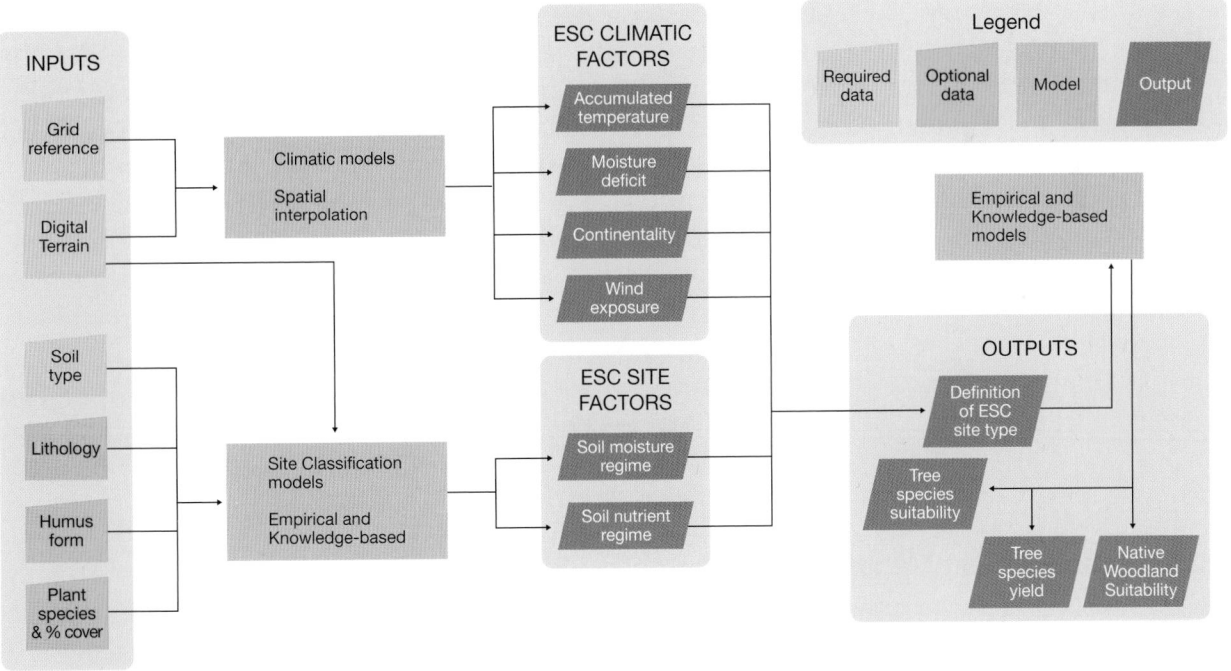

Figure 23.1 Schematic representation of Ecological Site Classification showing the bio-physical elements of the site classification system that cover climate and soil quality.

Recently, ESC has been further adapted to incorporate new climate projections and guidance (Ray, 2008). Figure 23.2 illustrates the use of ESC to model the impact of climate change projections on suitability for two species, Scots pine and Sitka spruce. The legend describes changes in suitability from the baseline climate to the projected climate in 2080 for the Low emissions (IPCC B1) and High emissions (IPCC A1FI) scenarios. The upper pair of maps show suitability changes for Sitka spruce, and depict conditions of generally increasing suitability in western Scotland – from Unsuitable to Suitable, and from Suitable to Very Suitable. However, in the east of Scotland suitability tends to decline – Very Suitable to Suitable, and Suitable to Unsuitable. These projected changes result from a warmer climate generally, with the potential to improve yield and suitability; in the east, projected higher moisture deficits of 180 mm or more would render sites too droughty for spruce. The lower pair of maps show a projected change in the suitability for Scots pine. Scots pine is more tolerant of a dry climate and dry sites than Sitka spruce, and so the Low emissions scenario climate of 2080 shows the suitability associated with the baseline climate is largely maintained, with some increase in east, central, and south Scotland. However, the projections of a more extreme moisture deficit in the High emissions scenario suggest a decline in the suitability and yield of Scots pine in parts of the eastern lowlands of Scotland, particularly Angus, Fife, Clackmannanshire, and the Lothians. It is worth remembering that these projections are based on average climatic conditions. It will be the increased frequency and severity of extreme events that will have most impact upon suitability of sites that are currently borderline for particular species.

There remain problems with representing the climatic extremes, including drought, wind and frost, as these are influential but poorly characterized thus far in climate projections. The forthcoming UKCP09 projections may provide more assistance, coupled with existing risk models such as ForestGALES (Gardiner and Quine, 2000). There are also substantial uncertainties over the potential for changing populations of pests and pathogens due to adjustments in ecology, phenology, epidemiology, and the complement of species associated with climate change. With respect to tree species choice, the most recent analysis recommended that care should be exercised in the selection of drought-sensitive species (including Sitka spruce) on freely draining soils in the east of Scotland, but that species choice may expand in a number of other locations (Ray, 2008). The analysis does not claim to be the final word but to contribute to, and provide early warning of the need for, adaptive management. In the absence of such prompts to think of the possible futures, it is likely that species choice for some sites will be based on the ease of early establishment rather than long-term growth and survival.

23.3.2 Establishment Management Information System (EMIS)

A second information system seeks to integrate the wide-ranging information needed to make decisions over establishment of new forests/trees so that they make a rapid and cost-effective contribution to woodland expansion or replacement (Perks *et al.*, 2007). EMIS draws upon information from many technical and scientific publications and is dynamically coupled with ESC, providing a web-delivered source of advice for tree establishment.

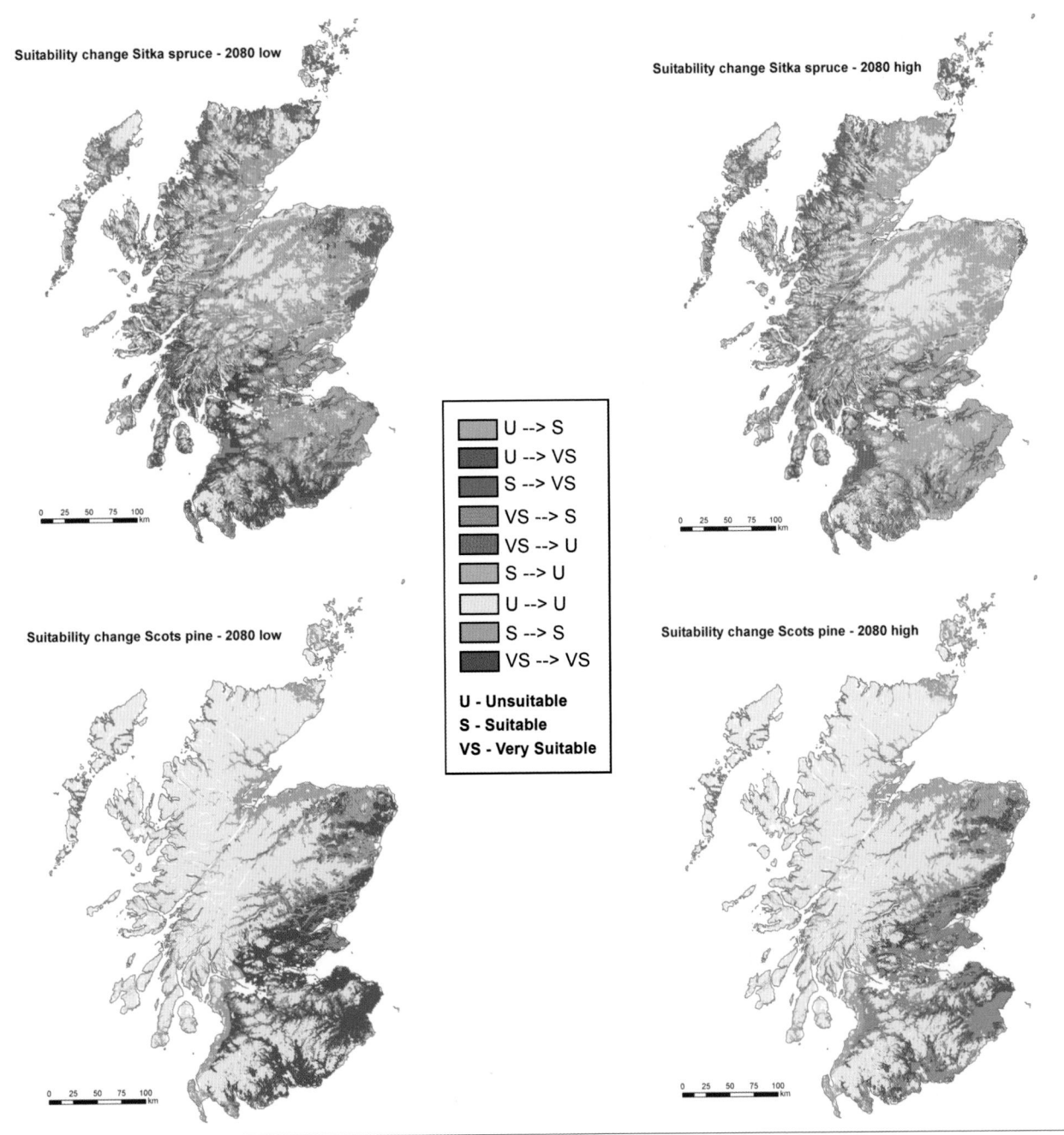

Suitability change Sitka spruce - 2080 low

Suitability change Sitka spruce - 2080 high

Suitability change Scots pine - 2080 low

Suitability change Scots pine - 2080 high

U --> S
U --> VS
S --> VS
VS --> S
VS --> U
S --> U
U --> U
S --> S
VS --> VS

U - Unsuitable
S - Suitable
VS - Very Suitable

Figure 23.2 Projected changes in the suitability of Sitka spruce (*Picea sitchensis*) and Scots pine (*Pinus sylvestris*) using Ecological Site Classification for the 30 year period climate projections (Low–IPCCB2; and High – IPCC A1 emissions scenarios) centred on 2080.

23.3.3 Multi-Criteria Decision Analysis (MCDA)

The range of contemporary drivers that is noted above is clearly challenging even when tools exist to provide some supporting knowledge. It is likely that new forms of decision-making are required that address the multiple influences, requirements and information sources (Reynolds *et al.*, 2007). One such technique is MCDA. This has been developed to guide where coniferous forest should be located, but the technique could also be applied to choice of species. At present, such decisions lack a formal structure and reflect the knowledge of the forest manager, the influence of advisers (particularly those offering incentives), and sometimes the views of consultees through an EIA (Environmental Impact Assessment) process.

23.3.4 A focus on adaptedness rather than nativeness?

At present there are two divergent trends in tree species management in forestry – the development of a 'land race' of introduced species to yield desirable timber; and an apparent default recommendation of 'native' (and occasionally 'site native') for any planting for the delivery of wider goods and services. Where the two trends converge is in the choice of 'local' material – not just native, but adapted by previous generations of presence on the site or similar sites. There appears to be scope for further sophistication and elaboration of such policy and practice. This deserves consideration because of the growing evidence for the substantial biodiversity within non-native forests (Brockerhoff *et al.*, 2008); and because 'many of the guidelines that emphasize the use of local stock were developed before the likely rate and magnitude of climate change were fully appreciated' (Hubert and Cottrell, 2007). There will undoubtedly remain a place for strict conservation of genetic integrity, but there will be many more situations where a more flexible approach is required to ensure that the tree species within woodlands are ecologically matched to both the present and the future climate. An appropriate use of genetic diversity could provide flexibility for forest management and a degree of risk reduction, for example avoiding poor performance or mass mortality. Hubert and Cottrell (2007) offer three strategies to accommodate climate change at a site through the choice of genetic material, and note that each has a mix of risks and benefits. They suggest that within these strategies, and most particularly when considering assisted migration, there is an implied choice – a preference for the maintenance of evolutionary processes, or a preference for the maintenance of functioning woodland. We clearly have some way to go to resolve the solution for this challenge!

23.3.5 Reluctant predictions of future composition

How might the make up of Scottish forests change in response to these drivers and these decision aids? Crystal-ball gazing is always risky! Who can say with confidence what type of world will Scotland occupy? The socio-economic characteristics, as well as the climate, will shape species choice in the future. Fuel security, carbon costs, and the need to make efficient use of a distinctly finite land area may focus interest in the productive potential of forests, perhaps using improved progeny exhibiting faster growth. The expense (ecological and energy wise) of site modifiers such as herbicides and fertilizer, may focus attention on matching ecological characteristics to the site type. A rapid shift to warmer and wetter climate may encourage use of a broader range of tree species. Acceptance of naturalized rather than nativeness as a key ecological character may be increasingly adopted, and compositional shifts in native woodland may be accepted in the face of naturally regenerating non-native species (and other calls on conservation budgets). But conservationists and foresters are inherently conservative and may prefer to adhere to the comfort of concepts such as 'native', and familiar species such as Sitka spruce. Our prediction – if forced – is for no major change in species composition, excepting small increases in southerly broadleaves (beech, sycamore), some new exotics that yield rapid carbon sequestration (eucalyptus, GM willow and poplar), but rather more significant changes to structure and layout of forests as management becomes increasingly sophisticated in its attempt to provide sustainable forests in a changing world.

23.4 Concluding remarks

The chapter has discussed some of the developments in the way foresters manage species in forests – most particularly through choice of tree species to plant. Indirect species management is, however, also likely to be of considerable significance to wider species guilds present in woodlands. The location of forests within landscapes may be influential in aiding the response of many woodland species to environmental change. As a consequence, tools are being developed to aid the development of habitat networks (Watts *et al.*, 2007, 2008). The management of stands and individual woods can substantially influence the quality of habitat provided by woodland (Humphrey *et al.*, 2006). Previous management history of reforested land is also critical to habitat quality (Honnay *et al.*, 1999). Relatively minor changes to practice can yield substantial benefits, e.g. deadwood management (Humphrey *et al.*, 2002), and targeted habitat management for rare priority and protected species (Ray *et al.*, 2007) such as capercaillie (Kortland, 2005). Increasingly foresters understand that a forest is composed of more than the species planted – and thus the choice of tree to plant is but one part of the species management that goes on (directly/indirectly; consciously/unwittingly) all the time.

Acknowledgement

The authors are grateful to colleagues and referees for their comments; the views expressed are our own.

References

Anderson, M.L. (1950). *The selection of tree species*. Oliver & Boyd, Edinburgh.

Anon. (1994). *Forest Landscape Design Guidelines*. Forestry Commission, Edinburgh.

Anon. (1998). *Forests and Soil Conservation Guidelines*. Forestry Commission, Edinburgh.

Anon. (2003). *Forests and Water Guidelines*. Forestry Commission, Edinburgh.

Anon. (2004). *The UK Forestry Standard* (2nd edition). Forestry Commission GB and Forest Service Northern Ireland, Edinburgh & Belfast.

Anon. (2006). *The Scottish Forestry Strategy*. Forestry Commission Scotland, Edinburgh.

Barbaro, L., Rossi, J.-P., Vetillard, F., Nezan, J. & Jactel, H. (2007). The spatial distribution of birds and carabid beetles in pine plantation forests: the role of landscape composition and structure. *Journal of Biogeography* **34**: 652-664.

Broadmeadow, M. & Matthews, R. (2003). Forests, carbon and climate change: the UK contribution. *Information Note 48*, Forestry Commission, Edinburgh.

Broadmeadow, M. & Ray, D. (2005). Climate Change and British Woodland. *Information Note 69*, Forestry Commission, Edinburgh.

Brockerhoff, E.G., Jactel, H., Parrotta, J.A., Quine, C.P. & Sayer, J. (2008). Plantation forests and biodiversity: oxymoron or opportunity? *Biodiversity Conservation* **17**: 925-951.

Broome, A., Quine, C., Trout, R., Poulsom, E. & Mayle, B. (2005). Research in support of the UK Biodiversity Action Plan: forest management and priority species. In *Forest Research Annual Report and Accounts 2003-2004*. Edinburgh, HMSO: 112-125.

Brown, A. & Webber, J. (2008). Red band needle blight of conifers in Britain. *Research Note 002*, Forestry Commission, Edinburgh.

Brown, A., Rose, D. & Webber, J. (2003). Red band needle blight of pine. *Information Note 49*, Forestry Commission, Edinburgh.

Davis, M.B. (1983). Quaternary History of Deciduous Forests of Eastern North America and Europe. *Annals of the Missouri Botanical Garden* **70**(3): 550-563.

Edwards, C. (2006). Managing and controlling invasive rhododendron. *Practice Guide*. Forestry Commission, Edinburgh.

Ellenberg, H. (1988). *Vegetation ecology of Central Europe*. Cambridge University Press, Cambridge.

Forestry Commission. (2007). *Forestry Facts and Figures*. Forestry Commission, Edinburgh.

Forrest, G.I. & Fletcher, A.M. (1995). Implications of genetics research for native pinewood conservation. In *'Our pinewood heritage'*, Ed. J.R. Aldhous. Forestry Commission, Royal Society for the Protection of Birds, and Scottish Natural Heritage, Edinburgh. pp. 97-106.

Frivold, L.H. & Frank, J. (2002). Growth of mixed birch-coniferous stands in relation to pure coniferous stands at similar sites in south-eastern Norway. *Scandinavian Journal of Forest Research* **17**: 139-149.

Gardiner, B.A. & Quine, C.P. (2000). Management of forests to reduce the risk of abiotic damage - a review with particular reference to the effects of strong winds. *Forest Ecology and Management* **135**: 261-277.

Gill, R. (2000). The Impact of Deer on Woodland Biodiversity. *Information Note 36*. Forestry Commission, Edinburgh.

Green, S. and Ray, D. (in press). Climate Change: Risks to Forestry in Scotland due to Drought and Fungal Disease. *Research Note*. Forestry Commission Edinburgh.

Honnay, O., Hermy, M. & Coppin, P. (1999). Impact of habitat quality on forest plant species colonisation. *Forest Ecology and Management* **115**: 157-170.

Hubert, J. & Cottrell, J. (2007). The role of forest genetic resources in helping British forests respond to climate change. *Information Note 86*, Forestry Commission, Edinburgh, UK.

Humphrey, J. W. (2005). Benefits to biodiversity from developing old-growth conditions in British upland conifer plantations: a review. *Forestry* **78**: 33-53.

Humphrey, J.W., Davey, S., Peace, A.J., Ferris, R. & Harding, K. (2002). Lichens and bryophyte communities of planted and semi-natural forests in Britain: the influence of site type, stand structure and deadwood. *Biological Conservation* **107**(2): 165-180.

Humphrey, J. W., Ferris, R. & Quine, C. P. (Eds). (2003). *Biodiversity in Britain's planted forests: results from the Forestry Commission's biodiversity assessment project.* Edinburgh, Forestry Commission.

Humphrey, J., Quine, C. & Watts, K. (2006). The influence of forest and woodland management on biodiversity in Scotland: recent findings and future prospects. In *Farming, forestry and the natural heritage: towards a more integrated approach,* Eds R. Davison and C.A. Galbraith, Scottish Natural Heritage, Edinburgh, pp. 59-75.

Humphrey, J.W., Ray, D., Brown, T., Stone, D., Watts, K. & Anderson, A.R. (2009). Using focal species modelling to evaluate the impact of land use change on forest and other habitat networks in western oceanic landscapes. *Forestry* **82**: 119-134.

Huntley, B. (1993). Species-richness in north-temperate zone forests. *Journal of Biogeography* **20**(2): 163-180.

Jactel, H. & Brockerhoff, E.G. (2007). Tree diversity reduces herbivory by forest insects. *Ecology Letters* **10**(9): 835-848.

Kortland, K. (2006). *Forest management for Capercaillie: an illustrated guide for forest managers.* Highland Birchwoods, Inverness.

Kuusipalo, J. (1985). An ecological study of upland forest site classification in Southern Finland. *Acta Forestalia Fennica* **192**: 1-78.

Lee, S. (2004). The Products of Conifer Tree Breeding in Britain. *Information Note 58*. Forestry Commission, Edinburgh.

Marquiss, M. & Rae, R. (2002). Ecological differentiation in relation to bill size amongst sympatric, genetically undifferentiated crossbills *Loxia* spp. *Ibis* **144**: 494-508.

Mayle, B., Ferryman, M. & Pepper, H. (2007). Controlling Grey Squirrel Damage to Woodlands. *Practice Note 4*. Forestry Commission, Edinburgh.

MCPFE. (1993). Helsinki Declaration. The second Ministerial Conference on the Protection of Forest in Europe. www.mcpfe.org/resolutions/helsinki

Newell, R.G. & Stavins, R.N. (2000). Climate Change and Forest Sinks: Factors Affecting the Costs of Carbon Sequestration. *Journal of Environmental Economics and Management* **40**: 211-235.

Nichols, J.D., Bristow, M. & Vanclay, J.K. (2006). Mixed-species plantations: Prospects and challenges. *Forest Ecology and Management* **233**(2-3): 383-390.

Perks, M.P., Harrison, A.J. & Bathgate, S.J. (2007). Establishment Management Information System (EMIS): Delivering Good Practice Advice on Tree Establishment in the Uplands of Britain. In *Sustainable Forestry: from monitoring and modelling to knowledge management and policy science,* Eds K.M. Reynolds, A.J.Thomson, M.Kohl, M.A.Shannon, D.Ray and K.Rennolls. CAB International, Wallingford, pp. 412-424.

Pojar, J., Klinka, K. & Meidinger, D.V. (1987). Biogeoclimatic Ecosystem Classification in British Columbia. *Forest Ecology and Management* **22**: 119-154.

Pyatt, D.G., Ray, D. & Fletcher, J. (2001). An Ecological Site Classification for Forestry in Great Britain. *Bulletin 124*. Forestry Commission, Edinburgh.

Quine, C. & Gardiner, B. (2002). Climate Change Impacts: Storms. In *Climate Change: Impacts on UK Forests,* Ed. by M.S.J. Broadmeadow. Forestry Commission Bulletin 125, Forestry Commission, Edinburgh, pp 41-52.

Quine, C. P., Fuller, R. J., Smith, K. W. & Grice, P. V. (2007). Stand management: a threat or opportunity for birds in British woodland? *Ibis* **149**(s2): 161-174.

Ray, D. (2008). Impacts of climate change on forests in Scotland – a preliminary synopsis of spatial modelling research. *Forestry Commission Research Note 001*. Forestry Commission, Edinburgh.

Ray, D. & Broome, A.C. (2007). An information retrieval system to support management of Habitats and Rare Priority and Protected Species(HaRPPS) in Britain. In *Sustainable Forestry: from Monitoring and Modelling to Knowledge Management and Policy Science,* Eds K.M. Reynolds, A.J.Thomson, M.Kohl, M.A.Shannon, D.Ray and K.Rennolls. CAB International, Wallingford, UK. pp480-496.

Ray, D., Broome, A.C., Brunt, A., Brown, T. & Vials, C. (2007). An information system to support sustainable management of Habitats and Rare Priority and Protected Species (HaRPPS) in British forests. In *Sustainable Forestry in Theory and Practice,* Ed. K.M. Reynolds. USDA Forest Service, Corvalis, USA.

Reynolds, K.M., Thomson, A.J., Kohl, M., Shannon, M.A., Ray, D. & Rennolls, K. (Eds). (2007). Sustainable Forestry: from monitoring and modelling to knowledge management and policy science. CAB International, Wallingford. 527pp.

Rodwell, J.S. & Patterson, G.S. (1994). Creating new native woodlands. *Forestry Commission Bulletin 112*. Forestry Commission, Edinburgh.

Rollinson, T. J. D. (2003). The UK policy context. In *The restoration of wooded landscapes,* Eds J. W. Humphrey, A. Newton, J. Latham, H. Gray, K. J. Kirby, E. G. Poulsom, and C. P. Quine. Forestry Commission, Edinburgh. pp. 3-6.

Royal Society of Edinburgh. (2008). *Inquiry into the future of Scotland's hills and islands*, Royal Society of Edinburgh, Edinburgh.

Stroud, D.A., Reed, T.M., Pienkowski, M.W. & Lindsay, R.A. (1988). *Birds, bogs and forestry - The peatlands of Caithness and Sutherland*. Eds D.A. Ratcliffe and P.H. Oswald, Nature Conservancy Council.

Wagenknecht, E., Scammoni, A., Richter, A. & Lehmann, J. (1956). *Eberswalde 1953: Wege zu Standortgerechter Forstwirtschaft*. Newmann Verlag, Berlin, 523 pp.

Watts, K., Ray, D., Quine, C., Humphrey, J. & Griffiths, M. (2007). Evaluating Biodiversity in Fragmented Landscapes: Applications of Landscape Ecology Tools. *Forestry Commission Information Note 085*, Forestry Commission, Edinburgh.

Watts, K., Quine, C.P., Ray, D., Eycott, A.E., Moseley, D. & Humphrey, J.W. (2008). Conserving Forest Biodiversity: Recent Approaches in UK Forest Planning and Management. In *Patterns and Processes in Forest Landscapes Multiple Use and Sustainable Management*, Eds R. Lafortezza, J. Chen, G. Sanesi, and T.R. Crow. Springer, Netherlands, pp 375-400.

Willoughby, I., Evans, H., Gibbs, J., Pepper, H., Gregory, S., Dewar, J., Pratt, J. & McKay, H. (2004). *Reducing pesticide use in forestry*. Forestry Commission Practice Guide, Forestry Commission, Edinburgh, 140pp.

Xenakis, G., Ray, D. & Mencuccini, M. (2008). Sensitivity and uncertainty analysis from a coupled 3-PG and soil organic matter decomposition model. *Ecological Modelling* **219**: 1-16.

Quine, C. and Ray, D. (2010). Sustainable forestry – which species for which site for which world? In: *Species Management: Challenges and Solutions for the 21st Century*, ed. by J.M. Baxter and C.A. Galbraith. TSO Scotland, Edinburgh. pp. 417-434

Chapter 24

Using technology to forward fisheries science: the sea scallop example

Kevin D.E. Stokesbury[1], Bradley P. Harris[1], Michael C. Marino II[1] and Catherine E. O'Keefe[1]

Summary

1. Sea scallops, *Placopecten magellanicus*, support one of the most valuable fishing industries in the United States. Large fluctuations in landings during the 1980s and a steady decline in harvest during the mid-1990s had severe effects on the fishing industry.

2. Fishing effort limits were implemented in 1994, but the sea scallop stock remained in an overfished condition. Three large areas, closed in 1994 to protect groundfish stocks, excluded scallopers from historically important fishing grounds on Georges Bank. At the time of closure, scallop densities in these areas were low and the fleet was fishing the Mid-Atlantic. After four years of closure, scallop biomasses were believed to be high within these areas, but the quantities were unknown.

3. In 1999, we developed a new cooperative video survey protocol designed to estimate the absolute number of scallops in closed and open areas. This coincided with a period of increased recruitment and reduced fishing mortality. Since then the sea scallop resource has made a spectacular recovery attaining record landings.

4. In 2003, the survey was expanded to the entire commercial sea scallop resource in US waters. Stock assessment results indicated that sea scallops were no longer overfished. In 2007, it was estimated there were 300 million lbs (130,000 mt) of harvestable scallops on the sea floor worth approximately US $2 billion. Management of this recovered resource, including the efficiency of area-rotational fishing, effects on marine habitat, and methods for tracking population status of the sea scallops are all under examination.

[1] Department of Fisheries Oceanography, School for Marine Science and Technology, Marine Fisheries Institute, University of Massachusetts Dartmouth, 200 Mill Road, Suite 300, Fairhaven, Massachusetts, USA 02719

Sea scallops (*Placopecten magellanicus*). © SMAST Scallop Survey Digital Still Imag

Estimating the abundance of marine species is difficult. Traditional fisheries assessments generally use modified commercial gear or fisheries landing data to provide relative abundance estimates recorded in catch per unit effort (CPUE) such as kg per tow. Critical population rates (e.g. recruitment, mortality) are derived from changes in CPUE over time. These sampling approaches generally focus on the target species of the fishery, and collect information on other species incidentally (by-catch). The efficiency and selectivity of this gear is usually unknown. With standardized sampling protocols, observed changes in CPUE are assumed to reflect changes in the populations surveyed not variations in the sample design (Hilborn and Walters, 1992; Gunderson, 1993). We believe that this assumption is often invalid and that sampling uncertainties are so large that they frequently mask vital population measures.

We argue that fisheries researchers should return to fundamental principles of field ecology; seek absolute measures (numbers per unit area) and determine the associated uncertainties (Stokesbury *et al,*. 2009). The implementation of these principles using new technology to examine the sea scallop fishery of the north-east Untied States is described.

24.1.1 The US sea scallop fishery

Sea scallops have been fished continuously on Georges Bank and in the Mid-Atlantic since the end of World War II, and are one of New England's major fisheries (Serchuck *et al.,* 1979; Caddy, 1989; Murawski *et al.*, 2000) (Figure 24.1). Two spatial management changes drastically altered fishing distribution replacing the traditional unrestricted movement of the fleet from one aggregation to another. In 1977 the Hague Line divided eastern Georges Bank between Canada and the United States. In 1994 three large areas (17,000 km^2) of the United States portion of Georges Bank were closed to mobile gear fisheries in an effort to protect depleted groundfish stocks (Murawski *et al.,* 2000) (Figure 24.2). These changes substantially reduced the scallop grounds available to the fishing fleet and concentrated intense fishing pressure on the remaining open areas.

Figure 24.1 Captain Tommy Manley onboard the F/V *Stardust* of New Bedford, Massachusetts. The commercial scallop dredge can be seen on the side of the vessel. © K. Stokesbury

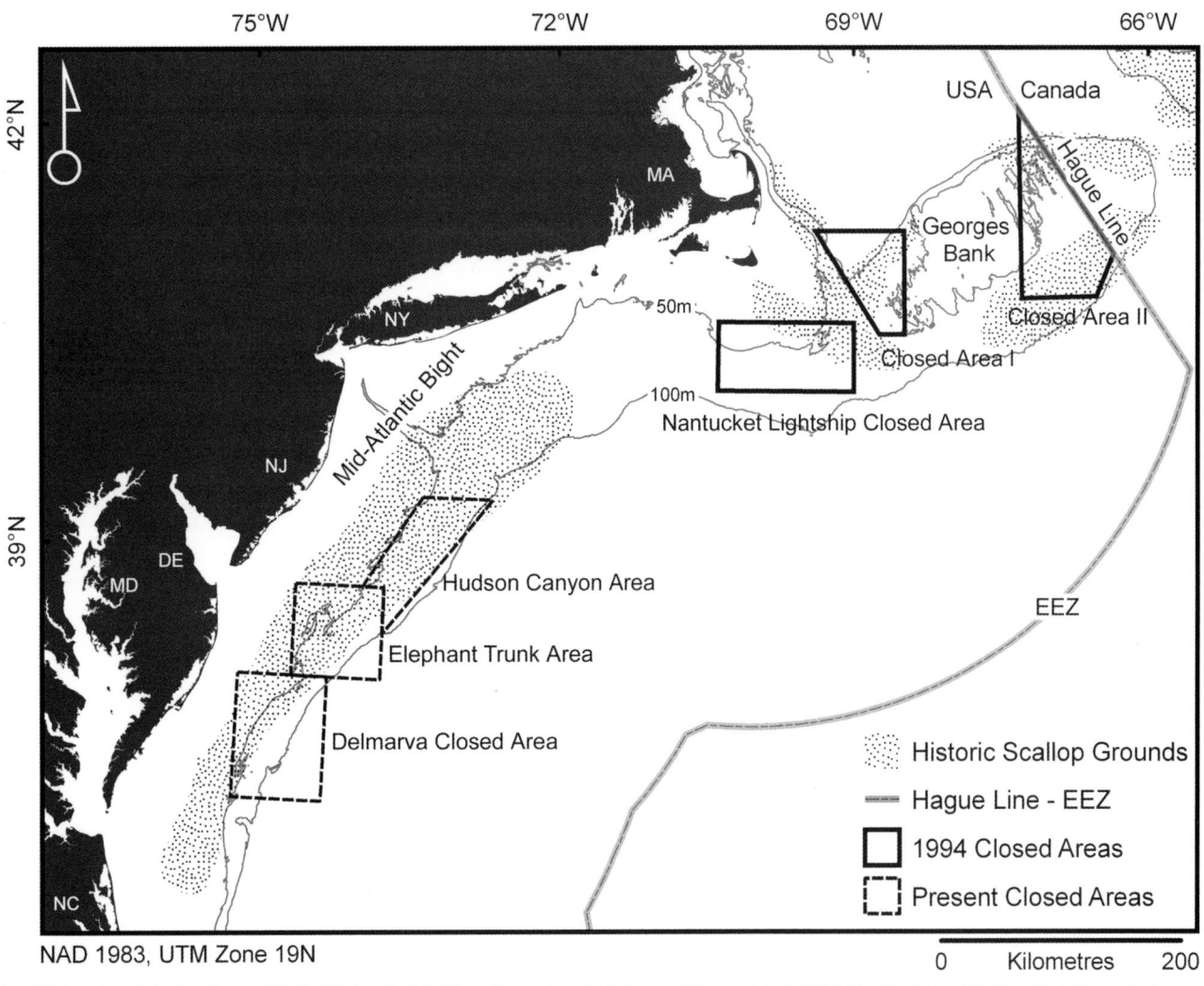

Figure 24.2 The historic sea scallop fishing grounds (Sinclair *et al.*, 1985; Brand, 2006) adapted with input from New Bedford scallop fishermen), including the groundfish closed areas on Georges Bank and the scallop closed areas in the Mid-Atlantic.

By 1998 the scallop fishery was facing severe restrictions. Landings had dropped by 68% from 17,288 mt in 1991 to 5,489 mt in 1997 (NMFS, 2007). Fishermen were desperate for access into the large closed areas of Georges Bank that had supported their traditional fishery, however, the National Marine Fisheries Service (NMFS) scallop survey suggested that scallop abundance was low within these areas (Atlantic Sea Scallop Fishery Management Plan Stock Assessment and Fishery Evaluation Report 1999, New England Fishery Management Council, 50 Water Street, Mill 2 Newburyport, MA, 01950, page 93).

The NMFS scallop survey uses a modified New Bedford style commercial dredge towed by a scientific research vessel, and a stratified random survey design (Hart and Rago, 2006). There is a great deal of uncertainty concerning the efficiency of scallop dredges and small differences may have large effects on biomass estimates. For example if the relative biomass estimate was 10,000 mt with a 40% dredge efficiency the biomass would be 25,000 mt but with a 20% efficiency the biomass would be 50,000 mt. Furthermore, the Georges Bank closed areas subdivided the existing survey strata confounding the assessment. The increased scallop densities in closed areas due to the reduction of fishing mortality violated the within-strata homogeneity assumptions of the stratified random sampling design (Krebs, 1979).

24.2 The SMAST sea scallop video survey

Working cooperatively with the scallop fishermen we set out to develop a video survey using quadrat techniques based on scuba diving studies (Stokesbury and Himmelman, 1993, 1995) that would provide spatially explicit, accurate, precise, absolute estimates of sea scallop density and size distributions along the off-shore north-east waters of the United States including the Georges Bank closed areas (Stokesbury, 2002; Stokesbury et al., 2004).

In designing this survey we tried to avoid the preconceived notions of formal fisheries stock assessments, such as:

1) estimating biomass rather than the number of individuals, and
2) assuming homogeneous densities within survey strata.

We met with fishermen who outlined their historic fishing grounds. With only very limited funds, sampling gear had to be inexpensive and readily available as a portable system deployable from any commercial scallop fishing vessel. It was also important to avoid the permitting process required to sample in closed areas with fishing gear, which often results in a six month to year delay (or denial). Three scientific principles guided the design:

1) *Scale*: According to scallop population biology, sampling grain needed to be at the scale of centimetres (i.e. individual distribution) and to the extent of 100-1000 of km2 (i.e. bed-level distribution; Stokesbury and Himmelman, 1993, 1995).
2) *Experimentation*: To measure the impact of the scallop fishery on the benthic habitats with a level of precision that allowed statistical testing of a Before-After-Control-Impact (BACI) experiment (Green, 1979; Stokesbury and Harris, 2006).
3) *Continuity*: Sampling in an expandable way such that subsequent surveys would build a mosaic suitable for mapping benthic substrates and macroinvertebrates.

A video-quadrat sampling pyramid with a multistage centric systematic design with three station grid resolutions (1.6, 2.3 and 5.6 km) was developed. Since 1999, 103 video cruises have been completed surveying Georges Bank and the Mid Atlantic (>600 days at sea).

The system is composed of a mobile video recording system compatible with any scallop vessel wheelhouse layout, an electro-hydraulic winch and a sampling pyramid. In its present configuration the sampling pyramid, supports four cameras and eight lights (Stokesbury, 2002; Stokesbury *et al.,* 2004; Figure 24.3).

Within each quadrat, macroinvertebrates and fish are counted and the substrates are identified (Stokesbury, 2002; Stokesbury *et al.,* 2004). Counts are standardized to individuals.m^{-2}. Mean densities and standard errors are calculated using equations for a two-stage sampling design (based on Cochran (1977); reviewed and published in Stokesbury, 2002; Stokesbury *et al.,* 2004, 2007; Harris and Stokesbury, 2006; Stokesbury and Harris, 2006; Marino *et al.,* 2007; Adams *et al.,* 2008).

Presently the video library contains over 240,000 georeferenced video samples covering the 70,000 km^2 of the US commercial scallop resource (Figure 24.4). The database includes over 1 million geological and 6 million biological records. These data permit spatial and temporal assessments of scallop distribution and density in closed and open areas of Georges Bank and the Mid Atlantic and are robust to spatial changes in fisheries management.

Figure 24.3 The SMAST video survey pyramid being prepared for deployment on th F/V *Huntress* by K. Stokesbury and B. Harris. The survey pyramid includes 3 DeepSea video cameras, a 10.1 megapixel digital still camera and 8 lights. In the foreground is the electro-hydraulic winch with a tension sensitive winding unit designed by S. Clingman. © B. Courchene

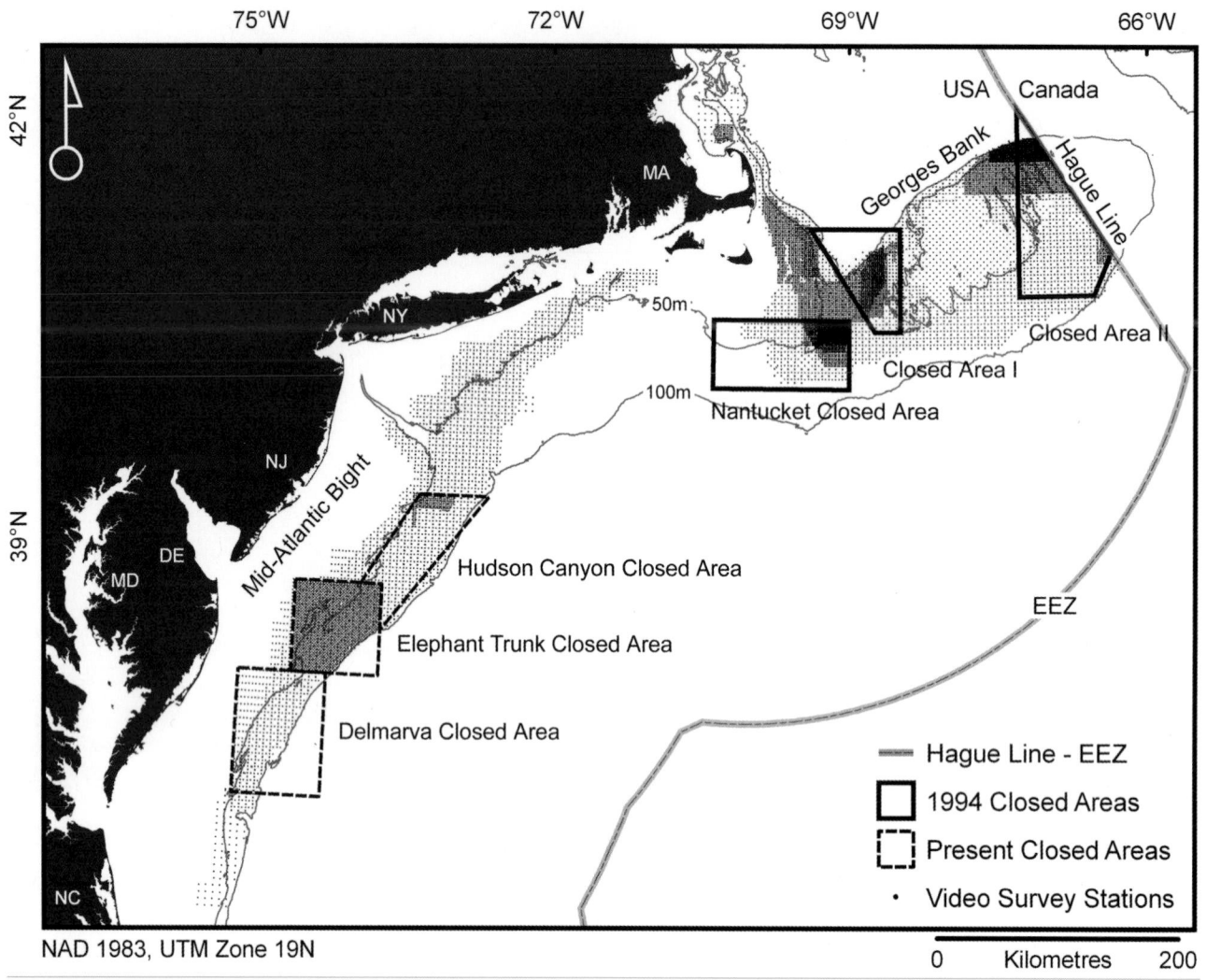

Figure 24.4 The Industry-SMAST video survey of the Mid Atlantic and Georges Bank sea scallop resource surveyed from 1999 to 2008. The survey area was based on the 2002 footprint of the scallop fishing fleet derived from the Vessel Monitoring System (Rago *et al.*, 2000) The annual continental shelf-scale survey stations (5.6 km^2 grid), and the high resolution survey stations (1.6 and 2.2 km^2 grids) are shown in the black areas.

24.3 Results of the video survey

24.3.1 Small-scale surveys

The initial work focused on estimating the density of sea scallops within the closed areas of Georges Bank, where densities ranged from 0.25 to 0.59 scallop.m^{-2} in the three surveyed areas, and 0.58 to

1.06 scallops.m^{-2} at stations where at least one scallop was observed. Sea scallops were highly aggregated into patches (beds) on the scale of km^2 and this distribution was strongly associated with the distribution of coarse sand-granule-pebble substrates (Figure 24.5). The three areas surveyed (total = 1,938 km^2) contained approximately 650 million scallops representing 17,000 mt of harvestable scallop meats. This is equivalent to 54% of the average harvestable scallop meat biomass from 1977 to 1988 and it occurred in 5% of the total scallop fishing grounds of Georges Bank (Stokesbury, 2002).

Figure 24.5 An aggregation of 19 sea scallops, representing three size classes, on a sand and granule pebble substrate in a 1.13 m^2 area. Sand dollars (*Echinarachnius parma*) are also present. © SMAST Scallop Survey Digital Still Image

24.3.2 Large-scale surveys

In 2003, at the request of the scallop fishing industry the video survey was expanded to cover the entire scallop resource in US waters based on the footprint of the 2002 fishery (Figure 24.2). Sea scallop densities in the Mid-Atlantic (26,270 km^2) and Georges Bank (28,523 km^2) ranged from 0.04 to 0.79 and 0.09 to

0.26 scallop.m^{-2}, respectively, and represented approximately 217,520 mt of scallop meats (approximately US $2.4 billion) about twice that estimated by the NMFS (J. Boreman, Director of NEFSC statement to The Standard Times, New Bedford, MA, USA, 4 November 2003). Sea scallops were highly aggregated in areas closed to mobile fishing gear. In the closed areas of the Georges Bank the proportion of sea scallop pre-recruits (<90 mm shell height) was low and sufficient to replace the adult population at an instantaneous mortality rate of 0.10 but not at a higher rate. In the Mid-Atlantic a large number of pre-recruit scallops were observed in the southern portion of the Hudson Canyon Closed Area extending south into open waters. This area, the Elephant Trunk, was closed in 2004, opened in 2007 and has sustained the fishery for the last several years. In some areas scallops were outnumbered by their primary predator, sea stars, by more than 2 to 1 (i.e. 39 to 16 billion) and these may have been responsible for a scallop mass-mortality in the southern portion of Closed Area II (CAII) (Stokesbury *et al.,* 2004) (Figure 24.6).

Figure 24.6 A blood star (*Henricia leviuscula*) and four boreal sea stars, (*Asterias vulgaris*), with six sea scallops and the sponge, (*Suberites ficus*), on a shell debris and granule pebble substrate. © SMAST Scallop Survey Digital Still Image

24.3.3 Mortality

As the first cohort of scallops that were protected by the closed areas aged, natural mortality increased. A mass mortality in the Nantucket Lightship Closed Area (NLCA) was observed between 2004 and 2005 where 80 % of the scallops had shell heights >130 mm (H_∞ = 155 mm), and were assumed to be approximately 10 years old. Individuals of this age may suffer the effects of senescence, including parasitism by shell borers and prokaryotic infection, which likely caused the mass mortality (Stokesbury *et al.*, 2007). The mass mortality equalled approximately 6,484 mt of harvestable scallop meat (US$ 100 million ex-vessel). Only 6 % of the decline was explained by fishing mortality.

24.3.4 Gear impacts on habitat

Whenever possible benthic habitat characteristics were examined before and after closed areas were opened to fishing; from 1999 to 2005 two impact and control areas on Georges Bank were recorded (Stokesbury and Harris, 2006). Changes in the number of taxonomic categories and the density of individuals within each category in the areas impacted by the fishery were similar to changes in the control areas that remained closed to fishing. Furthermore, sediment composition shifted between surveys more than epibenthic faunal composition suggesting that this community is adapted to a dynamic environment. Thus it was concluded that the limited short-term sea scallop fishery on Georges Bank appeared to alter the epibenthic community less than the natural dynamic environmental conditions.

By making the sampling design appropriate to the spatial distribution and density of the dominant commercial macroinvertebrate (sea scallops) it was possible to gather much more information on the make-up of the benthic community and the substrate of the sea floor. The expandable grid sampling approach enabled us to build a mosaic of the sea floor quadrats ideal for mapping habitat parameters like substrate coarseness and heterogeneity.

24.4 Discussion

A rotational management plan for sea scallops was established in 2004 in an amendment to the Magnuson-Stevens Act governing fisheries in US waters (Amendment 10). This plan limited the number of Days-At-Sea (DAS) each vessel could have within the fishing year, the number of crew (processing of the scallop is completed at sea so crew size directly affects the amount of product that can be harvested within a day) and the size of the rings in the dredge. From 2004 to 2008 vessels were limited to about 100 DAS, seven crew including the captain, and a 101.25 mm (4") ring was mandatory in all areas. Based on the density and size of scallops certain portions of the closed areas on Georges Bank and in the Mid-Atlantic were open to limited harvest and a set number of trips were allocated to each fishing vessel. This management strategy focused effort in areas with larger scallops, reducing both the amount of time the dredge was on the sea floor and the number of individuals harvested to make up the catch tonnage. Furthermore, areas with high proportions of pre-recruit scallops were closed to fishing, the largest of these being the Elephant Trunk closed area (ETCA) in the Mid-Atlantic in 2004 (Stokesbury *et al.,* 2004).

The ability to determine with a high degree of certainty the number of scallops, their size and distribution has enabled this rotational management plan. The first of these access programmes began in 1999-2000 and provided an instant increase in harvest of 2,400 mt worth $55 million (Stokesbury, 2002; Hart and Rago, 2006). The sea scallop stock has increased in abundance to a point where it is no longer overfished. The landings have increased nearly four-fold from a yearly average of 7,029 mt worth $87 million (1994 to 1998) to 26,177 mt worth $314 million (2002 to 2006) (NMFS, 2007) (Figure 24.7).

Currently the management decisions incorporate the SMAST video survey and the NMFS dredge survey results. Although the value of having two independent surveys to compare and contrast cannot be overstated, the use of a new cooperative survey design has met with some resistance. Critical to having SMAST data used is the involvement of the faculty and students from the Marine Fisheries Institute,

Figure 24.7 The crew of the F/V *Friendship* pick the pile. Sea scallops are sorted and processed at sea, only the meats are landed. Monkfish, *Lophius americanus*, flounders and skates are collected as by-catch. © Captain Gabe Miranda

University of Massachusetts, Dartmouth in the fisheries management process, acting as members of the Plan Development Teams and Science and Statistical review committees for the New England Fisheries Management Council.

24.5 Acknowledgements

We thank B.J. Rothschild for his support and guidance. We thank the students, staff, owners, Captains, and crews, who sailed with us. The manuscript was greatly improved by the suggestions of an anonymous reviewer and Editor J. M. Baxter. Aid was provided by SMAST, the Massachusetts Division of Marine Fisheries, NOAA awards: NA16FM1031, NA06FM1001, NA16FM2416, NA04NMF4720332, NA05NMF4721131 and NA06NMF472009, and the sea scallop fishery and supporting industries. The views expressed herein are those of the authors and do not necessarily reflect the views of NOAA or any other agencies.

References

Adams, C.F., Harris, B.P. & Stokesbury, K.D.E. (2008). Geostatistical comparison of two independent video surveys of sea scallop abundance in the Elephant Trunk Closed Area, USA. *ICES Journal of Marine Science* **65**: 995-1003.

Brand, A.R. (2006). Scallop ecology: distributions and behaviour. In: *Scallops: biology, ecology and aquaculture*. Eds Shumway, S.E. and Parson, G.J. Elsevier, Amsterdam, pp. 651-744.

Caddy, J.F. (1989). A perspective on the population dynamics and assessment of scallop fisheries, with special reference to sea scallop, *Placopecten magellanicus* (Gmelin). In: *Marine invertebrate fisheries: their assessment and management* Ed. Caddy, J.F. John Wiley & Sons, New York, pp. 559-589.

Cochran, W.G. (1977). *Sampling Techniques*. John Wiley & Sons, New York.

Green, R.H. (1979). *Sampling design and statistical methods for environmental biologists*. John Wiley & Sons, New York.

Gunderson, D.R. (1993). *Surveys of Fisheries Resources*. John Wiley& Sons, New York.

Harris, B.P. & Stokesbury, K.D.E. (2006). Shell growth of sea scallops (*Placopecten magellanicus* Gmelin, 1791) in the southern and northern Great South Channel, USA. *ICES Journal of Marine Science* **63**: 811-821.

Hart, D.R. & Rago, P.J. (2006). Long-term dynamics of U.S. Atlantic sea scallop *Placopecten magellanicus* populations. *North American Journal of Fisheries Management* **26**: 490-501.

Hilborn, R. & Walters, C.J. (1992). *Quantitative fisheries stock assessment: choice, dynamics and uncertainty*. Chapman & Hall, Inc., New York.

Krebs, C. J. (1989). *Ecological Methodology*. Harper & Row, New York.

Marino II, M.C., Juanes, F. & Stokesbury, K.D.E. (2007). Effect of closed areas on populations of sea star, *Asterias* spp., on Georges Bank. *Marine Ecology Progress Series* **347**: 39-49.

Murawski, S.A., Brown, R., Lai, H.-L., Rago, P.J. & Hendrickson, L. (2000). Large-scale closed areas as a fishery-management tool in temperate marine ecosystems: the Georges Bank experience. *Bulletin of Marine Science* **66**: 775-798.

NMFS. (2007). 45th Northeast regional stock assessment workshop. National Oceanic and Atmospheric Administration, National Marine Fisheries Service, Northeast Fisheries Science Center, Woods Hole, MA.

Rago, P.J., Murawski, S., Stokesbury, K.D.E., DuPaul, W. & McSherry, M. (2000). Integrated management of the sea scallop fishery in the northeast USA: research and commercial vessel surveys, observers, and vessel monitoring systems *ICES Marine Science Symposium* CM2000/W:**13**: pp. 18.

Serchuk, F.M., Wood, P.W., Posgay, J.A. & Brown, B.E. (1979). Assessment and status of sea scallop (*Placopecten magellanicus*) populations off the Northeast coast of the United States. *Proceedings of the National Shellfish Association* **69**: 161-191.

Sinclair, M., Mohn, R.K., Robert, G. & Roddick, D.L. (1985). Considerations for the effective management of Atlantic scallops. *Canadian Technical Report of Fisheries and Aquatic Sciences* **1382**: 1-99.

Stokesbury, K.D.E. (2002). Estimation of sea scallop, *Placopecten magellanicus*, abundance in closed areas of Georges Bank. *Transactions of the American Fisheries Society* **131**: 1081-1092.

Stokesbury, K.D.E. & Harris, B.P. (2006). Impact of a limited fishery for sea scallop, *Placopecten magellanicus*, on the epibenthic community of Georges Bank closed areas, *Marine Ecology Progress Series* **307**: 85-100.

Stokesbury, K.D.E. & Himmelman, J.H. (1993). Spatial distribution of the giant scallop *Placopecten magellanicus* in unharvested beds in the Baie des Chaleurs, Québec. *Marine Ecology Progress Series* **96**: 159-168.

Stokesbury, K.D.E. & Himmelman, J.H. (1995). Biological and physical variables associated with aggregations of the giant scallop *Placopecten magellanicus*. *Canadian Journal of Fisheries and Aquatic Sciences* **52**: 743-753.

Stokesbury, K.D.E., Harris, B.P., Marino II, M.C. & Nogueira, J.I. (2004). Estimation of sea scallop abundance using a video survey in off-shore USA waters. *Journal of Shellfish Research* **23**: 33-44.

Stokesbury, K.D.E., Harris, B.P., Marino II, M.C. & Nogueira, J. I. (2007). Sea Scallop Mass Mortality in a Marine Protected Area. *Marine Ecology Progress Series* **349**: 151-158.

Stokesbury, K.D.E., Harris, B.P. & Marino II, M.C. (2009). Astonishment, stupefaction, and a naturalist's approach to ecosystem-based fisheries studies. In *The Future of Fisheries* Eds Rothschild, B.J. & Beamish, R. American Institute of Fisheries Research Biologist , Fish and Fisheries Series 31, Springer. pp. 113-124.

Chapter 25

Harp seals: is the largest marine mammal harvest in the world sustainable?

Mike O. Hammill[1] and Garry B. Stenson[2]

Summary

1. The Canadian commercial harp seal hunt is the largest marine mammal harvest in the world. Highly controversial, this harvest has operated under various forms since the 1700s, with the largest harvests being taken in the early 1800s.
2. Beginning in 1996 when new markets were developed, an average of 264,000 animals has been reported harvested annually. Critics of the hunt argue that current harvests are not sustainable.
3. Resource management involves tradeoffs between conservation, economic and political concerns in establishing harvest levels. The Precautionary Approach (PA) brings various stakeholders together to identify clear management objectives and actions that would be triggered when a population approaches or falls below pre-defined biological reference levels.
4. Harvests in the Canadian commercial hunt are regulated under a Precautionary Management Framework. For harp seals the precautionary reference levels have been set quite high. As information on changes in the population and impact of poor ice conditions are incorporated into the assessments the Total Allowable Catch (TAC) is adjusted to conserve the resource above the precautionary level.

[1] Maurice Lamontage Institute, Fisheries and Oceans Canada, P.O. Box 1000, 850 route de la Mer, Mont-Joli, QC. Canada, G5H 3Z4
[2] Northwest Atlantic Fisheries Centre, Fisheries and Oceans Canada, P.O. Box 5667, St John's NL, Canada, A1C 5X1

25.1 Introduction

The harp seal (*Pagophilus groenlandicus*) is a medium sized seal, that reaches a length of about 170 cm and weighs on average 135 kg (Figure 25.1) (Hammill *et al.*,1995). Found only in the north Atlantic, three populations are recognized: the White Sea population that breeds on the pack ice in the White Sea and summers in the Barents Sea; the Greenland Sea population that breeds on the pack-ice off the east coast of Greenland near the island of Jan Mayen and summers in the north-eastern Atlantic Ocean, Norwegian and Barents Seas, and the North-west Atlantic population that breeds on the pack ice off eastern Canada and summers in the eastern Canadian Arctic and off the west Greenland coast (Sergeant, 1991) (Figure 25.2). Throughout much of the year North-west Atlantic harp seals are widely dispersed, but during the March breeding season animals are aggregated off the Newfoundland coast or in the Gulf of St. Lawrence. The pups are born with a white fur (lanugo) (Figure 25.1). They nurse for about 12-14 days, then are abandoned by the female. The adults mate, then disperse for a short period of time to feed before hauling out on the pack-ice in the northern Gulf of St Lawrence or off the north-east coast of Newfoundland to moult (Sergeant, 1991). The weaned young of the year remain on the ice

Figure 25.1 Harp seal (*Pagophilus groenlandicus*) female and whitecoat pup on the pack ice in the Gulf of St Lawrence near the Magdalen islands. © DFO Science

Plate 25.1 Sealers use various boats up to 65 feet (~ 21m) to hunt. Here hunters with a 21 footer have had some success. © DFO Science

for another 4-6 weeks. During this time, the lanugo is shed, to be replaced by fur that is similar in length to the adult fur, and at this stage they are known as beaters. Harp seals are assessed using a combination of aerial surveys to count the number of young that are born on the ice (Stenson *et al.*, 2003) and a population model, which incorporates the pup production estimates with information on reproductive rates, removals from the population through harvesting (including corrections for non-reporting), incidental catches by commercial fisheries and unusual mortality associated with unfavourable environmental conditions such as poor ice (Hammill and Stenson, 2005). Pup production of the North-west Atlantic harp seal population has increased from around 490,000 (SE=13,000) animals in 1960 to 986,000 (SE=78,000) in 2004, while total population size has increased from 2.2 million (SE=70,000) to 5.8 million (SE=900,000) (Figure 25.3) (Hammill and Stenson, 2005).

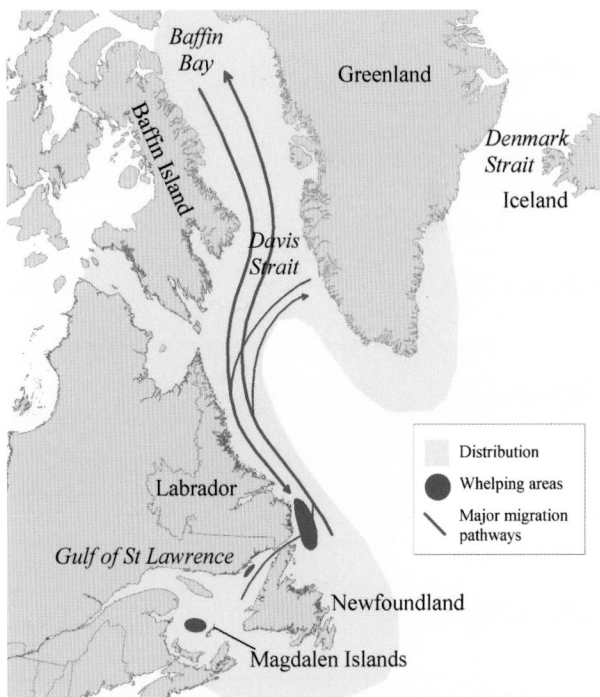

Figure 25.2 North-west Atlantic harp seals summer in the Arctic but move south in fall to over-winter and reproduce on the drifting pack-ice off north-eastern Newfoundland and in the Gulf of St Lawrence.

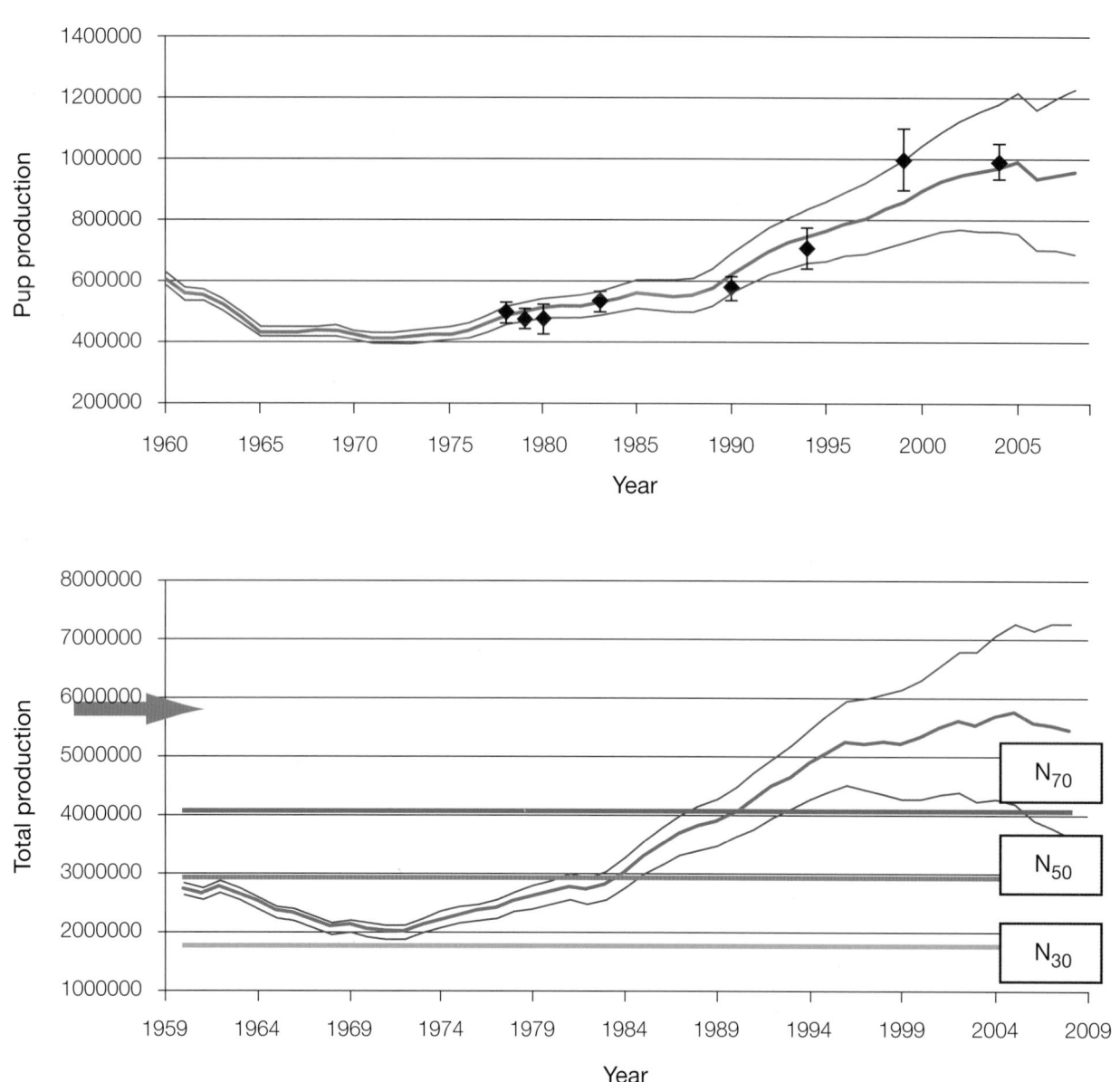

Figure 25.3 Changes in pup production (top) and total size of the North-west Atlantic harp seal total population between 1960 and 2005 (mean ± 1SE) (bottom). The survey estimates (mean ± 1SE) are based on mark-recapture estimates (prior to 1990), and aerial survey estimates (1990 and later). N70, N50 and N30 represent, precautionary and limit reference levels. They are set as 70%, 50% and 30% of the largest population estimated, which is approximately 5.8 million animals (arrow).

25.2 Historical hunt management

The hunt of harp seals in the North-west Atlantic is the largest marine mammal harvest in the world. They are hunted for commercial and subsistence uses in both Canada and Greenland. Highly controversial, the commercial harvest in Canada has operated under various forms since the 1700s with the largest harvests, on the order of 700,000 animals, being taken in the mid 1800s (Figure 25.4). An European Economic Community ban on the importation of whitecoat pelts in 1983 led to a collapse in the markets and Canadian catches declined from an average of 150,000 in the 1970s to 50,000 between 1983 and 1995. Beginning in 1996, new markets appeared, primarily for the fur of beaters, but also fine oil and health products derived from the blubber. Since 1996, an average of 264,000 animals has been reported harvested annually (Figure 25.4). In addition, approximately 90,000 harp seals are taken in the Greenland subsistence hunt each year.

Measures to limit hunting were first undertaken in 1883 with the passage of the Seal Fishery Amendment Act by the General Assembly of Newfoundland, which set opening dates of 1 March for

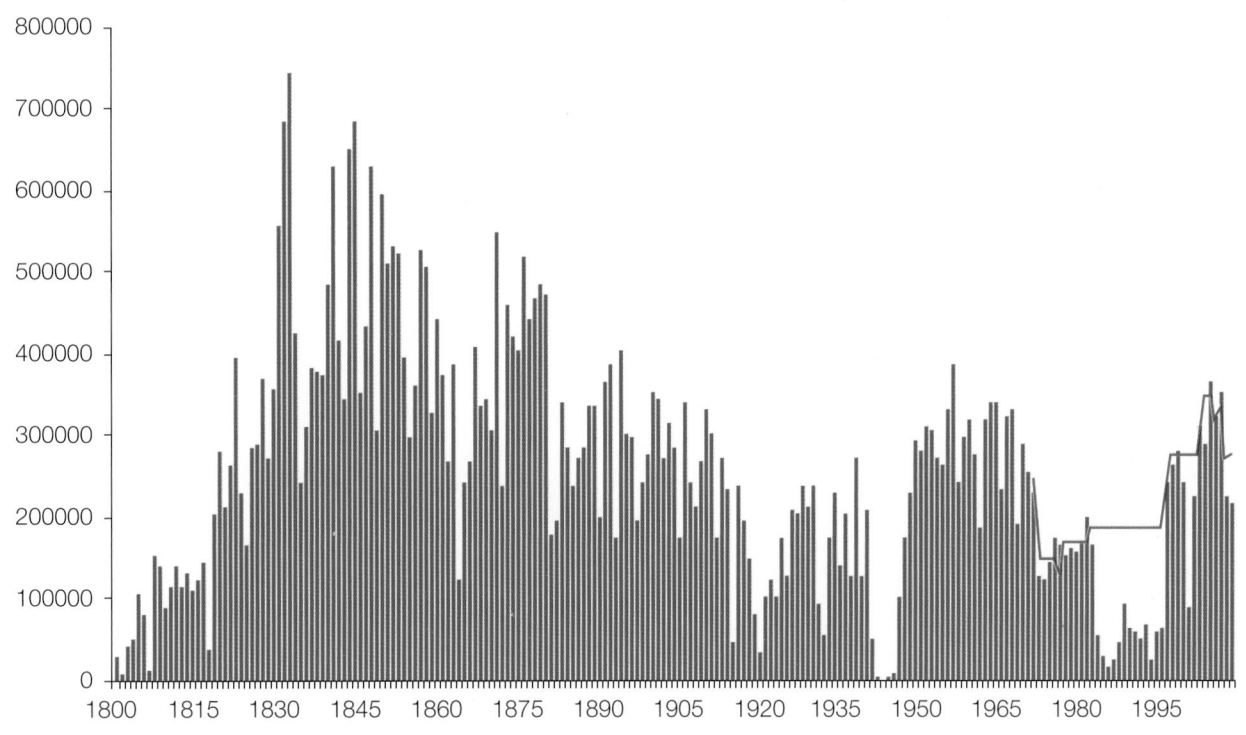

Figure 25.4 Reported catches (bars) and Total Allowable Catch (TAC) (line) of North-west Atlantic harp seals between 1800 and 2008 from Blanchard (Barchard, 1978; Stenson unpublished).

sailing ships and 10 March for steamers to travel to the herd (Sergeant, 1991). Quotas were first set in 1971 in response to indications of a significant decline in the herd and since then an annual Total Allowable Catch (TAC) has been set to restrict the maximum harvest. The current harvest is prosecuted as a sustainable economic activity; harvest levels vary between years as a function of markets (prices) and ice conditions which limit access to the resource. The seal hunt is economically important to Canadians living in traditional hunting areas such as Newfoundland and Quebec where alternative employment opportunities are limited. In 2006 (a peak year), the hunt generated more than $30 million (Canadian), providing up to 35% of the total annual income for some sealers. As can be expected with such a controversial activity, both the sustainability and economic importance of the hunt have been questioned (e.g. Johnston *et al.*, 2002; IFAW, 2007).

To manage the harvests sustainably, scientists provide regular advice to managers based on biological assessments of the exploited resource. These assessments attempt to predict changes in the resource by incorporating information on catches, estimates of recruitment, and indices of abundance into a population model and then translate these results into recommendations for a TAC (Cooke, 1999;

Plate 25.2 Young harp seal beaters on the pack ice. As young juveniles, beaters must learn to find food and make their way to the Arctic. © DFO Science

Butterworth, 2007). Because the information is often incomplete and estimated model parameters are subject to natural variability, the resulting advice has considerable uncertainty. In the past, failure to sufficiently recognize the consequences of this uncertainty led managers to require proof that populations or resources were in difficulty before remedial actions were taken (Taylor *et al.*, 2000). Unfortunately, by the time damage to the resource was identified, populations had often suffered serious harm. The collapse of North-west Atlantic cod stocks and many large whale populations are examples where traditional management approaches have failed (Rice and Rivard, 2003; Baker and Clapham, 2004).

Within the context of fisheries management, the Precautionary Approach (PA) strives to be more cautious when information is less certain, does not accept the absence of information as a reason for the failure to implement conservation measures, and defines, in advance, decision rules for stock management when the resource reaches clearly identified reference points (Punt and Smith, 2001). These points or levels are referred to as Conservation (Limit), Precautionary and Target Reference Points (ICES, 2001). The conservation, or limit, reference point is a level below which a population is considered to be in serious or irreversible harm. One of the basic principles of the PA is the need to account for the uncertainty associated with estimates and to develop a basis for taking action in cases with insufficient scientific understanding. One important aspect of the PA is to focus management of the resource above the precautionary reference levels, where the resource is abundant, rather than trying to manage the resource around the conservation limit reference level. If a population is in a healthy state, target reference points can be identified by management and industry. Thus, protocols are needed for situations where considerable data are available ('data-rich') as well as for situations where information concerning the resource is more limited ('data-poor') (Hammill and Stenson, 2007).

Since the late 1970s, the objective for the harp seal fishery was to set a TAC with reference to the annual replacement yield (RY). This is the level of catch that can be taken in one year that would result in the population remaining the same the following year. However, an independent review in 2001 pointed out that this approach was not precautionary since there was a high probability that the population would decline if the entire TAC was taken in each year (Mclaren *et al.*, 2001). In fact, there is a 50% probability that the population is above the mean and as well a 50% probability that the population is below this. Furthermore, although uncertainty around the size of the population will increase as we project into the future, it is evident that the mean is both non-precautionary and 'ill-equipped' to predict changes in this uncertainty into the future.

25.3 Current hunt management

In response to McLaren *et al.* (2001), Canada adopted a PA framework known as Objective Based Fisheries Management (OBFM) for the management of Atlantic seals (Hammill and Stenson, 2007). Under this approach, populations for which there is a good understanding of the population dynamics (e.g. recent abundance, fecundity and mortality) are considered to be 'data rich' while species for which there is more uncertainty are considered to be 'data poor' and must be managed more conservatively. Harp

Plate 25.3 Adult harp seals resting on the ice late in the breeding season. © DFO Science

seals satisfy the requirements for a 'data-rich' species, with a series of eight abundance estimates, the most recent completed in 2004, (Figure 25.3) as well as information on harvest levels and age specific reproductive rates (Hammill and Stenson, 2005). Under this PA framework, two precautionary levels called N70 and N50 and a conservation reference limit point (N30) were established at levels equal to 70%, 50% and 30% of the highest estimate population sizes known (Hammill and Stenson, 2007). Within this framework, the use of two precautionary levels reminds stakeholders and managers that the objective is to manage as far away as possible from the conservation reference point, and if the precautionary thresholds are exceeded, then the resource is declining and conservation must assume a higher priority in any management decision. Under OBFM, the management objective is to ensure an 80% likelihood that the population will remain above the N70 precautionary level, or conversely that the probability that the population will fall below N70 is less than 20% (referred to as L20) (Figure 25.5). Because the harvest control rule relies on L20, and the projection of L20 spreads out with increasing time from the last survey, this approach also captures the concept of increasing uncertainty in the population trend projecting into the future. As long as there is an 80% likelihood that the population remains above N70, higher risk harvest strategies can be adopted and managers can establish harvests based upon considerations such as ecosystem impacts and/or socio-economic benefits. If managers are uncomfortable with the increasing uncertainty, then they can request that a new survey be completed to provide an update of the current population status. If the population does fall below N70, then conservation becomes a higher priority and although harvesting can continue, the TAC is then set within the management objective that there is an 80% probability that the population will return above the N70 level within 10 years (DFO, 2008).

The North-west Atlantic harp seal population was estimated to number 5.8 million (95% CI: 4.1-7.6 million) seals in 2005, which is the largest population that has been documented (Figure 25.3). The resulting values of N70, N50 and N30 are 4.1, 2.9 and 1.7 million animals respectively. Harp seals are estimated to be above the N70 reference point and so, taking into consideration the uncertainty associated with population estimates, the current management objective is to maximize the economic return to sealers while ensuring an 80% probability that the population will remain above N70, i.e. above 4.1 million seals (DFO, 2003).

Canada implemented the precautionary OBFM approach to the management of Atlantic seals in 2003 (DFO, 2003) and the outline described here has been used in setting the TAC since then. Under the initial 2003-2005 plan, harvest levels were set at 975,000 over three years with an annual TAC up to 350,000 in any two years provided that there was a reduction in the other to ensure the overall total was not exceeded (DFO, 2003). In 2005, there was a new assessment of the population which included an update of pup production estimates from a 2004 aerial survey, and information on reproductive rates and catches. Under the 2006-2010 management plan the TAC is set annually to account for new information on the status of the population, changing environmental conditions, and changes in hunt levels in Arctic Canada and Greenland (DFO, 2008).

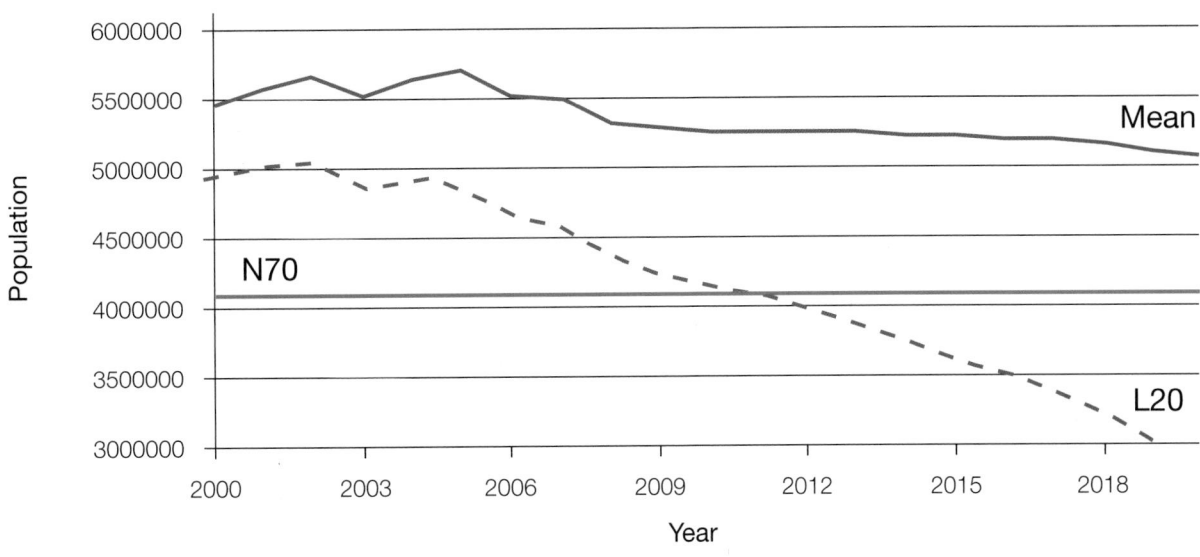

Figure 25.5 Predicted changes in the North-west Atlantic harp seal population assuming ice-related pup mortality of 26% overall, and under a TAC of 275,000, 250,000, and 200,000 animals in 2007, 2008, and 2009 followed by a TAC of 150,000 animals in 2010 and subsequent years. N70 represents the precautionary level set at 70% of the largest estimated population size observed, which was 5.8 million animals. Under the mean there is a 50% probability that the population is smaller than 5.8 million. For L20 there is a 20% probability that the population is less than the L20 line, or an 80% probability that the population is higher. The management objective is to maintain an 80% probability that the population will remain above N70. Under this scenario, if the complete TAC is taken, and there are no changes in other factors such as reported Greenland harvests, age-structure of the harvest etc, then L20 could fall below the Precautionary Level of N70 after the 2011 hunt.

The way in which the current management plan works can be illustrated in greater detail by focusing on events in 2007, a year in which there was very little ice in the southern Gulf of St Lawrence. Harp seals require ice for giving birth and nursing their pups. After weaning, the young animals also require ice to rest on. If animals do not have adequate ice during this period, they appear to suffer high mortality. Approximately 26% of the total North-west Atlantic harp seal births occur in the southern Gulf of St Lawrence. Although increased mortality of young animals due to poor ice conditions have been included in the assessment since 2003, there was concern that the extreme conditions in 2007 would have a serious impact on the population.

Prior to deciding upon a TAC, scientists were asked to estimate the impacts of various harvest levels on the population under conditions of no additional ice-related mortality, and additional ice-related mortalities of 50%, 75% and 100% of the southern Gulf component (equivalent to 13%, 20% and 26% of the pups born in the North-west Atlantic overall) (Table 25.1, Figure 25.5). Under one scenario that assumes 100% of the southern Gulf of St Lawrence pups would drown prior to the start of the hunt, and with a harvest of 275,000, 250,000, and 200,000 animals in 2007, 2008 and 2009 respectively, followed

Table 25.1 The table represents different harvest scenarios for the years 2007-2010, under different assumptions of ice related pup mortality (M) in 2007, expressed as a proportion of the total North-west Atlantic pup production. The years in the columns indicate the last year that a hunt could be prosecuted and still respect the management objective that there is an 80% probability that the population would remain above N_{70}.

Scenario	Additional pup mortality (M)			
('000s)	M=0% Year	M=13% Year	M=20% Year	M=26% Year
290,250,200,150,	2011	2010	2010	2009
275,250,200,150,	2011	2010	2010	2010
250,250,200,150,	2012	2011	2010	2010

by a continuing harvest of 150,000 animals, it is estimated that the population would decline slightly. However, the mean estimate of population would remain above 5 million animals at least until the year 2020 and well above our precautionary level set at N70 of 4.1 million animals (Figure 25.5). However, if the conditions in the scenario were to be met, i.e. the TAC was to be taken in full in each year, harvests in Greenland are as assumed and no change in the age composition of the harvest, then L20 would decline below N70 after the 2011 harvest. This would require reductions in future harvest levels to allow the L20 estimate of population size to recover above the precautionary level of 4.1 million animals.

Under another scenario of very high ice related mortality (100% of the southern Gulf pup production) and a TAC of 290,000 in 2007, followed by catches of 250,000, 200,000 and 150,000 in 2008, 2009, and 2010 and thereafter, the L20 line would fall below the N70 threshold in 2009, i.e. before the end of the 2006-2010 management plan. Therefore, this TAC was not accepted and in 2007, the TAC was set at 270,000. Although mortality did appear to be high, only 221,500 animals were reported taken in the commercial harvest. Conditions were re-examined in 2008 and as a result of the low catch the previous year, the TAC was set at 275,000 animals for the 2008 season, which would still maintain the population above the N70 level. Good ice conditions were observed in 2008, but access to animals was difficult resulting in a reported harvest of about 217,000 animals.

Within the precautionary framework of OBFM, as long as the resource remains above N70, managers can establish TAC levels based upon considerations such as ecosystem impacts and/or socio-economic benefits. Currently the North-west Atlantic harp seal population is near the highest levels seen in more than a century and the current high harvests have allowed some Atlantic Canadians to benefit economically from this abundant resource. The harp seal population will continue to be monitored to determine the impact of harvests and the TAC will be adjusted to ensure that the population remains healthy and above the precautionary level.

Plate 25.4 Adult female harp seal sunning on the ice in the Gulf of St Lawrence, Canada. © DFO Science

Although the framework described here was developed for the management of a hunted seal species, it could be applied to other situations including the management of terrestrial harvests, by-catch in commercial fisheries, subsistence harvests, or areas where industry-related mortality is of concern. It also provides a framework for considering the status of any species, including those considered to be at risk. A key factor in this approach is that scientists, stakeholders and managers can agree on what constitutes a healthy resource level and that specific management actions can be identified if certain thresholds are exceeded. Although simulation modelling is needed and may result in setting the precautionary and conservation reference limits at different levels from those identified here, particularly given different life history characteristics or knowledge, it is important that suitable reference limits be identified to focus management above the precautionary level, where the resource remains abundant and not around the conservation reference limit, where there is a much greater chance of serious damage to the resource occurring.

References

Baker, C.S. & Clapham, P.J. (2004). Modelling the past and future of whales and whaling. *Trends in Ecology and Evolution* **19**: 365-371.

Barchard, W.W. (1978). Estimates of historical stock size for Northwest Atlantic harp seals, *Pagophilus gronelandicus*. M.Sc. thesis, University of Guelph, Guelph, Ontario, Canada. 164 pp.

Butterworth, D. (2007). Why a management procedure approach? Some positives and negatives. *ICES Journal of Marine Science* **64**: 613-617.

Cooke, J.G. (1999). Improvement of fishery-management advice through simulation testing of harvest algorithms. *ICES Journal of Marine Science* **56**: 797-810.

DFO. (2003). Atlantic seal hunt 2003-2005 management plan. Available at:
http://www.dfo-mpo.gc.ca/seal-phoque/reports-rapports/mgtplan-plangest2003/mgtplan-plangest2003_e.htm

DFO. (2008). Atlantic seal hunt 2006-2010 management plan. Available at: http://www.dfo-mpo.gc.ca/seal-phoque/report-rapport_e.htm

Hammill, M.O. & Stenson, G.B. (2005). Abundance of Northwest Atlantic harp seals (1960-2005). *Canada Scientific Advisory Secretariat Research Document* 2005/090. 38 pp.

Hammill, M.O. & Stenson, G.B. (2007). Application of the Precautionary Approach and Conservation Reference Points to the management of Atlantic seals. *ICES Journal of Marine Science* **64**: 702–706.

Hammill, M.O., Kingsley,M.C.S., Beck, G. & Smith,T.G. (1995). Growth and condition in the Northwest Atlantic harp seal. *Canadian Journal of Fisheries and Aquatic Sciences* **52**: 478-488.

International Council for the Exploration of the Sea (ICES). (2001). Report of the study group on further developments of the precautionary approach to fishery management. ICES CM 2001/ACFM:11

IFAW. (2007). An overview of the economic importance of Canada's commercial seal hunt. 20 pp.

Johnston, D.W., Meisenheimer, P. & Lavigne, D.M. (2002). An evaluation of management objectives for Canada's commercial harp seal hunt, 1996-1998. *Conservation Biology* **14**: 729-737.

McLaren, I.A., Brault, S., Harwood, J. & Vardy, D. (2001). The eminent panel on seal management. 165 pp. Available at : www.dfo-mpo.gc.ca

Punt, A. E. & Smith, D. M. (2001). The gospel of maximum sustainable yield in fisheries management: birth, crucifixion and reincarnation. In: *Conservation of exploited species*, pp. 41-66. Eds J. D. Reynolds, G. M. Mace, K. H. Redford and J. G. Robinson. Cambridge University Press, Cambridge, UK.

Rice, J. & Rivard, D. (2003). Proceedings of the zonal assessment meeting—Atlantic cod. *Canada Scientific Advisory Secretariat Research Document* 2003/021. 133 pp. Available at: http://www.meds-sdmm.dfo-mpo.gc.ca/csas/applications/publications

Sergeant, D.E.A. (1991). Harp seals, man and ice. *Canadian Special Publication of Fisheries and Aquatic Sciences* 114. 153 pp.

Stenson, G.B., Rivest, L.-P., Hammill, M.O., Gosselin, J.-F. & Sjare, B. (2003). Estimating Pup Production of Harp Seals, *Phoca groenlandica*, in the Northwest Atlantic. *Marine Mammal Science* **19**: 141-160.

Taylor, B.L., Wade, P.R., DeMaster, D.P. & Barlow,J. (2000). Incorporating uncertainty into management models for marine mammals. *Conservation Biology* **14**: 1243-1252.

Hammill, M.O. and Stenson, G.B. (2010). Harp seals: is the largest marine mammal harvest in the world sustainable? In: *Species Management: Challenges and Solutions for the 21st Century*, ed. by J.M. Baxter and C.A. Galbraith. TSO Scotland, Edinburgh. pp. 447-460

Chapter 26

Sustainable use of mosses, lichens and fungi

David Genney[1] and Alison Dyke[2]

Summary

1. Mosses, fungi and lichens have been utilized by humans for millennia and represent a large and internationally important component of Scotland's biodiversity.
2. Patterns of use continually change in response to changes in society and technology.
3. Direct and indirect impacts of harvest are discussed along with some of the key management options.
4. The importance of codes of conduct is outlined as effective means of obtaining sustainable harvest.

[1] Scottish Natural Heritage, Great Glen House, Leachkin Road, Inverness, IV3 8NW, UK
[2] Reforesting Scotland, 58 Shandwick Place, Edinburgh, EH2 4RT, UK

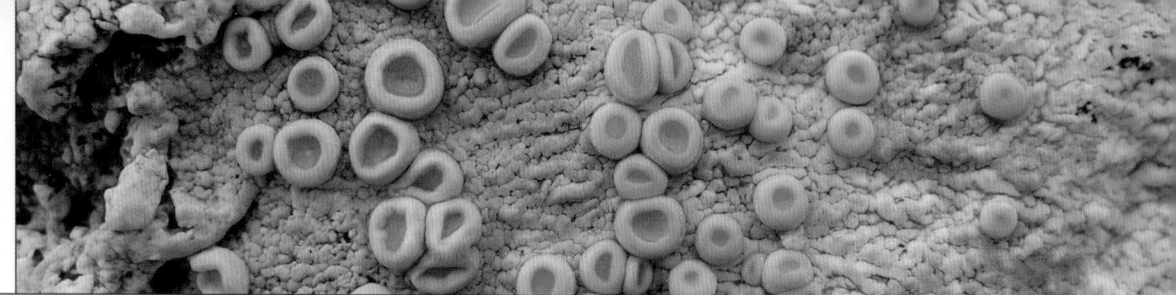

26.1 Introduction

'Orchil' or 'cudbear' (*Ochrolechia tartarea*). © David Genne

With some exceptions, mosses, fungi and lichens are not cultivated, but tend to be either harvested from natural and semi-natural habitats or as by-products of managed land e.g. forestry. It is this lack of cultivation, along with high terrestrial species diversity and commercial use that unifies these somewhat unrelated groups of species for consideration in this chapter.

Sustainability is a key concept in the management of our natural heritage. We define sustainable use as obtaining a biological resource under management practices that ensure replacement of the part or individual harvested, and associated species, by re-growth or reproduction, before another harvest occurs.

Mosses, fungi and lichens have, to a greater or lesser extent, been utilized by humans for millennia and in Scotland represent a large and internationally important component of our biodiversity. There are just under 800 species of mosses and about 1,500 species each of lichens and larger fungi (perhaps thousands more micro-fungi) in Scotland. However, only a small proportion of these species have been used directly. Changes in society and technology are altering patterns of both quantity and diversity of use, for example, some species are still used for traditional purposes, but are now harvested at a commercial scale. Such changes bring new challenges for managing their sustainable harvest.

Sustainable use of plant (and fungal) resources are enshrined within Objective 3 of the Convention on Biological Diversity's (CBD) Global Strategy for Plant Conservation (GSPC) and includes three main targets:

1. No species of wild flora endangered by international trade.
2. Thirty per cent of plant-based products derived from sources that are sustainably managed.
3. The decline of plant resources, and associated indigenous and local knowledge, innovations and practices that support sustainable livelihoods, local food security and health care, halted.

These targets are reflected in the European Strategy for Plant Conservation 2008-2014 (Planta Europa, 2008), the UK's Plant Diversity Challenge (Cheffings *et al.*, 2004) and locally in the Strategy for the Conservation of Lower Plants and Fungi in Scotland (Long and Ward, 2005). For these targets to be met, we need to understand how much of which species are used by whom and how. We also need to determine, for each species, what level of harvest is sustainable.

26.2 Historic uses

Given the large diversity and abundance of moss in Scotland, humans have made surprisingly little historic use of them. *Sphagnum*-peat is an obvious exception and has been used for many centuries as a fuel (Figure 26.1). In the past, mosses were used as an easily obtainable and multi-purpose packaging material. Mosses were used to protect vegetables in storage, and also as stuffing for bedding, along with bracken and straw (Rothero, 2005). Moss was used to pack the walls of stone houses, particularly near

Figure 26.1 *Sphagnum* peat has been used for many centuries as a fuel. © Lorne Gill/SNH

the chimney to keep out the wind and prevent the heat from setting fire to the wooden frame. In the Victorian era, moss was used around the base of potted plants and in flower arranging when 'moss-gathering' was a small industry. It is likely that moss has a long tradition of use for 'personal hygiene' due to its absorbent properties. In particular, *Sphagnum*, with its mild antiseptic properties resulted in its use for wound dressings. In the early 20th century there was widespread commercial production, reaching its peak in the First World War, when some one million *Sphagnum* dressings per month were used by the British forces (Rothero, 2005).

Scotland has until recently been considered a fungi phobic society, with little culinary tradition of use. While it is difficult to trace why this might be the case, it is thought to date from the exclusive right to use psychoactive and other fungi for shamanic purposes. This prohibition may have then been reinforced by the influence of early Christian settlers in Scotland. Other historic uses of fungi, including the culturally important use of yeast in fermentation, are discussed by Spooner and Roberts (2005).

By far the most important use of lichens in Scotland was for dyeing, first as a cottage industry and later on a commercial scale. The browns and fawns of Harris tweed were produced from a closely-related group of lichens called 'crottle' (*Parmelia* spp.) (Figure 26.2). The last commercial dyers and hand weavers of this cloth on Harris ceased production in 1997. The other main lichen dye produced in Scotland and exported all over Britain, was 'orchil' or 'cudbear' (*Ochrolechia tartarea*), which gave a purple or red colour.

Figure 26.2 Lichens were an important source of pigments used in the dyeing industry (e.g. Harris Tweed) © G.Satterley. 'Orchil' or 'cudbear' (*Ochrolechia tartarea*) (inset), which gave a purple or red colour. © David Genney

Its commercial value was so great that a factory producing this household dye was set up in Glasgow covering 17 acres and processing 250 tons of lichen each year (Gilbert, 2004). Lichens have been used for medicinal purposes, often due to the philosophy of the doctrine of signatures, established in the 1600s, where a species was thought to cure the particular part of the body or ailment that it resembled (Bennett, 2007). As a result, lungwort (*Lobaria pulmonaria*) (Figure 26.3) was thought to cure respiratory ailments because its lobes resemble a lung. Likewise, species of *Peltigera* (dog-lichens) were thought to cure rabies because the rhizines on the underside resemble the fangs of a dog. Many people still have faith in some of these remedies and large modern markets continue. For further uses of lichens, see Gilbert (2000).

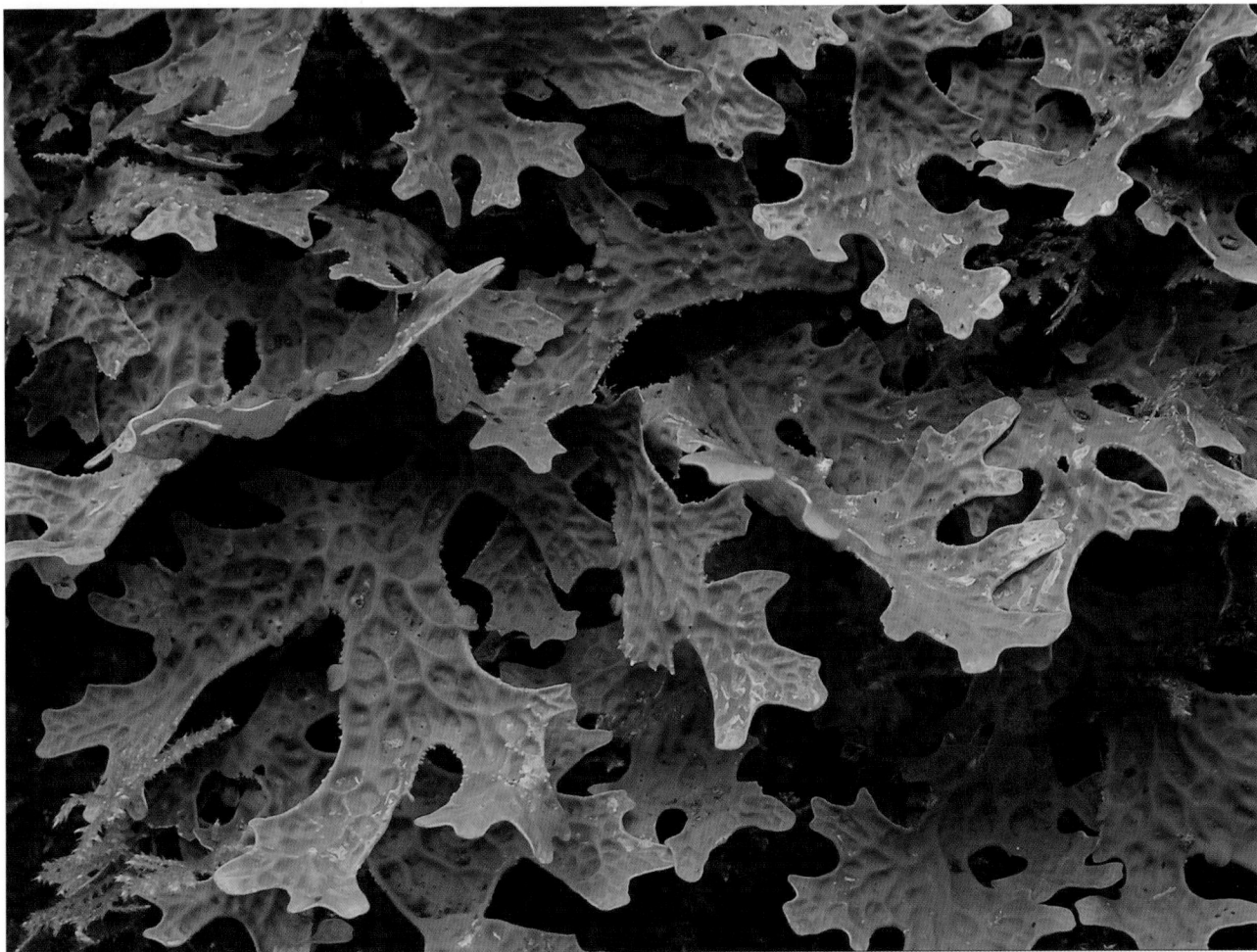

Figure 26.3 The lichen lungwort (*Lobaria pulmonaria*) was thought to cure respiratory ailments because its lobes resemble a lung. Demand for this species continues to present challenges for sustainable use. © David Genney

26.3 Changing trends and modern uses

26.3.1 Changing commercial harvests

Traditions of using wild plants survived longer in Scotland than elsewhere in the UK. Within this continuity of use, Darwin (1996) identifies a significant cultural gap in use following the Second World War, when social and economic changes led to the decline of centuries-old traditions. The use of fungi has undergone a renaissance in the past 40 years, during the 1970s a first wave of interest was sparked by books such as Richard Mabey's (1972) 'Food for Free', then during the 1990s demand from the continent for species such as chanterelle (*Cantharellus cibarius*) and cep (*Boletus edulis*) (Figure 26.4) led to the establishment of a number of commercial fungi buyers in Scotland. Initially the buyers began by supplying larger European buyers and London restaurants, but gradually their trade has broadened to include a wide variety of outlets in Scotland. A ten year old study set the value of the commercial harvest of Scottish fungi at £400,000 per year, more recent estimates indicate that this figure may have doubled (Dyke, 2006). Much of this harvesting occurs without the knowledge or consent of the landowner.

Figure 26.4 Chanterelle (*Cantharellus cibarius*) and cep (*Boletus edulis*) are two species of fungus harvested commercially and by individuals for personal use in Scotland. © David Genney

The increased commercial availability of wild fungi has in turn promoted an interest among celebrity chefs and the media. A search for press articles using the terms 'wild' and 'harvest' (and therefore by no means complete) in 2005 turned up 64 directly relevant articles either on harvesting or using wild harvested products, mainly foods. Many of these articles were published in the autumn and featured wild fungi (Dyke, 2006). This proliferation of press articles has been matched by a huge increase in the number of harvesting guides and recipe books. With the influx of migrants from the European Union's accession countries, which enjoy more extensive and continuous traditions of use, fungi in Scotland are being harvested to an even greater extent and management must adapt to a different set of harvesting practices and pressures.

In addition to these direct uses we have also seen a huge increase in the number of technological uses of fungi, for medicines and most recently as a potential energy source. A strain of the fungus *Gliocladium roseum*, discovered in Patagonian rainforests, naturally produces a suite of chemicals remarkably similar to diesel (Strobel *et al.*, 2008). These new products tend to come from fungi that are easily culturable and therefore present no sustainability issues, but do illustrate the importance of maintaining a genetically diverse resource from which new discoveries can be made.

In contrast, the harvests of mosses and lichens have declined, in both cases due to the availability of alternative products. In the case of moss, products such as coconut fibre began to be used in response to sustainability concerns around the harvest of *Sphagnum* moss. A significant market for moss remains, however, for use again as a packaging material by the horticultural industry and for hanging baskets and arrangements. A recent study of the moss harvest in Scotland put the value of the legal moss harvest at £0.5 million per year, with an equal amount of unauthorized harvesting (Staddon and Dyke, 2007). In turn, lichens are still used by hobbyists and craftspeople for dyeing, and recently a use of lungwort has reached Scotland from the continent, where it is used in homoeopathic cough remedies and where the species is in decline due to loss of habitat. The potential harvest of a species that indicates long periods of ecological continuity and associated high lichen diversity (Coppins and Coppins, 2002) has caused a great deal of controversy, but also presents an opportunity to manage a harvest before it has begun. Lungwort is currently being considered for listing on Schedule 8 of the Wildlife and Countryside Act (1981) under which commercial harvesting will have to be carried out under licence.

26.3.2 Harvests for personal use

While considering these commercial harvests it is important not to neglect harvests for personal use, a significant proportion of the population (25%) harvest some form of wild product every year (TNS Global, 2003; Snowley and Daly, 2005), in most cases, harvests for domestic use far exceed harvests for commercial purposes. These harvests have great cultural significance, they mark the changing of the seasons, moss for Christmas decorations and spring hanging baskets, fungi in the autumn. For those who harvest they represent a contribution to the household of fresh natural produce and a personal link with the local environment. There is often no strong dividing line between harvests for commercial purposes and domestic use, it is often the same people carrying out the harvests, perhaps even in the same visit to the woods.

Species Management: Challenges and Solutions for the 21st Century

26.3.3 Responding to changing use and harvest patterns

The species used today have very different histories and traditions of use, most having gone through periods where use was interrupted or abandoned. There are many different drivers of change: market demand, loss of habitat, changes in population size and cultural make up. The management and regulation of these harvests has to keep up with constant changes in the species harvested, size of harvests and harvesting and customary practices.

26.4 Impacts and management options

26.4.1 Direct impacts

There is very little formal scientific knowledge about the impacts of harvesting. At present management is based on an, at times, patchy mosaic of scientific knowledge, complemented in some cases with traditional knowledge and new expert knowledge developed by harvesters. For many species, there is not even the minimum species information required to estimate rates of sustainable use, i.e. rate of establishment, growth rate, reproductive age and vegetative regeneration potential.

There are some obvious reasons for this lack of species-level evidence. The high diversity of mosses, lichens and fungi alone means that it is less likely that data exist for an individual species. Geographic variation is also likely to have an impact on parameters that affect sustainability. As an example, the only data available to inform development of guidelines for lungwort harvest come from a Swiss study, where the species typically takes 20 years to produce the first fruiting bodies (apothecia) (Scheidegger *et al.*, 2007). However, the oceanic climate of the west coast of Scotland is thought to provide optimal conditions for lungwort and other *Lobaria* species, and sustainable levels of harvest may well be greater than would be estimated based on data from a continental climate alone.

Some good evidence does exist however; for example, there has been considerable concern about the impact of edible fungus harvest on subsequent years production. A 30 year study using replica plots has now demonstrated no direct impact of picking fungi on future production or diversity (Egli *et al.*, 2006). Estimates of sustainable epiphytic moss harvest have been made in the USA (Peck and Muir, 2001) but unfortunately there is little or no similar evidence to support sustainable harvest of Scottish mosses or lichens and we must base our estimates of sustainability on indirect evidence, such as the general knowledge that lichen growth rates can be very slow and measured in millimetres per year (Gilbert, 2000) and harvesters' own observations.

26.4.2 Indirect impact

Direct impacts of harvest are not the only issue in determining levels of sustainable use. Indirect impacts on other species in the habitats where the target species occur must also be considered. An analysis of commercial moss harvest in the Appalachian Mountains of West Virginia found that 73 bryophytes of low commercial value were collected along with the two or three commercially harvested species (Studlar and

468

Peck, 2008). Similarly, many species, such as beetles, flies and mammals, utilize fungi as a protein rich food source and some are obligate mycophages (Bruns, 1984). It is currently difficult to assess what the indirect impact of harvest is on these species. Lungwort is another good example, this species being the dominant component of a diverse and internationally important community of oceanic lichens called the Lobarion. The impact of harvest on other less common species in the Lobarion is a major concern to those wishing to develop sustainable guidelines for their harvest.

26.4.3 Management options

There are a number of ways that moss, lichen and fungus populations can be managed to achieve sustainable use, and these range from habitat management through to methods of harvest. Given the diversity of species and uses of moss, lichen and fungi, it is impossible to outline all available management options and only a selection are introduced here.

Habitat management aims to maintain healthy populations of target species to maximize the harvestable proportion of that population. For example, most species of edible fungi are mycorrhizal and depend on a continuity of woodland habitat. Here, control of grazing to allow woodland regeneration and control of invasive non-native plants are two habitat management options that will maintain the extent of habitat and therefore maximize future fungus harvests. Management may also aim to minimize negative ex-situ impacts, such as hyper-eutrophication, to which many fungi, mosses and lichens are particularly susceptible. In this case, careful location of nitrogen emitting pig and poultry farms, control of vehicle emissions and careful application of agricultural fertilizers are all important landscape scale management options.

Harvestable species often occur across a range of habitats, some of which are sensitive because they contain rare or threatened species and others that are dominated by the target commercial species. An assessment of habitat sensitivity is an important first step to achieve sustainable harvest and can often avoid unnecessary indirect impact on non-target species. Moss harvest is a good example, where ample supplies of commercial species can be gathered from forestry plantations prior to felling whilst avoiding more sensitive habitats such as bogs and native woodland. Importantly, such an approach avoids the need of harvesters to have detailed taxonomic expertise.

Any sustainable harvest must take the period of regeneration into account. Setting specific rotation periods may be desirable but can often be difficult, as described above, due to lack of species data. Another approach is to set targets for the condition or size of a population at a given harvest location before subsequent harvest takes place. This allows individual harvesters to adapt their rotation period to specific sites and also reduces the risk of double-cropping by different harvesters.

Consideration should be given to whether all or part of an organism is harvested. For fungi, this is not normally a problem because only the spore producing structure tends to be harvested rather than the greater proportion of the organism that lives as a mycelium in the soil or other substrate. For mosses, part harvest may not be an option, due to apical growth, but for lichens, it should be a serious consideration. Partial harvest is particularly important for species with poor recolonization rates or those that take a long time to reach reproductive maturity.

Post-harvest recovery of populations will be most rapid when the harvest efficiency is less than 100%. This can be achieved by either selecting a proportion of a population to be harvested prior to harvest, or by using deliberately inefficient harvest methods such as harvesting by hand rather than mechanical harvest. For some species, propagation and translocation can be another useful tool to enhance recovery and reduce the period between harvests.

Because mosses, lichens and fungi tend to be harvested by individuals rather than organized groups, management may need to be coordinated at the landowner or even governmental level. This is commonly done through either local or national licences and governed by legislation.

26.5 Legal status and customary practice

Three pieces of legislation currently affect wild-harvesting in Scotland and they have a bearing on how sustainable management can be achieved.

26.5.1 Scottish Common Law

Harvesting without the landowner's consent could be considered theft under Scottish Common Law. Property law in Scotland states that everything between the boundaries of the centre of the Earth and the Heavens belongs to the landowner. Much, is excluded from this right, but plants do not appear to be excluded. In fact, plants are classed as produce of the land, and become the property of the owner by 'accession of fruits', where produce of the land is treated as part of the land which produced it (Reid, 1996, p 457). Hence, regardless of whether harvesting is for commercial or recreational purposes the product remains the property of the landowner.

26.5.2 Wildlife and Countryside Act (1981)

In criminal law the Wildlife and Countryside Act (1981) (WCA), and amendments to that Act in the Nature Conservation (Scotland) Act 2004, states that it is an offence to uproot any wild plant without the permission of the landowner, (section 13 1b). Fungi are not directly referred to in the WCA but may, for the purposes of this act, be considered plants. Under the WCA some species have complete protection from harvesting (including seeds or spores), disturbance, and sale or possession with or without the landowners consent, and are listed in schedule 8 (section 13 1a and 2a).

26.5.3 Land Reform (Scotland) Act (2003)

Post devolution, the Scottish Parliament passed the third piece of legislation, the Land Reform (Scotland) Act 2003. Accompanying guidelines enabling the implementation of the new legislation came into force in spring 2004. Although this act makes no changes to the legality of commercial harvesting overall, it makes a significant distinction from Scottish Common Law, by excluding all harvesting for commercial purposes from the right of access. As the majority of commercial harvesting, particularly in the wild mushroom industry, occurs without the permission of the landowner (Dyke and Newton, 1999) this legislation in effect excludes the majority of commercial harvesters from accessing land. There is no specific provision in the Act for harvesting for non-commercial purposes, so the position on this remains as ambiguous as it is under Scottish Common Law. Commercially-run forays would appear not to be excluded from the right of access, but there has been no case law to test this.

26.5.4 Customary practice
In practice these legal measure are seldom challenged, so there is little case law and a great deal of confusion exists about harvesting rights. This leads to a situation where customary rights have far more influence on harvesting practice than legal rights. This situation is constantly in flux, reacting to the drivers of change mentioned earlier. Three main vectors influence the degree to which harvesters feel they have to seek permission (either from the landowner or a government agency): the scale and commercial nature of the harvest, their own 'localness' and the visibility of the harvest (for instance, moss harvesting has a high visual impact and may require vehicular access along extraction routes). For the majority of harvesters there is a long term incentive to protect harvests, and wild harvests are generally considered public goods (with a strong element of responsibility attached).

26.6 Codes

26.6.1 Developing codes
Given the difficulties in establishing firm scientific knowledge on sustainable harvest practices, a sensible approach is to promote responsible and courteous harvesting. Guidelines, or codes, are an important tool to do this and the process by which they are developed is as crucial as the final product. To be effective, it is important that everyone who wants to be involved can be and this may include representatives of conservation organizations, landowners, public land owning bodies, harvesters, buyers and distributors. The process of development must give everyone the opportunity to air concerns and bring together and acknowledge the different types of knowledge that each brings. Development of guidelines through participation helps different groups to understand each other's terminology and practices and thereby maximizes the success of their implementation.

Harvest guidelines for mosses, lichens and fungi have now been produced in a number of countries (e.g. Peck, 2006; Peck and Studlar, 2007; Scheidegger et al., 2007; State of Alaska Department of Natural Resources, 2008). With reference to the process described above, it is important that local guidelines are also developed to maximize local participation and take local variation in sustainable harvest rates and methods into account. In Scotland, harvest guidelines have already been produced for fungi (Box 26.1) and mosses (Box 26.2) using a structure of what (and what not), where (and where not), how (and how not) to harvest, a format that has been adopted as an international standard (Peck and Studlar, 2007).

Box 26.1 The Scottish Wild Mushroom Code.

The countryside is a working landscape. Please be aware of safety and follow the Scottish Outdoor Access Code. In accordance with this code, and as a matter of courtesy, you are advised to ask for permission before you pick mushrooms.

By respecting the natural environment you can help to manage and conserve the countryside. When picking mushrooms for any purpose, please consider the following points:

- Wildlife, especially insects, need mushrooms too, so only pick what you will use.

- Do not pick mushrooms until the cap has opened out and leave those that are past their best.

- The main part of the mushroom is below the surface; take care not to damage or trample it and not to disturb its surroundings.

- Scatter trimmings discreetly in the same area as the mushroom came from.

- Some mushrooms are poisonous and others rare and should not be picked – only pick what you know and take a field guide with you to identify mushrooms where you find them.

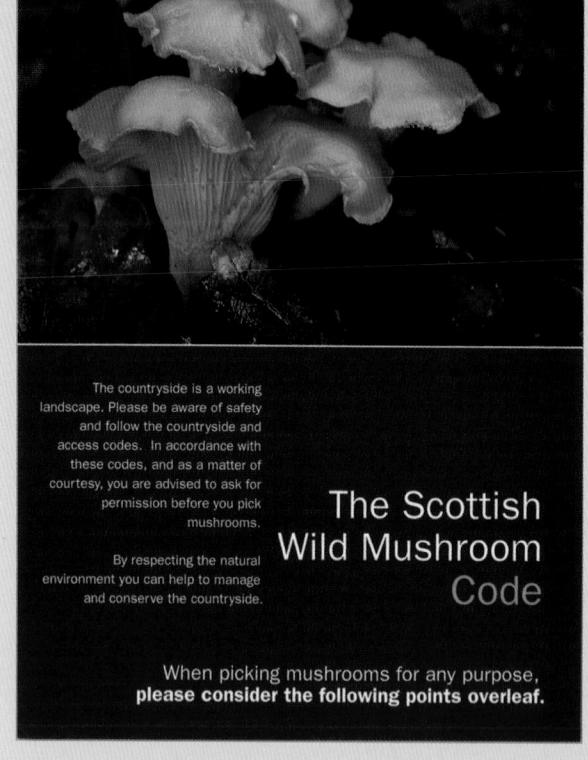

- Before you collect mushrooms at a nature reserve please always seek advice from the manager, as special conditions may apply.

If you own or manage land

- Be aware that your management activities may affect mushrooms.

If you run a foray or collect for scientific purposes

- Ensure the safety of your party, obtain permission in writing.

- Give a record of what you have found to the landowner or manager and explain the significance of your findings.

Box 26. 2 Scottish Moss Collection Code.

Please consider the following points when collecting moss. Please also contact the land manager who will help you to choose a suitable place. If you see evidence that other harvesters have not been following these guidelines, please report it to your local police and ask to speak to the Wildlife Crime Officer.

This code was created by a group representing the interests of conservation organisations, land managers and moss harvesters and buyers. The creation of the code was funded by Scottish Enterprise, the Forestry Commission, Scottish Natural Heritage and the Scottish Forestry Trust.

Where to collect

Mosses can be gathered from conifer plantations.

Please **avoid** places where rare mosses are most likely to be found, these are:

- Bogs, stream sides, springs, rock outcrops, walls, tree trunks and dead wood.
- Areas designated for nature conservation.
- Native woodlands (including pinewoods).
- Areas that appear to have been harvested recently.

How to collect

- Mosses should be collected by hand.
- Leave patches of moss so that it can re-grow, only collecting half of what is present.
- Please do not collect from the same patch for at least 5 years, this will allow time for the moss to recover.

What to collect

- Mosses that form a mat on the ground (weft-forming mosses) are least vulnerable to collection.
- It is illegal to collect certain mosses that are protected by law.

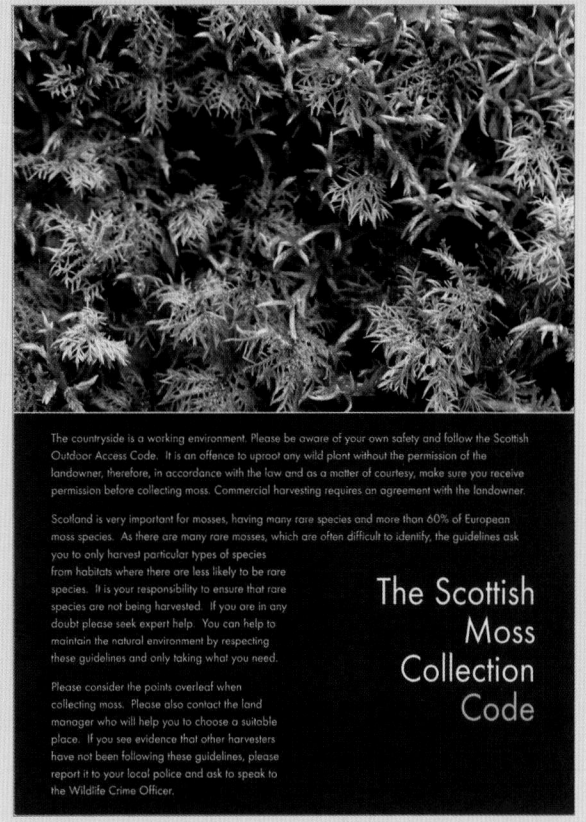

The countryside is a working environment. Please be aware of your own safety and follow the Scottish Outdoor Access Code. It is an offence to uproot any wild plant without the permission of the landowner, therefore, in accordance with the law and as a matter of courtesy, make sure you receive permission before collecting moss. Commercial harvesting requires an agreement with the landowner.

Scotland is very important for mosses, having many rare species and more than 60% of European moss species. As there are many rare mosses, which are often difficult to identify, the guidelines ask you to only harvest particular types of species from habitats where there are less likely to be rare species. It is your responsibility to ensure that rare species are not being harvested. If you are in any doubt please seek expert help. You can help to maintain the natural environment by respecting these guidelines and only taking what you need.

Please consider the points overleaf when collecting moss. Please also contact the land manager who will help you to choose a suitable place. If you see evidence that other harvesters have not been following these guidelines, please report it to your local police and ask to speak to the Wildlife Crime Officer.

The Scottish Moss Collection Code

26.6.2 Making the codes work

Guidelines should use the best available scientific knowledge to determine sustainable harvest. However, they can still be developed, and effective, when scientific knowledge is lacking and a 'common sense' approach is taken. Early guidelines may be precautionary, however, they should be regularly reviewed in light of new scientific evidence or common practice that allows confident sustainable harvest from different habitats or at different harvest rates.

Without the support of a dissemination and education strategy these codes will have little impact on harvesting practice. In order to reach the most receptive section of the harvester population, codes are currently available at various online sources and as A5 leaflets that are distributed through buyers, countryside rangers, through police wildlife crime officers, at fungi forays, etc. and are promoted to those who organize countryside activities. The codes are also being translated into relevant languages to target groups from The European Union accession countries.

Engaging harvesters in the regulation of their own activity places harvesting firmly where most harvesters see it: as a privilege with strong degree of responsibility.

References

Bennett, B.C. (2007). Doctrine of Signatures: An explanation of medicinal plant discovery or dissemination of knowledge? *Economic Botany* **61** (3): 246-255.

Bruns, T.D. (1984). Insect mycophagy in the *Boletales*: fungivore diversity and the mushroom habitat. In Wheeler, Q. & Blackwell, M. (Eds), *Fungus insect relationships. Perspectives in Ecology and Evolution*. pp. 91-129. New York: Columbia University Press.

Cheffings, C., Harper, M. & Jackson, A. (2004). *Plant Diversity Challenge: The UK's response to the Global Strategy for Plant Conservation*. JNCC. Peterborough, UK.

Coppins, A.M. & Coppins, B. J. (2002). Indices of ecological continuity for woodland epiphytic lichen habitats in the British Isles. *British Lichen Society*.

Darwin, T. (1996). *The Scots Herbal. The Plant Lore of Scotland.* Edinburgh: Mercat Press. pp 198.

Dyke, A.J. (2006). *The Practice, Politics and Ecology of NTFPs in Scotland*. University of Glasgow.

Dyke, A.J. & Newton, A.C. (1999). Commercial harvesting of wild mushrooms in Scottish forests: is it sustainable? *Scottish Forestry* **53**: 77–85.

Egli S., Peter M., Buser C., Stahel W. & Ayer F. (2006). Mushroom picking does not impair future harvests – results of a long-term study in Switzerland. *Biological Conservation* **129**: 271-276.

Gilbert, O. (2000). Lichens. *The New Naturalist Library*, **86**, Collins, London.

Gilbert, O. (2004). Lichens. *Naturally Scottish Series*. (Scottish Natural Heritage, Battleby).

Long, D. & Ward, S. (2005). *Strategy for the conservation of lower plants and fungi in Scotland*. Plantlife International (Salisbury, UK).

Mabey, R. (1972). *Food for free*. Collins (UK).

Peck, J.E. (2006). Towards sustainable commercial moss harvest in the Pacific Northwest of North America. *Biological Conservation* **28(3)**: 289-297.

Peck, J.E. & Muir, P.S. (2001a). Harvestable epiphytic bryophytes and their accumulation in Central Western Oregon. *The Bryologist* **104(2)**: 181-190.

Peck, J.E. & Studlar, S.M. (2007). Establishing international guidelines for the sustainable harvest of forest moss. *Evansia* **25(2)**: 65-71.

Planta Europa. (2008). A Sustainable Future for Europe; the European Strategy for Plant Conservation 2008-2014. *Plantlife International* (Salisbury, UK) and the *Council of Europe* (Strasbourg, France).

Reid, K.G.C. (1996). *The Law of Property in Scotland*. Edinburgh: Butterworths. pp 655.

Rothero, G.P. (2005). Mosses and liverworts. *Naturally Scottish Series*. Scottish Natural Heritage, Battleby.

Scheidegger, C., Stähli, I. & Ellenberger, A. (2007). Nachhaltige Wildsammlung und *in situ*-Vermehrung der geschützten Flechtenart *Lobaria pulmonaria* [Sustainable wild harvest and *in situ* propagation of the protected lichen species *Lobaria pulmonaria*.] In: Heilpflanzenforschung der WELEDA. Schwäbisch Gmünd, WELEDA-Naturals. 13-19.

Snowley, H. & Daly, C. (2005). *Scottish Public Opinion of Forestry Survey*. Edinburgh: Forestry Commission pp 53. www.forestry.gov.uk.

Spooner, B. & Roberts, P. (2005). Fungi. *The New Naturalist Library,* **96**, Collins, London, UK.

Staddon, S.C. & Dyke, A. (2007). Moss harvesting in Scottish forests. Its value and future. *Scottish Forestry* **61(3)**: 16-21.

State of Alaska Department of Natural Resources. (2008). Proposed Alaska non-timber forest products harvest manual for commercial harvest on state-owned lands. www.dnr.state.ak.us/mlw

Strobel, G., Knighton, B., Kluck, K., Ren, Y., Livinghouse, T., Griffin, M., Spakowicz, D. & Sears, J. (2008). The production of myco-diesel hydrocarbons and their derivatives by the endophytic fungus *Gliocladium roseum* (NRRL 50072). *Microbiology* **154**: 3319-3328.

Studlar, S.M. & Peck, J.E. (2008). Commercial moss harvest in the Appalachian Mountains of West Virginia : targeted species and incidental take. *The Bryologist* **110(4)**: 752-765.

TNS Global. (2003). *Woodland Research. Results of an Omnibus Survey into Non Timber Forest Product Use in Scotland. Edinburgh*: TNS Global pp 4.

Genney, D. and Dyke, A. (2010). Sustainable use of mosses, lichens and fungi. In: *Species Management: Challenges and Solutions for the 21st Century*, ed. by J.M. Baxter and C.A. Galbraith. TSO Scotland, Edinburgh. pp. 461-475

475

Chapter 27

Conservation of bumblebees

Dave Goulson[1]

Summary

1. Declines in bumblebee species in the last 60 years are well documented in Europe, where they are primarily driven by habitat loss and declines in floral abundance and diversity, in turn driven by changing agricultural practices. Impacts of habitat degradation and fragmentation are likely to be compounded by the social nature of bumblebees and their largely monogamous breeding system which renders their effective population size low.
2. Recent studies suggest that surviving populations of some rare species consist of <30 breeding females, and such populations are susceptible to chance extinction events and inbreeding.
3. In North America, catastrophic declines of some bumblebee species since the 1990s are probably attributable to the accidental introduction of a non-native parasite from Europe, a result of global trade in domesticated bumblebee colonies used for pollination of greenhouse crops.
4. Given the importance of bumblebees as pollinators of crops and wildflowers, it is vital that steps be taken to prevent further declines. Suggested measures include tight regulation of commercial bumblebee use and targeted use of agri-environment schemes to enhance floristic diversity in agricultural landscapes.

[1] School of Biological & Environmental Sciences, University of Stirling, Stirling, FK9 4LA, UK

27.1 Introduction

Machair grassland on South Uist. © D. Goulso

The world bumblebee (*Bombus*) fauna consists of approximately 250 known species, largely confined to temperate, alpine and arctic zones of the northern hemisphere (Williams, 1994). There is mounting evidence that many bumblebee species have declined in recent decades, particularly in developed regions such as Western Europe and North America (reviewed in Goulson, 2003a; Kosior *et al.*, 2007, see also Thorp and Shepherd, 2005). In the UK, three of the 25 native species have gone extinct and a further eight species have undergone major range declines (Goulson, 2003a). The most severely affected species tend to be those with long tongues associated with deep perennial flowers (Goulson *et al.*, 2005). Similar patterns are evident in Europe. In a review of declines in bumblebees of 11 central and western European countries, Kosior *et al.* (2007) describe extinctions of 13 species in at least one country between 1950 and 2000. Four species (*B. armeniacus*, *B. cullumanus*, *B. serrisquama*, *B. sidemii*) went extinct throughout the entire region.

A large number of wild plants are pollinated predominantly or exclusively by bumblebees, sometimes by particular species of bumblebee (Goulson, 2003a). Most bumblebees are generalist pollinators and most insect-pollinated plants use multiple pollinators (Waser *et al.*, 1996), so it could be argued that pollination networks are buffered against the loss of a few pollinator species. However, a recent study simulating the effects of removal of individual pollinators from pollination networks demonstrated that removal of highly linked pollinators such as bumblebees produced the greatest rate of decline in plant species diversity (Memmott *et al.*, 2004). Reduced pollination services can be particularly detrimental when plants are already scarce and threatened directly by the same changes in land use that threaten the bees (Goulson, 2003a; Goulson *et al.*, 2008).

Aside from the implications for conservation, there are good financial reasons for conserving bumblebees. The yields of many field, fruit and seed crops are enhanced by bumblebee visitation (Goulson, 2003c). For example, field beans in Europe are largely pollinated by longer tongued species such as *B. pascuorum* and *B. hortorum*, without which, yields are poor (Free and Williams, 1976). In the US there is an ongoing decline in managed honeybee populations due to disease, misuse of pesticides, loss of subsidies and dangers associated with invading Africanized honeybees (Kremen *et al.*, 2002). The value of crop pollination by honeybees in the US has been estimated at between 5 and 14 billion dollars per year, but beekeeping has diminished by around 50% over the last 50 years (Kremen *et al.*, 2002). This has given rise to concerns over the future of insect-pollinated crops such as cucumber, pumpkin, watermelon, blueberry and cranberry (Delaplane and Mayer, 2000; Richards, 2001; Kremen *et al.*, 2002). At sufficient densities, bumblebees pollinate many of these crops efficiently, often more so than honeybees (Stubbs and Drummond, 2001). However, the impoverished bumblebee communities often associated with agricultural landscapes may be insufficient to replace the services currently provided by honeybees.

Plate 27.1 *Bombus distinguendus*, one of the UK's rarest bumblebee species, feeding on red clover. © D. Goulson

27.2 Causes of bumblebee declines

Most researchers are convinced that the primary cause of bumblebee declines in Western Europe is the intensification of farming practices, particularly during the latter half of the 20th century (Goulson, 2003a, d). In the UK, a self-sufficiency drive in the wake of the Second World War led to a number of major changes. Permanent unimproved grassland was once highly valued for grazing and hay production but the development of cheap artificial fertilizers and new fast-growing grass varieties meant that farmers could improve productivity by ploughing up ancient grasslands. Hay meadows gave way to monocultures of grasses which are grazed or cut for silage. Between 1932 and 1984 over 90% of unimproved lowland grassland was lost in the UK (Howard *et al*., 2003).

There is evidence to suggest that bumblebee forage plants have suffered disproportionate declines. A recent study in the UK found that of 97 preferred bumblebee forage species, 69 (71%) have suffered range restrictions, and 74 (76%) have declined in abundance over the past 80 years, exceeding declines of non-forage species (Carvell *et al.*, 2006). Leguminous crops (notably clovers, *Trifolium* spp.) used to be an important part of crop rotations in much of Europe, and these are highly preferred food sources, particularly for long-tongued bumblebee species (Goulson *et al.*, 2005). Since the introduction of cheap artificial fertilizers, rotations involving legumes have been almost entirely abandoned, and it has been argued that this is one of the primary factors driving the decline of long-tongued bumblebees (Rasmont and Mersch, 1988; Goulson and Darvill, 2004).

Plate 27.2 Machair grassland on South Uist, a rare surviving example of species-rich grassland. © D. Goulson

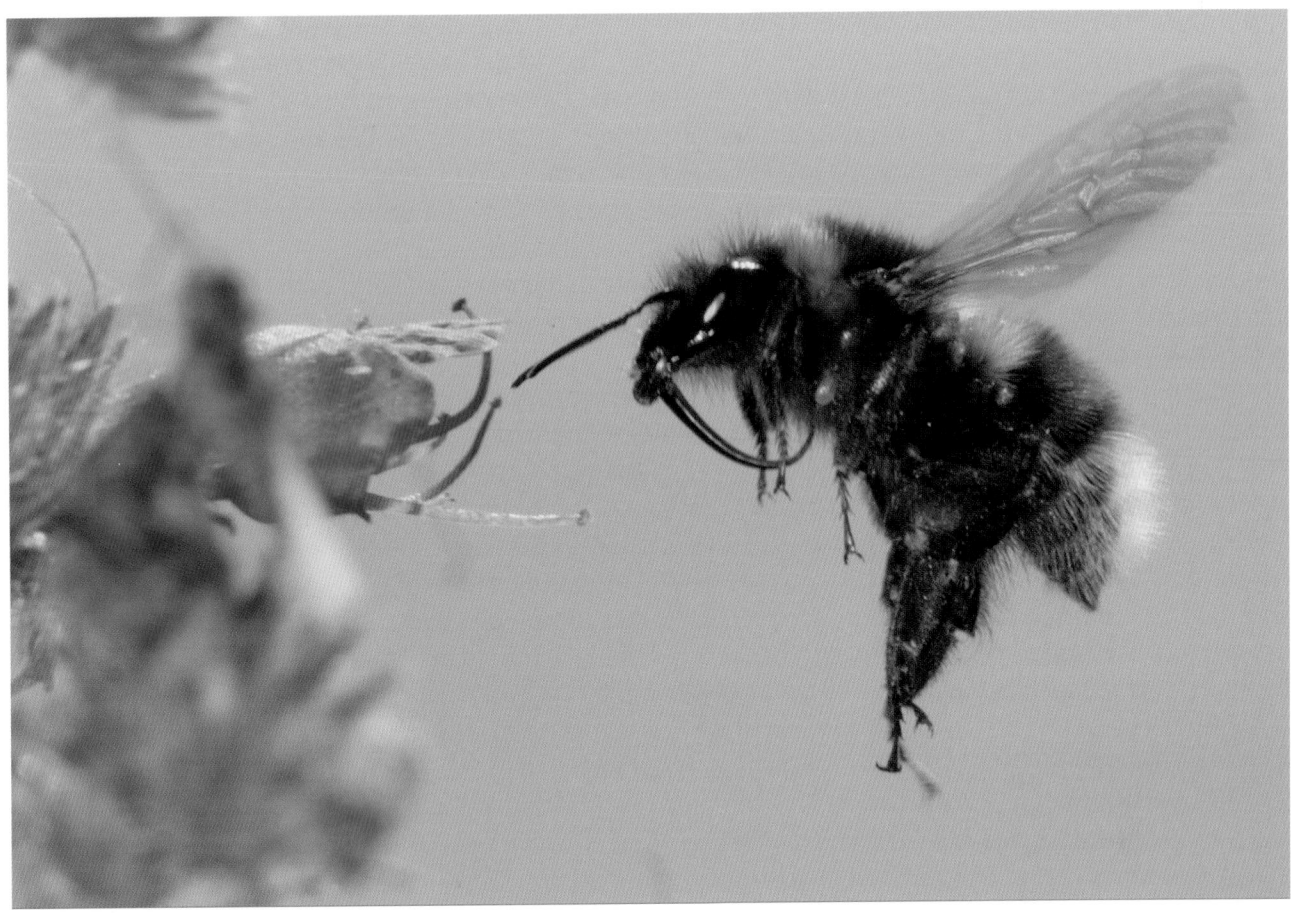

Plate 27.3 *Bombus hortorum*, the only long-tongued bumblebee that remains common in western Europe. © B. Darvill

Uncropped areas of farmland, such as hedgerows, field margins and borders of streams may provide flowers throughout the season, and therefore support greater numbers of foraging bumblebees than cultivated areas (Banaszak, 1992; Mänd *et al.*, 2002). However, these areas will be adequate only if there are enough of them, and if they have not been degraded by drift of herbicides and fertilizers. Insufficient flower-rich uncropped areas may lead to gaps in the succession of flowering plants during which bumblebee colonies may starve and die. With a decline in bees, the plants that they pollinate set less seed, resulting in less forage for the bees in subsequent years (Ockinger and Smith, 2007). The process by which mutually-dependent species drive each other to extinction is known as an 'extinction vortex'. We do not as yet know whether this process is really occurring, but it is clear that farmland provides less food for bees than it once would have done.

In addition to floral resources, bumblebees need suitable nesting sites, the precise requirements for which vary between species (Kells and Goulson, 2003). The carder bees (*Thoracobombus*) such as *B. pascuorum* tend to nest in dense grassy tussocks while other species such as *B. terrestris* nest underground in cavities. Both groups often use abandoned rodent nests. The loss of hedgerows and of unimproved pastures is likely to have reduced availability of nest sites for both above and below-ground nesting bumblebee species (Banaszak, 1992). Those species that nest above ground frequently have their nests destroyed by farm machinery, particularly by cutting for hay or silage. The scarcity of weeds and field-margin flowers on modern intensive farms means that there are less seeds, and therefore less food for voles and mice. Lower populations of these mammals will lead to fewer nest sites for both above and below-ground nesting bumblebee species.

In California, even on organically managed farms, the presence of bumblebees, in this case *B. vosnesenskii* and *B. californicus*, depends on proximity to areas of natural habitat in which the bees can nest (Kremen *et al.*, 2002). A study in Sweden found that field boundaries within 100m of a semi-natural grassland area contained a greater abundance and diversity of foraging bumblebees than similar sites > 1 km from such habitat. However, bumblebee abundance was found to be significantly lower in the semi-natural grasslands themselves suggesting that these sites were used primarily for nesting (Ockinger and Smith, 2007). Similarly, Greenleaf and Kremen (2006) found that tomato fields in northern California obtain high visitation rates from *B. vosnesenskii* only when they were positioned within 300m of a patch of natural habitat and if at least 40% of the land within a 2,100m radius of the farm was natural habitat.

27.2.1 Impacts of alien bees

It has been argued that the most immediate threat to bumblebees in the US, unlike in Western Europe, is the spread of disease due to widespread trafficking of commercial bumblebee hives (Thorp and Shepherd, 2005). Commercial bumblebee hives are used for greenhouse pollination all over the world, including; Israel, Korea, Japan, North America and Europe (Goulson, 2003b). In the US, colonies of *B. impatiens* and *B. occidentalis* have been commercially reared since the early 1990s for the pollination of greenhouse crops such as tomatoes (Whittington and Winston, 2004) and sweet peppers (Shipp *et al.*, 1994). These colonies have been found to have a greater parasite load than wild colonies with an elevated prevalence of the bumblebee specific protozoan pathogens *Crithidia bombi* and *Nosema bombi*, and of the tracheal mite *Locustacarus buchneri* (Colla *et al.*, 2006). These parasites have detrimental effects on colony survival and reproduction and/or the foraging efficiency of individual workers (Brown *et al.*, 2003; Gegear *et al.*, 2005; Otterstatter *et al.*, 2005).

There is little doubt that there are greenhouse escapes. In Japan, feral colonies of the non-native *B. terrestris* are now common (Inari *et al.*, 2005), and a recent study in Canada found that 73% of pollen carried by workers returning to commercial colonies originated from plants outside the greenhouse (Whittington *et al.*, 2004). Consequently, there is a high likelihood of interaction between wild and commercially reared bees at flowers, providing conditions for 'pathogen spillover' from the commercial population to wild populations. Significant increases in the prevalence of *C. bombi* and *N. bombi* have been found in wild bumblebee populations near to commercial greenhouses, compared to wild populations elsewhere (Colla *et al.*, 2006). In 1998, a *N. bombi* outbreak was reported in bumblebee production facilities in North America. This was thought to be a result of the importation of infected European *B. terrestris* colonies into Mexico in 1995 and 1996 (Winter *et al.*, 2006). Similarly, *C. bombi* has only been detected in the US since use of commercially reared bumblebees began and it is suspected that this parasite is not native to the US (Winter *et al.*, 2006). The introduction may have occurred as a result of the shipment of queens of *B. occidentalis* to Europe for commercial rearing before re-importation into the US in the early 1990s (Colla *et al.*, 2006; Winter *et al.*, 2006). Exposure to a non-native pathogen is a likely cause of the catastrophic declines in *B. terricola*, *B. affinis, B. franklini* and *B. occidentalis* (Whittington and Winston, 2004; Thorp, 2005; Thorp and Shepherd, 2005). However, we have a very poor understanding of the relative susceptibilities of bumblebee species to parasites, or of the natural distributions of these parasites, and work is urgently needed in this area. It is clear that tight controls are needed on transport of domesticated bumblebee hives.

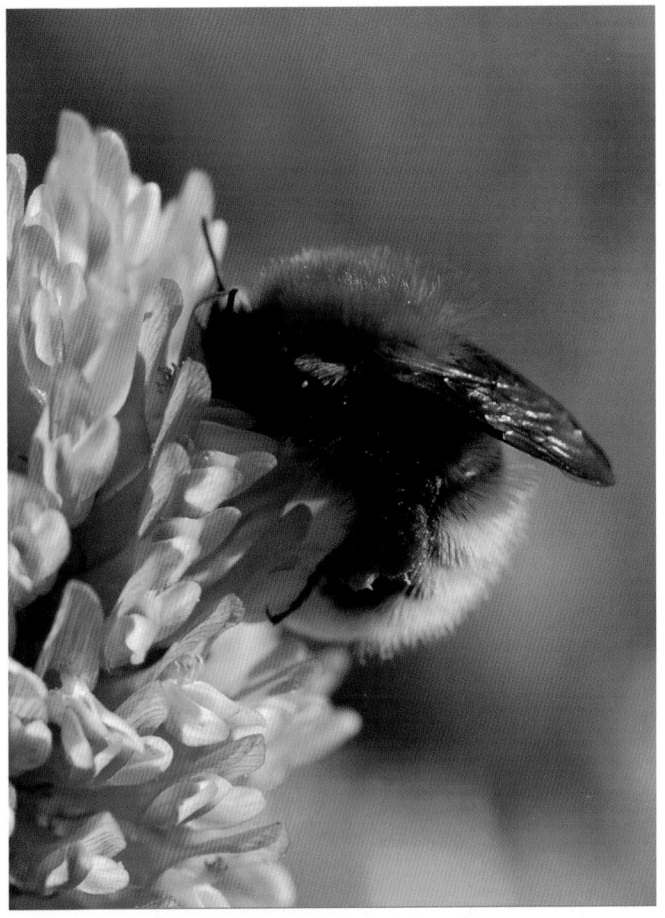

Plate 27.4 *Bombus muscorum*, has declined precipitously in England but healthy populations survive in the Western Isles. © D. Goulson

There are other dangers associated with commercial trafficking of bumblebees. *B. terrestris* is now naturalized in Japan and there are concerns regarding possible competitive effects of this species on native bumblebees. Studies have shown that *B. terrestris* has four times the reproductive output of native species (Matsumara *et al.,* 2004) and that there are considerable overlaps in forage use and timing of foraging (Inari *et al.*, 2005). There are similar concerns in the UK where around 10,000 colonies of a south-eastern European subspecies *Bombus terrestris dalmitinus* are imported each year (Ings *et al.*, 2006). Britain has an endemic subspecies of this bee, *Bombus terrestris audax*. Evidence suggests that there are dangers to the British subspecies in the form of parasite transmission (Ings *et al.*, 2005) or out-competition, particularly since the introduced subspecies has superior foraging efficiency and reproductive rate (Ings *et al.*, 2006). Also, *B. terrestris dalmitinus* and *B. terrestris audax* readily interbreed, so the native subspecies could be lost through introgression (Ings *et al.*, 2005).

In addition to non-native bumblebee species, native pollinator communities in many parts of the globe also have to contend with other introduced bee species, most notably honeybees (*Apis mellifera*). These natives of Europe, Africa and the Middle East have been introduced by man to almost every country in the world. Their impacts are reviewed by Goulson (2003b). Recent studies suggest that honeybees can have negative effects on bumblebees. Walther-Hellwig *et al.* (2006) found that short-tongued bumblebees avoided areas of forage close to honeybee hives, while carder (*Thoracobombus*) bumblebees switched to foraging later in the day and were displaced from their preferred foodplant. Thomson (2004) experimentally introduced honeybees and found that proximity to hives significantly reduced the foraging rates and reproductive success of *B. occidentalis* colonies. In eastern US, Thomson (2006) found a strong overlap between the foraging preferences of the two species, which peaked at the end of the season when floral resources were scarce, corresponding with a negative relationship between honeybee and bumblebee abundance.

There is increasing evidence that the spread of natural enemies of bumblebee colonies is being aided by honeybees. Honeybees can act as vectors for the bumblebee specific *C. bombi* via flowers (Ruiz-Gonzalez and Brown, 2006). The African honeybee parasite *Aethina tumida* (small hive beetle) recently invaded North America, Egypt and Australia, and attacks *B. impatiens* colonies where it causes considerable damage (Spiewok and Neumann, 2006). Deformed wing virus, a viral honeybee pathogen, has been found in commercial colonies of *B. terrestris*, transmitted between the two species as a result of the practice of placing honeybees with queens to induce colony founding (Genersch *et al.*, 2006). However, it has also been found in a wild colony of *B. pascuorum* which had been robbing a managed honeybee hive (Genersch *et al.*, 2006). This virus appears to have higher virulence to bumblebees than to honeybees and the findings raise important questions about transmission and cross-infectivity between bumblebees and honeybees.

27.2.2 Bumblebee population structure

As a consequence of the various factors discussed above, populations of a number of bumblebee species have become increasingly small, fragmented and separated from one another by large distances. In the UK, where distributions are best known, declines appear to have followed a characteristic pattern. The last bumblebee species to disappear from the UK (*B. subterraneus*), was once widespread across southern England, but declined rapidly in the years after the Second World War. By the 1980s the few remaining populations were small and isolated, surviving on habitat islands (nature reserves) that had escaped agricultural intensification. However, these populations subsequently disappeared despite the apparent suitability and protected status of the remaining habitat (Goulson, 2003a). The species was last recorded at Dungeness National Nature Reserve in 1988. Several other UK species such as

B. distinguendus and *B. sylvarum* are in the late stages of a similar process, and are likely to go extinct in the near future. Why do isolated populations go extinct? Understanding the consequences of the fragmentation of remnant populations of bumblebees is of great importance to conservationists, given the current distributions of many rare species.

Small populations of all taxa are inherently more vulnerable to local extinctions due to environmental and demographic stochasticity (Frankham *et al.*, 2002). If these populations form part of a broader metapopulation then regional extinctions can be balanced by subsequent recolonization, but if fragmentation is severe then extinct patches may never be repopulated. In addition, a functioning metapopulation ensures that dispersal maintains genetic cohesion. However, if habitat fragmentation results in the isolation of populations, then they may face an additional extinction threat through inbreeding (Frankham *et al.*, 2002). There are a number of reasons why bumblebees may be particularly badly affected by habitat fragmentation. It is the effective population size (Ne), rather than the census population size (Nc) which determines the rate of genetic drift in a population, and Ne may be several orders of magnitude lower than Nc. In bumblebees, as in many other social insects, Ne depends on the number of successful colonies. The Ne contributed by an individual colony depends on the number of egg-laying queens and the number of males they have mated with, but (unlike many other hymenopterans) bumblebee colonies are all founded by a single queen, and the vast majority of species are monoandrous (Estoup *et al.*, 1995; Schmid-Hempel and Schmid-Hempel, 2000). It seems therefore that population sizes of bumblebees may be low, even relative to other social insects, making them particularly susceptible to the loss of genetic diversity.

Given the potentially serious consequences of inbreeding in bumblebees, it is essential that we understand its prevalence within wild bumblebee populations. Until recently, studying the population genetics of rare bee species was extremely difficult, as lethal sampling was necessary. Work in this area was greatly aided by the development of a non-lethal DNA sampling technique (Holehouse *et al.*, 2003), and this has recently been applied to studies of fragmented populations of rare species: *B. muscorum* (Darvill *et al.*, 2006), *B. sylvarum* (Ellis *et al.*, 2006) and *B. distinguendus* (Bourke and Hammond, 2002). All three studies found significant population structuring. For example in *B. muscorum,* all populations >10 km apart were significantly differentiated, as were some populations just 3km apart, suggesting that this species has very limited dispersal abilities. Ellis *et al.* (2006) used microsatellite markers to group workers into sisterhoods and so estimated the number of colonies (and hence Ne) in populations of *B. sylvarum*, a species which is highly endangered in the UK. Estimates of Ne were very low (range 21-72) suggesting that these populations are very vulnerable to loss of genetic diversity through drift. In all rare species studied to date, genetic diversity (allelic richness and heterozygosity) is low compared to common species (Table 27.1). If fragmented populations of rare bumblebee species are suffering from reduced fitness through inbreeding then we must take steps to conserve what genetic diversity remains. Management strategies in vertebrates routinely consider genetic factors, and we may need to adopt similar measures in the management of rare bumblebee populations.

Table 27.1 Genetic diversity estimates for populations of a number of *Bombus* species (mean ± S.E.). Reviewed in Goulson *et al.* (2008).

Species	Population	Sample Size	Allelic Richness	H_E
B. ignitus	Beijing, China	33	12.2 ± 1.53*	0.85 ± 0.02
B. ignitus	Nagano, Japan	26	8.22 ± 0.72*	0.83 ± 0.03
B. pascuorum	Landford, UK	183	6.22 ± 1.19*	0.52 ± 0.15
B. pascuorum	Rothamsted, UK	125	5.71 ± 1.01	0.52 ± 0.11
B. pascuorum	Continental Europe	22.7 average	5.49 ± 0.16*	0.56 ± 0.01
B. terrestris	Continental Europe	37.5 average	5.96 ± 0.12*	0.61 ± 0.01
B. lucorum	Bern, Switzerland	40	7.00 ± 2.00*	0.60 ± 0.12
B. hypnorum	Various, Sweden	10	6.75 ± 1.03*	0.72 ± 0.14†
B. sylvarum	Southern UK	25.6 average	3.12 ± 0.10	0.39 ± 0.02
B. sylvarum	Epenede, France	10	4.00 ± 0.85	0.53 ± 0.09
B. muscorum	Outer Hebrides, UK	43.8 average	3.22 ± 0.12	0.39 ± 0.01
B. muscorum	Inner Hebrides, UK	62.7 average	3.21 ± 0.07	0.47 ± 0.01
B. muscorum	Southern UK	35.5 average	4.01 ± 0.06	0.51 ± 0.01
B. distinguendus	Scotland, UK	7.75 average	2.63 ± 0.23*	0.42 ± 0.01 †

* allelic richness was not available, and the average number of alleles per locus is presented. Allelic richness is a normalized measure which takes account of differing sample sizes to give a comparable figure for all populations.

† Expected heterozygosity (H_E) was not available, and observed heterozygosity is given. These measures are expected to be very similar for populations that are in Hardy-Weinberg equilibrium.

27.3 Conservation measures

A major cause of bumblebee declines is undoubtedly loss of habitat to intensive farming. However, there are moves to reverse this trend in Europe and North America where there is a growing emphasis on combining the goals of agriculture and conservation (Ovenden *et al.*, 1998; Kleijn and Sutherland, 2003). Subsidies are currently available in many countries for agri-environment schemes that promote biodiversity, including replanting of hedgerows, leaving land fallow, sowing wildflower strips, and restoring flower-rich grassland. Most of the management options promote floral abundance and diversity. It has been found that a 6m wide field margin kept free of crops and agrochemicals may contain six times as many flowering plants and ten times as many flowers than the equivalent cropped area (Kells *et al.*, 2001). The effects of UK field margin management options on bumblebee communities have been the focus of many studies in recent years.

The most valuable form of field margin management for bumblebees has been found to be the sowing of either wildflowers or a pollen and nectar mix consisting of agricultural cultivars of legume species (Carreck and Williams, 2002; Carvell *et al.*, 2004, 2007; Pywell *et al.*, 2005, 2006). Carvell *et al.* (2007) found that the pollen and nectar mixture produced the highest flower abundance with a succession of forage plants flowering over the 3-year trial period. The wildflower mixture produced few flowers in the first year but flower abundance increased over the three years as the mixture became established. Both treatments led to an increase in bumblebee species richness and abundance, and in the third year the wildflower mix was as valuable as the pollen and nectar mixture. Once established, the wildflower mix should persist for up to ten years, while the agricultural cultivars in the pollen and nectar mix are likely to need re-sowing within five years (Pywell *et al.*, 2002).

Plate 27.5 Overgrazed and degraded machair grassland with few flowers. The contrast with Plate 27.2 is striking. © N. Redpath

Bumblebees not only require a suitable source of forage, but also nest and hibernation sites. A popular agri-environment scheme in the UK is the sowing of field margins with tussocky grasses (Pywell et al., 2006). These habitats attract the small mammals whose abandoned holes are used by bumblebees for nest sites (Svensson et al., 2000), so it is likely that this form of management is of value to bumblebees. Carvell et al. (2004) found that field margins sown with a 'split' treatment consisting of a mixture of tussocky grasses and wildflower mix attracted almost as many bumblebees as margins sown solely with the wildflower seed suggesting that it is possible to provide both forage and nesting habitat in small areas.

27.4 Conclusions

Widespread declines of bumblebee species threaten pollination services to both wildflowers and crops. It is clear from studies of population structure that most bumblebee species cannot be conserved by managing small protected 'islands' of habitat within a 'sea' of unsuitable, intensively farmed land. Large areas of suitable habitat are needed to support viable populations in the long term. Also, studies of foraging range indicate that bumblebees exploit forage patches at a landscape scale, so that the scale of management must be appropriate. An integrated approach across large areas or several farms is more likely to succeed than localized efforts. Where small, isolated populations of rare species remain in habitat fragments, targeting the adjacent farms for uptake of suitable agri-environment schemes could increase the population size and so reduce the likelihood of stochastic extinction events and inbreeding. Similarly, such schemes could be used to provide linkage between habitat islands.

Unimproved flower-rich grassland is one of the most important habitats for bumblebees, but has been largely lost to agriculture in Western Europe and North America. Restoration of areas of this habitat will boost bumblebee populations and has been shown to provide improved pollination services on nearby farmed land. Substantial benefits could also be obtained by reintroducing clover (e.g. Trifolium pratense) ley crops into rotations, since this is a key forage source for many declining bumblebee species. This would also reduce dependency on artificial fertilizers.

In the US, recent declines in several bumblebee species have been linked to increases in the commercialization of bumblebees for greenhouse pollination and associated introductions of parasites. There are already restrictions in place on the importation and movement of bumblebees in Canada, Mexico and the US but there are calls for increased restrictions on transportation of bees and for stricter quarantine and monitoring systems (Winter et al., 2006). Similar systems are urgently needed in Europe.

References

Banaszak, J. (1992). Strategy for conservation of wild bees in an agricultural landscape. Agriculture, Ecosystems and Environment 40:179-192.

Bourke, A.F.G. & Hammond, R.L. (2002). Genetics of the scarce bumble bee, Bombus distinguendus, and nonlethal sampling of DNA from bumble bees. A Report for the RSPB, January 2002.

Brown, M.J.F., Schmid-Hempel, R. & Schmid-Hempel, P. (2003). Strong context-dependent virulence in a host-parasite system: reconciling genetic evidence with theory. *Journal of Animal Ecology* **72**: 994-1002.

Carreck, N.L. & Williams, I.H. (2002). Food for insect pollinators on farmland: insect visits to flowers of annual seed mixtures. *Journal of Insect Conservation* **6**: 13-23.

Carvell, C., Meek, W.R., Pywell, R.F. & Nowakowski, M. (2004). The response of bumblebees to successional change in newly created arable field margins. *Biological Conservation* **118**: 327-339.

Carvell, C., Roy, D.B., Smart, S.M., Pywell, R.F., Preston, C.D. & Goulson, D. (2006). Declines in forage availability for bumblebees at a national scale. *Biological Conservation* **132**: 481-489.

Carvell, C., Meek, W.R., Pywell, R.F., Goulson, D. & Nowakowski, M. (2007). Comparing the efficiency of agri-environment schemes to enhance bumble bee abundance and diversity on arable field margins. *Journal of Applied Ecology* **44**: 29-40.

Colla, S.R., Otterstatter, M.C., Gegear, R.J. & Thomson, J.D. (2006). Plight of the bumble bee: Pathogen spillover from commercial to wild populations. *Biological Conservation* **129**: 461-467.

Darvill, B., Ellis, J.S., Lye, G.C. & Goulson, D. (2006). Population structure and inbreeding in a rare and declining bumblebee, *Bombus muscorum* (Hymenoptera: Apidae). *Molecular Ecology* **15**: 601-611.

Delaplane, K.S. & Mayer, D.F. (2000). *Crop pollination by bees.* CABI Publishing, Wallingford, UK.

Ellis, J.S., Knight, M.E., Darvill, B. & Goulson, D. (2006). Extremely low effective population sizes, genetic structuring and reduced genetic diversity in a threatened bumblebee species, *Bombus sylvarum* (Hymenoptera: Apidae). *Molecular Ecology* **15**: 4375-4386.

Estoup, A., Scholl, A., Pouvreau, A. & Solignac, M. (1995). Monandry and polyandry in bumble bees (Hymenoptera, Bombinae) as evidenced by highly variable microsatellites. *Molecular Ecology* **4**: 89-93.

Frankham, R., Ballou, J.D. & Briscoe, D.A. (2002). *Introduction to Conservation Genetics.* Cambridge, UK: Cambridge University Press. 617 pp.

Free, J.B. & Williams, I.H. (1976). Pollination as a factor limiting the yield of field beans (*Vicia faba* L.). *Journal of Agricultural Science* **87**: 395-399.

Gegear, R.J., Otterstatter, M.C. & Thomson, J.D. (2005). Does parasitic infection impair the ability of bumblebees to learn flower-handling techniques? *Animal Behaviour* **70**: 209-215.

Genersch, E., Yue, C., Fries, I. & de Miranda, J.R. (2006). Detection of Deformed Wing Virus, a honey bee viral pathogen, in bumble bees (*Bombus terrestris* and *Bombus pascuorum*) with wing deformities. *Journal of Invertebrate Pathology* **91**: 61-63.

Goulson, D. (2003a). *Bumblebees: Behaviour and Ecology.* Oxford, UK: Oxford University Press.

Goulson, D. (2003b). Effects of introduced bees on native ecosystems. *Annual Review of Ecology, Evolution and Systematics* **34**: 1-26.

Goulson, D. (2003c). Conserving wild bees for crop pollination. *International Journal of Food, Agriulture and the. Environment* **1**: 142-144.

Goulson, D. (2003d). The conservation of bumblebees. *Bee World* **84**: 105-106.

Goulson, D. & Darvill, B. (2004). Niche overlap and diet breadth in bumblebees; are rare species more specialized in their choice of flowers? *Apidologie* **35**: 55-63.

Goulson, D., Hanley, M.E., Darvill, B., Ellis, J.S. & Knight, M.E. (2005). Causes of rarity in bumblebees. *Biological Conservation* **122**: 1-8.

Goulson, D., Lye, G.C. & Darvill, B. (2008). Decline and conservation of bumblebees. *Annual Review of Entomology* **53**: 191-208.

Greenleaf, S.S. & Kremen, C. (2006). Wild bee species increase tomato production and respond differently to surrounding land use in Northern California. *Biological Conservation* **133**: 81-87.

Holehouse, K.A., Hammond, R.L. & Bourke, A.F.G. (2003). Non-lethal sampling of DNA from bumble bees for conservation genetics. *Insectes Sociaux* **50**: 277-285.

Howard, D.C., Watkins, J.W., Clarke, R.T., Barnett, C.L. & Stark, G.J. (2003). Estimating the extent and change in broad habitats in Great Britain. *Journal of Environmental Management* **67**: 219-227.

Inari, N., Nagamitsu, T., Kenta, T., Goka, K. & Hiura, T. (2005). Spatial and temporal pattern of introduced *Bombus terrestris* abundance in Hokkaido, Japan, and its potential impact on native bumblebees. *Population Ecology* **47**: 77-82.

Ings, T.C., Raine, N.E. & Chittka, L. (2005). Mating preference of commercially imported bumblebees (*Bombus terrestris*) in Britain (Hymenoptera: Apidae). *Entomologia Generalis* **28**: 233-238.

Ings, T.C., Wards, N.L. & Chittka, L. (2006). Can commercially imported bumble bees out-compete their native conspecifics? *Journal of Applied Ecology* **43**: 940-948.

Kells, A.R. & Goulson, D. (2003). Preferred nesting sites of bumblebee queens (Hymenoptera: Apidae) in agroecosystems in the UK. *Biological Conservation* **109**: 165-174.

Kells, A.R., Holland, J.M. & Goulson, D. (2001). The value of uncropped field margins for foraging bumblebees. *Journal of Insect Conservation* **5**: 283-291.

Kleijn, D. & Sutherland, W.J. (2003). How effective are European agri-environment schemes in conserving and promoting biodiversity? *Journal of Applied Ecology* **40**: 947-969.

Kosior, A., Celary, W., Olejnikzak, P., Fijal, J., Krol, W., Solarz, W. & Plonka, P. (2007). The decline of the bumble bees and cuckoo bees (Hymenoptera: Apidae: Bombini) of Western and Central Europe. *Oryx* **41**: 79-88.

Kremen, C., Williams, N.M. & Thorp, R.W. (2002). Crop pollination from native bees at risk from agricultural intensification. *Proceedings of the National Academy of Sciences* **99**: 16812-16816.

Mänd, M., Mänd, R. & Williams, I.H. (2002). Bumblebees in the agricultural landscape of Estonia. *Agriculture, Ecosystems and Environment* **89**: 69-76.

Matsumara, C., Nakajima, M., Yokoyama, J. & Waishitini, I. (2004). High reproductive ability of an alien bumblebee invader, *Bombus terrestris*, L., in the Hidaka region of southern Hokkaido, Japan. *Japanese Journal of Conservation Ecology* **9**: 93-102.

Memmott, J., Waser, N.M. & Price, M.V. (2004). Tolerance of pollination networks to species extinctions. *Proceedings of the Royal Society, London (B).* **271**: 2605-2611.

Ockinger, E. & Smith, H.G. (2007). Semi-natural grasslands as population sources for pollinating insects in agricultural landscapes. *Journal of Applied Ecology* **44**: 50-59.

Otterstatter, M.C., Gegear, R.J., Colla, S. & Thompson, J.D. (2005). Effects of parasitic mites and protozoa on the flower constancy and foraging rate of bumble bees. *Behavioural Ecology and Sociobiology* **58**: 383-389.

Ovenden, G.N., Swash, A.R.H. & Smallshire, D. (1998). Agri-environment schemes and their contribution to the conservation of biodiversity in England. *Journal of Applied Ecology* **35**: 955-960.

Pywell, R.F., Bullock, J.M., Hopkins, A., Walker, K.J., Sparks, T.H., Burke, M.J.W. & Peel, S. (2002). Restoration of a species-rich grassland on arable land: assessing the limiting processes using a multi-site experiment. *Journal of Applied Ecology* **39**: 294-309.

Pywell, R.F., Warman, E.A., Carvell, C., Sparks, T.H., Dicks, L.V., Bennett, D., Wright, A., Critchley, C.N.R. & Sherwood, A. (2005). Providing forage resources for bumblebees in intensively farmed landscapes. *Biological Conservation* **121**: 479-494.

Pywell, R.F., Warman, E.A., Hulmes, L., Hulmes, S., Nuttall, P., Sparks, T.H., Critchley, C.N.R. & Sherwood, A. (2006). Effectiveness of new agri-environment schemes in providing foraging resources for bumblebees in intensively farmed landscapes. *Biological Conservation* **129**: 192-206.

Rasmont, P. & Mersch, P. (1988). Première estimation de la dérive faunique chez les bourdons de la Belgique (Hymenoptera, Apidae). *Annales de la Société Royale zoologique de Belgique* **118**: 141-147.

Richards, A.J. (2001). Does low biodiversity resulting from modern agricultural practice affect crop pollination and yield? *Annals of Botany* **88**: 165-172.

Ruiz-Gonzalez, M.X. & Brown, M.J.F. (2006). Honey bee and bumblebee trypanosomatids: specificity and potential for transmission. *Ecological Entomology* **31**: 616-622.

Schmid-Hempel, R. & Schmid-Hempel, P. (2000). Female mating frequencies in *Bombus* spp. from Central Europe. *Insectes Sociaux* **47**: 36-41.

Shipp, J.L., Whitfield, G.H. & Papadopoulos, A.P. (1994). Effectiveness of the bumble bee *Bombus impatiens* Cr. (Hymenoptera: Apidae), as a pollinator of greenhouse sweet pepper. *Scientia Horticulturae* **57**: 29-39.

Spiewok, S. & Neumann, P. (2006). Infestation of the commercial bumblebee (*Bombus impatiens*) field colonies by small hive beetles (*Aethina tumida*). *Ecological Entomology* **31**: 623-628.

Stubbs, C.S. & Drummond, F.A. (2001). *Bombus impatiens* (Hymenoptera: Apidae): An alternative to *Apis mellifera* (Hymenoptera: Apidae) for lowbush blueberry pollination. *Journal of Economic Entomology* **94**: 609-616.

Svensson, B., Lagerlöf, J. & Svensson, B.G. (2000). Habitat preferences of nest-seeking bumble bees (Hymenoptera: Apidae) in an agricultural landscape. *Agriculture, Ecosystems and Environment* **77**: 247-255.

Thomson, D.M. (2004). Detecting the effects of introduced species: a case study of competition between *Apis* and *Bombus*. *Oikos* **114**: 407-418.

Thomson, D.M. (2006). Competitive interactions between the invasive European honey bee and native bumble bees. *Ecology* **85**: 458-470.

Thorp, R.W. (2005). Species profile: *Bombus franklini*. In: *Red List of Pollinator Insects of North America*. Eds Shepherd, M.D., D.M. Vaughan and S.H. Black. The Xerces Society for Invertebrate Conservation.

Thorp, R.W. & Shepherd, M.D. (2005). Profile: Subgenus *Bombus*. In *Red List of Pollinator Insects of North America*. Eds Shepherd, M.D., D.M. Vaughan and S.H. Black. The Xerces Society for Invertebrate Conservation.

Walther-Hellwig, K., Fokul, G., Frankl, R., Buechler, R., Ekschmitt, K. & Wolters, V. (2006). Increased density of honeybee colonies affects foraging bumblebees. *Apidologie* **37**: 517-532.

Waser, N.M., Chittka, L., Price, M.V., Williams, N. & Ollerton, J. (1996). Generalization in pollinator systems and why it matters. *Ecology* **77**: 1043-1060.

Whittington, R. & Winston, M.L. (2004). Comparison and examination of *Bombus occidentalis* and *Bombus impatiens* (Hymenoptera: Apidae) in tomato greenhouses. *Journal of Economic Entomology* **97**: 1384-1389.

Whittington, R., Winston, M.L., Tucker, C. & Parachnowitsch, A.L. (2004). Plant-species identify of pollen collected by bumblebees placed in greenhouse for tomato pollination. *Canadian Journal of Plant Science* **84**: 599-602.

Williams, P.H. (1994). Phylogenetic relationships among bumble bees (*Bombus* Latr.): a reappraisal of morphological evidence. *Systematic Entomology* **19**: 327-344.

Winter, K., Adams, L., Thorp, R., Inouye, D., Day, L., Ascher, J. & Buchmann, S. (2006). Importation of non-native bumble bees into North America: potential consequences of using *Bombus terrestris* and other non-native bumble bees for greenhouse crop pollination in Canada, Mexico and the United States. A white paper of the North American Pollinator Protection Campaign (NAPPC).

Goulson D. (2010). Conservation of bumblebees. In: *Species Management: Challenges and Solutions for the 21st Century*, ed. by J.M. Baxter and C.A. Galbraith. TSO Scotland, Edinburgh. pp. 477-492

492

Part 6

The ecosystem approach: making the links

The focus of this book has been on the management of species in a range of different situations. This section of the book views species as components within an ecosystem, looking at how they interact and what role they perform within a wider, functioning system. As consideration of the ecosystem approach develops it seems likely that government and others will increasingly plan in a larger, more holistic way over longer timescales. Equally, the idea of "ecosystem services", is gaining much greater profile, hence there is a need to define, in a new way where species management fits into this approach and to clarify what role species play in the provision of particular services to the human population. The section examines also the impact that climate change may have on species in years to come. The environment has always changed in response to a multitude of factors of course, but perhaps it is the rate and nature of the changes that we are now experiencing that is so dramatic, and that may lead to significant changes in the ecology of many species.

Chris Spray reviews the relationship between species and ecosystems, noting that the traditional approach was for managers to focus on the needs of individual species or occasionally to consider them as part of a wider habitat, but almost never as part of a functioning ecosystem. Viewing issues at the ecosystem scale leads to consideration of wider countryside management, the role of ecological networks and landscape scale evaluation. The recent move to consider ecosystem services has placed biodiversity at the centre of land and water management, with the challenge to clarify its value and to manage it in a sustainable manner. Whilst a series of policy and other initiatives are helping to raise the awareness of the approach, there is still a need to develop standard methodologies for valuing ecosystem service and for placing species management in this context. Finally, Chris suggests that species managers have to embrace this new, wider approach and understand the value of ecosystems to society.

One of the issues appearing in many of the chapters of the book has been climate change. We are all climate forecasters; having our own views on the causes of climate change and on the likely severity of the changes we will witness in future years. Yet this is, in reality, a challenging area of science, and progressively underpinning opinion with fact will not be easy, especially as we seem to demand absolute accuracy in an area where uncertainty about the detail of changes will inevitably abound for years to come. Rhys Green and James Pearce-Higgins tackle the subject, reviewing the impact on species and considers what management measures could be put in place to lessen the impact, or to create conditions that might allow species to adapt to the changes. They suggest that management methods could be viewed in six categories; prioritization and planning, protection and creation of core areas, management of core areas, maintenance of suitable habitat in the wider landscape, protection from dispersed and remote human activities, and reintroduction and translocation. These categories all imply that proactive action is possible, rather than just adopting a fatalistic approach. This is important, as it would be all too easy to consider the problem of climate change to be too big to deal with. Action is possible, and is needed if we are to assist many species adapt. In conclusion, They note that future conservation management will require increased spatial scope in planning, better integration of effort, effective monitoring and a long term outlook. All this will need to lead to a new and more holistic approach.

Chapter 28

Targeted species management within a wider ecosystem approach

Chris J. Spray MBE[1]

Summary

1. Species management has traditionally been directed largely towards certain iconic and easily identifiable species at the top of food chains, or as components of habitats at risk from loss, rather than as key elements of functioning ecosystems.
2. Recognition of the role of individual species within the wider countryside and of the importance of ecological networks has grown, along with an emphasis on the need for conservation action at the landscape scale.
3. More recently, focus on ecosystem services and the Ecosystem Approach has placed biodiversity at the centre of land and water management decision-making, but targeted species management has not yet become an integral part of this.
4. A series of innovative policy, institutional and legislative initiatives in Scotland are helping promote wider acceptance of the Ecosystem Approach, but there is still a need for accepted methodologies for valuing ecosystem services and for placing species management within this context.
5. Targeted species management has to embrace this wider approach to understanding the value of ecosystems to society, and the role of species within effective functioning ecosystems.

[1] Professor of Water Science and Policy, UNESCO Centre for Water Law, Policy and Science, Dundee University, Dundee, DD1 4HN, UK

28.1 Introduction

Targeted species management has traditionally been achieved through the collection of data about species at risk (e.g. in the UK, the Birds of Conservation Concern - Eaton *et al*.,2009), combined with the delivery of resultant strategies and management programmes that address the underlying causes of any observed and unwelcome changes in species populations, distribution or behaviour. These species conservation programmes have mainly been undertaken in three ways – through direct action on the ground to protect or enhance species survival (e.g. through habitat management or reintroduction projects); through site protection (either through purchase or through financially backed management agreements); and through policies and legislation (both direct environmental regulation and indirectly by influencing other policies, such as planning or agriculture to include elements to enhance species conservation). This approach has proved the cornerstone of much of Scotland's conservation success in, for example, safeguarding species such as the Svalbard race of the barnacle goose (*Branta leucopsis*) or the reintroduction of sea eagles (*Haliaeetus albicilla*).

However, a focus on species management alone can only achieve so much. Individual species cannot exist for any length of time outwith their normal environment and individual habitat patches cannot themselves exist in isolation from other habitat patches. They themselves sit within wider ecological networks, extending across both time and space. Notwithstanding therefore the current attention placed on the UK and Scottish Biodiversity strategies, and the emphasis on delivery of individual Species Action Plans (SAPs) as the mechanism for driving species conservation, it is clear that to be sustainable, any long term approach to targeted species management must also address the fundamental issues relating to the healthy functioning of wider ecosystems.

This focus on ecosystems has recently been moved forward through the promotion of the Ecosystem Approach. The Convention on Biological Diversity defined the Ecosystem Approach is seen as a unifying strategy for "the integrated management of land, water and living resources that promotes conservation and sustainable use in an equitable way". Trying to incorporate this in to the previous strategies that focussed more on species conservation, provides both challenges and opportunities.

28.2 Species conservation paradigms

Historically, species management in native societies would have been purely concerned with sustainable harvesting of a wild resource - be that for food, for clothing, for fuel or for any other provisioning service that plants or animals provide. Knowledge of the ecology of such target species would have been only partial, based on local observation and oral history. Nevertheless, with low human population density, limited agricultural technology and despite little or no science base, targeted species management (in as much as that is what it was) would have been in harmony with ecosystem functions, human society and the carrying capacity of the local environment.

Plate 28.1 Gleann Màma, Arisaig. © John M. Baxter

More recently, as agriculture began to flourish and permanent settlements appeared, human society in Scotland began to fundamentally change the landscape. Sustainable harvesting would still have been important, but with it came permanent agriculture and the first moves towards the targeted protection of species. This would mainly have been quarry species, protected as a sustainable food resource and for "sport" - through legislation and exclusive land ownership. In effect royal hunting forests, moorland and salmon rivers became the first unofficial "nature preserves" of powerful landowners.

28.2.1 Single species management

The development of management strategies and programmes for the purpose of conserving species at risk in their own right (other than quarry) initially focused on a limited number of single species. Typically, these were large, "cuddly", easily identifiable, charismatic species, often at the top of their respective food chains (Bridgewater, this volume). Conservationists involved in species management could be sure that these iconic species, and the endangered plight in which their populations (or welfare) were described would be attractive to the general public and, critically would appeal to their financial support. As well as tracking population levels and highlighting the imminent danger of individual species extinction, the single species approach has also become associated recently with species reintroduction programmes. In Scotland, this has so far concentrated almost exclusively on birds, with the notable success of the return of the sea eagle and red kite (*Milvus milvus*) as breeding birds, following centuries of persecution. Corncrake (*Crex crex*), Eurasian crane (*Grus grus*), Eurasian beaver (*Castor fiber*), wolf (*Canis lupus*), Eurasian lynx (*Lynx lynx*) and a host of other species have been mooted as potential future targets for reintroduction.

Focusing on individual species clearly has advantages, not least its appeal to a wide range of people outside the ecological profession who can comprehend and engage with the fortunes of selected species - and it continues to form a key part of the species management approach in Scotland. In 2005 a list of species (and habitats) was published identifying those considered by Scottish ministers as important for biodiversity conservation in Scotland. It contained 197 marine species, and 1,086 terrestrial and freshwater species, including 61 endemic to Scotland. More recently, in 2007 Scottish Natural Heritage (SNH) launched a "Five Year Species Action Framework" (SNH, 2007), focusing attention on just 32 species and the actions (and partner organizations) that were needed to "make a difference for Scotland's species". Whilst the selection of the 32 species concerned by SNH may not have been outwardly driven by the ecosystem approach, the four criteria used for selection (species for conservation; invasive non-native species; species for conflict management; species for sustainable use) and the consultation process on which SNH engaged clearly follow many of the core principles of a practical ecosystem approach, as outlined in the Convention on Biological Diversity.

28.2.2 The Biodiversity Action Plan (BAP) framework

In 1994 the UK Government produced the UK Biodiversity Action Plan and in Scotland we saw the production of the Action for Scotland's Biodiversity (Scottish Biodiversity Group, 2000) and the Scottish

Biodiversity Strategy (Scottish Executive, 2004). Within these various strategies and action plans, priority species and habitats were identified for targeting conservation management.

The identification of Scottish priority species and the development of individual species action plans has gone a long way towards enabling clearer targeting of species management, but the sheer number of species involved is overwhelming. In August 2007 the UK Biodiversity Partnership published the revised UK BAP list of priority species and habitats, containing no less than 1,149 species (the previous list contained 577 species), of which some 610 species or subspecies occur in Scotland. Such a vast number provides practical difficulties in addressing what should be the current priorities for targeted species management. On its own, it also has no obvious direct connection to an ecosystem approach.

Another concern is the over-emphasis in both the UK and Scottish lists towards those species representing higher taxonomic orders, as opposed to their potential role in ecosystem functioning. Thus 138 vertebrates and 111 vascular plants occur in the list of 610 Scottish BAP species, compared to the estimated number of 539 vertebrates and 1,080 vascular plants occurring in Scotland (Scottish Biodiversity Group, 2000). By comparison, species of invertebrates (164), fungi and lichens (127), bryophytes (59) and algae (11) are very poorly represented in the BAP list compared to the total number of these species in Scotland (c.24,800 invertebrates; c.9,140 fungi and lichen; 928 bryophytes; and c.9,000 algae).

28.2.3 Habitat management

Whilst species action plans form a key part of the Scottish approach to species management, increasingly emphasis has been placed on achieving these and other species management targets through habitat-based delivery mechanisms; and the UK and Scottish Biodiversity Action Plans identify 65 and 60 priority habitats respectively.

The habitat management approach includes site protection as one of its main elements, and the importance of Scottish sites for species management is recognized in the designation of some 240 Special Areas of Conservation (SACs) for internationally important habitats, and over 140 Special Protection Areas (SPAs) to protect the breeding, feeding and roosting habitats of migratory birds. In addition, Scotland has over 1,450 Sites of Special Scientific Interest (SSSIs) covering 13% of the country. The nature reserves owned and managed by wildlife trusts and voluntary conservation organizations add further to the area protected for conservation of species through habitat management.

Underpinning this approach is the key assumption that habitat management will deliver species conservation – and targeted species management at that. The extent to which this is actually happening is less clear and, furthermore, whilst we may be able to promote and record expansion in terms of new areas of habitat, this will not necessarily be of equal quality. Indeed little may be known as to the robustness or functioning of component parts of such newly recreated habitats and their ecosystems. It also raises questions as to potential conflicts between species priorities within the same broad habitat.

Brotherton and Webb (this volume) have examined the relationship between habitat management and species conservation using heathlands as an example. This habitat was associated with some 90 UK BAP priority species, but of these only 8% actually required the ericaceous vegetation that for most site managers would be the main objective of any heathland management programme. Instead they showed that structural complexity was critical and that habitat heterogeneity (including the presence of scrub, temporary wetlands, bare ground, and grasslands) within the heathland sites was important both geographically and temporally. Targeted species management would require both geographical variation and variation in detailed habitat management at a range of sites to meet species' needs.

28.2.4 Ecological networks

Even before the major work on island biogeography (MacArthur and Wilson, 1967), it had been realized that habitat patches alone often fail to have the resilience to maintain individual species populations over long time periods. The natural processes of population dynamics (immigration and births, emigration and deaths) determine the chances of species extinction within any one habitat patch. For many social

Plate 28.2 Lochan and Creag Dubh, Beinn Eighe NNR. © Lorne Gill/SNH

insects, this is made even more challenging by the largely monogamous nature of their breeding system (Goulson, this volume). With the growing understanding of migration patterns, particularly those of birds, fish and mammals, species management has embraced the concepts of patch dynamics, of habitat connectivity and of ecological networks for targeting individual species survival needs.

Migratory waterfowl have possibly been the greatest beneficiaries of this approach to species management and the Ramsar Convention (on the conservation of wetlands of international importance especially as waterfowl habitat) signed by the UK and 17 other countries in Iran in 1971, can lay claim to being one of the oldest global environmental treaties. Along with the development of conservation programmes for species which depend on the African-Western Eurasian flyways (Davidson and Stroud, 2006), this framework sets the context for targeted species management of migratory waterfowl. Within Scotland, this approach to species management can readily be seen in the conservation management of the network of wetland sites that support tens of thousands of wintering swans, ducks and geese – including protected sites utilized by wintering Icelandic whooper swans (*Cygnus cygnus*) (Spray, 2007), and the entire global population of birds such as the Svalbard race of barnacle goose from Norway.

28.2.5 The landscape scale

Whilst there may appear to be little difference between targeting species management through ecological networks and patch dynamics on the one hand and approaching this at the landscape scale, species management in Scotland has struggled to adopt this wider approach in any meaningful manner. Calls for a "rewilding" of the Scottish landscape, for a bolder and wider approach to species management on a grand scale are becoming more frequent (Dennis, this volume), but are faced with many challenges – institutionally, legally, scientifically and in terms of public acceptance from certain stakeholders. Nevertheless, on the face of it larger populations of target species, within more sustainable ecosystems and with greater resilience to change can only but aid species conservation.

There have been some positive changes in policy development, particularly in the European context. The setting up of the Natura 2000 network of protected sites (SACs and SPAs) across Europe was certainly a move in this direction, though not itself based on a landscape approach. The EU Water Framework Directive and the EU Floods Directive both have river basins at the heart of their approach, with integrated river basin management planning expected to deliver "good ecological status" and sustainable flood risk management at the catchment scale, and there are opportunities to include species management requirements within this approach. Above all pressures, climate change is probably the most important in terms of its impact on the distribution and survival of populations of many Scottish species. Huntley *et al.* (2007) in mapping predicted changes in the distribution of breeding birds across Europe have highlighted how species management policies need to change to reflect the disruptions that will occur. Species can respond to climate change either by adapting (physically or behaviourally) or by moving – the alternative is extinction. Crucially, both positive options require time and space at the landscape scale. Green and Pearce-Higgins (this volume) also argue that scale is vital and that for some species it may be necessary to promote range extensions and create new habitats in new locations, as well as enhance the ability of species to move between habitat patches through the landscape.

28.3 Ecosystem services and the Ecosystem Approach

As defined in the Convention on Biological Diversity (CBD), the Ecosystem Approach is seen as a unifying strategy for "the integrated management of land, water and living resources that promotes conservation and sustainable use in an equitable way". It clearly recognizes the scientific basis of ecosystems as natural units of living and non-living elements acting together as an integrated system, but also promotes the emerging concept of ecosystem services which represent the much wider range of benefits that a healthy functioning ecosystem provides directly and indirectly.

The CBD identifies 12 priorities that should guide a practical approach to achieving this:

- Objectives of management of land, water and living resources are a matter of societal choice.
- Management should be decentralized to the lowest appropriate level.
- Consider the effects of activities on adjacent and other ecosystems.
- Need to understand and manage the ecosystem in an economic market:
  (a) reduce market distortions that adversely affect biological diversity
  (b) align incentives to promote biodiversity and sustainable use
  (c) internalize costs and benefits.
- Conservation of ecosystem structure and functioning services should be a priority target.
- Ecosystems must be managed within the limits of their functioning.
- Appropriate spatial and temporal scales.
- Objectives of ecosystem management should be set for the long term.
- Recognize that change is inevitable.
- Balance, conservation and use of biological diversity.
- All forms of relevant information, including scientific and indigenous and local knowledge.
- Involve all relevant sectors of society and scientific disciplines.

In this, ecosystem structure, processes and services are seen as the priority, rather than individual species conservation. The approach is not a detailed guidance manual for quantifying ecosystem services, nor a set planning methodology, rather an attempt to ensure environmental limits are respected in an holistic manner representing the true value of ecosystems to society.

In a ground-breaking paper in Nature, Costanza *et al*. (1997) attempted to put a global economic value to these ecosystem services ($33 trillion per annum on the basis of replacement costs) but, more importantly perhaps they focused attention on the real value of ecosystems, and by implication the species and habitats that make up functioning ecosystems.

This approach was taken a step further with the development of a broad framework for classifying and valuing services in the Millennium Ecosystem Assessment (2005). This grouped such services in four strands: provisioning services; regulatory services; cultural services; and supporting services (Figure 28.1)

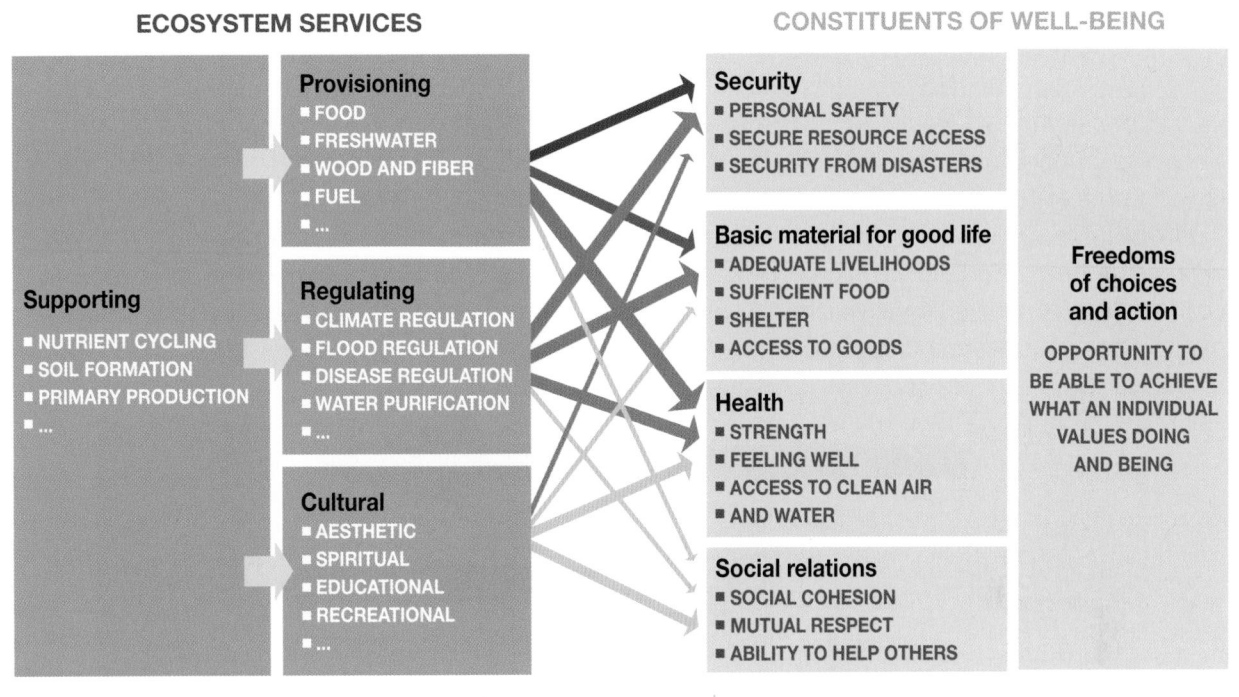

Figure 28.1 From: Millennium Ecosystem Assessment (2005).

28 3.1 Where does species management fit with an ecosystem approach?

Land (and water) management remains the key to effective species management. The various initiatives on valuing ecosystems promote the importance of sustainable use and of public participation in defining the objectives of land management - and thus influencing which species and habitats are seen as important targets for conservation action. This linkage between changes in land use (driven by pollution, climate change, resource exploitation, etc.) and subsequent changes in biodiversity, in ecosystem functions and in ecosystem services is a vital one in this context (Braat and ten Brink, 2008). Not only does it need to underpin a targeted approach to species management, it also leads to changes in the economic value of the ecosystem services and the subsequent impact this has on quality of life and human well-being.

Scottish ecosystems have been radically altered and modified, largely by human action. The SEPA report on the State of the Scottish Environment (2006) identifies conservation of biodiversity as one of the three key environmental challenges facing Scotland (alongside climate change and human health). It identifies increasing intensification of land use for agriculture, forestry and industry, alongside urbanization and population growth within the last 250 years, as being responsible for significant and at times rapid declines in species numbers.

In terms of species management, the Scottish Biodiversity Group Report (2000) identified seven such key drivers that continue to shape the landscape and impact on individual species survival. These are Forestry, farming and fisheries; Land development; Air quality; Water quality; Transport; Invasive non-native species; and Climate change. On top of this, they also recognized the importance of awareness raising and education.

Thus whilst the Ecosystem approach at one level might appear to take the focus away from single species management targets and action programmes, it firmly places biodiversity at the heart of decision-making and within a wider context of a participatory process for equitable sharing of the benefits of these natural resources and for delivering and sustaining human well-being (Figure 28.2).

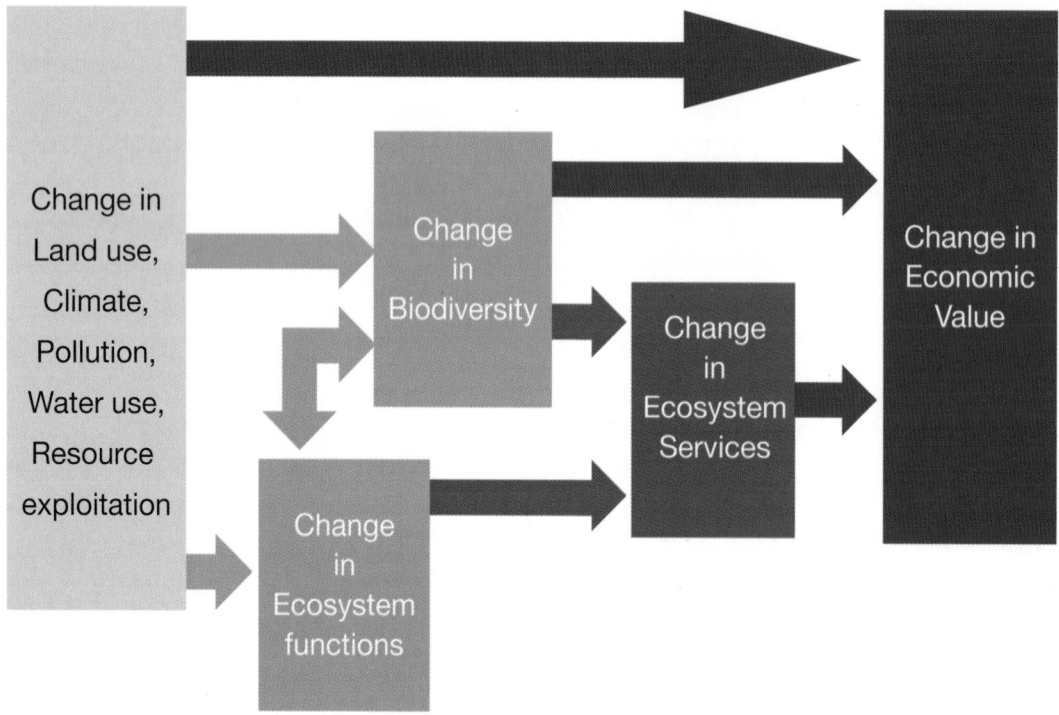

Figure 28.2 Adapted from Braat and ten Brink (2008): The Cost of Policy Inaction: the case of not meeting the 2010 biodiversity target.

Plate 28.3 Morton Loch. © Lorne Gill/SNH

28.4 Moving towards the Ecosystem Approach

As already noted, the Convention on Biological Diversity produced an early guide to implementing the Ecosystem Approach, identifying 12 priorities that should underpin it. In 2007, reflecting on the impact of the Stern Review of the Economics of Climate Change, the G8 and EU Environment Ministers meeting at Potsdam agreed a need for a similar study on the economics of the loss of ecosystems and biodiversity. In 2008 some of the interim results from this work (European Commission, 2008) and also work on the cost of policy inaction in the case of not meeting the 2010 target to significantly reduce the loss of biodiversity (Braat and ten Brink, 2008) were published.

At the same time, in 2007 DEFRA launched "Securing a healthy natural environment: an action plan for embedding an ecosystem approach" (DEFRA, 2007a) which aims to deliver a shift in the way that policy making and delivery encompass environmental issues, including the conservation of biodiversity. This report was accompanied by a new cross government Public Service Agreement on "securing a healthy natural environment for today and the future" which included as one of its elements "biodiversity valued, safeguarded and enhanced". Whilst neither this, nor the accompanying "Introductory Guide to valuing ecosystem services" (DEFRA, 2007b) focus on species management as such, they do recognize the significant evidence on the linkages between changes in biodiversity and changes in the way ecosystems function (Hooper *et al.*, 2005). They attempt to ensure that the true value of ecosystems (and therefore by implication the species they contain) and the services they provide are taken in to account in policy decision-making.

28.4.1 Scottish institutional and policy initiatives

The responsibility for delivery of actions under the UK BAP for the conservation of priority species in Scotland rests with the Scottish Government. In 2008, responding to the principles underlying this new Ecosystem Approach, they reorganized the structures that were in place to deliver the Scottish Biodiversity Strategy. A key move was to create five Ecosystem Groups, reflecting the broad ecosystems characteristic of Scotland (Freshwater/wetland; Lowland/farmland; Upland; Woodland; and Marine/coastal). These are now responsible for coordinating action for the groups of habitats and species that make up each Group, and for ensuring that issues such as the development of ecological networks and habitat mosaics are addressed in an holistic manner. Similar actions for species conservation can be brought together as broad habitat management actions that could in large be delivered by wider policies affecting land use management – for example agricultural support mechanisms, strategic planning, or actions to combat climate change. However, it is recognized that there is still the need for individual species action programmes alongside this.

Each species listed in the BAP has been assigned to one primary Ecosystem Group, based on habitat occurrence and conservation need. Thus, for the Freshwater/wetlands group, there are 75 such UK priority species found in Scotland, along with another 22 which have secondary linkages to this broad ecosystem grouping. In this manner, targeted species management has been integrated with the wider ecosystem approach. However, there is still a real imbalance in the representation of different taxonomic groups between the number of priority species listed and the actual numbers occurring in Scotland, and this would appear not to recognize their relative importance to the functioning of healthy ecosystems; instead perhaps reflecting more societal preferences and scientific data availability.

Alongside these institutional changes, the Scottish Government have recently launched three other policy initiatives: on rural land use; on a model ecosystem framework; and participation in a UK Millennium Ecosystem Assessment. Whilst not directly concerned with targeted species management per se, each policy initiative will be vital in informing the direction in which species conservation in Scotland goes.

The Scottish Rural Land Use Study was launched by the Environment Minister, Richard Lockhead in September 2008. Framed by the triple challenges of future food security, energy security and water security at a time of rapid environmental change, the study will explore the potential for delivery of multiple benefits from the management of the Scottish landscape. Conservation of biodiversity is identified as one such crucial benefit; the valuation and delivery of which needs to be integrated with other costs and benefits to help create an evidence base for long-term sustainable decision-making. This initiative will help inform the government's wider programme for encouraging the incorporation of the ecosystem approach in all areas of policy-making where decisions affect the environment.

Also begun in autumn 2008, is a project to develop the ecosystem concept into a workable methodology for Scottish conditions. This is being taken forward in two phases: firstly to investigate the appropriate scope and scale for an ecosystem approach, including developing an outline framework; and, secondly to develop this outline in more detail to create a model ecosystem framework for the pilot area in Aberdeenshire at a number of scales. This should enable land management decisions to be seen in a more holistic manner, such that changes to ecosystem services are recognized, valued and addressed – changes that will have inevitable consequences for species conservation. At the same time, targeted actions for species conservation can potentially be framed within the wider context of the value of the ecosystem services that these actions themselves will help support.

Finally, the Scottish Government have committed to participation in the UK Ecosystem Assessment, based on a similar methodology to the Millennium Ecosystem Assessment. This will provide policy-makers with the scientific evidence describing the state of Scotland's (and the UK's) ecosystems, including species and habitats, and identifying the services they provide. This in turn will inform policy options to conserve these ecosystem services, the functioning ecosystems themselves and the species that make them up.

28.4.2 Legislative progress and opportunities

Recent European and Scottish legislation have provided a number of opportunities to place species conservation within the wider ecosystem context. Of these, the EU Water Framework Directive, EU Floods Directive and EU Marine Strategy are three key drivers. The resultant Scottish legislation – the Water Environment Water Services Act; the Flood Risk Management (Scotland) Act; and the Marine Bill all take the ecosystem approach forward. Indeed each one is slightly more progressive in this respect than its predecessor. The Marine Bill includes specific reference to marine ecosystem objectives and the need for strategic goals that translate the principles of the ecosystem approach in to practice.

The aim of the Water Framework Directive is to achieve and maintain "good water status" for individual water bodies, through the development and delivery of River Basin Management Plans. These plans clearly encompass many of the elements of the ecosystem approach through the integration of the management of land and water. They include identification of significant management issues that are impacting on these ecosystems; linkages with other statutory development strategies and policies; public participation in decision-making through Area Advisory Groups; and assessment of economic costs and benefits, as well as setting long-term targets for sustainable improvement. There is, however, no attempt to identify, quantify or value the actual costs and benefits of ecosystem services themselves within individual water bodies, or at catchment scale.

Targeted species conservation is less apparent as such, but can be seen in the recognition of the importance of "protected areas" within river basin plans, including Special Protection Areas, Special Areas of Conservation and Sites of Special Scientific Interest. In addition, the very basis for measuring "good water status" is through monitoring of selected species within the freshwater environment, though these are not necessarily the species of highest conservation concern. The plans will also have to tackle the issue of non-native invasive species, such as signal crayfish (*Pacifastacus leniusculus*) – and in this, they will be directly targeting what are increasingly important species management issues.

The Flood Risk Management (Scotland) Act is not directed at species management, and at first sight therefore might not seem to be a mechanism for targeted actions. However, it does provide an opportunity to focus on hydro-ecological processes, linking upstream sources of water, flood plains and downstream receptors. In doing so, it moves attention away from the river channel and physical flood defences, towards options for sustainable land and water management. By promoting a variety of management interventions at a catchment scale (such as changes to upland drainage patterns to control run off in the headwaters), the potential exists for targeted species management actions in the form of large-scale habitat changes. Quite how this approach to sustainable catchment flood risk management will recognize and then value the costs and benefits that the delivery of such ecosystem services provide is unclear. However, many wetland species, especially those associated with flood plain habitats are a key target of conservation concern, and it will be important to include species conservation benefits as part of the package of multiple benefits that sustainable flood risk management can provide.

28.5 Combining species management with the Ecosystem Approach

How to take forward these emerging concepts of species conservation and ecosystem services at the landscape scale has been the subject of a number of initiatives from organizations in Scotland, notably in the voluntary conservation sector and statutory agencies. Scottish Wildlife Trust, for example, has called for a new vision for re-building Scotland's wildlife at the landscape scale with their report on ecosystem-based conservation in Scotland (Hughes and Brooks, 2009), including a greater role for public engagement. Meanwhile, WWF have championed the potential for integrated natural flood management to provide benefits for wetland species conservation, and the RSPB's conservation plan (Future Directions IV) highlights the need for landscape-scale conservation for targeted species management at an ecosystem level (what they term futurescapes). In Scotland this includes programmes to recreate large areas of native pinewood at Abernethy Forest for capercaillie (*Tetrao urogallus*), red squirrels (*Sciurus vulgaris*) and a host of threatened invertebrates; and at Forsinard to restore the open peatlands of the Flow country for wading birds such as greenshank (*Tringa nubularia*). And whilst site conservation is one element of this, they also recognize the need to advance at the policy level as well.

The main Scottish statutory environmental agencies are also engaged in targeted species management in their respective activities. SNH play the key role in progressing the ecosystem approach through the Scottish Biodiversity Strategy and in advising government and others as to inclusion in their

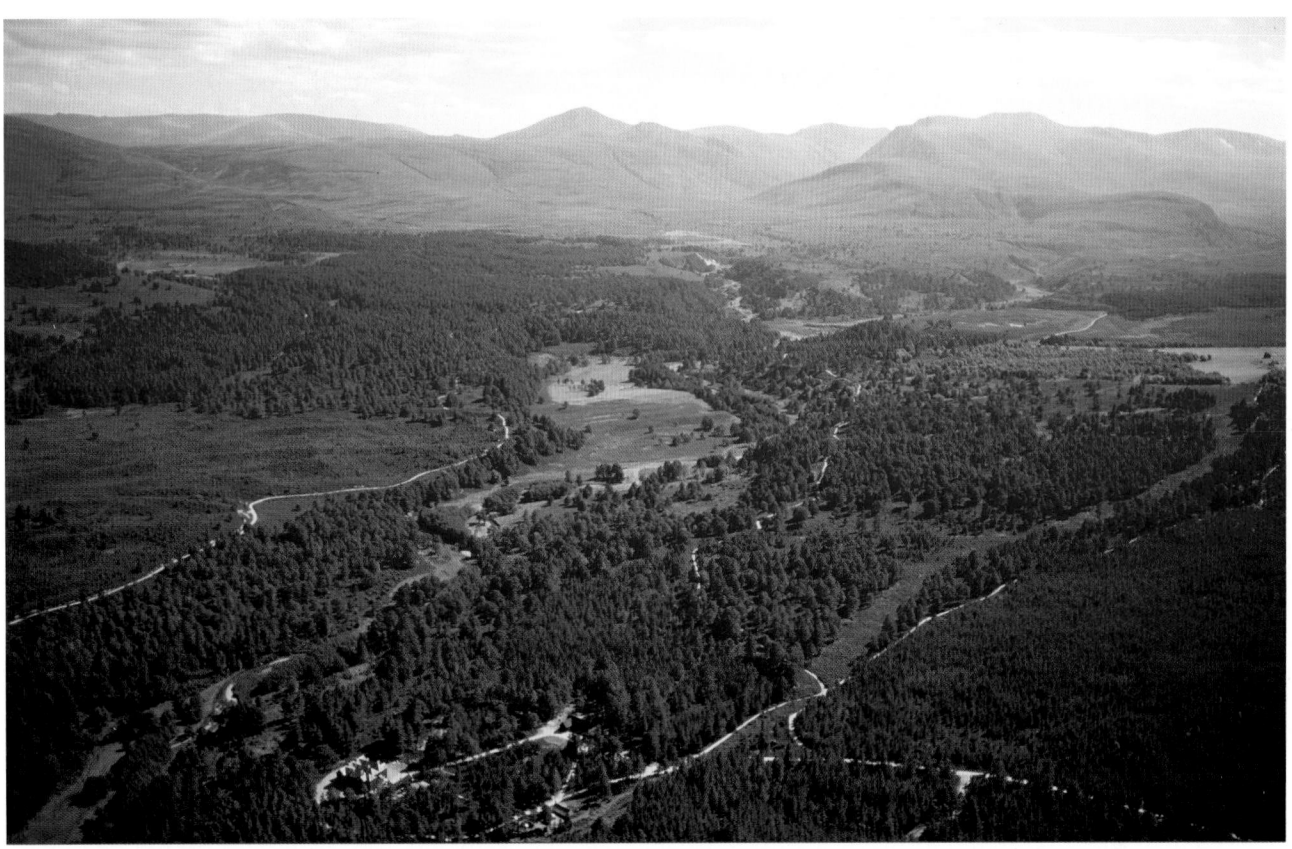

Plate 28.4 Abernethy Forest the native pinewood is essential for the conservation of the capercaillie and red squirrel populations. © Patricia and Angus Macdonald/SNH

plans and policies. SEPA are developing a wetland inventory and advice on incorporating the ecosystem approach in river basin management to promote biodiversity and other multiple benefits. The Forestry Commission have included many aspects of the ecosystem approach, including extensive public consultation in their Scottish Forestry strategy, delivering action for species conservation alongside multiple economic and cultural benefits to society.

What these and other such programmes do not have though, is any direct link between those species targeted for conservation support and the ecosystem services provided by the healthy functioning of the ecosystems of which the species are an integral part. Critically, in most case, neither the value of either the species nor the ecosystem services themselves are identified or costed.

Fundamental to the ongoing development and actual delivery of the ecosystem approach on the ground is the need to develop standardized methodologies for valuing the services that ecosystems provide. One of the 12 principles identified by the CBD is to understand and manage ecosystems in an economic market so as to reduce market distortions that adversely affect biological diversity and influence land use management options for species and habitat conservation. Whilst Costanza *et al.* (1997) provided a first global assessment of the total economic value of ecosystem services (and for Scotland see Williams *et al.* (2003)), there is no consensus amongst the many evaluation methodologies proposed for either individual services, distinct ecosystems, or the value of individual species in this context. Phase 2 of the EU project on the Economics of Ecosystems and Biodiversity, which reports in 2010 is due to provide further

Plate 28.4 Greenshank (*Tringa nubularia*). © Paul Robertson

standard guidance on evaluation for biodiversity and ecosystem services. In the UK, DEFRA produced an introductory guide to ecosystem service valuation in 2007 and NERC have commissioned reviews of the current state of knowledge on valuation of biodiversity and of natural resources for 2009.

In the meanwhile, markets have been established around the world for some ecosystem services – most notably carbon trading in relation to the costs of climate change. Payments for ecosystem services have also been developed in other arenas, particularly for forestry and for wetlands through both public and private schemes.

Actual examples of payments for ecosystem services that have been successfully running for more than a few years though are rare, but that of the New York City watershed protection programme is perhaps one of the most extensive and long-running and gives an idea of what might be feasible and at just what scale it could operate. Whilst the primary aim of the programme which began in 1990 was clearly not targeted species management, or indeed conservation of biodiversity per se, through working in a manner that clearly parallels the ecosystem approach, this is exactly one of the multiple outcomes it delivers (Coombe, 2003; Snow, pers. comm.).

In this instance the payments come from the 9 million consumers of New York City's water supply and are made to the farmers, foresters and other land managers in the 2,000 square mile catchments covering the Catskill mountains and Croton watershed, from where their water supply originates. The arrangement protects the largest unfiltered water supply in the world, at a cost of just over $1 billion in ten years, paid by the city to the land managers of the Catskills. It has saved New York City from the much larger costs of building and running new treatment facilities downstream (estimated at $8 billion capital and $350 million annual operations). No detailed account was made of value or economic cost or benefits of the individual elements of this programme, so many of the potential arguments on valuation methodologies have been effectively bypassed (Coombe, 2003; Snow, pers. comm.).

The watershed protection programme includes targeted land acquisition and management programmes that are based on scientific evidence of the key hydrological and ecological impacts and interests. Working with the New York State Department of Environmental Conservation and others, conservation of biodiversity now forms one of the guiding aspects behind the programme. Protection of the water environment includes a conservation reserves enhancement programme, stream habitat restoration and management, agricultural and forestry management programmes, as well as economic and social support to the communities who live in the catchment. It involves the whole community on the ground largely through the work of the Watershed Agricultural Council, a non-governmental organization established in 1993 to promote the voluntary participation of landowners in environmental protection of the watershed (Coombe, 2003; Snow, pers. comm.).

One of the key lessons from New England is that a really detailed evaluation of the value of individual species (economic, social, cultural or whatever) is not necessary for action to begin. What is essential though is that we get society as a whole to understand the value of ecosystem services (in this case water quality protection) to their lives. Species management should both play a key role in the restoration and maintenance of healthy functioning ecosystems from which these services flow, and also should be one of the targets of such management and restoration programmes in the first place.

28.6 Conclusions and the future

Monitoring of the population trends of key species in Scotland remains a conservation priority. The creation of ever more accurate lists of those species in urgent need of conservation management is ongoing (e.g. Eaton *et al.*, 2009), and the science evidence base behind this population work remains essential. Similarly, research to understand the drivers behind observed population changes and to develop and test actions to reverse them will always remain a cornerstone of an approach to species management. It enables the prioritization of resources and informs the choice of options for intervention (be they on the ground, at management or policy level) to achieve conservation objectives.

Where the Ecosystem Approach now takes us is to place this work in the wider context of ecosystem services, the evaluation of multiple costs and benefits, and to the engagement with society in defining the objectives and deliverables of targeted species management at the landscape scale.

Targeted species management clearly has to be part of this wider approach to understanding the value of ecosystems. A long-term, landscape scale approach will enable the delivery of multiple benefits for the environment, society and ultimately the economy. Costs need to be paid by the beneficiaries of these services, where ever they may be "downstream" and not hidden. Society has to be involved in designing the potential solutions, which will need to embrace economic and social aspects as well as environmental ones. This can only be done with a partnership approach delivering at various geographical and temporal scales, underpinned by access to sound scientific data. A key element of this data will be information on species, their distribution, ecology and population trends, which together help create the basis for targeted action.

28.7 Acknowledgements

My thanks to Scottish Natural Heritage for the invitation to contribute to this conference and publication, and to colleagues in the Scottish Environment Protection Agency for invaluable discussions and their support of this work.

References

Braat, L. & ten Brink, P. (2008). The Cost of Policy Inaction: The Case of Not Meeting the 2010 Biodiversity Target. Report for the European Commission, Wageningen/Brussels.

Bridgewater, P. (2010). What management? Which species? In: Baxter J.M. & Galbraith C.A. (Eds). *Species Management: Challenges and Solutions for the 21st Century*. Edinburgh: TSO Scotland, pp. 3-19.

Brotherton, P. & Webb, J. (2010). Achieving species conservation through habitat-based approaches In: Baxter J.M. & Galbraith C.A. (Eds). *Species Management: Challenges and Solutions for the 21st Century*. Edinburgh: TSO Scotland, pp. 75-89.

Coombe, R.I.C. (2003). Watershed Protection: a better way. Paper presented at the International Association of Hydrogeologists (Irish Group) Groundwater Seminar, April 2003, Tullamore, Ireland.

Costanza, R., d'Arge, R., de Groot, R., Farber, S., Grasso, M., Hannon, B., Limburg, K., Naeem, S., O'Neill, R.V., Paruelo, J., Raskin, R.G., Sutton, P. & van den Belt, M. (1997). The value of the world's ecosystem services and natural capital. *Nature* **387**: 253-260.

Davidson, N.C. & Stroud, D.C. (2006). African-Western Eurasian Flyways: current knowledge, population status and future challenges. In *Waterbirds around the World,* Eds G.C. Boere, C.A.Galbraith & D.A.Stroud. The Stationery Office, Edinburgh. pp. 63-73.

DEFRA. (2007a). Securing a healthy natural environment: An action plan for embedding an ecosystems approach.

DEFRA. (2007b). An introductory guide to valuing ecosystem services.

Dennis, R. (2010). Bigger, better – it's when, not if In: Baxter J.M. & Galbraith C.A. (Eds). *Species Management: Challenges and Solutions for the 21st Century*. Edinburgh: TSO Scotland, pp. 65-73.

Eaton, M.A., Brown, A.F., Noble, D.G., Musgrove, A.J., Hearn, R., Aebischer, N.J., Gibbons, D.W., Evans, A. & Gregory, R.D. (2009). Birds of Conservation Concern 3: the population status of birds in the United Kingdom, Channel Islands and the Isle of Man. *British Birds* **102**: 296-341.

European Commission (2008). The economics of ecosystems & biodiversity. An interim report.

Goulson, D. (2010). Conservation of bumblebees In: Baxter J.M. & Galbraith C.A. (Eds). *Species Management: Challenges and Solutions for the 21st Century*. Edinburgh: TSO Scotland, pp.477-494.

Green, R.E. & Pearce-Higgins, J. (2010). Species management in the face of a changing climate In: Baxter J.M. & Galbraith C.A. (Eds). *Species Management: Challenges and Solutions for the 21st Century*. Edinburgh: TSO Scotland, pp. 517-538.

Hooper, D.U., Chapin III, F.S., Ewel, J.J., Hector, A., Inchausti, P., Lavorel, S., Lawton, J.A., Lodge, D.M., Loreau, M., Naeem, S., Schmid, B., Setälä, H., Symstad, A.J., Vandermeer, J. & Wardle, D.A. (2005). Effects of biodiversity on ecosystem functioning: a consensus of current knowledge. *Ecological Monographs* **75**: No. 1, pp. 3-35.

Hughes, J. & Brooks, S. (2009). Living landscapes: towards ecosystem-based conservation in Scotland. Scottish Wildlife Trust. Edinburgh.

Huntley, B., Green, R.E., Collingham, Y.C. & Willis, S.G. (2007). A climatic atlas of European breeding birds. Durham University, the RSPB & Lynx Edicions. Barcelona.

MacArthur, R. & Wilson, E.O. (1967). *The theory of island biogeography.* Princeton University Press. Princeton.

Millennium Ecosystem Assessment. (2005). Millennium Ecosystem Assessment: Ecosystems and human well-being, Summary for decision-makers. Washington.

Scottish Biodiversity Group. (2000). Action for Scotland's Biodiversity.

Scottish Environment Protection Agency. (2006). State of Scotland's Environment.

Scottish Executive. (2004). Scotland's Biodiversity *It's in Your Hands* A strategy for the conservation and enhancement of biodiversity in Scotland. Edinburgh, TSO Scotland.

Scottish Natural Heritage. (2007). A Five Year Species Action Framework: Making a difference for Scotland's Species. Battleby, Perth.

Spray, C.J. (2007). The Whooper Swan. In *Birds of Scotland,* Eds R. Forrester & I. Andrews. SOC, Aberlady. pp. 133-136.

UK Government. (1994). Biodiversity The UK Action Plan.

Williams, E., Firn, J.R., Kind, V., Roberts, M. & McGlashan, D. (2003). The value of Scotland's ecosystem services and natural capital. *European Environment* **13**: 67-78.

Spray, C.J. MBE. (2010). Targeted species management within a wider ecosystem approach. In: *Species Management: Challenges and Solutions for the 21st Century*, ed. by J.M. Baxter and C.A. Galbraith. TSO Scotland, Edinburgh. pp. 497-515

Chapter 29

Species management in the face of a changing climate

Rhys E. Green[1] and James Pearce-Higgins[1]

Summary

1. Anthropogenic climate change has affected the distribution and abundance of many species and will do so in future.
2. Species management methods are placed in six categories: prioritization and planning, protection and creation of core areas, management of core areas, creation and maintenance of suitable habitat in the wider landscape, protection of species from dispersed and remote human activities, and reintroduction and translocation.
3. These methods are reviewed to assess their usefulness in the face of rapid climate change. All are found to have an important future role in adapting species conservation to the effects of climate change.
4. Effective future conservation management will require increased spatial scope of planning, better integration of different conservation tools, high quality monitoring and a longer-term outlook.

[1] RSPB and Conservation Science Group, Department of Zoology, University of Cambridge, Downing Street, Cambridge, CB2 3EJ, UK
[1] RSPB Scotland, Dunedin House, 25 Ravelston Terrace, Edinburgh, EH4 3TP, UK

29.1 Introduction

Marsh harrier (*Circus aeruginosus*). © Andy Hay (rspb-images.com)

Climate change has affected the distribution and abundance of many species in recent decades (Parmesan and Yohe, 2003; Root *et al.*, 2003; Fischlin *et al.*, 2007; Green *et al.*, 2008) and projections of anthropogenic climate change indicate even larger effects in future (Thomas *et al.*, 2004; Jetz *et al.*, 2007; Huntley *et al.*, 2008). Does this render established approaches to species management ineffective? Here, we use the main elements of species conservation management as it has been practised recently, based upon categories developed by the World Conservation Union – Conservation Measures Partnership (2006), as our basis for discussion, suggesting ways in which these need to be adapted to cope with ongoing and probable future climate change. We identify six main elements of species conservation management as follows:

1. Prioritization and planning
2. Protection and creation of core sites
3. Management of core sites
4. Creation and maintenance of suitable habitat in the wider landscape
5. Protection of species from dispersed and remote human activities
6. Reintroduction and translocation

29.2 Adapting the tool-kit and its use to cope with climate change

It has been suggested that adaptation of biodiversity conservation to climate change requires a paradigm shift in attitudes to conservation (Mitchell *et al.*, 2007). This has sometimes been interpreted to mean that long-established types of conservation intervention, such as protected area designation, will no longer be of value because of their fixed location. We differ from this view and argue that the tools for species conservation management described above will remain potentially effective during a period of rapid climate change. However, the ways in which the tools are deployed and the spatial and temporal scales over which their use is planned and coordinated may need to change, as follows.

29.2.1 Prioritization and planning

Much thought has already gone into the identification of species requiring special conservation efforts to allow them to persist in the face of continuing loss and degradation of habitat because of human land use, into designing the networks of habitat required to support them, and into identifying unfilled gaps in such networks (Gaston *et al.*, 2008). However, most priority-setting activity so far has assumed that the potential geographical range and habitat requirements of species remain constant, which may not be valid during a period of rapid climate change. Species prioritization for conservation action needs also to consider information on the potential impacts of projected future climate change. Currently, the only practical way to achieve this for a large number of species is to make and apply climate envelope models that describe current distribution or abundance in relation to climate. This model is then used, in combination with a projection of future climate, to predict the location of the species' future potential range, on the assumption that it will continue to occupy the same climate space. It is relatively straightforward to model distributions of large numbers of species in terms of a limited number of readily available explanatory climatic variables, whose future average values can be projected using global circulation models and emissions scenarios, and then rank those species according to the extent of projected range changes. For example, some species might be projected to become rarer or more narrowly distributed, whilst others are expected to maintain or increase their distribution. Species might also need to accomplish large shifts in their geographical range in order to maintain their extent. Appropriate translation of these projected changes into conservation priorities depends upon several factors, particularly the degree of confidence associated with the predictions.

At a coarse scale, such climate envelope models can provide good descriptions of current geographical range, especially for small-bodied species without special habitat requirements and without a history of extensive range restriction by human persecution and exploitation (Huntley et al., 2007). Beale et al. (2008) suggest that the reliability of climate envelope models should be assessed by significance tests of the degree to which they fit observed static distributions. However, the only stringent tests of reliability are those that either involve the independent prediction of species distribution in a different region to that in which the model was fitted, or predictions or retrodictions of change in distribution or abundance during a period of rapid climate change using a model fitted during a period of slow climate change. Few tests of these kinds have been carried out. However, a correlation between observed and predicted abundance changes in the UK provides support for the validity of this approach, although with much unexplained variation among species in terms of the rates of observed change (Green et al., 2008). Some of this might arise because direct and indirect effects of climate change do not have much influence on distribution and abundance. However, as there are an increasing number of examples of significant climate change impacts on populations and distributions (e.g. Both et al., 2006; Hickling et al., 2006), it is more likely that climate change is only one of several influences on observed changes in a species' status or that changes in distribution or abundance will only occur after a delay.

Most large-scale climate envelope modelling excludes non-climatic variables. Although this may reduce its realism in describing current distributions, it prevents the introduction of large and unquantifiable uncertainty about future values of these other effects, such as predicting future land use change. Existing models could certainly be further developed by including the effects of additional non-climate variables that are less affected by socio-economic factors, such as soil type and topography; developments which are likely to further improve the efficacy of this method over the next few years. As a rough guide to the current reliability of climate envelope projections of future range changes to assess conservation status, we suggest that projections for species' groups with artificial gaps in the distribution data used to obtain the climate envelope model should be regarded with caution. This includes species whose recent geographical range has been extensively modified by human activities such as over-exploitation, persecution, habitat destruction and pollution, and includes birds of prey and other large-bodied bird species (Newton, 1979). For these species, other sources of information are required to assess their likely vulnerability to climate change, such as from ecological knowledge, or other studies of climate change impacts. For example, recent food-related declines in the productivity of UK seabirds may be used to increase their conservation priority in the expectation of such trends continuing as sea temperatures warm (Frederikson *et al.,* 2006; Irons *et al.,* 2008). On the other hand, projections for groups of species which appear to have no such distributional problems, or which can be validated against recent changes in abundance or distribution, may be regarded as reliable. These projections, in combination with other ecological information, can be used to modify conservation status. For example, the projected reduction of the potential range of the pied flycatcher (*Ficedula hypoleuca*) in central Europe (Huntley *et al.,* 2007) is reinforced by the results of studies from Holland which show that phenological mismatch between the timing of breeding and peak food supply are causing population declines (Both *et al.,* 2006).

A further advantage of the climate envelope approach is that it allows projections of future status to vary throughout the range, enabling conservation priorities to be modified in different areas. Take a hypothetical species whose combined present and future potential range spans several countries (Figure 29.1). The species' potential future range is likely to remain of similar size to the present range, but to shift location substantially so that only a small proportion of the present range is expected to remain suitable in the long term (Part A). In other areas where the species does not occur at present, the climate is projected to become suitable for it in future (Part B) and in yet other areas climatic conditions in the present range are projected to become unsuitable in future (Part C). The projection is thought to be reliable, but the species is a poor disperser inhabiting a patchily distributed habitat, and therefore is unlikely to easily occupy the whole of the potential future range. The influence of the climate impact projection on conservation management priorities and

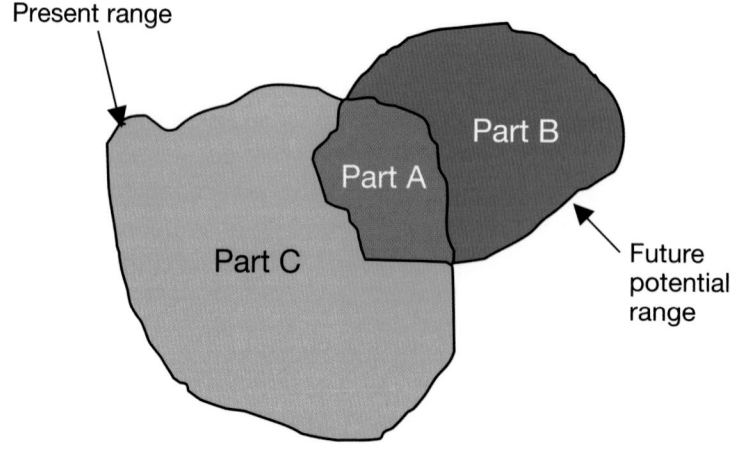

Present range

Part B

Part A

Part C

Future potential range

Figure 29.1 Schematic map of the present and future potential geographical ranges of a hypothetical species affected by climatic change. The future potential range is the geographical area where climatic conditions become potentially suitable for the species at a future time. The combined present and future geographical range is divided into three parts: A- the overlap between the present and future potential ranges, B – the area potentially suitable in future that is currently unoccupied, and C – the currently occupied range which is expected to become climatically unsuitable in future.

Plate 29.1 A mosaic of lochans, moorland and machair in South Uist. © Lorne Gill/SNH

objectives should differ in these three parts of the range. If the species' status can be improved by the designation of existing critical habitats as protected areas and management, regardless of climate change, then expanding the extent and quality of such habitat in Part A is the highest priority, because this will increase the population in the area most secure against effects of future climate change. Hence, this is a "no regrets" option that will also increase the flow of propagules to colonize Part B of the range. In Part B, the extent of potentially suitable habitat should be surveyed, particularly in areas close to current range boundary, and if scarce, should be increased. If the prime habitat is patchily distributed, consideration should be given to improving the permeability of the matrix between habitat patches to aid dispersal (see below). Even in parts of the range where the species is predicted to disappear (Part C), it should not be removed from the list of conservation priorities. Because projections of climate change remain uncertain, monitoring of the species and its habitats should be carried out to assess whether the predicted deterioration in status caused by climate change is really occurring. If it is, consideration should be given to special counteracting or compensatory management within existing sites holding the species or expansion of protected habitat (see below). Even if the species eventually declines to extinction in Part C, maintaining its population and hence maximizing propagule production in the short to medium term will promote dispersal to other parts of the range.

Although decisions about priorities are generally made at national levels, the process outlined above argues for the projected future international importance of the country for each species to play a part in current priority-setting, which requires species management to be coordinated internationally to a greater extent than at present.

It is likely that over the next few years, there will be increasing evidence for the effects of climate change on species abundance and distributions, which can be used to refine and update these predictions (e.g. Green et al., 2008). Given the potential uncertainty in current predictions, it is important to establish and maintain high quality monitoring programmes to enable climate-related changes in populations to be rapidly identified and incorporated into decisions about priorities. The results of such monitoring should be used to validate and refine predictions, and provide an early warning of species declining as a result of climate change.

29.2.2 Protection and creation of core sites

Protection of core sites for priority species has long been vital for species conservation, and is likely to remain an essential tool for conservation management, particularly for species which occur only in natural or semi-natural landscapes. Core sites for species conservation are generally chosen to hold a significant proportion of the regional, national or international population and to have near-optimal habitats in which survival and reproduction are sufficient to at least maintain population size. Given recent global trends in human population and diet and in the loss of such habitats for food and biofuel production (Green et al., 2005; Fitzherbert et al., 2008), the importance of core sites to conserve such species is likely to increase. However, it should not be assumed that the set of species for which a particular nature reserve or

Plate 29.2 Bittern (*Botaurus stellaris*). © Andy Hay (rspb-images.com)

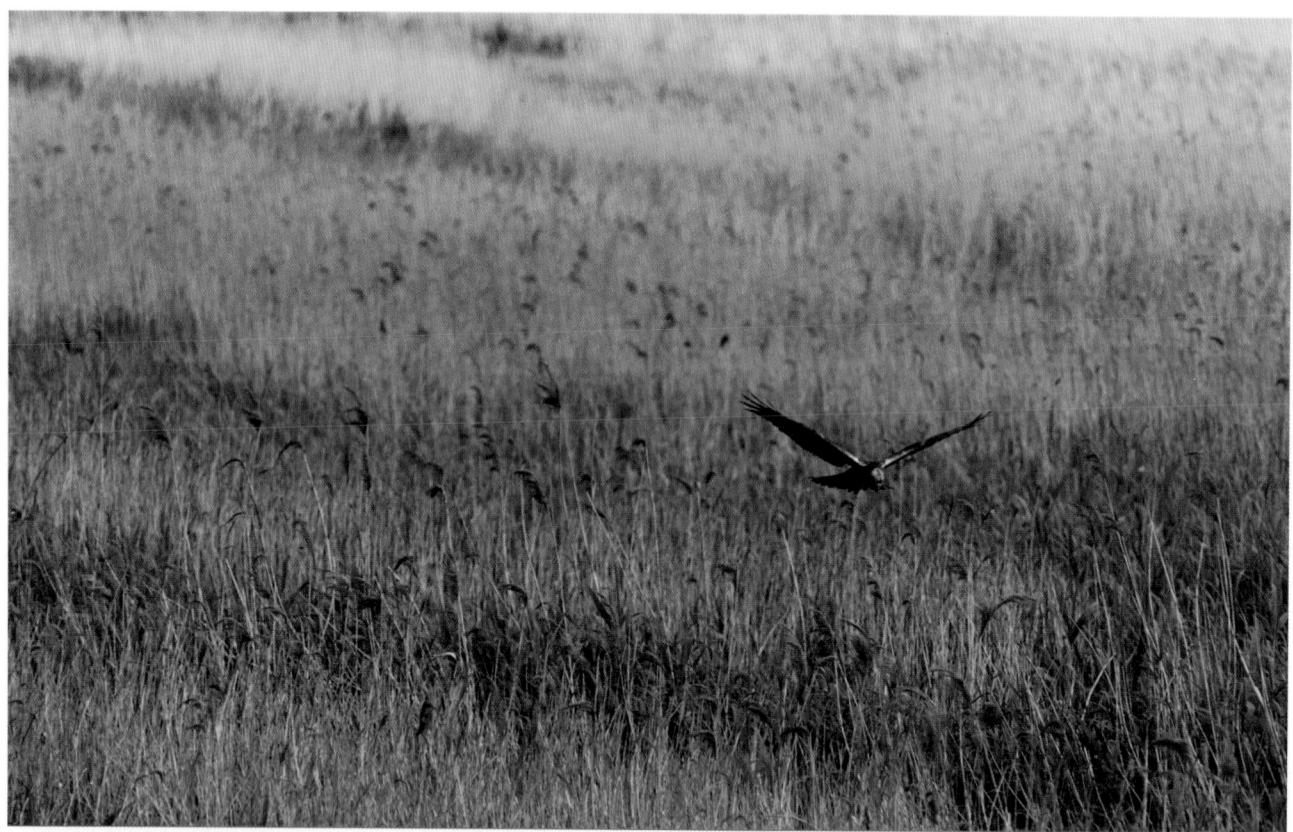

Plate 29.3 Marsh harrier (*Circus aeruginosus*) in flight. © Andy Hay (rspb-images.com)

protected area are important will remain the same in the future. The previous discussion of climate envelope models highlights how species' ranges may change in future, meaning that the assemblage of species occupying a particular site may also change. For example, wetland nature reserves in southern England which currently support species like bittern (*Botaurus stellaris*), marsh harrier (*Circus aeruginosus*) and bearded reedling (*Panurus biarmicus*), are likely to be colonized by more southerly distributed species, such as little bittern (*Ixobrychus minutus*), night heron (*Nycticorax nycticorax*) and zitting cisticola (*Cisticola juncidis*) (Huntley *et al.,* 2007). The most valuable core areas to protect will therefore be those which currently protect significant populations of a range of threatened species, and which will provide colonization opportunities for other threatened species likely to advance their range in response to climate change. These will generally be of rare natural or semi-natural habitats.

More subtle changes in the dependence of different species on protected areas are also likely to occur in future. Some species may become more reliant on protected sites as a result of twin pressures of unfavourable changes in land use in the wider countryside and climate change. In the UK, waders of lowland wet grassland have become increasingly restricted to core areas as management of farmland, especially land drainage, has removed much of their breeding habitat in the wider countryside (Wilson *et al.*, 2005). Climate change, acting via effects on farming or on the water budget of grassland, might be expected to produce a similar additional effect through higher spring and summer temperatures and lower precipitation. By contrast, other species may become more widely distributed than currently. For example, the habitat associations of the silver-spotted skipper (*Hesperia comma*) in the UK have altered as a result of climate warming, increasing the range of sites available for colonization, and meaning that conservation efforts need not be so targeted at a small number of sites and to create a specific sward structure (e.g. Davies *et al.*, 2006). The recent expansion of stonechat (*Saxicola torquata*) into the UK uplands (Sim *et al.*, 2005) probably results from a reduction in the severity of winter weather, enabling the species to colonize areas of extensively managed heather moorland (Pearce-Higgins and Grant, 2006) ecologically different from the lowland, coastal and western heaths which the species previously occupied (Gibbons *et al.*, 1993).

Climate change might reduce the population density of a species within suitable habitat in a region, but perhaps not immediately cause it to disappear. However, if the extent of suitable habitat stays the same, the total population may fall below the minimum viable population size, leading to eventual extinction in the region. This problem could be countered by expanding the area of suitable habitat to maintain population size. Such expansion, if within or around a protected site along ecological or topographic gradients, might produce further benefit by allowing species to persist even though currently occupied parts of the site become unsuitable because of climate change. This principle may be particularly relevant to mountain environments. For some species, action to increase the number and extent of core sites is especially urgent. In the UK, many of the key reed-bed breeding sites for the bittern are coastal, and increasingly vulnerable to saltwater incursions because of isostatic lowering of land levels, sea-level rise and more frequent storm surges caused by climate change. The policy of managed retreat, in which existing sea defences are abandoned, is leading to the loss of these sites. If the recent recovery in the bittern population is to be maintained, it is necessary to create or extend reed-beds in other areas away from the coast, but within the likely dispersal range of the species, and, to delay saltwater incursion at key coastal sites until these new sites are ready (Gilbert, 2008).

29.2.3 Management of core sites

The persistence of species at core sites often depends upon specific management targeted at supporting them. In the face of climate change, such management may become increasingly important, to maintain population densities, even though climate change would otherwise cause these to decline. Such management falls into two categories; *counteracting* and *compensatory*. *Counteracting* management arrests or reverses a deleterious effect on the species caused or triggered by climate change. Climate change has its effects on the distribution and abundance of species by directly or indirectly changing demographic rates; survival, fecundity and immigration and emigration rates. In some cases, understanding the mechanism of these effects may provide enough insight to suggest management to counteract the change. For example, an invasive species which is a pathogen, predator or competitor of the species of conservation concern and whose spread or impact has been enhanced by climate change, might be controlled by culling. Deleterious effects of increased temperature of the microhabitat important to a species might be counteracted by habitat management. This approach may require complex understanding of a system, with climate impacts spanning trophic levels. Higher temperatures in UK peatland areas in August tend to be followed by lower abundance of emerging craneflies (Diptera: Tipulidae) in the following year (Pearce-Higgins et al., 2009). The precise mechanism of this effect is uncertain, but it is likely that summer warming reduces the survival of cranefly eggs and early larval instars, either through the desiccation due to the drying out of the peat surface or other physiological mechanisms (Coulson et al., 1976; Bale et al., 2002). This seasonal emergence of craneflies provides a key food for a wide-range of UK peatland bird species (Buchanan et al., 2006), including the golden plover (Pluvialis apricaria), for which chick growth and survival are positively related to cranefly abundance (Pearce-Higgins and Yalden, 2004). As a result, fluctuations in a peatland population of golden plovers were negatively correlated with August temperature, with a one-year lag. According to a simulation model, future increases in August temperature would cause rapid declines in at least some UK golden plover populations (Pearce-Higgins, 2009). Climate envelope models also project a decline in range for this species (Huntley et al., 2007). Many peatland areas in the UK are in suboptimal condition for biodiversity as a result of the construction of drainage ditches for past agricultural and silvicultural management (Holden et al., 2007). It is possible that by blocking these ditches, water levels could be raised, increasing the resilience of cranefly populations, and hence golden plovers and other peatland birds, to summer warming.

The alternative *compensatory* management approach to preventing deleterious impacts of climate change is to allow the climate-induced effect to proceed unchecked, but to compensate for its effects through the positive influence of management operating through a different mechanism. The negative effects on survival of a new pathogen encouraged by climate change might be compensated for by decreased mortality due to other causes, brought about by changes in the management of habitat, predators or competitors. This principle could again be illustrated in relation to the golden plover in the UK. If summer warming does indeed reduce productivity as a result of declines in cranefly abundance, it might be possible to compensate for these losses by reducing the number of nests and chicks which are lost to predators. There is evidence that the nests and chicks are vulnerable to predation by corvids and mammalian predators (Parr, 1992; Pearce-Higgins and Yalden, 2003), and that golden plover populations may benefit from the control of such predators (Tharme et al., 2001). Depending on the relative magnitude of chick mortality through reductions in prey abundance, and relative benefit accrued through controlling predators, the latter may be employed as compensatory management at some sites.

Plate 29.4 Golden plover (*Pluvialis apricaria*). © Lorne Gill

29.2.4 Creation and maintenance of suitable habitat in the wider landscape

For widely distributed declining species, it may be beneficial to provide suitable habitats within areas dominated by human use, such as production landscapes, used for agriculture and forestry, and urban areas. Agri-environment and forestry and woodland management grant schemes are a possible means to achieve this. This is likely to become increasingly important in a changing climate, as the ability of a species to move beyond the boundaries of large patches of high quality habitat which may be present in protected core sites is essential for the persistence of most species (Hanski, 1999). Although core sites may hold high population densities, they are often restricted in extent and therefore have a smaller total population than that supported outside the core by small patches of partly degraded habitat scattered through production landscapes set within the matrix of unsuitable land cover between core sites. If population density in all parts of a region declines because of climate change, then increasing the quality, size and number of small patches of suboptimal habitat may help maintain the total population size of the region.

Plate 29.5 Nuthatch (*Sitta europaea*). © Ben Hall (rspb-images.com)

Whether this is effective will depend in part upon the marginal cost of maintaining a unit of population size in small patches, relative to the cost of achieving the same result in the core sites. However, the population balance, dependent upon survival and fecundity, may also differ between the scattered small patches and core sites and this needs to be taken into account. The ability of species to exist in small habitat patches within the matrix between core sites also allows dispersal among the core sites. In principle, it should be possible to use models to design a network of habitat patches to maximize the population size and chance of long-term persistence for a particular species. However, there is considerable uncertainty regarding model parameters (site-specific productivity and survival rates, dispersal distances, effects of patch distribution and matrix habitat on dispersal success, etc.) which make this extremely difficult to achieve in practice (Bailey, 2007), although there are particular, well-studied species, such as the speckled wood butterfly (*Pararge aegeria*) and the nuthatch (*Sitta europaea*), for which such a formal approach should be possible.

The properties of the distribution of habitat patches across the landscape that promote connections among sub-populations, and, hence, metapopulation persistence in the absence of climate change, are similar to those that permit rapid extension of the geographic range as a response to climate change (Opdam and Wascher, 2004). There are at least two potential benefits from increased connectivity in relation to climate change. First, if local extinctions or severe reductions of sub-populations at core sites within the current range become more frequent, perhaps because of more frequent extreme weather, recolonizations or rescue events during periods of favourable climate will be more likely if dispersal is enhanced by increased numbers of patches and permeability of the matrix. Second, maintenance of total range size and population of a species in future may depend upon it being able to colonize patches of habitat in areas where it is not currently present, but where the climatic conditions become more favourable (see above). This principle is illustrated by the expansion of the speckled wood butterfly in the UK, which has been facilitated by the availability of suitable habitat patches (Hill *et al.,* 2001). However, the expansion of other butterfly species with more specialized habitat needs into areas in which the climate has recently become favourable has been prevented by the lack of habitat (Warren *et al.,* 2001). The ability to disperse through the matrix is likely to speed up future colonization of habitat patches outside the current range.

In the absence of specific information about a particular species, a number of principles can be adopted to assist with the development of particular networks and landscapes. The maintenance and expansion of existing core sites should be given a greater priority than the creation of new core sites, whilst any new sites should increase functional connectivity through physical linkages between existing sites either directly, or by functioning as stepping stones. In addition to focusing on core sites, the quality of the intervening landscape matrix should be maximized. Finally, clear conservation objectives should be established for the implementation of a particular network, including the species which the network should benefit, and monitoring should be established to test the effectiveness of any established network (see above).

There is currently a high degree of interest in applying these principles to landscape conservation, with simple modelling tools being developed to maximize the connectivity of particular habitats, such as woodland, within real landscapes (e.g. Watts *et al.,* 2007). When based upon the principles outlined above, these tools may be of benefit, although because of the uncertain outcomes of such approaches (Bailey, 2007), clear species objectives that can be monitored should be established. Indeed, the current evidence suggests that the species most likely to benefit from such generic approaches will be generalists (Dolman *et al.,* 2007), whilst the arguably more vulnerable specialists may require more species-specific action. The potential risks of increasing connectivity should also be recognized; these are increased spread of disease and invasive competitors, both of which are likely to become increasingly important as a result of climate change. This principle is illustrated by the conservation of native red squirrels (*Sciurus vulgaris*) in Scotland, which depends upon the existence of isolated woodland areas that have not been colonized by grey squirrels (*Sciurus carolinensis*), which are competitors and a reservoir of disease (Tompkins *et al.,* 2003; Poulsom *et al.,* 2005).

Financial support to farmers for the creation and maintenance of suitable habitat for species on farmland through agri-environment schemes is a potential method to increase both the population density of a priority species on farmland and the permeability of the matrix to enhance dispersal (Donald and Evans, 2006). The provision in production landscapes of corridors (e.g. hedges, ditches and strips of native grass and herbs species at field margins) to connect core patches or small habitat patches to act as stepping stones have both been suggested as means to increase connectivity. However, more needs to be known about the effectiveness of these approaches, especially as regards the type and quantity of habitat required and its distribution in the landscape.

29.2.5 Protection of species from dispersed and remote human activities

There is often a need for conservation measures to protect species from adverse effects that are not addressed by measures to protect particular sites and habitats. These include deliberate killing, disturbance and pollution. Climate change will further modify human activities and land use (e.g. agricultural management, renewable energy development, water management and recreational activities) in ways that are difficult to predict (see above), but yet are likely to impact on populations of wild species in this way. Conservation management will need to respond to these changes when they threaten a species, whilst reducing existing adverse effects from dispersed and remote human activities may compensate for other climate impacts.

The impacts of many agricultural and land-use changes can already be assessed from existing knowledge. For example, continuation of the recent destruction of tropical forests to make way for biofuel plantations will be detrimental to the conservation of a wide range of already threatened species (Fitzherbert *et al.*, 2008), and has already led to changes in conservation priority of some forest species (Buchanan *et al.*, 2008). Similarly, there is a wealth of literature associated with the effects of farming on biodiversity (Wilson *et al.*, 2009) which can be used to assess the likely effects of changes in cropping patterns and agricultural intensity. However, there is less certainty associated with the effects of some emerging technologies, such as forms of renewable energy generation, upon wildlife. One of the most widespread and rapidly increasing sources of renewable energy is wind power, which in certain circumstances, has the potential to cause high rates of mortality in birds (Barrios and Rodriquez, 2004; Everaert and Stienen, 2007; Smallwood and Thelander, 2008) and bats (Baerwald *et al.*, 2008), with additional consequences of displacement and disturbance to individuals, barriers to migration and habitat loss (Drewitt and Langston, 2006). However, there is considerable uncertainty about the conditions in which such effects occur (Drewitt and Langston, 2006), making it difficult to develop strategies for the development and location of wind turbines that are consistent with biodiversity conservation. Research may reduce these uncertainties in future, but it is also possible to develop a framework to inform current decision making. This is illustrated by the development of a sensitivity map to highlight areas of potential conflict between bird conservation and wind farm development, achieved by combining the likely sensitivity of species to wind farms from the literature with distribution maps (Bright *et al.*, 2008). This map highlights the sensitivity of parts of the north-west Highlands, Western and Northern Isles to wind farms, suggesting that such

Plate 29.6 Great bustard (*Otis tarda*) in flight. © David Kjaer (rspb-images.com)

developments would have least impact if concentrated in southern, central and eastern Scotland, close to the conurbations with high energy demand.

Climate change may permit or enhance range extensions and population increases by introduced alien competitors, predators and parasites (Dukes and Mooney, 1999), which may affect the status of priority species and necessitate remedial action. For example, recent outbreaks of the West Nile Virus, which cause mortality in birds and other animals, and occasionally have human health consequences, may have been facilitated by rising winter temperature and drought (Epstein, 2001).

29.2.6 Reintroduction and translocation

These techniques have become increasingly employed to restore populations to areas from where they have been lost, and in extreme cases, may involve the establishment of captive populations in case wild populations become extinct. The potential effects of climate change should be considered when planning reintroduction into parts of a species' historical range from which it has been eliminated by human activities. Climate change may make historical occupancy a less reliable guide to current and future climatic suitability than was previously the case. Climate envelope models may seem to offer some guidance on whether the location of a reintroduction is likely to remain suitable for some species, but in this instance, such predictions could be unreliable, because the very species that conservation managers wish to reintroduce are usually the large-bodied species whose recent geographical ranges have been drastically altered by human activity (see above). Unless climate envelope models can be fitted using the historical unmodified range boundaries, their projections may be faulty. A list of actual and planned bird reintroductions in the UK; white-tailed eagle (*Haliaeetus albicilla*), golden eagle (*Aquila chrysaetos*) (to Northern Ireland), osprey (*Pandion halietus*) (to England), red kite (*Milvus milvus*), great bustard (*Otis tarda*) and common crane (*Grus grus*) illustrates this point: all of these species have had their ranges drastically curtailed by humans.

The effectiveness of reintroduction and translocation as tools for species' conservation in a changing climate is likely to increase with time and experience. For poorly dispersing species where the existing range is largely disjunct from the potential future range, it may be possible to use translocation to enable the colonization of areas of suitable habitat in regions where conditions have become favourable because of climate change. Among the many likely problems is that of ensuring that all the necessary components of the habitat for that species are in place where the translocation will occur. We therefore suggest that translocations require detailed research before implementation and careful monitoring afterwards.

29.3 Conclusions

The current tools used for species management will all remain essential in the face of rapid climate change. Although climate change is a newly recognized source of additional pressure on the conservation of biodiversity, the existing pressures from increasing human populations and demands for goods, enabled by technological change, have been enormous for decades, and will continue to be so. The main changes to conservation management required as a result of climate change are to increase the spatial scope of conservation planning, to integrate the different conservation tools to a greater extent, to establish monitoring programmes to identify potentially rapid change in time for action, and to make decisions with a longer-term outlook. These changes may require new approaches to dealing with associated uncertainty.

References

Bailey, S. (2007). Increasing connectivity in fragmented landscapes: An investigation of evidence for biodiversity gain in woodlands. *Forest Ecology and Management* **238**: 7-23.

Bale, J.S., Masters, G.M., Hodkinson, I.D., Awmack, C.S., Bezemer, T.M., Brown, V.K., Butterfield, J., Buse, A., Coulson, J.C., Farrar, J., Good, J.E.G., Harrington, R., Hartley, S., Jones, T.H., Lindroth, R.L., Press, M.C., Symrnioudis, I., Watt, A.D. & Whittaker, J.B. (2002). Herbivory in global climate change research: direct effects of rising temperature on insect herbivores. *Global Change Biology* **8**: 1–16.

Barrios, L. & Rodrıguez, A. (2004). Behavioural and environmental correlates of soaring bird mortality at on-shore wind turbines. *Journal of Applied Ecology* **41**: 72–81.

Baerwald, E.F., D'Armours, G.H., Klug, B.J. & Barclay, R.M.R. (2008). Barotrauma is a significant cause of bat fatalities at wind turbines. *Current Biology* **18**: 695-696.

Both, C., Bouwhuis, S., Lessells, C.M. & Visser, M.E. (2006). Climate change and population declines in a long-distance migratory bird. *Nature* **441**: 81-83.

Beale, C.M., Lennon, J.J. & Gimona, A. (2008). Opening the Climate Envelope reveals no Macroscale Associations with Climate in European Birds. *Proceedings of the National Academy of Sciences* **105**: 14908-14912.

Bright, J., Langston, R., Bullman, R., Evans, R., Gardner, S. & Pearce-Higgins, J. (2008). Map of bird sensitivities to wind farms in Scotland: A tool to aid planning and conservation. *Biological Conservation* **141**: 2342-2356.

Buchanan, G.M., Grant, M.C., Sanderson, R.A. & Pearce-Higgins, J.W. (2006). The contribution of invertebrate taxa to moorland bird diets and the potential implications of land-use management. *Ibis* **148**: 615-628.

Buchanan, G.M., Butchart, S.H.M., Dutson, G., Pilgrim, J.D., Steininger M.K., Bishop, K.D. & Mayaux, P. (2008). Using remote sensing to inform conservation status assessment: Estimates of recent deforestation rates on New Britain and the impacts upon endemic birds. *Biological Conservation* **141**: 56-66.

Coulson, J.C., Horobin, J.C., Butterfield, J.E.C. & Smith, G.R.J. (1976). The maintenance of annual life-cycles in two species of Tipulidae (Diptera); a field study relating development, temperature and altitude. *Journal of Animal Ecology* **45**: 215-233.

Davies, Z.G., Wilson, R.J., Coles, S. & Thomas, C.D. (2006). Changing habitat associations of a thermally constrained species, the silver-spotted skipper butterfly, in response to climate warming. *Journal of Animal Ecology* **75**: 247-256.

Dolman, P.W., Hinsley, S.A., Bellamy, P.E. & Watts, K. (2007). Woodland birds in patchy landscapes: the evidence base for strategic networks. *Ibis* **149 s2**: 146-160.

Donald, P.F. & A.D. Evans. (2006). Habitat connectivity and matrix restoration: the wider implications of agri-environment schemes. *Journal of Applied Ecology* **43**: 209-218.

Drewitt, A.L. & Langston, R.H.W. (2006). Assessing the impacts of wind farms on birds. *Ibis* **148**: 29-42.

Dukes, J.S. & Mooney, H.A. (1999). Does global change increase the success of biological invaders? *Trends in Evolution and Ecology* **14**: 135-139.

Epstein, P.R. (2001). West Nile virus and the climate. *Journal of Urban Health* **78**: 367-371.

Everaert, J. & Stienen, E.W.M. (2007). Impact of wind turbines on birds in Zeebrugge (Belgium). Significant effect on breeding tern colony due to collisions. *Biodiversity and Conservation* **16**: 3345-3359.

Fischlin, A., Midgley, G.F., Price, J.T., Leemans, R., Gopal, B., Turley, C., Rounsevell, M.D.A., Dube, O.P., Tarazona, J. & Velichko, A.A. (2007). Ecosystems, their properties, goods, and services. Pages 211-272 in *Climate Change 2007: Impacts, Adaptation and Vulnerability, Contribution of Working Group II to the Fourth Assessment Report of the Intergovernmental Panel on Climate Change.* M. L. Parry, O. F. Canziani, J. P. Palutikof, P. J. van der Linden and C. E. Hanson, (Eds). Cambridge University Press, Cambridge, U. K.

Fitzherbert, E.B., Stuebig, M.J., Morel, A., Danielsen, F., Bruhl, C.A., Donald, P.F. & Phalan, B. (2008). How will oil palm expansion affect biodiversity? *Trends in Evolution and Ecology* **23**: 538-545.

Frederiksen, M., Edwards, M., Richardson, A.J., Halliday, N.C. & Wanless, S. (2006). From plankton to top predators: bottom-up control of a marine food web across four trophic levels. *Journal of Animal Ecology* **75**: 1259-1268.

Gaston, K.J., Jackson, S.F., Nagy, A., Cantu-Salazar, L. & Johnson, M. (2008). Protected Areas in Europe: Principle and Practice. *Annals of the New York Academy of Sciences* **1134**: 97-119.

Gibbons, D.W., Reid, J.B. & Chapman, R.A. (1993). *The New Atlas of Breeding Birds in Britain and Ireland: (1988–1991).* Poyser, London.

Gilbert, G. (2008). Bittern recovery, a Wetland Vision and hope for the future. *Conservation Science in the RSPB 2008*, 32-33.

Green, R.E., Cornell, S.J., Scharlemann, J.P.W. & Balmford, A. (2005). Farming and the fate of wild nature. *Science* **307**: 550-555.

Green, R.E., Collingham, Y,C. Willis, S.G., Gregory, R.D. & Smith, K.W. (2008). Performance of climate envelope models in retrodicting recent changes in bird population size from observed climatic change. *Biology Letters* **4**: 599-602.

Hanski, I. (1999). *Metapopulation Ecology.* Oxford University Press: Oxford.

Hickling, R., Roy, D.B., Hill, J.K., Fox, R. & Thomas, C.D. (2006). The distributions of a wide range of taxonomic groups are expanding polewards. *Global Change Biology* **12**: 450-455.

Hill, J.K., Collingham, Y.C., Thomas, C.D., Blakeley, D.S., Fox, R., Moss, D. & Huntley, B. (2001). Impacts of landscape structure on butterfly range expansion. *Ecology Letters* **4**: 313-321.

Holden J., Shotbolt L., Bonn A., Burt, T.P., Chapman, P.J., Dougill, A.J., Fraser, E.D.G., Hubacek, K., Irvine, B., Kirkby, M.J., Reed, M.S., Prell, C., Stagl, S., Stringer, L.C., Turner, A. & Worrall, F. (2007). Environmental change in moorland landscapes. *Earth-Science Reviews* **82**: 75-100.

Huntley, B., Green, R.E., Collingham, Y.C. & Willis, S.G. (2007). *A Climatic Atlas of European Breeding Birds.* Barcelona: Lynx Edicions.

Huntley, B., Collingham, Y.C., Willis, S.G. & Green, R.E. (2008). Potential impacts of climatic change on European breeding birds. *PLoS ONE* **3**: e1439. doi:10.1371/journal.pone.0001439.

Irons, D.B., Anker-Nilssen, T., Gaston, A.J., Byrd, G.V., Falk, K., Gilchrist, G., Hario, M., Hjernquist, M., Krasnov, Y.V., Mosbech, A., Olsen, B., Petersen, A., Reid, J.B., Robertson, G.J., Strøm, H. & Wohl, K.D. (2008). Fluctuations in circumpolar seabird populations linked to climate oscillations. *Global Change Biology* **14B**: 1455 – 1463.

Jetz, W., Wilcove, D.S. & Dobson, A.P. (2007). Projected Impacts of Climate and Land-Use Change on the Global Diversity of Birds. *PLoS Biology* 5: e157 doi:10.1371/journal.pbio.0050157.

Mitchell, R. J., Morecroft, M.D., Acreman, M., Crick, H.Q.P., Frost, M., Harley, M., Maclean, I.M.D., Mountford, O., Piper, J., Pontier, H., Rehfisch, M.M., Ross, L.C., Smithers, R.J., Stott, A., Walmsley, C.A., Watts, O. & Wilson, E. (2007). England biodiversity strategy: Towards adaptation to climate change. Department of Environment Food and World Affairs, London, U.K. Available from: http://www.defra.gov.uk/wildlife-countryside/resprog/findings/ebs-climate-change.pdf (accessed October 2008).

Newton, I. (1979). *Population Ecology of Raptors.* Poyser: Berkhamsted.

Opdam, P. & Wascher, D. (2004). Climate change meets habitat fragmentation: linking landscape and biogeographical scale levels in research and conservation. *Biological Conservation* 117: 285-297.

Parmesan, C. & Yohe, G. (2003). A globally coherent fingerprint of climate change impacts across natural systems. *Nature* 421: 37-42.

Parr, R. (1992). The decline to extinction of a population of Golden Plover in north-east Scotland. *Ornis Scandinavica* 23: 152-158.

Pearce-Higgins, J.W. (2009). Effects of climate change on golden plovers. *Conservation Science in the RSPB 2008*, pp. 42-43.

Pearce-Higgins, J.W. & Grant, M.C. (2006). Relationships between bird abundance and the composition and structure of moorland vegetation. *Bird Study* 53: 112–125.

Pearce-Higgins, J.W. & Yalden, D.W. (2003). Golden Plover *Pluvialis apricaria* breeding success on a moor managed for shooting Red Grouse *Lagopus lagopus*. *Bird Study* 50:170-177.

Pearce-Higgins, J.W. & Yalden, D.W. (2004). Habitat selection, diet, arthropod availability and growth of a moorland wader: the ecology of European Golden Plover *Pluvialis apricaria* chicks. *Ibis* 146: 335-346.

Pearce-Higgins, J.W., Dennis, P., Whittingham, M.J. & Yalden, D.W. (2009). Impacts of climate on prey abundance account for fluctuations in a population of a northern wader at the southern edge of its range. *Global Change Biology*, doi 10.1111/j.1365-2486.2009.01883.x

Poulsom, L., Griffiths, M., Broome, A. & Mayle, B. (2005). *Identification of priority woodlands for red squirrel conservation in North and Central Scotland: a preliminary analysis.* Scottish Natural Heritage Commissioned Report No. 089 (ROAME No. F02AC334).

Root, T. L., Price, J.T., Hall, K.R., Schneider, S.H., Rosenzweig, C. & Pounds, J.A. (2003). Fingerprints of global warming on wild animals and plants. *Nature* 421: 57-60.

Sim, I.M.W., Gregory, R.D., Hancock, M.H. & Brown, A.F. (2005). Recent changes in the abundance of British upland breeding birds. *Bird Study* 52: 261–275.

Smallwood, K.S. & Thelander, C.G. (2008). Bird mortality in the Altamont Pass. *Journal of Wildlife Management* 72: 215–223.

Tharme, A.P., Green, R.E., Baines, D., Bainbridge, I.P. & O'Brien, M. (2001). The effect of management for red grouse shooting on the population density of breeding birds on heather – dominated moorland. *Journal of Applied Ecology* 38: 439 – 457.

Thomas, C.D., Cameron, A., Green, R.E., Bakkenes, M., Beaumont, L.J., Collingham, Y.C., Erasmus, B.F.N., De Siquiera, M.F., Grainger, A., Hannah, L., Hughes, L., Huntley, B., Van Jaarsveld, A.S., Midgley, G.F., Miles, L., Ortega-Huerta, M.A., Peterson, A.T., Phillips, O. & Williams, S.E. (2004). Extinction risk from climate change. *Nature* 427: 145-148.

Tompkins, D.M., White, A.R. & Boots, M. (2003). Ecological replacement of native red squirrels by invasive greys driven by disease. *Ecology Letters* 6: 189–196.

Warren, M.S., Hill, J.K., Thomas,J.A., Asher, J., Fox, R., Huntley, B., Roy, D.B., Telfer, M.G., Jeffcoate, S., Harding, P., Jeffcoate, G., Willis,S.G., Greatorex-Davies, J.N., Moss, D. & Thomas, C.D. (2001). Rapid responses of British butterflies to opposing forces of climate and habitat change. *Nature* **414**: 65-69.

Watts, K., Ray, D., Quine, C.P., Humphrey, J.W. & Griffiths, M. (2007). *Evaluating biodiversity in fragmented landscapes: Applications of landscape ecology tools.* Forestry Commission Information Note 85. Forestry Commission, Edinburgh.

Wilson, A.M., Ausden, M. & Milsom, T.P. (2005). Changes in breeding wader populations on lowland wet grassland in England and Wales: causes and potential solutions. *Ibis* **146 s2**: 32-40.

Wilson, J.D., Evans, A.D. & Gryce, P.V. (2009). *Bird conservation and agriculture.* Cambridge: Cambridge University Press.

World Conservation Union – Conservation Measures Partnership. (2006). Unified Classification of Conservation Actions. Conservation Measures Partnership, Bethesda, Maryland. Available from: http://www.fosonline.org/CMP/IUCN/browse.cfm?TaxID=ConservationActions (accessed October 2008).

Green, R.E. and Pearce-Higgins, J. (2010). Species management in the face of a changing climate. In: *Species Management: Challenges and Solutions for the 21st Century*, ed. by J.M. Baxter and C.A. Galbraith. TSO Scotland, Edinburgh. pp. 517-536

Part 7

Chapter 30: Conclusions

Colin A. Galbraith and John M. Baxter

The studies and situations reported in this book demonstrate that the management of species is complex, at times difficult, and that the issues involved are changing in response to our expectations and desires for the environment around us. Interest in nature, and in wildlife in particular, has never been greater in the UK, yet in some ways the daily lives of most of the population has never been more distant from the environment. Increasing real involvement in the management of species and the wider landscape is important for the future.

What is particularly striking in many of the chapters is the rate of change in the environment itself and in the ways that we are beginning to respond. The recent increase in awareness about the impact that climate change is having is perhaps the best example of this, but these changes need to be seen alongside others that are the result of how we manage the countryside more deliberately. For example, changes in agricultural support policies or in the management of marine fisheries can cause real shifts in the wider environment, leading in turn to changes in the distribution and ecology of many species. The combined effect of these multiple changes has been profound and the environment is now perhaps more challenging for many species, and for us, than ever before.

Much of what we have read is a testimony to the hard work and dedication of the researchers and others involved in the particular projects and situations being reported here. One important theme that emerges is the need for a detailed understanding of the issues involved, and especially an intimate knowledge of the ecology of the species concerned. Getting this level of information is expensive and in the current economic climate every pound spent has, rightly, to be justified, but without this knowledge it is difficult to see how management can have any credible basis for action. Equally, it is no longer enough just to have the data and information on species ecology; it must be made readily available, interpreted, utilized as the basis for advice and fed into policy discussions, and ultimately used as the basis for action. The Millennium Ecosystem Assessment (2005) suggested that at the global scale we may be entering a new and major phase of species extinctions hence the need for action not only at the local level but also globally. The principle of using "the best available information" still seems to hold true to us; waiting for a perfect understanding before taking action is unrealistic in the present climate of change. The balance between the degree of certainty and the risks of getting it wrong will need to be carefully weighed in all of the situations concerning the management of species.

It is not all bad news, thankfully, and the recent move to embrace the use of the ecosystem approach in planning by Governments and others does offer the hope of developing holistic, longer-term plans for the management of species and of the environment more generally. Linked to this, the present level of interest in "ecosystem services", is beginning to change the way the natural world is viewed from somewhat remote and something of a luxury, to being the critical "life support system" for the future. This is an important change and whilst it is a major step forward, it does pose many questions and challenges for those directly involved in the management of species. How will a truly multi-species approach to conservation in any area work? What does taking an ecosystem approach mean for individual species action? What part do species play in the provision of ecosystem services? These and other questions will need to be addressed while attempting to deliver effective species conservation in the face of climate change. These are real challenges for the future!

The SNH Species Action Framework has identified a number of priority species for action; taking difficult decisions and prioritizing those most in need of a variety of types of management action, from direct support for populations, to the active control of non-native invasive species. This approach identifies the need for action based on four types of management, namely; species management for conservation, dealing with invasive non-native species, addressing conflicts of interest involving native species and finally, delivering the sustainable use of species. These categories appear to be applicable to species management situations in countries around the world and may help clarify the different approaches needed in each case.

The need to prioritize actions and to take far reaching decisions to manage species is obvious, however, the process of decision taking is sometimes less so. How we view particular situations has been shown to be a mixture of cultural and individual preference and opinion, with the present legal framework relating to species protection being an expression of what we think is right and important. The question for the future is how these views and opinions will need to change given all the pressures we noted above. There will undoubtedly be a need for some form of assessment or triage of situations where those populations that are in need of action are prioritized and action is taken, where this is likely to succeed. Perhaps more controversially, it is likely that the triage will result in some populations being assessed as beyond reasonable action. Reaching this view will be a particular challenge for the conservation movement to consider and to resolve.

This year, 2010, sees a renewed focus on the conservation of biodiversity and on the role it plays in our lives. We have seen that there is a need for detailed monitoring of species populations and that the translation of research into action is key. There is, however, another need in this important year, and that is to celebrate what we still have. It is all too easy for conservationists and others to focus on the problems and that is, of course, legitimate but we are enormously fortunate in Scotland to have a wonderful diversity of both animal and plant life readily available for everyone to experience and enjoy. The continued survival of these species is due to the actions of the multitude of conservationists, land-owners and managers who, over the years have created suitable habitats in which they can thrive. We have an excellent science base related to the natural environment, probably one of the best in the world, and have better data and information than many other countries regarding the state of our biodiversity. So we have much to be proud of, and much to contribute to the rest of the world in terms of showing what we have done and how we have achieved it. We do of course need to continue to learn from others and to seek out best practice in the management of species and then to deploy that in our work.

In that context we hope that this book is seen as a valuable contribution to discussions about the management of species and to the management of the environment more widely.

Index

Note: **Emboldened** references indicate **chapter** extents. *Italicized* references are to *species*, *illustrations*, *tables* and *boxes*. There is often additional text on these pages.

CL

639.
909
411
SPE